THE YAK
SECOND EDITION

-O-

FIRST EDITION

CAI LI
B.Sc.

Professor of Animal Science and vice-chairperson of the Academic Committee,
Southwest Nationalities College and deputy director of the Animal Science and
Veterinary Medicine Institute (SWNC), Chengdu, Sichuan, China

GERALD WIENER
B.Sc., Ph.D., D.Sc., F.R.S.E., C.Biol. F.I.Biol.

Honorary Professor, Gansu Agricultural University, China; Centre for Tropical
Veterinary Medicine, University of Edinburgh and Roslin Institute, Edinburgh, UK.
Lately deputy director of former AFRC Animal Breeding Research Organization, UK

SECOND EDITION
REVISED AND ENLARGED *by*

GERALD WIENER
B.Sc., Ph.D., D.Sc., F.R.S.E., C.Biol. F.I.Biol.

Honorary Professor, Gansu Agricultural University, China; Centre for Tropical
Veterinary Medicine, University of Edinburgh and Roslin Institute, Edinburgh, UK.
Lately deputy director of former AFRC Animal Breeding Research Organization, UK

HAN JIANLIN
B.Sc., Ph.D.

Molecular Geneticist, International Livestock Research Institute, Kenya; Professor of Animal Genetics
and Breeding, Gansu Agricultural University, China; Executive Secretary of the International Yak
Information Center and China Yak Breed Association, Lanzhou, China

LONG RUIJUN
B.Sc., M.Sc., Ph.D.

Professor of Pastoral Science and Dean of Faculty of Grassland Science, Gansu Agricultural University,
China; Senior Scientist, Northwest Plateau Institute of Biology, the Chinese Academy Science, China;
vice-chairperson of Chinese Grassland Society, China

RAP publication 2003/06

THE YAK
SECOND EDITION

REVISED AND ENLARGED
By

GERALD WIENER
HAN JIANLIN
LONG RUIJUN

ISBN 92-5-104965-3

Published by the Regional Office for Asia and the Pacific
Food and Agriculture Organization of the United Nations, Bangkok, Thailand

**Food and Agriculture Organization of the United Nations
Regional Office for Asia and the Pacific
Bangkok, Thailand**

This publication is produced by

FAO Regional Office for Asia and the Pacific

Research funded by
**FAO Regional Project
"Conservation and Use of Animal Genetic Resources in Asia and the Pacific"**
(GCP/RAS/144/JPN)
The Government of Japan

Jacket design and illustration and frontispiece by John Frisby, RIAS

© FAO 2003

ISBN 92-5-104965-3

For copies write to: The Animal Production Officer
FAO Regional Office for Asia and the Pacific
39 Phra Atit Road
Bangkok 10200 Thailand
Tel : +66 2 697-4000
Fax : +66 2 697 4445

PREFACE TO THE SECOND EDITION

Some background to the yak book was provided in the preface to the first edition and this is therefore reprinted below. The second edition represents an extensive revision of the chapters in the first edition and a substantial enlargement through the addition of five new chapters. Sadly, the death of Professor Cai Li in 1997 has meant that his expertise in what he termed "yakology" could not be brought to bear on the revision. Two scientists of a younger generation, eminent in their own specialist subjects but with a major involvement in yak research, have joined this endeavour from Gansu Agricultural University in northwest China – a university that stands in friendly rivalry, in its concern with yak, with the late Professor Cai Li's Southwest Nationalities College.

Apart from the continuing growth of the scientific literature on yak that has added to this edition, it had become apparent that two matters were insufficiently dealt with previously. One of these is the crucial role that culture and social context play in yak keeping. Although these issues were recognized and alluded to before, the topic has now been expanded into a new chapter. The second matter is the continuing search for the scientific basis underlying yak production. The subjects involved have become increasingly specialized and provide, for the present, perhaps more insights for the scientists than for practitioners of yak keeping – but they are the foundation for future developments. These issues and the understandings derived from them form the basis of three new chapters. The first of these looks in some detail at the alpine rangeland ecosystem and its management. The second deals with fundamental processes in yak nutrition, and the third is concerned with advances in the genetics of yak at the molecular and cytogenetic level.

The discussion of yak in different regions has been greatly enlarged into a chapter divided into three parts. The first part provides information, for the first time in this book, on the special features of yak keeping in six provinces of China – the six that account for most of the yak in that country. The second part, revised and enlarged from an earlier chapter, provides much information on yak keeping and yak research in other countries that have a long history and tradition of yak keeping; this includes a new section that takes a broad sweep over yak in Western High Asia, and includes some of the more remote countries of the region with small but locally important yak populations. The section on Mongolia has been re-written by a new author; some of the others have been re-written or revised by their former authors or with new collaborators. It is a matter of regret that no one could be found willing to write on behalf of the countries of the Russian Federation (with the honourable exception of Buryatia) and that section is therefore based on available literature. The third part of this long chapter has been added to provide a little evidence on yak in countries with environments that are not traditional for yak – principally yak kept commercially in North America, as well as a few in Europe and elsewhere and yak kept in zoos and wild animal parks.

It is hoped, therefore, that the book will continue to appeal to those with an interest in yak but wishing to delve also a little below the surface. It is hoped also that the more esoteric science in the book will provide a review of the subjects treated for those with specialist interests and will be seen by general readers as showing how yak research is being integrated with that on other ruminants. An overview is provided at the start of each chapter for those who do not want the detail. As before, the concluding thoughts in the final chapter are written from my perspective as an outsider to the actual art of keeping yak. An "outsider's perspective" should at least have the merit of being in tune with one of the important aims of the book, which is to make knowledge of yak more widely accessible to the world outside the yak territories.

Much care has gone into the production of this volume and much help received (see acknowledgements to both editions). Inevitably, some inadequacies may remain. Some will be of our own making and some due to lack of information on certain points. Hopefully, such problems will be few compared to the wealth of information presented.

Gerald Wiener
June 2003

ACKNOWLEDGEMENTS
(second and first editions)

The acknowledgements for help and advice with the second edition of this book should be read in conjunction with the thanks extended in relation to the first edition. These former thanks are clearly still relevant and are also shown below.

Much encouragement and advice was received for the revised and enlarged edition of this book.

From the FAO Regional Office for Asia and the Pacific those involved were principally Denis Hoffmann, a former senior animal health production officer from 1997 to 2002, and David Steane, a freelance livestock consultant.

More specifically, thanks go first to those who have contributed new chapters or sections. The authors concerned are shown at the beginning of each of these chapters or sections and their affiliations as footnotes. Their names will not therefore be listed here, but their collaboration is greatly appreciated. Particularly in relation to countries within the traditional yak zone but outside China, several of the contributors differ from those who participated in the first edition.

Advice and help was sought from and given by many individuals, some on general matters and some in relation to specific chapters. In relation to the more technical new chapters, the help provided in terms of time and expertise is greatly appreciated not only by the compilers of this volume but also by the authors of the relevant chapters. Those to whom profound thanks are due are shown below in alphabetical order (in two cases, they are also authors or co-authors of other sections in the book):

Shikui Dong (formerly, Gansu Agricultural University, China); John Frame (formerly, Scottish Agricultural College, UK); Professor James F. D. Greenhalgh (formerly, Aberdeen University, UK); Chris Haley (Roslin Institute, UK); Professor Corneille Jest (Centre Nationale de la Recherche Scientifique, France); W. Scott Johnston (formerly, Scottish Agricultural College, UK); Professor Hermann Kreutzmann (University Erlangen, Germany); Walter Roder (Advisor, Bhutan); David Steane (formerly FAO).

Appreciation for additional information and help not specifically acknowledged in the text, is also due to the following:

James Delaney (International Yak Association, USA); Nick Lindsay (Senior Curator, Whipsnade Wild Animal Park, UK); Daniel J. Miller (Rangeland consultant, USA); Camille Richard (International centre for integrated mountain development, Nepal);

Dan Wharton and staff (wildlife conservation society, NY, USA); Nyima Tashi and Ji Qiumei (Tibetan academy of agriculture and animal sciences, Tibet, China); Qi Xuebin (Gansu, China); Liu Yingchun (Qinghai, China); Professor Pu Jiabi (Heifer Project International, Sichuan, China); Fu Changxiu (Sichuan, China); Associate Professor Wei Xiaohong (Gansu Agricultural University, China).

Also, other support was provided by Hans-Gerhard Wagner, FAO animal production officer, and by Chanrit Uawongkun, Animal Production and Health Commission for Asia and the Pacific for page layout and page setup.

The editorial assistance of Karen Emmons is appreciated.

The following were the acknowledgements in the first edition of the book:

Help and encouragement has been received by the authors from many sources and these are most happily acknowledged. Our thanks are listed under headings:

FAO Regional Office for Asia and the Pacific

We are very grateful to Obaidullah Khan (Assistant Director-General and Regional representative for Asia and the Pacific) for his support and kindly writing the Foreword for this book. We are particularly indebted to David Steane (Chief technical advisor, conservation and use of animal genetic resources) for actively promoting the publication of this book, for making most of the arrangements for this and also for comments on scientific matters. We are also grateful to Masao Sasaki (FAO regional animal production and health officer) for his support of the project.

Material for book

The authors are indebted to those who personally contributed material for this book, mostly found in chapter 11. Particular thanks are due to Professors M. Tumurjav and M. Olonbayar (Mongolia), E. V. Katzina (Buryatia), R. N. Pal (India), D. D. Joshi (Nepal), Lham Tshering (Bhutan), and A. H. Cheema and A. Ghaffar (Pakistan). Their various and varied contributions have helped greatly to broaden the perspectives of this book. N. Lindsay (Curator) and E. Flack (Veterinarian) kindly provided information on yak at Whipsnade Wild Animal Park (England).

Scientific help

The authors are most grateful for the time and effort given by J. M. M. Cunningham (Emeritus Professor, Glasgow University) and A. J. Smith (Centre for tropical veterinary medicine, University of Edinburgh). Each read an entire draft of this book. Their comments and questions and the discussions held with them by one of us (G.W.) were most helpful in the development and revision of the manuscript. Professor Crad Roberts (University of Wales) should also be thanked for some initial suggestions on content. Helpful comments on Chapter 5 were also given by R. Webb (Roslin Institute), on Chapter 9 by A. G. Hunter (Centre for tropical veterinary medicine, University of Edinburgh) and on Chapter 4, in relation to haematology, by David Doxey (Veterinary field station, University of Edinburgh).

Translation

An initial translation of the Chinese manuscript of the book by Professor Cai Li, *China yak* (1992) (which provided a basis for the FAO book) was made into English by Ma Li and Zi Xiang-dong (both on the staff of the Southwest Nationalities College). Their time and effort are greatly appreciated. Subsequently, almost the entire burden of translation from Chinese into English and vice versa, during the preparation of this book, fell on Zi Xiang-dong. This was a formidable task owing to the copious correspondence between the authors, neither of whom speak each other's language. The work of translation must have greatly interfered with Zi's academic teaching commitments and with his personal life. We cannot thank him enough.

A relatively small but important amount of translation was done by J. G. Gong (Roslin Institute, Edinburgh) to whom we are also grateful.

Other help

Professor Graham Bulfield (Director, Roslin Institute) is thanked for use (by G.W.) of the facilities of the Roslin Institute. Its three library staff helped, beyond the call of duty, in tracing and obtaining books and reprints of articles needed for reference but often difficult to locate. Frances Anderson undertook the skilled job of preparing camera-ready copy from the material and diskettes supplied by G.W.

Photographs: by Cai Li except where otherwise acknowledged.

FOREWORD TO THE FIRST EDITION

It is fitting that in this year, the 50th anniversary of FAO, the Regional Office for Asia and the Pacific acknowledges, by this publication, the unique and special role of the Yak whose natural environment is almost totally within this region.

The Yak is a relatively insignificant species in global terms, yet it is critical to the livelihood security of the herders in a rather difficult environment.

The Yak's ability to survive in harsh conditions and the peoples' ability to derive sustenance from it are classic examples of adaptation by both the animals and the human beings. The need to ensure the maintenance of domestic animal diversity, therefore, cannot be overstated.

The book is not a purely technical publication but tries, through the use of the scientific and other literature available, to provide a comprehensive document describing all aspects of the Yak and its husbandry. It is, however, unique in providing for the first time such a comprehensive document on the Yak in the English language. It will enable a wide audience to learn and appreciate the contribution the Yak makes both to human survival in an inhospitable environment and to biological diversity.

Obaidullah Khan
Assistant Director-General and
FAO Regional Representative for Asia and the Pacific

PREFACE TO THE FIRST EDITION

A preface should perhaps be in the name of both the authors. That convention is broken here in order to provide me, the "foreign" co-author, with an opportunity to pay particular tribute to Professor Cai Li. He has dedicated an entire lifetime, helped by colleagues, students and co-workers, to observing, recording and trying to understand the yak and its characteristics and attributes and its role in the life, culture and economy of the mountainous regions of central Asia. Some of this study has involved personal hardship, which most young scientists nowadays would find hard to imagine.

The areas of the world in which yak are kept are in many cases, even now, isolated by distance and difficult terrain. Much of yak husbandry is still steeped in tradition and values, which may not be encountered by "animal improvers" elsewhere. It is no mean feat therefore to have gathered the information on which this book is based and it is no discredit to its value that some of the expectations of modern data recording and analysis could not always be observed. Numbers involved in comparisons are often fewer than the observers would have wished, and one of the recurring regrets is that some factors remain confounded – for example, between breeds or types of yak and the location where they are found. It is thus not often possible to say whether a particular type of animal is better, or whether it is the conditions under which it lives which is the deciding factor.

The backbone of this book is the work of Professor Cai Li, particularly in his home province of Sichuan. Much of his work has been quoted by direct reference to specific publications, but other information on yak, when not attributed to a specific source also derives from Professor Cai Li's studies. However, it is hoped that readers will also quickly note that this book is based on a large array of information and a mass of data from many different sources and places. It follows that this book differs in breadth and depth from the many popular and a few review articles on the yak, which represent the bulk of the information published in the English language. (In addition there is a growing number of scientific papers on specific topics concerned with yak, also in the English language - and some in French and German). The more general of these articles mostly set out to say how remarkable an animal the yak is, because it has adapted to life in an extraordinarily hostile environment, and then give just a taste of information on body size, reproductive rate, milk yield, and perhaps little else. Usually, this provides no clue to the wide range of variation in performance and habitat of the yak and to the potential of the yak for change. Such conclusions need to be based on a more detailed assessment of the yak and critical evaluation of the results. Nonetheless, taken together, these articles and specific studies provide an impressive addition to the literature in the traditional languages for yak publications (mostly Chinese, but also many in Russian), and they have been quoted here whenever appropriate.

It is hoped, therefore, that this book will fill a gap in knowledge and understanding, not only among those concerned with the science of animal production, but also those just interested in the yak and wishing to dig a bit deeper. To accommodate especially the more general reader, an overview has been provided at the beginning of each chapter.

In spite of the claim to breadth and depth for this book, it has to be acknowledged that not every possible piece of information published on the yak has been used. Much of the wealth of articles in scientific journals, reports and proceedings of technical meetings (mainly in the Chinese or Russian language) deals with specific detail under specific circumstances. While it is one of the aims of this book to demonstrate the range of variation found in the management and performance of yak in both practical and experimental situations, and to provide a clue to the underlying factors, it was not thought desirable to make the references exhaustive. To do so would also have required some means of interpreting the causes of the plethora of small differences in performance, or characteristics, of the yak that would emerge. Such interpretation is not possible in the absence of a level and scale of experimentation, which has not been undertaken with the yak (or indeed with other types of domestic livestock, if considered over the kind of vast area encompassed by yak territory). The separate chapter on yak husbandry in different countries should go some way towards widening the picture as far as possible.

The publication of this book was requested by the Regional Office for Asia and the Pacific of the Food and Agriculture Organisation of the United Nations to coincide with the 50th anniversary of FAO's foundation. Due to restrictions on time, it has not been possible, in every case, to obtain information for chapter 11, on yak husbandry in different countries, direct from those involved – as was originally hoped. Thus, some of the information for that chapter has had to be compiled from existing, published information.

This preface must end with an apology. The problem of transliterating Chinese, and to a much lesser extent Russian, into the English alphabet may mean that some of the names of authors and the titles of papers and sources given in the list of references may not be totally correct in every detail. Also, it is a matter of regret that some of the references listed will be found difficult to access, even in the form of abstracts, by those wishing to do so. It is hoped that the revolution in communication, in which we find ourselves at the end of the 20th century, will also, in the future, apply to publication across far distant national boundaries for subjects such as the yak.

Gerald Wiener
September 1995

CONTENTS

1 ORIGINS, DOMESTICATION AND DISTRIBUTION OF YAK

OVERVIEW

Fossil remains of the domestic yak and its wild ancestor date back to the Pleistocene period. Over the past 10 000 years or so, the yak developed on the Qinghai-Tibetan Plateau, extending over about 2.5 million sq km and often called the "roof of the world". Although this is still the centre of the yak's distribution, yak have spread northward and southward and also, albeit in relatively small numbers, to other parts of the world. Yak are usually found at elevations between 2 000 and 5 000 m (the lower elevations at the more northerly latitudes).

The wild yak may have been tamed and domesticated by the ancient Qiang people. Chinese documents from ancient times (eighth century B.C.) testify to a long-established role of the yak in the culture and life of the people. From the south to the north, the distribution of the domestic yak now extends from the southern slopes of the Himalayas to the Altai and west to east from the Pamir to the Minshan mountains. In relatively recent times the area of distribution has further extended to, for example, the Caucasus and North America. In addition, yak are found in zoos and wild animal parks in many countries.

At the present time, the total yak population is estimated to number around 14.2 million, of which 13.3 million are in Chinese territories, about 0.6 million in Mongolia and the rest in other countries, notably those bordering the Himalayas and countries of the Commonwealth of Independent States (formerly the Soviet Union). Their numbers are said to be increasing in some areas of China. In addition, hybridization of yak with cattle – most usually the local cattle of the area – is widely practised. Hybrids of yak with "improved" European breeds are also produced, though in relatively small numbers.

The wild yak population, as distinct from the domestic yak, is now very restricted in distribution. Numbers are likely to be fewer than 15 000. Although the animals are "protected", illegal hunting still represents a major problem to their survival. Wild yak are larger in size than the domestic ones. Because the two types readily interbreed, there is interest in the use of wild yak to improve the performance of the domestic type.

The yak is integrally associated with the culture, religion and social life of its herders, their families and communities. However, with outside pressures influencing the life of the people and with technical developments impinging on yak husbandry, it seems likely that the nature of yak keeping has entered a period of change.

Introduction

The yak *(Poephagus grunniens* or *Bos grunniens)* must be regarded as one of the world's most remarkable domestic animals as it thrives in conditions of extreme harshness and deprivation while providing a livelihood for people. A herbivore, the yak lives predominantly on the "roof of the world", as the Qinghai-Tibetan Plateau is often called. The Plateau itself extends over 2.5 million sq km (about 1 million square miles) and was described by Miller (1990) as the most extensive high-elevation region on earth and the best grazing lands in all of Asia. For those more familiar with the western hemisphere, Miller (1990) equated the vast size of this Plateau to the combined areas in the United States of America of Montana, Wyoming, Idaho, Utah, Nevada, Colorado, Arizona and New Mexico. From the central "core" of the yak's habitat, the species has spread to adjacent territories. These areas are, to a large extent, above the tree line where there is virtually no cropping. There is no frost-free period during any part of the year. At its high elevation, the territory overall is characterized by a harsh climate of cool moist summers, severely cold winters and grazing resources restricted by very short growing seasons. More than 13 million yak thus live and provide food, transport, shelter and fuel where few other animals will survive. About 30 million sheep and goats (Miller, 1990) – and the herdsmen's horses – co-exist with yak over large parts of the Plateau. But these are not serious competitors to the yak in much of yak territory, and they do not have the same economic importance. However, yak and sheep are, to some extent, complementary to each other in their grazing habits. In some of the alpine regions, the terrain is also treacherous. Chinese historians have argued that without the yak's capacity to live in such a hostile environment, human civilization might not have established and flourished in these remote areas.

This book traces briefly the development of this remarkable animal and then describes in some detail its characteristics and performance and its products. There is also a discussion of the more recent research and development projects that may provide a basis for improvements in yak performance and in the utilization of the rangelands. The research and development may also lead to a wider distribution for the yak and to a better utilization of yak products. Any marked changes in yak husbandry are also likely to have far-reaching consequences for the social fabric of a society of pastoralists.

Origins

Unequivocal evidence to link the modern yak to its earliest ancestors is not available. Fossil evidence suggests that yak were extensively distributed in north-eastern Eurasia in the late Tertiary period (2.5 million years ago) and that these are the forerunners of wild yak found as Pleistocene fossils in northern China, Inner Mongolia (China), eastern Siberia and northern mid-Asia and on a line roughly connecting these locations (Dyblor, 1957;

2

Belyar, 1980; Flerow, 1980; Olsen, 1991; but see also Chapter 15, Systematics and phylogeny).

The principal area of distribution for the remaining wild yak of modern times is discussed in the section on wild yak later in this chapter. The Himalayas rose to their present elevation above 4 500 m only in the late Pleistocene epoch. Their rise obstructed the warm and damp airflow from the south and significantly changed the climate of the central area of what is now the Qinghai-Tibetan Plateau. Forest disappeared from the Plateau and was replaced by alpine meadow. Wild yak migrated from northeastern Eurasia and adapted to life on the Plateau and domestication followed.

Domestication and historical distribution

The present domestic yak is descended from wild yak, which may have been caught and tamed by ancient Qiang people in the *Changtang* (a Tibetan term meaning "the empty highland of the north"), an area that covers more than half of Tibet.

This process is thought to have begun in the late Stone Age, about 10 000 years ago, and led to the primary yak industry, beginning in the period of the Longshan Culture of the late New Stone Age (2 800 - 2 300 B.C.) (Qian Yanwen, 1979). The history of China's yak industry is thus at least 4 500 years old. Chinese historians regard the ancient Qiang people living around 30 000 years ago as the first intelligent humans. They lived and roamed the present Qinghai-Tibetan Plateau, though its average altitude then, at around 3 000 m, was lower than it is now. These people developed quite possibly the earliest animal husbandry culture of excellence in the world – the Qiang Culture. This development is of a different type from that based on agriculture in ancient Mesopotamia, widely regarded as the cradle of civilization. The outstanding achievement of the Qiang Culture was the taming of wild beasts for domestic purposes. Sheep and goats had already been tamed successfully and this led to the taming of yak, horse and other herbivores and the development of a society based on animal husbandry. Domestication of yak in particular led to progress, prosperity and economic advancement for the people because of the value of the yak as a beast of burden and its products of milk, hair, hides and meat – and the availability of its dung as a fuel in the areas above the tree line.

Yak expanded outward from that original area of domestication on the Plateau. To the east, yak migrated from the Bayan Kala mountains into the Songpan grasslands (located in what are now the Aba, Ruoergai and Hongyuan counties of Sichuan province) and into the Danba mountains. To the south, the migration went through passes in the Himalayas to the mountainous grasslands of the southern slopes of the range. To the west, yak entered Kashmir through the western Tibet grasslands. And to the north the migration took the yak over the Kunlun mountains into northern Pamir, northern and southern Tianshan and Altai.

The present-day distribution of the yak developed gradually from these migrations (see Figure 1.1).

Figure 1.1 Principal area (hatched) of the distribution of domestic yak

Nearly all the nationalities that now keep yak are thought to be related to the ancient Qiang people, including, for example, the Suchas and Tibetans. Others such as the Menba, Luoba and the Sherpa people of Nepal were separated from the original Qiang only when they entered the southern slopes of the Himalayan range. The Luoba became the Yi nationality when they migrated to the Yungui Plateau from the east. Similarly, nationalities in central Asia and the Tianshan area are related to the Qiang people, as are the Mongolian and other southern nationalities.

Many old Chinese documents illustrate these links and the associations with the yak. For example, the *Guoyu chuyu* describes events in the late Western Zhou Dynasty (ca. 841 B.C.): "… The Bapu's rhinoceros and yak cannot be destroyed …" (Bapu was the northern part of the ancient Ba nation located in the present Daba mountains area of Sichuan province). The old text describes how yak were raised in large numbers.

A geological document, the *Shanhaijing Zhongshanjing*, dating from 400 B.C., states: "In the northeast there is a mountain called Jingshan. Its northern slope abounds with iron and the southern slopes are rich in gold. There are many yak on the mountain …." The Jingshan is at the extremity of the Daba range in what is now the Xiangyan area of Hubei province.

Many other Chinese documents dating from the fourth to the first century B.C. attest to the abundance of yak on the mountainous slopes. They also describe the migration, often forced by oppression from despotic rulers, of the Qiang people who took their yak with them. The Qiang people thus branched into what became different races living in isolation from each other. One of these was the sixth Mao Niu race – a name synonymous with one of the names for yak (Tong Pingya and Zhao Guopan, 1990).

4

Another branch of the Qiang people deserves particular attention because of their association with the Jiulong yak, which is now, in terms of its performance, among the most renowned native breeds of China. These people migrated to southern Kangding in what is now the Ganzi Tibetan autonomous prefecture of Sichuan province. They called themselves *muya*, meaning "yak country". The centre of this territory was in the Mula region of Yajiang county of the prefecture, the original home of the Jiulong breed. The people and therefore the area of distribution of this breed spread, as the yak industry developed, to include several other counties within Sichuan (Kangding, Jiulong, Daofu and Litang) as well as Zhongdian county of Yunnan province.

Thus, the raising of yak was a national characteristic of the ancient Qiang people. Their nomadic lifestyle has carried over into much of yak keeping to this day.

Gradually, the distribution of the yak expanded. But only in relatively modern times did it reach some of the areas where yak are now regarded as important. For example, the raising of yak in the Tianshan mountain area of the Xinjiang Uygur Autonomous Region is only about 100 years old. A century ago, 6 male and 170 female yak were taken from Tibet to Hejing county in the centre of the Tianshan mountain range and the whole of Tianshan (Yu Daxin and Qian Defang, 1983).

Present distribution

In Asia and traditional territories

Yak are found extensively on the plateau of western China in alpine and subalpine regions at altitudes from 2 000 - 5 000 m with a cold, semi-humid climate. The area, as seen in Figure 1.1, extends from the southern slopes of the Himalayas in the south to the Altai in the north and from the Pamir in the west to the Minshan mountains in the east. The centre of the yak's distribution is the Qinghai-Tibetan Plateau, which is interspersed with several mountain ranges. From the most recently available information (mostly 1997), the number of yak in Chinese territories is estimated to exceed 13 million, of which about 15 percent are hybrids with (mostly) *Bos taurus* cattle of local types. The majority of the yak, as shown in Table 1.1, are concentrated in four of that region's provinces. The rest of the world accounts for another million or so yak.

The majority of the yak in Mongolia are found in the Hangay and Hovsgol mountains and in the high altitude area of the Mongolian Altai – on the western and northern side of the country (cf. Chapter 11, part 2).

The yak in countries of the Commonwealth of Independent States (CIS, formerly the Soviet Union) are distributed in the narrow mountain area on the borders with China and Mongolia from Pamir in the west to Lake Baikal in the east. Yak were also introduced to the high alpine areas of the northern Caucasus in 1970, and reintroduced to the Yakutsk valley of Siberia (Yakutia) as recently as 1971 (Verdiev and Erin, 1981), to exploit the potential for meat production from otherwise inhospitable alpine grasslands. The yak of Nepal and Bhutan are on the southern slopes of the Himalayas while those of India are distributed in the high altitude northern provinces and in the small territory of Sikkim. Other pockets of yak populations are in alpine areas of Afghanistan and Pakistan, adjacent to the Qinghai-Tibetan Plateau. These areas of the yak distribution are dealt with in more detail in Chapter 11, part 2.

In the 1970s and 1980s, the yak was introduced to mountainous areas in northern China (but at lower altitudes of 1 500 - 1 800 m) to increase utilization of the grasslands in these cold areas. The results in Weichang county of Hebei province and in the Lingshan area of Beijing suggest a useful role for the yak there (Langjie Zeren *et al.*, 1987; Zhong Guanhui *et al.*, 1986).

Yak in China thus represent about 94 percent of the world's total number of yak but account for only a small proportion of the 140 million bovines in China (numbers in 1996, according to Xu Shangzhon, 1998).

According to Guo Shijan and Chen Weisheng (1996), 1.3 million yak were marketed in China annually. It was also estimated that the annual production from yak was 226 000 tonnes of meat, 13 000 tonnes of fibre and 170 000 pieces of skin (Xu Guifang and Wang Zhigang, 1998). Milk production was quoted as 1.4 million tonnes for 1989 by Li Yifang (1999) and 715 000 tonnes by Xu Guifang and Wang Zhigang (1998) for the year 1997. However, as roughly 40 percent of the meat, 60 percent of the milk and milk products and 80 percent of the fibre produced from yak are used by the herders' families for their own consumption (Guo Shijian and Chen Weisheng, 1996), all these estimates may fall well short of the actual contribution made by yak to the total economy.

Distribution outside Asia in modern times

Export of yak to parts of Europe, North America and other parts of Asia began in the mid-nineteenth century. The purpose was mostly for research and for the possible utilization of cold pastureland. Before that, Samuel Turner, a Briton, sent two yak bulls from Tibet to England in 1783. One died on the way there, and the other, after recovering from the journey, was mated to British cows. Several calves were born, but only one female survived to breed (with an Indian bull) (Turner, 1800).

In 1854, a total of 12 male and female yak were imported into France, also from Tibet. They appeared to acclimatise successfully but performed differently in different areas due to variations in feeding. They did best in the Cantal province of the central French Plateau.

Table 1.1 Distribution of yak and numbers (1997 - 2000 data for China*)

Country	Province or region	Distribution at location	Number ('000)
China			
	Qinghai	All	3 716 (in 2000)
	Tibet	All	3 916 (in 1999)
	Sichuan	Western plateau and alpine	4 084 (in 2000)
	Gansu	area	
		Southern grasslands and	904 (in 1997)
	Xinjiang	Qilian	230 (in 1997)
	Yunnan	mountain area	50 (in 1997)
	Inner	Middle of the Tianshan	0.2 (in 2001)
	Mongolia	mountains	0.9 (in 1983)
	Hebei	Northwestern alpine area	0.1 (in 1983)
	Beijing	Helan mountain area	
Mongolia		Northern mountainous area	610
Countries of		Xishan cold mountainous area	100 (?)
CIS			20 (+40 hybrid)
Nepal			38
Bhutan			40-51 (?)
India			11
Pakistan			2 (?)
Afghanistan			2 (?)
North America			

*Recent reports suggest that numbers in some areas of China may be higher than those derived from less-recent official statistics shown in the Table. Estimates with question marks attached may be less reliable than others.

Hybrids with cattle were produced in both possible ways – calves from native cows and calves from yak cows - with calves of the latter being reported as the better. However, although the yak disappeared after 1862, local stories lived on about animals at high altitudes that were strong, tolerant of rough conditions and with the tail of a horse (Boulnois, 1976). The horse-like tail, derived from the yak, led to the legend that the original crosses had been between cattle and horses. Clearly, the yak left an impression, but no descendants.

Small herds of yak are found in other parts of Europe, including Switzerland and Austria (Agir, 1997; Michael Goe, personal communication, 2002; Horst Geilhausen, personal communication, 2002). More detail is given in Chapter 11, part 3.

A number of yak were sent to Canada, first in 1909 and again in 1921 for trials, including hybridization with domestic cattle and with American bison in an attempt, later discontinued, to produce an animal capable of meat production in the harsh pastoral conditions of northern Canada. A similar project using only domestic cattle for the hybridizing, was conceived and carried out for some years in Alaska, starting with yak born in Canada (White *et al.*, 1946).

Some yak were present in the late 1980s in the Polar Park of Edmonton, Alberta, Canada. Since then, the yak has expanded in numbers in Canada and the United States for commercial use in meat production. In addition, there are yak in a several zoological and wild animal parks in Europe, North America and elsewhere. More reference to these yak populations, some in environmental conditions thought to be atypical for yak, is included in Chapter 4 in relation to adaptation and in more detail in Chapter 11, part 3.

The name of the yak – a historical note

In the Tibetan language, yak is pronounced as "yag"; although in that form, it usually applies to the yak bull – with *dri* the equivalent Tibetan term for the female yak. Other languages follow this name closely. This use of the same name in numerous languages is considered unusual.

The ancient Chinese people called the animal *Ya Niu*. In the Shang dynasty (before 3 000 B.C.), yak was vividly written as 牜, denoting the yak's large body, outstretched horns, long hair and big tail. In time, the name was reduced to a word pronounced as "ya". Later still, this was mispronounced as "mao" – and many homophones began to appear after the Qin and Han dynasties. These words referred not only to the yak but also to yak hair products (because 髦 *mao* means "hair" in Chinese). Some people wrote 毛, pronounced "mao", as 犛, pronounced "li", and then called the yak *Li Niu*. The tiny alteration in the script led to a change of name. And this provides an interesting object lesson for good handwriting! A distinction between *Li* and *Mao* to denote yak was first made in the *Compendium of materia medica*, published by Li Shizhen in 1578. *Li Niu* was said to live in the mountains and denoted the wild yak, while *Mao Niu* was used to denote the domestic yak (Li Ruimin, 1986).

Present-day names, in spite of a common thread, vary for the yak from country to country and often from locality to locality within a country. The male and the female are generally known by different names and there is a plethora of different names for the hybrids of yak with other cattle. (For the sake of clarity in this book, the species of either sex will be referred to by its common name of "yak" and the sexes will be distinguished by the prefix "male" and "female", but with an occasional use of "bull", "steer" [castrated male] and "cow").

Some observations on the wild yak

Before the wild yak became known as *Li*, it was called *Zhong* in the Tibetan language and *Zuo* by the ancient Chinese in central China.

Li Shizhen in his *Compendium of materia medica* of 1578, said: "In the southwestern area around yak country, *Li Niu* (the wild yak) lives in the high mountains. Its appearance, hair colour and tail are the same as those of the domestic yak, but its body is larger." In 1875, N.M. Przewalski, named the wild yak *Bos mutus Prze*, in the belief that the wild yak did not make a sound or "cry". In fact, although the wild yak does not normally cry, it will let out squeaks and cries during oestrus and the breeding season and if it meets other wild beasts, just as does the domestic yak.

According to Miller and Steane (1996), wild yak once numbered in the millions in the central and eastern border areas of the Qinghai-Tibetan Plateau. Herds of them also existed on the cold pastures of western Sichuan province up to the middle of the twentieth century. Male wild yak could be seen mingling and mating with herds of female domestic yak. A few individuals with hair colour characteristics of wild yak can be seen in domestic herds to the present day – the principal visual difference being grey-white hairs, which are normally absent in the domestic yak, found around the mouth. The domestic yak that do have such grey-white hairs are those that have had, at some stage, an infusion of wild yak blood. This is particularly found among the Plateau breed of yak in Qinghai.

Excessive hunting of wild yak for food drove them from the plateau areas into mountainous areas at even higher altitudes, above 4 500 m and right to the tops of the mountains at 6 000 m. By the 1970s, wild yak were thought to be on the verge of extinction. Some survived in China's Kunlun mountains and due to protective measures by the Chinese Government, some wild herds are reported to have reappeared at elevations between 4 000 and 4 500 m. Schaller (1998) gives an authoritative account of the distribution and herd dynamics of wild yak. He reports finding few animals, except in the Changtang reserve, in the course of extensive visits to areas of the wild yak's present and former range. Schaller's estimate of likely total numbers is around 15 000. However, in view of improved access to much of the territory by road and continuing reports of illegal hunting, survival of the wild yak does not seem assured.

The wild yak is large in body and strong (Figure 1.2). Thick, long hair covers the whole body. The colour of the hair is jet brown or jet black. This is virtually the exclusive colour, but Schaller (1998) reported a golden brown mutation among wild yak seen in the Aru Basin of northwestern Tibet. A colour line down the back of the body and behind the withers is silver grey and there are grey-white hairs around the muzzle. (As referred to earlier, the latter feature is found only in domestic yak that have some wild yak blood.)

Figure 1.2 Wild yak bull of the Kunlun type (Photo courtesy of Lu Zhonglin)

The horns are round and very thick, 15 - 20 cm in diameter. (Some herdsmen used these horns as milking vessels and this can still be found in some remote areas of the country.) The horn arch of the wild yak is open (Figure 1.3), and the head shape has a fierce appearance.

Figure 1.3 Horn arch and part of a wild yak skull (undated) discovered in the middle reaches of the Heihe River in Ruoergai county, Sichuan province

The skull illustrated in Figure 1.3 is the largest of several skulls found in the middle and lower reaches of the Heihe Riverof Ruoergai county, Sichuan province and presumed to be ancient remains of wild yak. Measurements of the skull are as follows:

Forehead width – highest	34 cm
Forehead width – lowest	28 cm
Distance between base of horns	27 cm
Circumference of base of horns	44 cm
Horn length	99 cm
Largest distance between horns	146 cm
Distance between tips of horns	126 cm

On the basis of these measurements, it was estimated that this yak had been 170 cm high at its withers, had a body length (pin bone to shoulder) of 190 cm, a heart girth of 250 cm and weighed approximately 950 kg, which is 1.5 times the average for domestic yak bulls in the same area (Cai Li, 1989). Schaller (1998) quotes figures based on a number of published studies suggesting a shoulder height for adult wild yak bulls of 175 - 203 cm and of 137-156 cm for adult females. A total body length is given as 358 - 381 cm for bulls. Wild yak bulls are said to be about 35 percent heavier than the cows. The length of 53 horns of wild yak bulls found in the Changtang reserve is reported by Schaller (1998) to have averaged 75.7 ± 10.7 cm along the outside curve.

Wild yak prefer to live in herds of tens or even hundreds of animals. The wild yak has a very acute sense of smell, is highly alert and timid; it tries to escape immediately on sensing or seeing people or other animals. Wild yak stampede readily, but if angered or cornered they are fierce and will attack an intruder. Wild yak dislike heat but are highly tolerant of cold and starvation. Wild yak bulls often wander off individually during the non-breeding season to hill areas away from the high mountains. Such males are known to attack people on remote roads.

In times when wild yak were more prevalent, they were known to come down from the mountains to mate with female domestic yak during the breeding season. The first crossbred generation (F1[1]) between the wild and the domestic yak was similar in appearance to the wild yak and had a larger body and fiercer temper than the typical domestic yak. The crosses are difficult to manage, but the herdsmen like them because of their apparently better growth and development compared to pure domestic yak. They are also liked because the crossbred males are perceived as protecting the herd better than their domestic counterparts. There is now an attempt, organized by provincial yak breeding centres, to exploit the potential benefits of such crossbreeding through the use of semen from wild yak bulls to inseminate domestic yak cows. Some observations on the body size and performance of such crosses are included in Chapter 3.

Feral yak

Recently, 250 - 300 feral yak were discovered in the Helan mountains of Inner Mongolia at an elevation of 2 500 - 3 000 m (Han Jianlin personal communication, 2002). These animals are thought to be the offspring of yak that lived about 200 years ago that were used at that time by lamas to transport Tibetan religious books from Qinghai to Gansu. The herd contains a high proportion of white animals, which suggests they may be related to Tianzhu White yak. Currently, there is no confirmation of this. Some of the oldest residents in the region contend that these yak are only about half the size that they were 50

---

[1]The F1 in this book denotes the first generation of offspring from a cross of two pure breeds, or a hybrid of yak and cattle. F2 is then the generation produced by mating F1 to F1. Matings of F1 back to one of the parental types is referred to as B - with an appropriate suffix – denoting a backcross.

years ago. This is attributed, with agreement from local technical staff, to inbreeding in the herd. Local farmers also believe the lack of salt in the area may have contributed to what is described as the degeneration of the animals over the years. These yak are said to have shorter and thinner coats than what is normal for other yak and this is attributed to the fact that the area is warmer than typical for yak-producing areas. It would be useful to have more detailed studies of these animals to determine their kinship to other yak and possibly their inbreeding status and to have some record of their performance, reproduction and survival rates.

Yak in the culture of the people

As noted earlier, the yak has a long documented history stretching into ancient times. As the people who kept them migrated, they took their yak with them into wider territory. It is important to stress how closely involved the yak has been, and is, with the culture, religion and social life of the pastoral people of the cold, high-mountainous regions of Asia – at least among those people who can trace their history of yak keeping back over the centuries. This will be given more detailed consideration in Chapter 12 (see also Miller, 2002). The traditions and traditional knowledge of yak keeping provide a suitable counterbalance for the scientific and technological considerations – the main concerns in this book. It is possible, of course, that the cultural and social context of yak herding may diminish in the future in the face of the introduction of market-driven economics and of improved transport and communication. It is also possible that the spread, however slow, of modern concepts of feeding, management and breeding, and the pressures on yak husbandry from those proffering such technological advice, might further erode the force of traditional values. In some areas, such as Nepal, social change in relation to its yak economy, as documented by, for example, Bishop (1989), has led to a great reduction in yak numbers. It would be a pity if the natural resources of the vast territories now purposefully exploited by the yak were to become less productive or deserted through insensitive management of change.

The yak takes its place alongside other animals, both real and mythical, in the history, legends and mythology of the Tibetan region and neighbouring territories, as illustrated with examples by Cayla (1976). The yak and yak emblems are closely associated with many aspects of religious practice of Tibetan Buddhism and depicted widely in temple art, as described succinctly by Olsen (1990). The use of the yak as provider of components for local medicines is but one aspect of their near-mystical importance. Meyer (1976) described some of these medicines and remedies associated with the yak.

As discussed in more detail in Chapter 12, religion, ceremony, social customs and attitudes to wealth and its symbols are all intertwined with each other in the life of the people and with the integral role of the yak in all aspects of that life. This intertwining has counterparts among nomadic people of Africa but is rarely applicable to animal husbandry in the western part of the world. It is important to bear these points in mind, lest it be assumed that knowledge of the reproductive and productive attributes of the yak and of modern management practices are all that is required to bring about "improvements" in the economy of yak keeping.

The spread of knowledge of the yak outside its "native" area

The relative isolation of both wild and domesticated yak in the mountainous regions of central Asia, around the Qinghai-Tibetan Plateau, is illustrated by the dearth of mention of the yak in the West until relatively modern times. If early travellers to the East had attempted to export yak, they might have been frustrated by a reputedly poor tolerance of the yak to prolonged exposure to heat at lower altitudes - particularly if this involved a relatively rapid transition from cold to hot areas. Although, as already mentioned, yak now exist in zoos and wild animal parks in many parts of the world and commercially in North America. This suggests that the degree of tolerance of the yak to heat and its adaptability to different environments may be better than traditionally thought and that this subject requires reappraisal (see Chapter 11, part 3).

Lydekker (1912) asserted that yak were known by repute in western Europe in the classical Grecian times and given the name of *poiphogoi*, or "eaters of poa grass", because they were said to feed exclusively on grass. Also, Zeuner (1963) in his *A history of domesticated animals* provided two early references to yak. The first of these dates to the latter part of the first century A.D. when Martial (a Roman poet) alluded to the use, by the ladies of Rome, of the tail of some kind of ox (*Muscarium bubulus*) as a fly-whisk, or clothes brush. Zeuner deduced that the tail was that of the yak and goes on to point out that this, in turn, suggests that overland trading routes to the East must have been fully open then. (The yak-tail fly-whisk has been well-known in India for centuries). Zeuner further referred to accounts of the thirteenth-century travels of Marco Polo, who clearly exaggerated the size of the yak when equating it to an elephant.

Boulnois (1976) provided a much fuller background to the knowledge of the yak made available by Western travellers in early times, especially from the seventeenth century onwards.

It is therefore apparent that factual information on the yak, as distinct from anecdotes, came to Europe rather late, compared to China, as seen from the many references in ancient Chinese literature. Perhaps the first Western account was by Samuel Turner, who was sufficiently impressed by the yak to send two to Europe. His book, *An account of an embassy to the Court of the Teshoo Lama in Tibet*, was published in 1800 and republished in 1971; in it he vividly described the characteristics of the yak and its environs.

In respect to more recent times, there are, apart from much documentation of the yak by Chinese authors and a substantial body of publications in Russian, two substantive accounts in English on the general performance of the yak in China. These reports resulted from visits to various parts of yak country in the 1940s by distinguished American experts in animal husbandry (Phillips *et al.*, 1945, 1946). In the past few decades, relatively brief, general accounts of the yak in English have appeared in textbooks and in FAO publications dealing with the livestock of China and the former USSR. In addition, there are a number of "popular" articles about the yak though they are of the "isn't-it-wonderful" or "quaint" variety. Fortunately, there are a substantial number of technical papers on specialist research topics regarding the yak and the ecology of its territories published in English, French, German and other languages that are more widely accessible to readers in the West. Many of these are reference sources for this book in addition to the great number from traditional yak-rearing countries. Special mention must be made of the substantial and well-documented study by a team of French scholars (*The yak – its role in the economic and cultural life of its breeders in central Asia*) sponsored by the Société d'Ethnozootechnie au Museum National d'Histoire Naturelle (Paris) (1976).

A recent source of information on the commercial use of yak is the promotional literature and Web site of the International Yak Association, formed by yak breeders in North America.

References

Agir (1997). Elevages exotiques en Suisse. *Actualités,* 30 Août 1997.

Belyar, D.K. (1980). *Domestication of yakutsk*. Siberian Publication House.

Bishop, N.H. (1989). From zomo to yak: Change in a Sherpa village. *Human Ecology*, 17:177-204.

Boulnois, L. (1976). The yak and the travels of western naturalists. *In Le Yak*. Son role dans la vie materielle et culturelle des eleveurs d' Asie centrale. Ethnozootechie, No.15, France. pp. 7-22.

Cai Li (1989). *Sichuan yak*. Chengdu, China. Sichuan Nationality Press. 223 pp.

Cayla, L. (1976). Some mythological aspects of yak in Tibet. In: *Le Yak*. Son role dans la vie materielle et culturelle des eleveurs d' Asie centrale. Ethnozootechie, No.15, France. pp. 23-34.

Dyblor, E. (1957). The first time to discovery of yak fossils in Yakutsk. *Vertebrate Palasiatica*, 1 (4): 293-300.

Flerow, C.C. (1980). On the geographic distribution of the genus Poephagus during the Pleistocene and Holocene. *Quaternary Paleontol. (East) Berlin*, 4:123-126.

Guo Shijian & Chen Weisheng (1996). The situation of yaks in China. In: Miller D.G., Craig S.R. and Rana G.M. (ed), *Proceedings of a workshop on conservation and management of yak genetic diversity, at ICIMOD, Kathmandu, 29-31 October 1996*. ICIMOD (International Centre for Integrated Mountain Development), Kathmandu. pp. 25-28.

Langjie Zeren *et al.* (1987). Supplementary feeding trial for fattening hybrid of Holstein-Friesian and yak in warm season. *Journal of China Yak*, 4: pp. 51-55.

Li Ruimin (1986). Records of bovine species in ancient Chinese history. In: Zhang Zhongge and Zhu Xianhuang (ed), *Proceedings of papers about history of animal husbandry in China.* Beijing, China Science Press. pp. 146-149.

Li Shih-Chen (Li Shizhen (1596). *Compendium of materia medica,* or *The great herbal. (Pen ts'ao kang mu,* or *Ben cao gang mu)*

Li Yifang (1999). *Past, present and future of milk industry in China.* Beijing, China Agriculture Press.

Lydekker, R. (1912). *The ox and its kindred.* London. Methuen & Co. Ltd.

Meyer, F. (1976). Notes on products from the yak and its crosses used in Tibetan medicine. *In Le Yak.* Son role dans la vie materielle et culturelle des eleveurs d' Asie centrale. Ethnozootechie, No.15, France. pp. 35-45.

Miller, D.J. (1990). Grassland of the Tibetan Plateau. *Rangelands,* 12:159-163.

Miller, D.J. & Steane, D.E. (1996). Conclusions. In: Miller D.G., Craig S.R. and Rana G.M. (ed), *Proceedings of a workshop on conservation and management of yak genetic diversity, at ICIMOD, Kathmandu, 29-31 October 1996.* ICIMOD (International Centre for Integrated Mountain Development), Kathmandu. pp.191-209.

Miller, D.J. (2002). The importance of China's nomads. Rangelands, 24(1): 22-24.

Olsen, S.J. (1990). Fossil ancestry of the yak, its cultural significance and domestication in Tibet. *Proceedings of the Academy of Natural Sciences of Philadelphia,* 142:73-100.

Olsen, S.J. (1991). Confused yak taxonomy and evidence of domestication. *Illinois State Museum Scientific Papers,* Vol. 23:387-393.

Phillips, R.W., Johnson, R.G. & Moyer, R.T. (1945). *The livestock of China.* U.S. State Department Publication, No. 2249.

Phillips, R.W., Tolstoy, I.A. & Johnson, R.G. (1946). Yaks and yak-cattle hybrids in Asia. *Journal of Heredity,* 37: 163-170, 207-215.

Prezewalski, N.M. (1883). *From Zaisan Lake through the Kham region of Tibet and the head of the Yellow River.* Second edition (1948). Moscow.

Qian Yanwen (1979). *The origin of domesticated animal: biohistory.* Beijing, China Science Press.

Schaller, G.B. (1998). Wild yak. Chapter 7 in *Wildlife of the Tibetan Steppe.* University of Chicago Press. 125-142

Tong Pingya & Zhao Guopan (1990). *Brief history about livestock and poultry in China.* Beijing, Scientific Books Press. 46-47.

Turner, Samuel (1800). (1971 reprint of original edition). *An account of an embassy to the Court of the Teshout Lama in Tibet.* Original edition: G. & W. Nicol, Booksellers, London, Reprint: Bibliotheca Himalayica, Series I, vol. 4. New Delhi, Manjusri Publishing House.

Verdiev, Z. & Erin, I. (1981). Yak farming is milk and meat production. *Molochnoe I miasnoe skotovodstvo,* 2: pp. 16-17.

White, W.T., Phillips, R.W. & Elting, E.C. (1946). Yaks and yak-cattle hybrids in Alaska. *Journal of Heredity,* 37:355-358.

Xu Guifang & Wang Zhigang (1998). Present situation and proposal for future development of yak industry in China. *Forage and Livestock,* Supplement: 6-8.

Xu Shangzhon (1998). Development strategies for the beef industry in China in the twenty-first century. *Forage and Livestock,* Supplement:1-6.

Yu Daxin & Qian Defang (1983). General situation of Xinjiang yak. *Journal of China Yak,* 1:57-64.

Zeuner, F.E. (1963). *A history of domesticated animals*. London, Hutchinson. pp. 352-353.

Zhong Guanhui *et al.* (1986). Observation on the adaptability of yak introduced into Lingshan area of Beijing. *Journal of Southwest Nationalities College* (Animal Husbandry and Veterinary Sciences Edition), 1:9-14.

OVERVIEW

According to the (Chinese) *Provincial annals of livestock breeds*, there are 12 officially recognized breeds of domestic yak in China: the Jiulong yak and Maiwa yak in Sichuan, Tianzhu White yak and Gannan yak in Gansu, Pali yak, Jiali ("Alpine") yak and Sibu yak in Tibet, Huanhu yak and Plateau yak in Qinghai, Bazhou yak in Xinjiang and Zhongdian yak in Yunnan, and one other, the "Long-hair-forehead yak" in Qinghai – which does not, however, meet all the criteria used to define a yak breed. Among these, the Plateau yak, Maiwa yak, Jiulong yak, Tianzhu White yak and Jiali ("Alpine") yak are also included in the publication *Bovine breeds in China*.

The yak of the Qinghai-Tibetan Plateau yak (often called Plateau or Grassland yak) and those of the Henduan mountain Alpine yak (often called Alpine or Valley yak) have long been regarded as "types". This classification was initially based on the geographic and topographic parameters of their habitats and on the body size of different yak populations in the different environments. Although there are some differences between the main types in appearance and in aspects of their performance – as there are also among the breeds – it is not yet resolved to what extent such differences are genetic and to what extent they derive from varying conditions in the areas in which these yak populations are found.

In this chapter, the main characters of 11 of the principal breeds are reviewed. In addition, information is given on an "improved" strain of yak, named Datong yak, which was started by crossbreeding between Huanhu yak and wild yak (using artificial insemination) and subsequently developed on the Datong Yak Farm in Qinghai. (The Datong yak is not at present classified as a breed because of its limited numbers).

Outside China, most notably in Mongolia and in countries of the CIS (formerly Soviet Union), yak are usually referred to by a name designating the area where they are kept or the area from which they have come. Whether this constitutes different breeds in the genetic sense is a matter for debate and is not generally claimed.

Introduction

The yak was listed by Linnaeus (1766) as *Bos grunniens*, the same genus as other domestic cattle. However, in the middle of the nineteenth century the yak was listed as *Poephagus grunniens* (Gray, 1843) on the grounds of morphological distinctions from both other cattle and from bison. There was a return to *Bos grunniens* following Lydekker (1898), and this form has continued to be used to the present. More recently, however, the *Poephagus* classification has returned and been considered as the most appropriate for reasons discussed by Corbet (1978) and by Olsen (1990, 1991) following a re-examination of the available fossil evidence. The name *Poephagus grunniens* has been adopted increasingly, over recent years – but is by no means universally accepted. Clearly, this is a matter of considerable interest and concern to taxonomists. Since both the *Bos* and the *Poephagus* genera have their strong adherents in respect to the yak, it will be surprising if this debate ends anytime soon (see also Chapter 15 for new evidence favouring *Poephagus*). Fortunately, both camps agree on the species name of *grunniens* on account of the characteristic grunting noise made by the yak.

The yak has the same number of chromosomes (60) as *Bos taurus* and *Bos indicus* and interbreeds with both; the female hybrids being fertile and the male hybrids sterile. The yak will also interbreed with bison – again, the female hybrids are fertile, but not the males (Deakin *et al.*, 1935). (These authors also report that the yak-bison hybrid showed stamina and speed to a "remarkable degree".)

Breeds in China

Domestic yak differ from wild yak in being smaller and, not surprisingly, in temperament (see Chapter 1). It is not clear whether these differences have arisen because of differences in the selection pressures on wild and domestic yak or whether and to what extent genetic drift and inbreeding have contributed. However, there are many attributes in common between wild and domestic yak; broadly speaking, they share a similar environment and, as already noted, they will interbreed without difficulty, given the opportunity.

By crossing wild yak bulls with the Huanhu yak on the Datong Yak Farm, using artificial insemination, a "new" strain of yak has been developed (see section, A new strain of Datong yak in Qinghai). Moreover, the semen from the wild yak and semi-wild yak bulls have been extensively used with the intention of improving domestic yak productivity in Qinghai, Tibet, Sichuan, Gansu and Xinjiang (see Chapter 11, part 1). In former times, it was not uncommon for wild yak bulls to wander among domestic yak herds within their territory and mate with them (cf. Chapter 10). Crosses of wild and domestic yak and, consequently, their special qualities have been known for a long time to herdsmen in the vicinity of wild yak territory.

Twelve yak breeds were officially recognized by committees of yak experts on the basis of intensive investigations in the six main yak-raising provinces in China. Results of these deliberations published in the provincial annals of livestock breeds in the 1980s and discussed in many other publications (Lei Huanzhang, 1982; Editing Committee [Qinghai], 1983; Department of Animal Husbandry and Veterinary Medicine in Gansu, 1986; Editing Committee [Sichuan], 1987; Liu Zubo *et al.*, 1989; Cai Li, 1989, 1992; Zhang Rongchang, 1989; Zhong Jincheng, 1996; Bhu Chong, 1998; Han Jianlin, 2000; Ji Qiumei, *et al.*, 2002). The recognized breeds are the Jiulong yak and Maiwa yak in Sichuan, Tianzhu White yak and Gannan yak in Gansu, Pali yak, Jiali (Alpine) yak and Sibu yak in Tibet, Huanhu yak, Plateau yak and the "long-hair-forehead" yak in Qinghai, Bazhou yak in Xinjiang and Zhongdian yak in Yunnan. For this book's present purpose, the "long-hair-forehead yak" of Qinghai province is not considered further because it does not match the definition of a breed due to its random distribution in herds of both the Huanhu and Plateau yak. The remaining 11 breeds will be described here in some detail. However, all 11 breeds are distinguished only by origin, location and some small differences in productive characteristics (which might be attributable to the locality). There is almost no evidence available of the magnitude of any genetic differences.

The domestic yak of the Qinghai-Tibetan Plateau (known as the Plateau or Grassland yak) and those of the Henduan mountain range (known as Alpine or Valley yak) in China have been regarded as "types" for a long time. This classification was initially based on the geographic and topographic parameters of their habitats and on the body size of the different yak populations (Cai Li, 1985). In 1982, a number of Chinese experts on the yak agreed to a broad classification of domestic yak into these two principal types (Plateau and Alpine) based on body conformation. The classification also took account of the ecological and social-economic conditions in which the yak were kept and evidence of any selection that had taken place. In general, it was thought that artificial selection applied to the Qinghai-Tibetan Plateau type during its development was less than that applied to the Henduan Alpine type (Cai Li, 1989).

Other classification suggestions have arisen from time to time but have not been subsequently adopted. Although there are some differences between the main types in appearance and in aspects of their performance – as there are among the breeds – it is not yet resolved to what extent such differences are genetic and to what extent they derive from the different conditions in the areas in which these yak populations are found. Even the once apparently clear distinction between the Qinghai-Tibet Plateau and the Henduan Alpine types has become blurred or ignored in recent literature.

To resolve the question of the relative contribution of heredity and environment to the apparent differences among the breeds of yak, one would require comparisons of them and of the crosses between them at the same location and at the same time. Better still, such comparisons should be repeated at a number of different locations typical of the different ecological habitats associated with the breeds of yak. If that were done, it might be expected that outward appearance associated with colour, hair and horn types and, to some extent, body conformation would remain largely distinct. However, differences in aspects such as body size and milk production, as well as reproductive performance, might converge in a common environment. But the extent of such effects cannot be predicted. Currently, genetic approaches using chromosomal and protein polymorphisms, mitochondrial DNA RFLP (restricted fragment length polymorphism), mitochondrial DNA sequencing and microsatellite genotyping are being introduced to the study of yak to estimate the genetic distance among breeds and some aspects of breed differentiation (see Chapter 15).

Plateau yak of Qinghai

This yak, now classified as a breed, is found on the cold highland pasture of southern and northern Qinghai province where the wild yak distribution overlapped with it, particularly in former times. Crossing between them is thus assumed to have taken place. Its population numbers around three million (Han Jianlin, 2000). The Plateau yak of Qinghai looks similar to the wild yak in body conformation. Among domestic yak breeds it stands tall, has a relatively large body weight and big head. Both sexes are horned. Similar to wild yak, it has greyish-white hair down its back and around the muzzle and eye sockets. It adapts well to the cold and humid climate at high elevation (see Table 2.1a). The majority of these yak are black-brown in colour (71.8 percent) and the rest are chestnut (7.8 percent), grey (6 percent), spotted (1.7 percent) and white (0.8 percent) (Lei Huanzhang, 1982; Editing Committee [Qinghai], 1983; Liu Zubo *et al.*, 1989). Their productivity is shown in Table 2.1b.

Huanhu yak of Qinghai

This breed is found in the transitional zone around the Qinghai Lake in Qinghai province where the grasslands are predominantly semi-arid and consist of meadow pasture and neighbouring areas consist of dry Gobi and semi-Gobi pastures. It is believed that herds of this strain were domesticated and transferred to this area by the Qiang people, the predecessors of the present Tibetans, and by the Tufan people, beginning 10 000 years ago up through their later migrations. Around 310 A.D., Mongolian immigrants used Mongolian cattle to hybridize with the local yak to improve the relatively low productivity of the animals. Accordingly, the Huanhu yak, numbering about one million (Han Jianlin, 2000), contains some remnants of cattle blood from the time of its origins, and this may account for some of its differences from the Plateau yak (Liu Zubo *et al.*, 1989). Compared to the Plateau yak, the Huanhu has a relatively smaller body size and finer structure, a wedge-shaped head, a narrower and longer nose that is mostly concave in the middle, a smaller but broad mouth, a thinner neck, deeper chest, narrower buttock, longer legs and smaller, but strong solid feet with a hard base to them. Most of the animals are hornless; those with horns have a fine, long and slightly curved set of horns. The colours are varied, but the majority is black-brown (64.3 percent); among the rest, there are grey animals (10.3 percent), white-spotted (10.7 percent) chestnut-brown (4.7 percent), white (3 percent) and other colours (6.9 percent) (Lei Huanzhang, 1982; Editing Committee [Qinghai], 1983; Liu Zubo *et al.*, 1989). Their productivity is shown in Table 2.1b.

Tianzhu White yak of Gansu

The Tianzhu White breed (see Figure 2.1) is found in Tianzhu county of Gansu province, which is located in the eastern end of the Qilian mountains and the northern edge of the Qinghai-Tibetan Plateau (102°02' - 103°29'E; 36°29' - 37°41'N). Its main distribution borders the Menyuan and Huzhu counties of Qinghai where a few white yak are also found. Generally, 2 - 3 percent of all yak populations are white individuals – though these are not regarded as part of the Tianzhu White breed. Because the white yak hair is easily dyed into different colours, it has been highly valued in local markets. On account of this, herdsmen who had migrated from Qinghai started to select and breed pure white herds

20

about 120 years ago. A more intensive breeding programme started in 1981. Currently, there are around 60 000 of the white individuals (Liang Yulin and Zhang Haimin, 1998; Zhang Haimin and Liang Yulin, 1998). The breed has a medium body size and fine structure, a well-developed forepart but a less-developed rear part and strong but short legs. And there are big differences in size between the two sexes. Compared to the females, the males have larger heads with a wider forehead, longer and coarser horns with a visible contour, a larger mouth and broader muzzle, thinner lips, smaller nose and a coarser neck. The sex dimorphism is greater in the Tianzhu White yak than in other breeds. In the total population of the Tianzhu White breed in Gansu and Qinghai, around half the individuals have only white hair and skin with slightly red eye sockets. They are typical albinos. The rest are white but with coloured spots, mostly around the eye sockets. This colour helps to reduce problems to the eyes from the strong ultraviolet irradiation at high altitudes (Pu Ruitang *et al.*, 1982; Department of Animal Husbandry and Veterinary Medicine in Gansu, 1986; Zhang Rongchang, 1989). Their productivity is shown in Table 2.1b.

Gannan yak of Gansu

Yak raising in the Gannan Tibetan autonomous prefecture of Gansu (100°46' - 104°45'E; 33°06' - 35°43'N), bordering Sichuan and Qinghai, for long has been based on the same yak from the Qinghai-Tibetan Plateau. Frequent exchange of breeding animals continues. There are about 700 000 animals of this breed (Han Jianlin, 2000). It has a strong body conformation and well-developed muscles, a relatively large skull, a short, wide and slightly protruding forehead, a long and concave nose with externally expanded muzzle, a square mouth with thin lips, horned (48 - 97 percent in different herds) or hornless, small ears, round eyes, a well-developed chest and belly and short, strong legs with small feet. Black is the predominant colour (76.8 percent of the animals); among the rest, the colours are white-spotted on black (15.8 percent), grey (6 percent) and yellow and white (1.4 percent). The males have longer and coarser horns with wider distance between the bases and a stronger neck than the females. The females have a small udder with short nipples (Department of Animal Husbandry and Veterinary Medicine in Gansu, 1986; Zhang Rongchang, 1989). Their productivity is shown in Table 2.1b.

Pali yak of Tibet

This breed is mainly found in Yadong county of Shigatse prefecture of the Tibetan Autonomous Region (approximately 88°8'E, 27°5'N), which borders western Bhutan and India. It has a strong and well-developed body conformation that is rectangular, a short skull with a wide forehead, a big round mouth with thin lips, small eyes, broad muzzle, small nose, a short, strong neck, a deep wide chest and large heart girth, a large belly and short, strong legs with small solid feet. Most of the animals have horns with wide bases. Black is the dominant body colour (87 percent); the rest are spotted black (11 percent) and brown (2 percent) (Tang Zhenyu *et al.*, 1981; Liu Zubo *et al.*, 1989). Their productivity is shown in Table 2.1b.

21

Sibu yak of Tibet

This breed is found in Medrogungkar county (approximately 92°40'E; 29°120'N) in the southeastern Lhasa municipality of Tibet. It has a large head with externally expanded horns, a rectangular-shaped body conformation with a straight back (Dou Yaozong *et al.*, 1984; Liu Zubo *et al.*, 1989). Their productivity is shown in Table 2.1b.

Jiali (Alpine) yak of Tibet

This breed is found in the Jiali (Lhari in Tibetan) county of the Nakchu prefecture (approximately 93°40'E; 31°N) of Tibet at the southern edge of the Nyenchen Thangla mountains. It has a relatively large body shape with a deep and wide chest, and it is mostly horned (83 percent). Compared to the females, males have coarser and stronger horns with a wide distance between the bases. Females have a thinner neck, straighter back, a larger belly and shorter legs than the males. Eighty percent of the animals have a white-spotted head or a completely white head. Half of them are white-spotted black, 41 percent are pure black or with only a white tail and the remaining 9 percent are white, brown or grey (NIAH *et al.*, 1982; Liu Zubo *et al.* 1989). Their productivity is shown in Table 2.1b.

Jiulong yak of Sichuan

This breed (see Figure 2.2) belongs to the Jiulong county of Sichuan province, which is located on the southeastern edge of the Qinghai-Tibetan Plateau (approximately 101°33'E, 28°39'N). It has a long history of development, but today's herds are the descendants of a relatively small population that survived a severe outbreak of Rinderpest some 150 years ago. The population now numbers around 50 000 animals (Zhong Jincheng, 1996; Lin Xiaowei and Zhong Guanghui, 1998). The Jiulong yak has a large body height and body size, with a deep and wide chest and a medium-sized head. The breed is horned. Males, compared to females, have a shorter head but with a wider forehead and wider-based horns, bigger eyes, thinner lips and well-developed teeth, a finer neck, straighter back and shorter legs. Females have a relatively long neck. Black is the predominant colour (61.7 percent); the rest are black-and-white (24.6 percent) and white-spotted on black (13.7 percent) (Editing Committee [Sichuan], 1987; Cai Li, 1989, 1992; Liu Zubo *et al.* 1989). Their productivity is shown in Table 2.1b.

Maiwa yak of Sichuan

This breed (see Figure 2.3), numbering around 600 000 animals (Lin Xiaowei and Zhong Guanghui, 1998), belongs to Hongyuan county of Sichuan province (approximately 102°33'E; 32°48'N), which borders Gansu and Qinghai provinces The breed originated from almost the same locality as the present-day Jiulong yak. However, it was taken by a migratory tribe to its present habitat, passing through southern Qinghai, in the 1910s. During that migration, matings occurred with other domestic yak on route and with wild yak when it first settled in Hongyuan, when wild yak were still known to come down from Qinghai. The resulting infusions of genes are thought to have improved the original type. The better pasture and ecological environment of the new habitat assisted its development. It has a medium-sized head and a wide flat forehead, straight back, a well-developed belly, a long body with short legs and small solid feet. Most of the animals are horned.   Black accounts for 64.2 percent of the population's colouring; the rest are black with a white-spotted head and tail (16.8 percent), cyan (a very dark blue) (8.1 percent), brown (5.2 percent), black-and-white (4.2 percent) or other colours (1.5 percent) (Cai Bolin, 1981; Editing Committee [Sichuan], 1987; Cai Li, 1989, 1992; Liu Zubo *et al*. 1989). Their productivity is shown in Table 2.1b.

Bazhou yak of Xinjiang

This breed is found mainly in Hejing county (83° - 93°56'E, 36°11' - 43°20'N) in Xinjiang Uyghur Autonomous Region. Their presence dates to 1890 when around 60 animals were brought from Tibet (Zhou Yiqing, 1980); another 176 animals were introduced in 1920 (Dong Baoshen, 1986). In the late 1980s, some breeding bulls were purchased from the Datong Yak Farm in Qinghai to refresh the blood (Dong Baoshen, 1986). There are now about 70 000 Bazhou yak (Fang Guangxin and Liu Wujun, 1998). This breed has a large rectangular body, a heavy head, a short and wide forehead, big round eyes, small ears, a broad muzzle and thin lips, a wide chest, large belly and strong legs with small, solid feet. The majority (77.3 percent) have fine, long horns. Black is the main colour, but some are black and white, brown or grey and white (Gala *et al.*, 1983; Yu Daxin and Qian Defang, 1983; Zhang Rongchang, 1989). Their productivity is shown in Table 2.1b.

Zhongdian yak of Yunnan

This breed is found in the Zhongdian and Deqin counties (99°50' - 100 50'E, 26°85' - 28 40'N) in the very northern part of Yunnan province, at the southern end of the Qinghai-Tibetan Plateau where it borders Tibet and Sichuan. In general, the Zhongdian yak has had frequent exchanges of blood with yak in Sichuan. There are about 20 000 animals of this breed (Zhong Jincheng, 1996; Han Jianlin, 2000). It has a strong body conformation, large round eyes, small ears, a wide forehead, a deep chest, straight back, well-developed legs with large feet and a short tail. Both sexes have horns. There is relatively large variation in body size. The majority of the animals are black (62.4 percent), a black-and-white colouring is found among 27.5 percent of them, while the rest are black with white-spots on the forehead, legs and tail (Liu Guoliang, 1980; Duan Zhongxuan and Huang Fenyin, 1982; Zhang Rongchang, 1989). Their productivity is shown in Table 2.1b.

A new strain of Datong yak in Qinghai

This is the only improved yak population developed deliberately by crossing wild yak bulls with domestic yak females with the intention of creating a new breed of yak. The development is taking place on the Datong Yak Farm in Qinghai (approximately 101°70'E, 32°N and at an altitude of around 3 200 m). For this purpose, one wild yak bull captured in the Kunlun mountains and two in the Qilian mountains (with an altitude of more than 5 000 m) were taken to Datong Yak Farm and trained for semen collection between 1983 and 1986.

Figure 2.1 Tianzhu White yak (Qinghai-Tibetan Plateau type)

a   b

Figure 2.2 Jiulong yak (Henduan Alpine type) a) male; b) female

a   b

Figure 2.3 Maiwa yak (Qinghai-Tibetan Plateau type) a) male; b) female

The semen of these three bulls is used to artificially inseminate the Huanhu yak cows. To date this has produced 1 086 crossbred animals (F1), which formed the foundation generation. Then six F1 breeding bulls were selected from that group. The next generation consisted of 1 700 breeding cows, which were of both the F2 type (from mating F1 females to F1 males) and back-crosses (B1) (from mating F1 males with the domestic yak females). The subsequent generation (designated the second generation in the programme) of 29 breeding bulls and 542 breeding cows was obtained by mating B1 to each other, F1 males with the B1 females and B1 males with the F1 females. That generation, in turn, was used to create a nucleus herd. A third generation was created by intermating the offspring from the second generation. In a similar way, a fourth generation was produced from the third. By the year 2000, there were about 2 000 animals in the nucleus herd at the Datong Yak Farm where most performance records have been taken and where most of the selection was practiced. A further 20 000 animals in multiplier herds were situated at three locations: the Datong Yak Farm in Qinghai and the Shandan and Liqiaru farms in Gansu. The animals in the multiplier herds derived from the third and fourth generations at the Datong Yak Farm. In total, 8 700 breeding animals, from the foundation to the third generation, had their productivity recorded over a 15-year period.

The objective in the nucleus herd was to control inbreeding and to select breeding bulls to improve yak productivity. The average inbreeding coefficient was estimated as 0.094 (0.031 - 0.125). The selection of bulls was made first around the time of birth using their own birth weight (adjusted for the parity of the dam) and the body conformation, birth weights and growth of their parents. Ten percent of the bulls were discarded at this stage. A second selection took place when the bull calves were six months old. Body weight and conformation before winter were considered, and weight was adjusted for parity and month of calving. Between 30 and 50 percent of the bull calves were rejected at that stage. A third selection was conducted at age 18 months. This was regarded as a particularly important time for further selection as the animals were weaned and had had the opportunity to express their performance, in terms of growth and body conformation, under both a harsh winter season and the following summer season with adequate nutrition. Sixty percent of those so evaluated were rejected from further consideration. A final selection was made when the animals were between two and a half and three and half years old. At this time, the bulls were each mated to between 15 and 20 cows to check for their reproductive capacity and the offspring phenotype of potential replacement bulls. Each bull's own growth and body conformation was also reconsidered. Half of the bulls taking part at this stage were discarded. After these four selections, around 11 percent of the original group remained for use as replacement breeding bulls.

The Datong yak looks not dissimilar to the wild yak with its greyish-white mouth, nose, sockets and grey back line. The males are horned and females are either horned or hornless. The body conformation seems to be of a meat type with good body weight, straight back, a wide chest, and long, strong legs. The body colour is typically black, though there may also be a few brown hairs. The body measurements and the selection progress of the Datong yak are shown in Tables 2.2 and 2.3. In addition, the milk and fibre yields of the Datong yak were recorded and compared with the Huanhu yak and are reported in a number of publications (Bo Jialin *et al.*, 1998a, b; Wang Minqiang *et al.*, 1998).

Postscript on breeds in China

Not surprisingly in view of the relative isolation of different areas from each other, at least in times past, many distinct breeds of yak have developed in China. Five of them are listed as breeds at national level in the *Bovine breeds of China* (Institute of Animal Science [China], 1986). These are the Plateau yak, Maiwa yak, Jiulong yak, Tianzhu White yak and Jiali (Alpine) yak. The Provincial Administration of Standardization in both Gansu and Sichuan also issued breed criteria for the Maiwa yak, the Jiulong yak and the Tianzhu White yak (TAHVS and DAS, 1985; Zhong Guanghui *et al.*, 1995; Wen Yongli *et al.*, 1995).

Some information on the various breeds is shown in Tables 2.1a and 2.1b. Three of the breeds are shown in Figures 2.1, 2.2 and 2.3.

Breeds in countries apart from China

From the available literature, it appears that yak in most countries outside China are not specifically classified as "breeds". Instead, they are referred to as yak of a particular area in which they are found or from which they have been brought, or they may take their name from the people of the area. For example, Sarbagishev *et al.* (1989) referred in this manner to the yak in various parts of the former USSR: "Yaks bred in Kirgizia are considerably larger than those in Tajikistan." They are careful to note a management difference between these two populations of yak so as not to draw the conclusion that the differences are necessarily genetic. In the same manner, Zagdsuren (1994) referred to the country of origin when discussing hybridization of yak with cattle of other species. Smirnov *et al.* (1990) referred to yak of "Tuva type" when writing about meat production trials in the northern Caucasus. Verdiev and Erin (1981) referred to Pamir, Altai and Buryatia types, which are the names for the areas or country where the yak are located. In writing about domestic livestock in Nepal, Epstein (1977) also did not separate yak into breeds. It thus appears that differences among "local" populations of yak are recognized, but whether these constitute different breeds, in the genetic sense, is a matter for further investigation. Pal *et al.* (1994) classified the yak of India into a number of types, as described in the section on India in Chapter 11, part 2. For further general information on yak in other countries, see also Chapter 11.

Table 2.1a Main breeds of yak in China and observations on distribution and characteristics
[Source: adapted and revised from Cai Li, 1985]

Location (province or autonomous region)	Breed	Main area	No. ('000)	Topography	Pasture type	Grass type (predominant type)	Altitude (m)	Average annual temp. (°C)	Rainfall (mm)
Sichuan	Jiulong*	Jiulong county and Shade district of Kangding county in Ganzi Tibetan autonomous prefecture	30	High mountain intersecting valleys	Alpine bush and meadow	Mixed sward	>3 500	2.0	900
	Maiwa*	Hongyuan and Ruoergai counties in Aba Tibetan and Qiang autonomous prefecture	200	Hill-shaped plateau	Cold meadow and marsh	Gramineae, cyperaceae	3 400-3 600	1.1	728
Yunnan	Zhongdian	Zhongdian county in Diqing Tibetan autonomous prefecture		Hill-shaped plain among mountains	Alpine bush and meadow	Mixed sward and grass	3 276	5.4	620
Gansu	Tianzhu White*	Tianzhu Tibetan autonomous county	30	Broad plateau and valley	Sub-alpine meadow	Many bush on n. slopes; Gramineae Cyperaceae	[3 000]	0.1	300-416
	Gannan	Gannan Tibetan autonomous prefecture		Hill-shaped plateau	Alpine and sub-alpine	Gramineae, Cyperaceae	3 300-4 400	0.4	664
Qinghai	Plateau*	Northern and southern Qinghai	3 400	Plateau	Alpine meadow	Gramineae, Cyperaceae	3 700-4 700	From -2 to -5.7	282-774
	Huanhu	Mountainous region around the Qinghai Lake		Mountain	Sub-alpine meadow, part forest grassland	Grass	2 000-3 400	From 0.1 to 5.1	269-595
Tibet	Jiali (Alpine)*	Alpine area of Tibet; Jiali county	1 400	Plateau, mountain	Alpine bush and meadow	Mixed sward	>4 000	0	694
	Pali	Yadong county		Plateau, mountain	Alpine meadow	Gramineae, Cyperaceae	4 300	1.7	468
	Sibu	Medrogungkar county		Plateau, mountain	Alpine bush and meadow	Mixed sward	4 000-5 500	0	700
Xinjang	Bazhou	Centre of Tianshan mountains		Mountain	Sub-alpine meadow	Grass	2 400	-4.7	285

* Listed as national breeds in China. ** Estimated body weight = {(heart girth [m])^2 x (body length [m]) x 70}.

Table 2.1b Main breeds of yak in China and observations on distribution and characteristics

Breed		Sex	No.	Body measurements (cm)				Body weight** (kg)	Source
				Height at withers	Body length	Heart girth	Cannon bone circumference		
Sichuan	Jiulong*	M	15	138	178	219	23.6	594	GAAHB and YRO, 1980a, b; Cai Li, 1989
		F	708	117	140	179	18.2	314	
	Maiwa*	M	17	126	157	193	19.8	414	Cai Li, 1989
		F	219	106	131	155	15.6	222	
Yunnan	Zhongdian	M	23	119	127	162	17.6	235	Duan Zhongxuan and Huang Fenying, 1982
		F	186	105	117	154	16.1	193	
Gansu	Tianzhu White*	M	17	121	123	164	18.3	264	Pu Ruitang et al., 1982; Zhang Rongchang, 1989
		F	88	108	114	154	16.8	190	
	Gannan	M	10	126	141	189	22.4	354	Department of Animal Husbandry and Veterinary Medicine in Gansu, 1986; Zhang Rongchang, 1989
		F	159	109	122	157	16.1	210	
Qinghai	Plateau*	M	21	129	151	194	20.1	398	Editing Committee [Qinghai], 1983
		F	208	111	132	157	15.8	228	
	Huanhu	M	14	114	144	169	18.3	287	Editing Committee [Qinghai], 1983
Tibet	Jiali (Alpine)*	M	8	130	154	197	22.4	421	NIAH et al., 1982; Liu Zubo et al., 1989
		F	187	107	133	162	16.1	243	
	Pali	M	59	111	123	155	18.3	288	Tang Zhenyu et al., 1981; Liu Zubo et al., 1989
		F	321	109	121	152	15.2	217	
	Sibu	M	4	132	149	185	21.0	358	Dou Yaozong et al., 1984; Liu Zubo et al., 1989
		F	53	109	127	153	15.9	212	
Xinjiang	Bazhou	M	33	127	140	192	20.7	359	Dong Baoshen, 1986
		F	265	111	124	171	16.3	257	

* Listed as national breeds in China. ** Estimated body weight = {(heart girth [m])^2 x (body length [m]) x 70}.

Table 2.2 Body measurements and weights of the first generation Datong yak in comparison to the Huanhu yak on the Datong Yak Farm [Source: Bo Jialin et al., 1998b]

Group	No.	Age (month)	Height at withers (cm)	Body length (cm)	Heart girth (cm)	Cannon bone circumf. (cm)	Body weight (kg)
Datong yak	7[a]	6	88.4 ± 5.6	87.1 ± 5.2	106.8 ± 4.8	12.0 ± 0.7	74.7 ± 10.4
Huanhu yak	7	6	79.4 ± 3.4	52.0 ± 4.6	96.4 ± 5.1	11.3 ± 1.1	58.8 ± 10.2
Difference			5.1*	5.1*	10.4**	0.7	14.88**
Datong yak	7	18	103.1 ± 2.4	108.5 ± 4.7	141.6 ± 4.7	14.6 ± 0.9	150.5 ± 56.1
Huanhu yak	7	18	100.1 ± 3.5	103.2 ± 2.8	131.3 ± 4.5	13.7 ± 0.4	117.7 ± 17.4
Difference			2.7*	5.3*	10.3**	0.9	32.8**

Note: *$P<0.05$; **$P<0.01$. a: Pooled data from 4 females and 3 males of both groups.

Table 2.3 Generation progress of body weights of animals in the nucleus herd at the Datong Yak Farm (data from males [M] and females [F] pooled) [Source: Wang Minqiang et al., 1998]

Item	Generation 0	1st generation	2nd generation
Birth weight	11.49 ± 0.98	12.04 ± 0.89	12.42 ± 0.89
No.	10 M and 11 F	12 M and 15 F	14 M and 19 F
Weight at 6 months	71.02 ± 7.80	74.71 ± 10.47	82.19 ± 12.91
No.	10 M and 15 F	4 M and 3 F	12 M and 19 F
Weight at 18 months	135.08 ± 10.18	150.50 ± 6.07	154.40 ± 11.18
No.	8 M and 12 F	9 M and 12 F	8 M and 12 F

References

Bhu Chong (1998). Present situation of research and production of yak husbandry in Tibet. *Forage and Livestock*, Supplement: 38-40.

Bo Jialin *et al.* (1998a). Raising of the Datong new yak breed. *Forage and Livestock*, Supplement: 9-13.

Bo Jialin *et al.* (1998b). Meat production performance from generation Datong yak in China. *Forage and Livestock*, Supplement: 15-18.

Bo Jialin *et al.* (1998c). Milk production from one generation Datong yak in China. *Forage and Livestock*, Supplement: 19-20.

Cai Bolin (1981). Introduction to the Maiwa yak. *Journal of China Yak*, 1: 33-36.

Cai Li (1985). Yak breeds (or populations). *In* Chen Pieliu (ed), *Domestic animal breeds and their ecological characteristics in China*. Beijing, China Agricultural Press pp. 45-59.

Cai Li (1989). *Sichuan yak*. Chengdu, China, Sichuan Nationality Press. 223 pp.

Cai Li (1992). *China yak*. Beijing, China Agriculture Press. 254 pp.

Corbet, G.B. (1978). *The mammals of the Palaearctic Region: a taxonomic review*. British Museum (Nat. Hist.), Ithaca, New York, Cornell Univ. Press. 314 pp.

Deakin, A., Muir, G.W. & Smith, A.G. (1935). *Hybridisation of domestic cattle, bison and yak. Report of Wainwright experiment*. Publication 479, Technical Bulletin 2, Dominion of Canada, Department of Agriculture, Ottawa.

Department of Animal Husbandry and Veterinary Medicine in Gansu (1986). *Annals of livestock and poultry breeds in Gansu*. Lanzhou, China, Gansu People's Press.

Dong Baoshen (1986). Source, economic traits and development of Hejing yak. *Journal of China Yak*, 2: 33-37.

Dou Yaozong *et al.* (1984). Tibetan yak. *Journal of Tibetan Animal Husbandry and Veterinary Medicine*, 2: 12-34.

Duan Zhongxuan & Huang Fenying (1982). Report of survey on the Zhongdian yak. *Journal of China Yak*, 1: 75-82.

Editing Committee [Qinghai] (1983). *Annals of livestock and poultry breed in Qinghai*. Xining, China.

Editing Committee [Sichuan] (1987). *Annals of livestock and poultry breeds in Sichuan*. Chengdu, China, Sichuan Scientific and Technology Press.

Epstein, H. (1977). *Domestic animals of Nepal*. New York, Holmes & Heier. pp. 20-37.

Fang Guangxin & Liu Wujun (1998). Present situation, constraints and future actions of yak husbandry in Xinjiang. *Forage and Livestock*, Supplement: 50-51.

GAAHB (Ganzi Agricultural and Animal Husbandry Bureau) and YRO (Yak Research Office of Southwest Nationalities College) (1980a). The good meat-purpose yak – the investigation and study of Jiulong yak. *Journal of China Yak*, 1: 14-33.

GAAHB (Ganzi Agricultural and Animal Husbandry Bureau) and YRO (Yak Research Office of Southwest Nationalities College) (1980b). The general survey and identification for Jiulong yak. *Journal of China Yak*, 3: 17-24.

Gala, Mao Guangtong *et al.* (1983). Bazhou yak in Xinjiang. *Journal of China Yak*, 2: 46-50.

Gray, J.E. (1843). *List of mammals in the British Museum*. London, British Museum.

Han Jianlin (2000). Conservation of yak genetic diversity in the Hindu Kush Himalayan region and central Asian steppes. *In* Shrestha, J.N.B. (ed), *Proceedings of the fourth global conference on conservation of domestic animal genetic resources, in Kathmandu, 17-21 August 1998.* pp. 113-116.

Institute of Animal Science [China] (1986). *Bovine breeds in China.* Shanghai, China, Shanghai Scientific and Technology Press. pp. 117-132.

Ji Qiumei *et al.* (2002). Resources of yak production in Tibet and reasons for the degeneration of productive performances. *Proceedings of the third international congress on yak, in Lhasa, China, 4-9 September 2002.* Nairobi, International Livestock Research Institute (ILRI). pp 300-307.

Lei Huanzhang (1982). Discussion of types and utilization of Qinghai yak. *Journal of China Yak*, 2: 1-3.

Liang Yulin & Zhang Haimin (1998). Conservation and utilization of Tianzhu White yak. *Forage and Livestock*, Supplement: 56-57.

Linnaeus, C. (1766). *Systema naturae per regna tria naturae, secundum classes, ordines, genera, species, cum characteribus, differentiis synonymis, locis.* Vol 1, Regnum Animale, pt. 1, pp. 1-532.

Lin Xiaowei & Zhong Guanghui (1998). Present situation and development strategy of yak husbandry in Sichuan. *Forage and Livestock*, Supplement: 26-28.

Liu Guoliang (1980). Zhongdian yak. *Journal of China Yak*, 2: 75-82.

Liu Zubo, Wang Chengzhi & Chen Yongning (1989). Yak resources and qualified populations in China. *In Chinese Yakology*. Chengdu, China, Sichuan Scientific and Technology Press. pp. 36-77.

Lydekker, R. (1898). *Wild Oxen, sheep and goats of all lands*. London, Rowland Ward Ltd. 314 pp.

NIAH (Nagqu Institute of Animal Husbandry), Jiali Farm and Jiali Veterinary Station (1982). Report of investigation of the Jiali yak. *Journal of China Yak*, 3: 51-56.

Olsen, S. J. (1990). Fossil ancestry of the yak, its cultural significance and domestication in Tibet. *Proceedings of the Academy of Natural Sciences of Philadelphia*, 142: 73-100.

Olsen, S.J. (1991). Confused yak taxonomy and evidence of domestication. *Illinois State Museum Scientific Papers*, Vol. 23: 387-393.

Pal, R.N., Barari, S.K. & Basu, A. (1994). Yak (*Poephagus grunniens* L.), its type – a field study. *Indian Journal of Animal Sciences*, 64: 853-856.

Pu Ruitang, Zhang Rongchang, Zhao Yiner & Den Shizhang (1982). Introduction to the Tianzhu White yak. *Journal of China Yak*, 1: 64-74.

Sarbagishev, B.S., Rabochev, V.K. & Terebaev, A.I. (1989). Yaks. *In* Dmitriev N.G. & Emst, L.K. (ed), *Animal genetic resources of the USSR*. FAO Animal Production and Health Paper, No. 65, Rome. pp. 357-364.

Smirnov, D.A. *et al.* (1990). Meat yield and meat quality of yaks. *Sel'skokkhozyaistvennykh Nauk Im. V.I. Lenina. (Soviet Agricultural Sciences)*, No. 1: 46-49.

TAHVS (Tianzhu Animal Husbandry and Veterinary Station) and DAS (Department of Animal Science of Gansu Agricultural University) (1985). *Breed criterion of the Tianzhu White yak in Gansu Province (Gan Q/NM4-85)*. Issued by Provincial Administration of Standardization on 2 January 1985 and effective 1 April 1985.

Tang Zhenyu *et al.* (1981). Survey of the yak in Pali district of Yadong county in Tibet. *Journal of China Yak*, 2: 46-50.

Verdiev, Z. & Erin, I. (1981). Yak farming is milk and meat production. *Molochnoe I miasnoe skotovodstvo*, 2: 16-17.

Wang Minqiang *et al.* (1998). Selection and breeding for bulls and the generation progress of the mass breeding in raising of the Datong new yak breed. *Forage and Livestock*, Supplement: 13-15.

Wen Yongli *et al.* (1995). *Breed criterion of the Maiwa yak in Sichuan Province (DB51/249-95).* Issued by Provincial Administration of Standardization on 14 December 1995 and effective 1 January 1996.

Yang Bohui *et al.* (1998). Study on the fair and underwool production of Datong yak. *Forage and Livestock*, Supplement: 21-23.

Yu Daxin & Qian Defang (1983). General situation of Xinjiang yak. *Journal of China Yak*, 1: 57-64.

Zagdsuren, Yo (1994). Heterosis in yak hybrids. Proceedings of the first international congress on yak. *Journal of Gansu Agricultural University* (Special issue June 1994). pp. 59-62.

Zhang Haimin & Liang Yulin (1998). Survey on herd structure and management of Tianzhu White yak. *Forage and Livestock*, Supplement: 57-58.

Zhang Rongchang (1989). *China: the yak.* Lanzhou, China, Gansu Scientific and Technology Press. 386 pp.

Zhong Guanghui *et al.* (1995). *Breed criterion of the Jiulong yak in Sichuan Province (DB51/250-95).* Issued by Provincial Administration of Standardization on 14 December 1995 and effective 1 January 1996.

Zhong Jincheng (1996). *Yak genetics and breeding.* Chengdu, China, Sichuan Scientific and Technology Press. 271 pp.

Zhou Yiqing (1980). Brief introduction to the Hejing yak in Xinjiang. *Journal of China Yak*, 1: 91.

3   BREEDING, CROSSBREEDING AND HYBRIDIZING OF YAK

OVERVIEW

Pure-breeding is the predominant practice with yak. Apart from a scheme involving selection in crossbreds of wild yak with domestic yak in a process of breed development (see Chapter 2), no information has become available on rigorous selection programmes consistently applied for the improvement of the performance of yak in China. However, some selection schemes appear to be under consideration both in China and other countries. The dearth of organized selection schemes is not surprising with an absence of written records of performance and pedigrees and because of the location of yak in harsh environments and remote regions. Herdsmen in some areas, such as those of the Jiulong yak, have a traditional system of selection for replacement bulls. The Jiulong scheme considers the performances of the sires and maternal performance, as well as the physical appearance of the individual. It has to be remembered that the capacity to survive must be one of the chief attributes in the genetic makeup of the yak. This characteristic is likely to be under constant pressure from natural selection.

There is circumstantial evidence that some inbreeding is likely to have occurred with yak as a result of traditional pure-breeding methods and, in some countries, because of insufficient interchange of breeding stock across national boundaries. This can be expected to have harmful effects on the performance of yak.

Crossbreeding among the different types and breeds of yak does not appear to be systematic, but, on theoretical grounds, should be advantageous. Crossing domestic yak with wild yak is receiving widespread attention and favourable results are reported, with indications of heterosis. Crosses of domestic yak with wild yak are also thought to provide a basis for selection in new breed formation (cf. Chapter 2).

Hybridizing of yak with other species of cattle (mainly *Bos taurus* but also *Bos indicus* in some countries) is widely practised. Bulls of local breeds of cattle are used for natural service. But for hybridizing of yak with relatively high-yielding "exotic" breeds of cattle, the use of AI with frozen semen is normal, as the bulls of these breeds have not, in the past, survived for long in the mountainous regions. Hybridizing of yak with cattle is advocated in several countries as a means of increasing milk and meat output from the mountainous regions. Only the first generation of hybrids (F1) is favoured, as later generations of backcrosses have poorer performance (and hybrid males are sterile). However, the F1 females can usefully be mated to males specially chosen for "meat" production. There are both economic and biological limits on the extent to which interspecies hybridization can be carried out. The biological limit is set by the low reproductive rate of yak and by survival rates. A large proportion of the female yak population is required simply to replace the pure-bred yak – even if the size of that population were to remain static and not increase, as seems often desired by herders.

Pure-breeding

Ways of improving yak productivity by selection might be of great importance to the people who depend on yak for their livelihood. As discussed earlier, the yak is the dominant domestic animal in the alpine regions and the mountain plateaux of western China and adjacent areas to the south and north – dominant in economic, though not necessarily in numerical, terms. The yak also has great importance in Mongolia and several other countries (see Chapter 11, part 2). It is an integral component of the socio-economic system of people in many remote areas and, often along with sheep and goat, it is the main contributor to the livelihood of the herdsmen and their families. And yet, several factors militate against systematic breeding programmes.

The first of these constraints on improvement by genetic selection is that yak are still widely regarded, especially among Tibetan people, as a symbol of wealth. The more yak a family or a village owns, the richer and stronger it is considered to be. To maintain or increase the number of yak can take precedence over improvements in quality, or even overall productivity. Thus, animals are often kept until they die rather than culled for reasons of poor productivity. This can lead to overstocking of pastures and to a potential reduction in the output from the herd as a whole (see Chapters 12 and 13). "Quality" of the herd can become more of a consideration in situations where "competing" families or villages already own similar numbers of animals. Observation also suggests that smaller herds are sometimes of better quality because more pasture resource is available for a given number of animals and greater individual care is given to the animals by the herders.

A second important reason why genetic selection by herdsmen, or by extension officers acting on their behalf, is impeded is the absence of the necessary performance and parentage records – although herdsmen will often claim to know the parents of yak, especially bulls. It is doubtful if the accuracy of this knowledge is ever tested. In some nucleus breeding herds set up recently on the state farms in Qinghai, Tibet, Gansu and Sichuan, pedigrees but not performance were recorded.

Third, survival of the yak in a harsh, even hostile, environment is of paramount importance, perhaps of higher priority than any other single performance trait (though it is unlikely that this matter has been quantified). In terms of selection for survival under these conditions, natural selection is almost certainly more effective than any current procedure devised by man.

In relation to selection for the main products from the yak – milk, meat and fibre – the only convincing evidence of changes resulting from selection applies to fibre, where selection of a "fibre line" in the Jiulong breed appears to have produced far higher yields than in contemporary animals not selected for this trait (Cai Li *et al.*, 1980). Because fibre traits are quite strongly inherited and much more so (at least in other species) than milk yield or growth traits, selection progress is relatively easier to achieve with fibre production traits.

The milk yield of yak is very low, relative to other cattle, particularly those specializing in milk production. It has been suggested that the amount of milk produced by yak is only the quantity that would normally be needed to rear its calf. Thus, yak calves that receive only some of their dams' milk, because the rest is taken for human consumption, grow significantly less well (see Chapter 6). An incentive to select for a higher yield in yak is most likely to arise only where there is an expanded market for milk destined for sale.

In respect to meat output from yak, three problems arise that may create conflict with opportunities for selection for growth rate or "size" (meat production), even if these traits were somehow measured. One is the fact that a significant proportion of each year's growth of the animals during the warm season is lost over the period of nutrient deficiency in winter and early spring. This makes it difficult to see what an appropriate selection strategy should be. If the strategy were to be the increase in the size of the adult animal, say at the end of a growing season, the selection process would be delayed to late in life and hence would make slow progress. A second constraint is that when milk is taken from yak for human consumption and the calf is left short, the precise effect on each individual calf is difficult to estimate (even though an average effect of rearing practice is known). And in any case, there is variation in the quantity of milk produced by the dams. Selection among calves for growth rate therefore would be less accurate than in a totally uniform rearing system. A third problem is the opportunistic nature of the disposal of surplus stock that frequently occurs. The lack of a regular marketing strategy for well-grown animals, combined with the relatively rudimentary nature of the current marketing system, particularly in the remote areas, works against selection for "meat".

Nonetheless, in the regions where yak products are in great demand in the marketplace, it seems that herdsmen have acquired both the knowledge and skill to improve production traits – even though it may be done unsystematically and perhaps unconsciously. This is a possible reason why some breeds are held in higher esteem than others. But different breeds are rarely compared with each other in the same place and at the same time. So it is difficult to quantify the extent of any genetic differences in performance of the breeds, as distinct from differences in their looks.

Selection objectives for the chief yak breeds in China

In general, there are no clearly defined breeding objectives and no developed breed structure among herdsmen. Chinese animal scientists, however, decided towards the end of the 1980s to develop breeding objectives for the principal yak breeds. The intention was to provide technical assistance for a more systematic approach to yak breeding and to aim for earlier maturity, to improve the animal's shape for meat production and to develop strains for either milk or meat, or for meat and hair production. The criteria to be adopted therefore stressed body size, growth rate, dressing and meat percentages, milk yield and fat percentage, as well as the yield of hair – both coarse and down, but with an emphasis on the down.

The criteria proposed were approved in Sichuan and Qinghai for the Jiulong, Maiwa, Plateau and Huanhu breeds of yak (Zhong Guanghui *et al.*, 1995; Wen Yongli *et al.*, 1995) and a corresponding scheme was developed in Gansu for the Tianzhu White breed in 1985 (TAHVS and DAS, 1985). Some information and comments about these schemes appear below, but first though, attention is drawn to a selection procedure used by herdsmen. The procedure in the Jiulong breed is regarded as traditional because it occurred before the advent of the recent provincial schemes and also had particular involvement from the late Professor Cai Li and his colleagues (1980; GAAHB and YRO, 1980a, b).

A "traditional" selection procedure used by herdsmen in the Jiulong area of Sichuan

Selection of yak by the herdsmen in the Jiulong area is relatively systematic. Herdsmen pay more attention to choice of yak bulls for breeding than they do to the cows. The guiding principle for the herdsmen is to check the ancestors (the parents) first and the bull second. Selection of replacement males starts in the herd with calves from cows that have good conformation and high milk yield over two parities of calving. The herdsmen require that the sire of the males being chosen as replacement bulls should have copious hair and a large number of progeny. The bulls being selected should have good conformation. In particular, the herdsmen require that the horns of the selected bulls stretch outward from a rough base and that there is a long distance between the horns. The forehead, head, muzzle and mouth have to be broad; the neck thick and the lips thin and long; withers should be high and brisket wide; the back, loin and rump should be wide and flat; the tail hairy; forelimbs straight and hind legs curved; the scrotum should be shrunken. Acceptable coat colours are black or black with some white specks on the forehead and at the extremities of the body (e.g. legs or tail), but not on the body itself.

It is of interest that selection of bulls in the Jiulong area is made in three stages. The first is a pre-selection at the age of one to one and a half years. There is a second selection from among the first group at the age of three years and a final selection at the age of four to five and a half years. (The relative importance given to different traits at each stage is **not** specified). Bulls that are culled are castrated and used for meat or draught purposes. After initial mating with cows, bulls that are found to have been defeated in the normal competition for mates, which occurs among the bulls, and males found to have physical defects or bad conformation are then also culled. The herdsmen aim to have two or three successors to an excellent, dominant bull that has been working in the cow herd.

In 1979, in accordance with newly instituted breeding plans, nearly 7 000 reproductive bulls and cows (about a third of the total) were evaluated on physical conformation and body weight (GAAHB and YRO, 1980b). As a result, four adult yak bulls were identified that met or approached the predetermined performance levels. However, by the time the bulls were identified they were too old for use. Clearly, this was an uncertain start to selective breeding and was more akin to a process of population screening (a search for exceptional individuals) than a process of continuous genetic selection. This particular scheme could not be continued, but consideration was subsequently given to selection of yak at various locations and in different counties where the Jiulong yak are kept (Cai Li, 1989). A standardized evaluation scheme for the Jiulong yak was drafted and approved to assist individual evaluation and selection (Zhong Guanghui *et al.*, 1995). Finally, a nucleus herd with 412 breeding animals was established in the centre of the Jiulong yak territory and 106 individuals were maintained on a state farm to implement a breed-improvement programme (Lin Xiaowei and Zhong Guanghui, 1998).

The traditional selection methods for Jiulong yak appear to have produced over a period of many decades, perhaps centuries, an improved breed of yak that is highly regarded. Clearly, the criteria applied contain elements that are related to important aspects of production in the yak. However, a cautionary comment should be added, lest it be thought that these methods have to be unreservedly commended because they have tradition and herdsmen's experience on their side. Geneticists would wish to suggest that there is great scope for improving these procedures, even in the absence of sophisticated indices of breeding value and modern computational procedures. To start with, they would ask how closely related the physical appearance of the yak, so much emphasized by the herdsmen, is to actual performance of the herd – in terms of, say, growth, milk yield or reproductive rate. Usually the relationship is not high. A geneticist would also wish to encourage the herdsmen to pay most attention to those characteristics of the yak that provide the greatest economic return irrespective of whether the products from the yak are for home or commercial use. For that reason, it would also be urged that the number of criteria considered for selection be restricted to an essential minimum. Improvement of the important traits is diluted, or even lost, when a lot of attention is paid to less important, even trivial, matters – as may be the case now.

More recent provincial schemes: the example of the Tianzhu White

The Provincial Administration of Standardization in Gansu adopted criteria in 1985 to standardize the assessment of grading for the Tianzhu White yak and to evaluate breeding value as an aid to selection (TAHVS and DAS, 1985; Zhang Rongchang, 1989). The aim was to improve the breed for meat and hair.

Scores are allocated for aspects of general conformation, the body, testes for males and udder for females, legs, feet and the coat. Calves and adults are graded to somewhat different criteria. Weight and height classes are designed according to age and sex of animal and assigned to four grade classes. The use of selected breeding bulls is recommended, and newborn animals may be assigned a grade on the basis of the grades of their parents. Breeding bulls, in turn, are classified into four grades on the basis of the grades attained by their offspring. There are eight nucleus herds with a total of about 400 breeding animals maintained in the central area of this breed and 40 multiplier herds with approximately 20 000 individuals in surrounding areas (Zhang Haimin and Liang Yulin, 1998).

On the face of it, this scheme, like the "traditional" Jiulong scheme, pays considerable attention to aspects of the animals' appearance. This may well detract herders from considering more single-mindedly the performance aspects that matter most, namely, in line with the objectives for this breed, meat and hair production and the underlying factors of reproduction and vigour. Also, as has been found elsewhere with breeding schemes, if too many traits are considered there is a likelihood that none are improved (unless combined in highly sophisticated, statistically complex and computerized schemes).

In spite of reservations about the selection schemes, there appears to have been significant progress in the Tianzhu White yak since the 1980s. For example, the body height of adult breeding bulls and cows older than four and a half years increased from 108.1 cm and 104.3 cm (average of 17 males and 88 females) in 1981 to 110.2 cm and 104.7 cm (20 males and 44 females) in 1987 and to 114 cm and 112.9 cm (98 males and 826 females) in 1997. Corresponding body weights changed for males and females from 189.7 kg and 171.4 kg to 199.2 kg and 179.6 kg and to 202.8 kg and 192.7 kg respectively over those same years (Zhang Rongchang, 1989; Wang Yuchang and Wang Yanhong 1994; Zhang Haimin and Liang Yulin, 1998). However, these data were collected in a simple survey on various farms over a period of years. It is not possible, therefore, to distinguish any contributions from genetic improvement from those in management and feeding (or simply from year effects). There is a presumption, though, that management and feeding practices have remained largely unchanged over this period.

Other schemes

Sarbagishev *et al.* (1989) referred to an organized breeding programme in Kyrgyzstan based on specifications for yak males and females that were concerned primarily with conformation, growth rate and body size. Pedigrees were included and breeding values constructed. The improvement scheme was spread over a number of stock-breeding farms.

But the main scientific effort towards genetic improvement of productivity of yak, in many countries, has been directed at hybridization with *Bos taurus* and, to a lesser extent, *Bos indicus* cattle, rather than to selection. Some consideration has also been given to introducing, by crossbreeding, genes from wild yak into the domestic yak population as a means of improving productivity (see the following section). Lei *et al.* (1994) reported a scheme that uses performance criteria of individual yak and the potential benefits of introducing wild yak.

In the late 1980s, the first Wild Yak Frozen Semen Station was established on the Datong Yak Farm in Qinghai with three wild yak bulls (two captured from the Qilian mountains and one from the Kunlun mountains (Lu Zhonglin and Li Kongliang, 1994; Bo Jialin *et al.*, 1998). Another Yak Frozen Semen Station is now in operation at Damxung in Tibet (Zhang Yun, 1994). These are the only A.I. centres in China specific to yak. By 1995, 8 700 crossbred animals of the wild yak with domestic yak had been produced in Qinghai and Gansu that served as the base herds for further selection and breeding of the new improved yak strain of Datong yak (Bo Jialin *et al.*, 1998). The scheme used in this development of a "new" breed is described in Chapter 2.

Zhang Yun (1994) reported that there were ten yak bulls from the Sibu and Jiali yak breeds in Tibet and 28 semi-wild yak (F1, or backcrosses) at the Damxung station, though this number had been reduced to 17 in use. At the time of Zhang's report, 50 000 doses of semen had been produced and 2 000 yak cows inseminated – as well as a much larger number of yellow cattle to produce hybrids with the yak.

As yet there is no information on progeny records from these A.I. bulls. The full potential of using such information in selection procedures for improved performance of yak has not yet been realized. However, Zhang also suggested that the distribution of yak semen from this station could play a significant role in counteracting adverse effects of inbreeding, which have been thought to occur in yak in some areas. (The need to introduce yak "blood" from outside sources, to counteract inbreeding in the yak population of different areas, is also referred to by Pal in relation to India [see Chapter 11, part 2].)

Group breeding schemes
Because of the potential advantages of group-breeding schemes in promoting genetic improvement, especially when the participating herds are each relatively small,

consideration is being given to setting up such schemes for yak. At present, as far as is known, these remain in the planning stages.

In the early 1990s an "open-nucleus" herd was established at Longri farm in Hongyuan county. This set-up included a small trial to check problems in the recording of accurate pedigrees for purposes of estimating genetic parameters (Zhong Guanghui, 1998). The nucleus herd to promote the improvement of Maiwa yak consists of 12 breeding bulls, tested for their performance, and 180 breeding cows (Lin Xiaowei and Zhong Guanghui, 1998). Records of growth, milk and reproduction have been collected continuously.

Consideration of inbreeding in yak

Inbreeding has harmful effects on nearly all aspects of livestock performance. Inbreeding reduces, for example, reproductive capacity, growth rate, adult size, and milk production and increases mortality, especially among the newborn and young. The amount of harm is usually quite closely related to the degree to which inbreeding occurs. It is a matter that should be considered in relation to yak because the traditional pattern of breeding may encourage inbreeding (cf. Chapter 5). In this system, bulls compete for mates and, in due course, these bulls are often replaced in the hierarchy of the herd by their offspring. This makes it inevitable that some inbreeding occurs. Inbreeding can be much reduced if bulls are exchanged across herds and greater distances – even then the problem may not be avoided but only postponed if two villages, for example, were consistently to exchange breeding stock only with each other. Controlled mating, whereby the herdsman decides on the mates for a particular bull, is similar in that it may reduce or postpone inbreeding, but rarely avoids it for long.

The absence of the pedigrees of animals in yak herds has made it impossible in the past to know the actual extent to which inbreeding has occurred. However, recently, microsatellite markers were used to analyse the genetic structure of different yak breeds/herds in China and other parts of the world and hence to estimate a general inbreeding effect. An assumption is made that the fewer alleles found at any one locus in a breed or herd, the higher will be the degree of inbreeding in that population. These investigations may help clarify the inbreeding issue specific to yak herds or breeds (cf. Chapter 15). However, the actual effects in yak are not known since this requires comparison of the performance of groups differing in their degree of inbreeding. This, in turn, requires performance records linked to pedigrees. For the time being, the probability of harmful consequences of inbreeding in yak is therefore inferred from known, corresponding effects in cattle, sheep and other livestock.

In some countries, such as Bhutan, Nepal and India (see Chapter 11, part 2), concerns about the effects of inbreeding have been expressed by those on the spot. The yak populations in these countries have become relatively closed. This is a consequence of that, in turn, increases the likelihood that related animals are mated to each other. The effects of inbreeding must be suspected whenever the general performance of the stock is known, or thought, to have declined relative to an earlier era, and when other systematic changes in husbandry practices, such as overgrazing, for example, cannot account for it. Thus Kozlovskii (1960) stated that yak in the Gorno-Altai region were becoming closely inbred, which, if true, could well account for the earlier view of Denisov (1935) that the yak of that area were inferior, at that time, to those of other regions. Kozlovskii advocated, by way of remedy, the introduction of unrelated yak males and/or of hybridization with other cattle.

Inbreeding occurs whenever animals that are more closely related to each other than "average" are mated to each other. For example, if a son or sons of a popular bull are used in a herd as his replacement, they, in turn, are liable to mate with some of their half-sisters or cousins. Moreover, such bulls are likely to serve other less closely related females, but related through common ancestors more generations back (grandparents or great-grandparents). Mating of full siblings to each other, or parents to their offspring, which is regarded as close inbreeding, can easily occur if steps are not taken to avoid it. Pal *et al.* (1994), writing in relation to yak in India, stated that farmers may use the same male to serve females of two to three successive generations.

Inbreeding also occurs as a consequence of selection, even though selection is widely and correctly advocated and practised for the genetic improvement of livestock. Selection has the inevitable consequence of bringing about an increase in inbreeding, simply as a consequence of restricting the number of animals that become parents of the next generation. The objective in selection schemes must ensure that the beneficial effects of selecting superior stock outweigh the harmful effects of the consequent inbreeding. This consideration is nowadays a routine part of large-scale and long-term breeding plans, such as cattle improvement programmes involving the widespread use of a few bulls through artificial insemination.

The reason for having dealt with the topic of inbreeding at some length is that experience suggests that the effects of inbreeding are easily ignored because they are not readily recognized in the short term. However, the circumstantial evidence for inbreeding is strong in some yak populations, and the potential for inbreeding should not, therefore, be ignored when yak are allowed to mate.

Crossbreeding within the yak species

No systematic crossbreeding appears to be practised among the different breeds or local populations of yak. This is not surprising considering the relative isolation of different communities and the distances separating them. But it is more surprising that it does not seem, so far, to have played more than a minor role in investigations to find out whether hybrid vigour would result from such crossbreeding. There is a likelihood that hybrid vigour would result, although the magnitude cannot be predicted. The likelihood of heterosis from breed crossing can be argued from the relative isolation, over a long time, of discrete populations of domestic yak in different localities and from the likelihood that breeding practices within herds have led to inbreeding (although, again, some would dispute this). Crossing under these circumstances could have merits. From past experiments in China where Jiulong yak and Tianzhu White yak were introduced to other localities for crossing with the local yak, the crosses were at least heavier and larger than the local yak (Ren Chen Luoerri *et al.*, 1995; Liang Hongyun *et al.*, 1997). However, in the absence of results from the pure-bred animals of the introduced breed in the same locality, it is difficult to know to what extent this improvement represents the effects of heterosis or the consequence of bringing in "superior" genes from the new breed. Table 3.1 gives some of these results for crosses with the Jiulong yak.

Table 3.1 Improvement of the yak in Luhuo county in Sichuan by crossing
with the Jiulong yak [Source: Zhong Jincheng, 1996]

Type	Age (year)	Sex	No.	Average body weight (kg)	Average body measurements (cm)		
					Height	Length	Heart girth
F1	Birth	M	10	13.8	54.4	48.1	57.6
(Jiulong		F	12	13.2	54.4	49.2	56.8
crossed	0.5	M	8	46.9	71.0	77.4	89.7
with local)		F	10	41.5	68.4	73.6	86.2
	1.0	M	8	85.0	95.7	107.7	127.3
		F	8	80.2	90.3	103.3	122.7
Local Luhuo	Birth	M	6	11.9	53.5	46.3	56.2
yak		F	6	11.0	51.6	46.0	54.0
	0.5	M	6	36.6	66.3	69.3	82.0
		F	4	29.9	63.3	67.8	81.3
	1.0	M	3	81.3	85.0	93.3	109.3
		F	3	77.8	80.3	90.7	106.0

Further support for the potential usefulness of crossbreeding comes from the attention paid more recently to crossing of domestic yak with wild yak and the claims of improved performance from such crossbreeding.

In the results presented from such trials, it is also not possible to differentiate clearly between the additive genetic effects (e.g. the fact that wild yak are larger than domestic yak) and the occurrence and magnitude of heterosis as a result of the crossing; but some results from such crosses are shown in Table 3.4.

Size of pure wild yak

Measurements were made in the 1960s on five adult male wild yak by the Agriculture and Animal Husbandry Department of Tibetan government (Study Group [Qiangtang], 1978). These animals had been caught in the Qiangtang area of northern Tibet. Their measurements are shown in Table 3.2.

Table 3.2 Body dimensions and weight of five male wild yak from Tibet

Body dimensions (cm), weight (kg)	Average	Range
Head length	61.1	(55 - 67)
Forehead width	27.3	(26 - 32)
Circumference of base of horn		(30 - 40)
Body length	179.3	(171 - 193)
Height at withers	158.8	(152 - 163)
Heart girth	240.6	(218 - 264)
Chest depth	91.1	(90 - 92)
Chest width	61.6	(53 - 78)
Cannon bone circumference		(22 - 24)
Estimated body weight	1 000.0	

Some wild yak calves caught by staff of the Animal Husbandry Institute of the Yushu Tibetan autonomous prefecture of Qinghai province were compared with domestic yak calves under the same conditions of feeding and management (Xu Guilin, 1985). Table 3.3 shows the weights and weight gains of the two groups. It can be seen from these results that the wild yak calves were 86 percent heavier than the domestic yak calves at three months of age but, relative to their weight, grew more slowly (though not necessarily less in absolute terms) so that by the age of 16 months the wild yak were only 63 percent heavier than the domestic ones.

Table 3.3 A comparison of the body weights and weight gains at various ages of five wild yak and 19 domestic yak kept under the same conditions of feeding and management [Source: Xu Guilin, 1985]

Age (months)		3	4	5	6	12	16
Domestic yak	Weight	33.6	39.2	48.2	51.5	59.1	67.4
	gain (kg)	5.6	9.0	3.3	7.6	8.3	
Wild yak	Weight	62.5	71.9	77.3	81.5	92.5	110.1
	gain (kg)	9.4	5.4	4.2	11.0	17.6	

Crossbreeding of wild yak with domestic yak

Some results from the crossing of wild yak with domestic yak are available. Provided the progeny from such crosses of domestic with wild yak have not been given preferential treatment over the domestic yak alongside them (and that may be a matter in question), the results suggest that the crosses have an advantage. Lu Hongji *et al.* (1987), for example, showed that the birth weight of crosses between domestic and wild yak were more than 30 percent heavier at birth than domestic yak calves. By age six months, the advantage in favour of the cross had increased to more than 50 percent. Calves with only one quarter wild-yak blood were 16 percent and 35 percent heavier at birth and six months of age, respectively.

Staff at the Lanzhou Institute of Animal Husbandry and Veterinary Science of the Chinese Academy of Sciences used some frozen wild yak semen to inseminate female domestic yak on the Datong Yak Farm of Qinghai province (Lu Hongji *et al.*, 1987). They also produced some backcrosses of the F1 to local domestic yak (to produce 0.25 percent wild yak) and mated some local domestic yak to males of the Jiulong (domestic) breed of yak (cf. Chapter 2, Datong breed). The results are shown in Table 3.4 and suggest that crossing to the wild yak increased body weights and weight gains over the first six months of life. These weight gains were greater, relative to the birth weights, in the crosses with wild yak than in crosses with the Jiulong. The local domestic yak showed the lowest relative weight gains to six months old. There were no measurements beyond that age. Some of the wild-domestic crossbred yak at the Datong farm are illustrated in Figure 3.1.

Table 3.4 Body weights (kg ± SD) of local domestic yak and crosses with Jiulong yak and wild yak [Source: Lu Hongji *et al.*, 1987]

	Type of calf			
	Local yak	Local x Jiulong (F1)	Local x F1 (wild) (25% wild)	Local x wild yak (F1)
Birth weight	13.2 ± 2.3 (n = 25)	14.0 (n = 2)	15.3 ± 1.9 (n = 76)	17.3 ± 2.3 (n = 77)
6-month weight	65.2 ± 10.5 (n = 64)	73.7 ± 6.9 (n = 9)	86.1 ± 4.6 (n=21)	101.3 ± 9.4 (n = 33)

In the 1990s, there was intensive use in Qinghai of the wild yak semen by A.I., or the use of semi-wild yak bulls with natural mating, to try to improve the domestic yak productivity and "rejuvenate" the yak population. Some comparable data from observations of the F1 (half wild yak blood), B1 (one quarter wild yak blood) and local yak under the same feeding and management system in southern Qinghai are shown in Table 3.5

(Yan Shoudong, 1998). It was found that the body measurements and weights of the semi-(F1) and quarter-wild yak (B1) were higher than those of domestic yak within the same age groups. As seen from Table 3.5, birth weight, height, length and heart girth of the F1 were greater than of the domestic yak calves and particularly at 18 months old, the measurements of both the F1 and the B1 were greater than of domestic yak.

Interest in the use of the wild yak to improve production of domestic yak was exemplified by the presentation of a number of papers on this topic at the first, second and third international congresses on yak, held in China in 1994, 1997 and 2000 (Zhang Rongchang et al., 1994; Yang Rongzhen et al., 1997a; Han Jianlin et al., 2002; Zhao Bingyao and Zhang Jianwen, 1994). It was noted in those papers that, historically, herdsmen in the Gannan area of Gansu drove their domestic yak females into regions where wild yak lived, in order to allow natural mating with wild yak bulls. The crossbred progeny would later be selected to improve the domestic yak population. Based on this popular experience, more systematic studies using frozen semen from wild yak bulls are in progress. Substantial numbers of first-cross and backcross (25 percent wild yak) offspring have been born and are reported to grow significantly larger than the local domestic yak. The benefits of wild yak blood, as noted in these studies, have also carried over into crossing with the local yellow cattle. When yak bulls that had 50 percent wild yak blood were mated to yellow cattle, the resulting F1 hybrids were of the order of 20 percent larger at six months old than comparable F1 hybrids of yellow cattle with domestic yak. Yang et al. (1997b), Lu and Zhao (1997), Yan Shoudong (2002) and Amarsanaa et al. (2002) presented similar findings using wild yak to increase the growth and the related meat production of the domestic yak.

It is not known, from any of the studies previously referred to, what is the relative importance of the role of heterosis and of the additive genetic contribution from the wild yak to its cross with the domestic yak, as discussed earlier in relation to crosses among domestic breeds of yak.

Results of studies in another area of Gansu (Lu Zhonglin and Li Kongliang, 1994) suggested that substantial increases in body size, hair production and meat output were achieved in first crosses of wild with domestic yak, relative to the latter. Milk yield was found to have increased by more than 10 percent. Yan Ping et al. (1994) reported, more specifically, that the fleece weight of adult females was 1.76 kg, 1.65 kg and 1.47 kg for half-wild, quarter-wild and domestic yak, respectively. These authors also found that, importantly, the proportion of the undercoat was increased substantially with the introduction of wild yak blood – but the strength of the fibres was not affected. The use of wild yak to improve domestic yak performance through a process of crossing and selection was also reported to be under investigation in Qinghai (*Lei Huanzhang et al.*, 1994).

But clearly, only the additive genetic contribution from the wild yak genes will be useful in the actual process of subsequent selection (though the cross will retain some of the advantages from the initial heterosis). It is the perceived advantages of the introduction of wild yak blood into domestic yak populations that led to a project to develop a new breed from such a crossbred foundation (see Chapter 2).

Breed conservation

Taking into account the size of the present domestic yak population as a whole, it would be difficult to argue that conservation measures are a matter of urgency at this time. This might change if social or economic pressures were to reduce the extent of yak keeping – as is already evident in some areas, such as Nepal – or if predicted changes in global climate (over decades and centuries) have the effect of restricting the future distribution and size of the yak population.

Preservation of some of the remarkable traits of the yak in terms of its adaptation to a harsh environment and to long periods of severe deprivation should, nonetheless, be of interest to animal breeders worldwide. There are parts of the world where these characteristics could assist in establishing animal production and other parts where such resilience, on the part of the animal, could lead to better utilization of natural resources. Currently, however, the gene pool of the domestic yak as a whole is not endangered.

A different situation seems to exist for some of the more localized, and to an extent differentiated, populations or breeds of yak. The total numbers in some of these breeds is not large and hybridization with *Bos taurus* and *Bos indicus* cattle further reduces the proportion of the yak population available for its replacement.

For example, the Jiulong yak, possibly the best producer among the yak breeds, numbers 50 000 animals (Zhong Jincheng, 1996; Lin Xiaowei and Zhong Guanghui, 1998). The total numbers, however, tell only a small part of the story. Starting from a small herd, the Jiulong breed of yak has been a closed population for hundreds of years. Throughout the breed's history, herdsmen are said to have avoided introducing outside blood. Moreover, the system of selection practised by the herdsmen (previously described), and the natural competition among bulls for dominance makes it virtually certain that the effective size of the population is small and that inbreeding occurs (though the extent of this is a matter for debate). Thus, if the particular properties of the Jiulong are worth preserving and are not to be lost through genetic drift, special measures may be required. This was recognized by Chinese experts some years ago and led to the setting up of a random-breeding herd of 100 yak females and 20 males maintained per generation (Zhong Jincheng, 1996).

Table 3.5 Body weight and measurements of F1 and B1 of wild yak crossed with domestic yak in southern Qinghai [Source: Yan Shoudong, 1998]

Group	Sex	Age (month)	No.	Height (cm)	Length (cm)	Heart girth (cm)	Cannon bone Circumference (cm)	Body Weight (kg)
F1	m	At birth	21	56.1 ± 3.4	52.3 ± 4.6	59.6 ± 4.6	8.10 ± 0.38	14.9 ± 1.8
	m	6	19	80.8 ± 6.0	81.8 ± 7.5	94.3 ± 7.3	9.74 ± 0.42	49.6 ± 6.7
	m	12	11	80.7 ± 4.4	82.6 ± 6.7	92.5 ± 7.3	10.23 ± 0.61	45.9 ± 7.2
	m	18	13	91.8 ± 6.4	96.5 ± 8.7	117.5 ± 9.4	11.85 ± 0.83	98.9 ± 27.8
	f	At birth	31	56.2 ± 3.7	52.5 ± 5.2	59.6 ± 3.8	8.10 ± 0.57	14.6 ± 2.3
	f	6	30	79.3 ± 5.7	80.8 ± 9.0	93.1 ± 8.3	9.62 ± 0.68	45.8 ± 9.0
	f	12	20	81.6 ± 6.3	81.7 ± 8.6	97.6 ± 8.0	10.30 ± 0.64	49.4 ± 8.9
	f	18	19	90.0 ± 3.9	94.6 ± 11.6	114.6 ± 6.2	11.84 ± 0.67	90.9 ± 22.5
B1	m	At birth	41	55.2 ± 4.3	51.2 ± 4.4	59.8 ± 7.2	8.27 ± 0.39	14.8 ± 2.5
	m	6	39	78.1 ± 7.5	78.5 ± 7.3	94.2 ± 10.4	10.18 ± 1.33	50.7 ± 13.7
	m	12	20	83.5 ± 7.8	85.0 ± 8.7	98.6 ± 8.8	10.30 ± 1.49	54.5 ± 13.5
	m	18	23	92.8 ± 7.3	97.3 ± 10.0	115.9 ± 7.7	11.48 ± 0.72	95.7 ± 23.2
	f	At birth	64	54.6 ± 3.4	51.5 ± 4.4	58.7 ± 4.5	7.89 ± 0.66	14.7 ± 2.6
	f	6	64	77.3 ± 7.4	77.2 ± 7.9	92.7 ± 9.6	9.86 ± 0.97	47.9 ± 13.0
	f	12	37	82.2 ± 5.3	83.7 ± 7.3	99.3 ± 8.2	10.49 ± 0.80	54.7 ± 10.1
	f	18	37	91.4 ± 6.0	96.3 ± 7.9	116.3 ± 6.8	11.62 ± 0.87	94.3 ± 15.4
Domestic yak	m	At birth	81	53.1 ± 4.1	48.8 ± 4.0	57.5 ± 3.9	7.83 ± 0.63	13.6 ± 2.3
	m	6	76	77.4 ± 5.2	79.5 ± 8.1	92.8 ± 7.1	9.18 ± 0.71	48.1 ± 9.4
	m	12	50	80.9 ± 5.0	81.8 ± 5.9	97.8 ± 7.8	10.34 ± 0.73	53.6 ± 10.0
	m	18	49	89.7 ± 5.4	94.3 ± 8.0	113.6 ± 7.8	11.44 ± 0.90	88.7 ± 19.6
	f	At birth	92	52.8 ± 3.8	47.9 ± 4.0	56.8 ± 4.0	7.58 ± 0.54	12.9 ± 2.1
	f	6	88	76.6 ± 6.3	79.7 ± 6.5	93.6 ± 7.2	9.62 ± 0.78	48.1 ± 9.5
	f	12	66	81.2 ± 6.0	82.1 ± 6.4	97.9 ± 6.9	10.20 ± 0.86	51.5 ± 9.5
	f	18	62	89.6 ± 5.6	94.4 ± 8.1	114.8 ± 8.2	11.47 ± 0.96	93.2 ± 21.0

This was managed in the Hongba area of Jiulong county and was the responsibility of the Animal Husbandry Station there. Income from the sale of milk and culled animals met some of the costs. There was also a subsidy from local government to assist the project. This type of approach is clearly commendable as one way forward in terms of breed conservation. A random-breeding herd has, however, a further potential advantage in that it can also serve as a yardstick against which to measure progress from any genetic selection in other parts of the breed population.

Other yak breeds may be in a similar situation to the Jiulong, with total numbers not large and the size of the "effective" breeding population possibly quite small. The Tianzhu White breed, in an area of Gansu province, could be one and its conservation is being considered (Wang Yuchang and Wang Yanhong, 1994). Zhang Haimin and Liang Yulin (1998) indicated that the number and proportion of the pure white yak in Tianzhu have increased as a result of the protection programs; for example, in 1952, the proportion of pure white animals was 20.3 percent and in 1981 it was 31.5 percent. It increased to 44 percent in 1998. Interestingly, the price of a white tail was double that of a black one in 1998 (120 yuan per kg compared to 60 yuan per kg).

Local breeds may have special merits or special characteristics that could be lost in the absence of positive action to maintain such breeds. Investigation of the need for conservation in the yak should therefore receive some attention even if local rather than general action may be called for. A useful start might be an up-to-date census of the yak population, its various types and breeds and current breeding practices. In combination, such information would help to indicate the (genetically) effective size of the different breeding populations, both in China and elsewhere. A census of numbers alone, as regularly practised in some countries such as Mongolia, though helpful, is not enough for this particular purpose.

Too often in matters of conservation, action has been delayed until damage to the breed, or even extinction of the species, has become imminent. This must not be allowed to happen with the yak.

The genetic approaches using chromosomal and protein polymorphisms, mitochondrial DNA RFLP and sequencing, and microsatellite genotyping (referred to in Chapter 2) to estimate genetic distances among breeds should go some way towards determining priorities for breed conservation (Han Jianlin, 1996, 2000). (The technology is discussed in more detail in Chapter 15).

For the wild yak, it is widely accepted that conservation is a matter of importance and urgency. Accounts, from as recently as the nineteenth century, testified to vast herds of wild yak in the Kunlun mountains of Tibet and Qinghai. These are no longer seen. Miller *et al.* (1994) estimated that wild yak of all ages and both sexes may still have numbered around 15 000 in the early 1990s, and this is also the number quoted more recently by Schaller (1998). Miller and Schaller (1996) claimed an estimated 7 000 - 7 500 wild yak remained in the Chang Tang Wildlife Reserve in Tibet at the time of their survey. But this number does not necessarily give an accurate picture of the threat confronting this wild species. Wild yak in China are included in the country's wildlife-protection legislation, but, according to Miller *et al.* (1994), the Departments concerned have inadequate resources for enforcement. The factors that have led to a dramatic decline in wild yak numbers over the past century still operate, even if to a lesser extent. These factors include excessive hunting, partly for food, the encroachment of the infrastructure of modern society, such as roads, and the increasing competition for grazing land from domestic livestock (Miller *et al.*, 1994).

Hybridization of yak with cattle of other species

Ancient documents show that yak have been hybridized with ordinary cattle (*Bos taurus*) for at least 3 000 years. Documents from the eleventh century China, in the Zhou dynasty, suggest that hybridization of yak with cattle by the Qiang people gave benefits that nowadays would be called heterosis (or hybrid vigour). The name *Pian Niu* and variants of it have been used for these hybrids from earliest times (Ceng Wenqiong and Chen Yishi, 1980; Xie Chenxia, 1985; Cai Li, 1989). However, many other names exist (see section on local names). In some areas, such as northern India, Nepal and Bhutan, hybridizing with *Bos indicus* cattle also occurs.

Systematic hybridization of yak with other cattle has been recommended and practised for many years – and certainly as long as hybridization by plant breeders has been in fashion. The hybrids find a special niche with herdsmen in providing extra milk and as draught animals, usually at somewhat lower altitudes than the typical yak country. Hybridization is carried out primarily with yak females mated to bulls of local cattle.

This is regarded as the normal hybridization and, in China the F1 is called "true *Pian Niu*" (or simply *Pian Niu*). The reciprocal hybridization of female cattle to yak bulls is also practised and regarded as "counter-hybridization" with the progeny called "false *Pian Niu*" (see Figure 3.2) and many other local names.

The hybrids are always mated back to either yak or cattle males. There is no alternative to this as the F1 males are sterile. The herdsmen use, for the most part, the cattle available to them in their area; in China, for example, they are the local, so-called "yellow cattle". The hybrid progeny of the F1 generation are then called "local *Pian Niu*". However, much investigation has gone into the use of "improved" breeds of cattle of dairy, beef and dual-purpose types. Results of hybridizing with both local and "improved" cattle breeds are given in Chapter 7. The name that is given to the first hybridizing of yak with "improved" cattle breeds is "improved *Pian Niu*" – in order to distinguish it from the "local *Pian Niu*".

Information on the production of hybrids between yak and cattle will also be found in Chapter 11 in relation to individual countries.

In the course of experiments in the 1920s and 1930s at Buffalo Park, Wainwright, Canada, aimed at developing a meat animal for the cold northern regions, including Alaska, a small number of hybrids were also successfully produced between yak (male) and female American bison and half-bison (bison crossed with a cattle cross) (Deakin *et al.*, 1935).

Figure 3.1 *Pian Niu* female
(F1 from yak dam and local,
yellow cattle sire)

Figure 3.2 çFalseé *Pian Niu* female
(F1 from local, yellow cattle
dam and yak sire)

Local names for hybrids

Names for the first generation hybrids of yak and cattle include the name *dzo* in Tibetan areas, variants of which extend into Mongolia and other countries, and *chauri*, the name used in Nepal. The various types of backcross hybrid, both to cattle and to yak, have an especially rich variety of names that differ in different parts of China and elsewhere. Descriptions of these names have been given by, among others, Zhao Zhengrong (1957), Hu Angang *et al.* (1960), Cai Li (1980), Joshi (1982), Zhang Rongchang (1989) and Pal (1993). The uninitiated traveller may find himself confused by the fact that the local people in China are said to call the hybrids of yak with cattle çimproved cattleé ñ this usage is avoided here.

Distribution of hybrids

In the areas of the Henduan Alpine type of pasture, hybridizing of yak females with cattle males is not widely practised, nor is interspecies hybridization common in the pastoral regions at high elevation to which cattle cannot adapt. Such hybridization is, however, widespread in areas of mixed pastoral and agricultural production at lower altitudes. Table 3.6 shows, by way of example, the relative proportions of pure yak to hybrids and yellow cattle in two such areas in Sichuan. In the main yak-producing areas, hybridization with cattle is normally restricted to only a small proportion of the yak herd (see section, Limits to hybridization).

Nomenclature

Because of the diversity of local names for different stages of hybridizing and in order to avoid confusion in the presentation of results in this and later chapters, the scientifically more formal nomenclature of F1 (first-generation hybrids), and B1 (backcrosses), etc. will be used. It should be noted that in publications from China and some other countries, the backcross-hybrid generations are often denoted as F2, F3, F4, etc. This nomenclature will not be used here as it also could lead to confusion among readers, geneticists in particular, who will be accustomed to these notations denoting successive generations of crosses (or hybrids) mated among themselves. Backcross hybrids will be described here by the letter B, with a number denoting the generation and a letter to show whether the last male used was cattle or yak – when that has been specified. (Thus, B1(C) would denote a backcross-hybrid animal produced from the mating of a F1 female to a cattle bull, etc.). In the same way, in cases where doubt could arise, the F1 generation will indicate whether the sire was a cattle breed or a yak.

Table 3.6 Proportions of yak, *Bos taurus* cattle and hybrids in Ganzi county of Sichuan

Type	Pastoral area (%)	Agricultural area (%)
Yak	91.4	16.8
F1	7.8	55.8
B1(C)	0.7	3.7
Cattle	<0.1	21.9
Total No.	41 541	25 560

The hybrid females are an important source of milk and milk products, for home consumption or for sale, and the males, since they cannot be used for breeding, are used for draught purposes, or are slaughtered for meat (see Chapter 7).

In China, the reciprocal hybridization procedure between yak bulls and yellow cattle females is carried out mainly in the cattle-producing areas of the cold Minshan mountains, especially in the Min county of Gansu province and Pingwu county in Sichuan province. These hybrids do not give much milk and are used mainly for draught purposes.

Hybridization policy

The first generation of hybrids of yak and "ordinary" cattle adapt well to the conditions in which they are used. They have some of the good characteristics of both parental types: resistance to a harsh environment from the yak and extra productivity, milk in particular (but with a lower fat percentage), from the cattle. Backcross hybrids to cattle, however, are less well adapted to the environment, and their productivity is often little better than that of yak – most probably through loss of heterosis (although there is no strict quantification of this). Backcross hybrids to cattle are not therefore favoured – one practice being to dispose of these hybrid calves immediately after birth, in order to have all the milk from the dam available for use or sale by the herders.

The alternative of backcrossing to the yak does, however, provide a particularly good source of animals for meat production. This system is encouraged and practised in China and elsewhere.

Cai Li *et al.* (YRO and XLF, 1983; YRO and GISP, 1984) showed, from a comparison of two neighbouring and otherwise similar grassland farms in Sichuan, that the output per head of animal, per unit of land and per unit of labour can be seriously reduced if the proportion of B1 hybrids is allowed to become too high. On the Xiangdong Livestock Farm, the proportion of B1 hybrids was not allowed to exceed 5 percent of the total herd and some selection was practised of those retained. On the other farm, Axi Livestock farm, the backcross progeny of the F1 hybrid generation were retained in full. The results of the comparison are shown in Table 3.7.

The use of "improved" breeds.

In China, starting at Datong in Qinghai province around 1939 and in the area now known as the Ganzi Tibetan autonomous prefecture in Sichuan from 1941, some yak were crossed with Dutch Holstein-Friesian bulls. Such hybridization did not become systematic until the mid-1950s when 200 bulls of various breeds were introduced to the yak-producing areas of China (Zhang Rongchang, 1989). The breeds included the Holstein-Friesian, Shorthorn, Simmental; Latvia, Ala-Tau, Kostrome cattle, the Mongolian, Binzhou, Sanhe, Qinchuan, Yinging and others. More recently, Charolais, Hereford, Limousine and others have been added to those available for hybridizing with yak. Mating was tried initially by natural mating, but artificial insemination was also used and continues as the predominant practice (Cai Li, 1989; Zhang Rongchang, 1989). From 1979 to 1985, a yak research team coordinated the hybridizing with such exotic breeds in the five principal provinces with yak in China, and some 32 000 hybrids were produced. As so often happens with fieldwork, relatively little of this work has provided comparative performance results – those available are quoted in Chapter 7.

Table 3.7 Comparison of output of animal products from two neighbouring and similar farms in pastoral areas of Sichuan province (1977 - 1981)

	Xiangdong	Axi
Total stock	2721	4346
Yak (%)	69.7	31.5
F1 (%)	25.4	21.1
B1 hybrids* (%)	4.7	47.1
Ordinary cattle (%)	0.2	0.3
Output value** of:		
Milk	49 673	64 565
Cheese	2 405	2 931
Hide	1 753	1 789
Hair and down	1 914	1 258
Market animals	38 760	54 825
Total value	*94 505*	*125 368*
Average output per:		
Head of stock	34.7	28.9
Head of staff	716	412.4
6.7 ha grassland	92.8	53.5

*B1 hybrids here are mostly backcrosses to cattle bulls – very few to yak.

**Output value (yuan; US$1=1.7 yuan) as the mean of 1979 - 1981 calculated according to fixed prices in 1980 as follows: milk 0.33 yuan/kg; cheese 0.56 yuan/kg; hide 8.9 yuan each; hair and down 1.74 yuan/kg; market cattle 85 yuan/head.

To better exploit the advantages of hybridization while avoiding the reproductive problems caused by using large "exotic" bulls, an alternative has been devised in parts of China whereby crossbred cattle, instead of large exotic breeds, are hybridized with the yak. For example, the Holstein Friesian or Simmental breed was used to produce F1 breeding bulls by crossing them first, by A.I., with the local cattle. The F1 crossbred bulls, with their relatively smaller body size, were then used on the yak to produce a hybrid F1 through natural mating.

Although the growth and performance of the hybrids for both milk and meat production was highly regarded (see Chapter 7, for performance results) the bulls of these various "improved" breeds (and 75 percent grade bulls of these breeds with yellow cattle) did not adapt to the local conditions and high altitudes in China. Most of the bulls died of mountain sickness or for other reasons within two years of introduction, and many died within the first few months. The bulls introduced in the mid- and late 1950s left fewer than 1 000 F1 and B1 hybrid progeny over a more than 20-year period.

Hybridization of yak with these "improved" breeds of cattle is now carried out by A.I. with frozen semen. This procedure inevitably restricts the utilization of these breeds to the more accessible and well-organized yak herds. In practice in many areas, therefore, the *Bos taurus* (and *Bos indicus*) cattle used for hybridizing with the yak will continue to be the local types of cattle.

Hybridization of yak with "exotic" breeds of cattle has also been practised in other countries for a long time (see Chapter 11, part 2), such as in as, some countries of the former USSR. Thus, Denisov (1938) reported on hybrids of yak and Schwyz (Brown Swiss) cattle, and more recently Katzina *et al.* (1994) added the Jersey and the Galloway and a continuing use of the Schwyz (now of American origin, hence probably the American Brown Swiss) to the list of exotic breeds referred to previously. Several of the breeds referred to are also used in Mongolia (Zagdsuren, 1994).

Limits to hybridization

The relatively low reproductive rate of the yak sets severe limits on the proportion of the female yak population that can be used for hybridizing with cattle if the numbers of the pure yak population are to be maintained, or possibly increased. In practice, it has been found best to restrict production of hybrids to the F1 generation only (whose offspring, in turn, are then slaughtered for meat). The male sterility of the hybrids prevents *inter-se* crossing systems and allows only the mating of the F1 hybrid back to yak or cattle bulls. Reduced productivity, relative to the F1, makes the B1 and later backcross generations unattractive commercially.

The actual proportion of the female yak population that can be hybridized with cattle depends on the reproductive rate, the replacement rate for cows (depending on the rate of death and disposal of the cows) and the loss of female calves before they reach reproductive age. These factors will vary from region to region and from year to year.

If it were assumed that:
- the yak population remained static in numbers,
- an average reproductive rate for the yak cow is around of 0.5 (equivalent to a live calf every second year),
- 10 percent of cows are eliminated annually and
- 10 percent of calves are lost before breeding age,

then 50 percent of the yak cow population could be available for hybridization. (These assumptions are equivalent, on average, to a yak cow producing, in her lifetime, two female progeny that survive to breeding age.) Any intention to expand the yak population would reduce the proportion that could be hybridized. If an increase of 10 percent in population numbers were required (and, as indicated earlier, herdsmen like to increase the number of animals they own), then only 10 percent of the yak cows could be hybridized with cattle – when the other assumptions remain the same.

Other assumptions would be entirely reasonable. Thus, higher replacement rates for cows and poorer survival of calves would reduce the proportion of yak females available for hybridization. For example, if replacement rates for cows and mortality among calves were both as high as 20 percent, as happens in some situations and some years, no yak cows would be available for hybridization if the reproductive rate of the yak did not exceed 50 percent – even with a static yak population. Matters would be even worse if snow disasters strike in particular years and localities and the rebuilding of the pure yak population becomes the top priority. On the other hand, in some regions and countries, where reproductive rate over a lifetime of the yak may be higher than in the examples given, the proportion of the yak female population available for hybridization can be increased.

The precise proportions of the yak population available for hybridization thus depend on the circumstances in any particular herd or group of herds. The point has been made often (see also Chapter 7) that the production of yak-cattle hybrids can play a useful role in improving the economics of animal production in the mountainous regions and particularly at the lower elevations of the yak territory and in the proximity to markets where the extra produce can be sold. But it also needs to be said that such hybridization is not a panacea. The pure yak must, perforce, remain the major proportion of the total bovine population in the mountainous regions. The attractions of hybridizing yak with cattle should not be allowed to detract from the need to consider genetic and husbandry improvements for the yak itself. In fact, improvements in the productivity and reproductive rate of the yak would also in turn increase the opportunities for hybridizing of yak with cattle, as already apparent in some areas.

There is clearly an opportunity to produce additional hybrids from the reverse process, that of mating cows of other local, domestic cattle species to yak bulls or using the semen of yak for insemination – although it appears that this hybrid (the "false *Pian Niu*") is traditionally used mainly for ploughing (see Chapter 7). This process also depends on having available a reproductive surplus in the cattle population.

Recently, Professor Jack Rutledge (personal communication, 2002) made a technology-based proposal for trials to produce hybrids from "improved" (e.g. Holstein) cattle and yak by *in vitro* production of embryos – using oocytes from slaughter cattle and yak semen. The resulting embryos then need recipient dams for their further development to birth. This proposal was conceived in the context of a situation (in a part of the Andes) where such hybrids might become a suitable dairy animal in the absence of either the yak or of a sufficiently productive cattle population or alternative milk producer. Although these procedures may have little immediate relevance to traditional yak-rearing areas, the idea is intriguing (see also Chapter 16)

References

Amarsanaa, B., *et al.* (2002). Growth patterns of F_1 calves of wild × domestic yak. *Proceedings of the third international congress on yak, in Lhasa,China, 4-9 September 2000.* International Livestock Research Institute (ILRI), Nairobi. pp 420-422.

Bo Jialin *et al.* (1998). Raising of the Datong new yak breed. *Forage and Livestock*, Supplement: 9-13.

Cai Li (1980). Nomenclature of the hybrids between yak and cattle. *Journal of China Yak.*

Cai Li (1980). Selection and breeding of yak – suggestions to pure-breeding of Jiulong yak. *Journal of China Yak*, 1: 58-65.

Cai Li (1989). *Sichuan yak.* Chengdu, China, Sichuan Nationality Press. 223 pp.

Ceng Wenqiong & Chen Yishi (1980). Yak in ancient China. *Journal of China Yak*, 1: 71-74.

Deakin, A., Muir, G.W. & Smith, A.G. (1935). *Hybridization of domestic cattle, bison and yak. Report of Wainwright experiment.* Publication 479, Technical Bulletin 2, Dominion of Canada, Department of Agriculture, Ottawa.

Denisov, V.F. (1935). Some data on the yak and its hybrids in Kirghizstan. *Trud. Kirgiz. Kompl. Eksp.*, 4: 115-171. (Cited from *CAB Animal Breeding Abstracts*, 4: 298-300.)

Denisov, V.F. (1938). Hybridization of the yak with Kirghiz cattle and the Schwyz. *Izv. Acad. Nauk. USSR (Otd. mat. est., Ser. boil)*, 863-878. (Cited from *CAB Animal Breeding Abstracts*, 7: 116-117.)

GAAHB (Ganzi Agricultural and Animal Husbandry Bureau) and YRO (Yak Research Office of Southwest Nationalities College) (1980a). The good meat-purpose yak – the investigation and study of Jiulong yak. *Journal of China Yak*, 1: 14-33.

GAAHB (Ganzi Agricultural and Animal Husbandry Bureau) and YRO (Yak Research Office of Southwest Nationalities College) (1980b). Phenotypic characterization of Jiulong yak. *Journal of China Yak*, 3: 17-24.

GISP (Grassland Institute of Sichuan Province) and LF (Longri Farm) (1993). Summary of the project titled "Study on the selection and breeding to improve production performances of Maiwa yak". *Journal of China Yak*, 3: 2-10.

Han Jianlin (1996). Yak genetic resources in China: evaluation of chromosome, protein and mtDNA polymorphism. In: Miller D.G., Craig S.R. and Rana G.M. (ed), Proceedings of a workshop on conservation and management of yak genetic diversity, at ICIMOD, Kathmandu, Nepal, 29-31 October 1996. ICIMOD (International Centre for Integrated Mountain Development), Kathmandu. pp. 175-183.

Han Jianlin (2000). Conservation of yak genetic diversity in the Hindu Kush Himalayan region and central Asian steppes. *In* Shrestha, J.N.B. (ed), Proceedings of the fourth global conference on conservation of domestic animal genetic resources, in Kathmandu, 17-21 August 1998. pp. 113-116.

Han Jianlin *et al.* (2002). *Yak production in Central Asian highland.* Proceedings of the third international congress on yak, in Lhasa, China, 4-9 September 2000. ILRI (International Livestock Research Institute), Nairobi. 572 pp.

Hu Angang, Cai Li & Du Shaodeng (1960). An investigation on yak in Ganzi County. *Journal of Southwest Nationalities College* (Animal Husbandry and Veterinary Sciences Edition), 4: 46-50.

Joshi, D.D. (1982). *Yak and chauri husbandry in Nepal*. Kathmandu, H.M. Government Press, Singha Durbar. 145 pp.

Katzina, E.V., Davydov, V.N. & Baldanov, N.D. (1994). Elaboration of the scheme of production and usage of industrial hybrids of yak and meat cattle. Proceedings of the first international congress on yak. *Journal of Gansu Agricultural University* (Special issue June 1994). pp. 44-48.

Kozlovskii, B. (1960). The greater use of commercial crossing in yak breeding. *Molochnoe I Myasnoe Skotovodstvo*, 5 (11): 32-26. (Cited from *CAB Animal Breeding Abstracts*, 29: 270.)

Lei Huanzhang *et al.* (1994). Studies on yak selection (1982-1986). Proceedings of the first international congress on yak. *Journal of Gansu Agricultural University* (Special issue, June 1994) pp. 139-143.

Liang, Hongyun *et al.* (1997). Analysis on crossbreeding and improving results for introduced Tianzhu White yak. Proceedings of the second international congress on yak held in Xining, China, 1-6 September 1997. Xining, China, Qinghai People's Publishing House. pp. 76-78.

Lin Xiaowei & Zhong Guanghui (1998). Present situation and development strategy of yak husbandry in Sichuan. *Forage and Livestock*, Supplement: 26-28.

Lu Hongji *et al.* (1987). A test on improving yak's productive performances by introducing wild yak blood. *Journal of China Yak*, 2: 8-12.

Lu Zhonglin & Li Kongliang (1994). Distribution, types and utilisation of wild yak in China. Proceedings of the ffirst international congress on yak. *Journal of Gansu Agricultural University* (Special issue June 1994) pp. 23-26.

Lu, Zhonglin & Zhao, L.Q. (1997). Great change in production system of yak. Proceedings of the second international congress on yak, in Xining, China, 1-6 September 1997. Xining, China, Qinghai People's Publishing House. pp. 26-28.

Miller, D.J. & Schaller, G.B. (1996). Threats to the Chang Tang Wildlife Reserve, Tibet. Rangelands 18 (3): 91-96.

Miller, D.J., Harris, R.B. & Cui-Quan Cai (1994). Wild yak and their conservation in the Tibetan Plateau. Proceedings of the first international congress on yak. *Journal of Gansu Agricultural University* (Special issue June 1994) pp. 27-35.

Pal, R.N. (1993). Domestic yak (Poephagus grunniens L.): a research review. *Indian Journal of Animal Sciences*, 63: 743-753.

Pal, R.N., Barari, S.K. & Biswas, D. (1994). Yak (*Poephagus grunniens* L.) husbandry in India. Proceedings of the first international congress on yak. *Journal of Gansu Agricultural University* (Special issue June 1994) pp. 16-21.

Ren Chen Luoerri, Wu Zhengning & Zhou Juli (1995). Analysis of the usefulness by crossing the Jiulong yak bulls with the local Li County in Sichuan. Journal of China Yak, 2: 32-35.

Sarbagishev, B.S., Rabochev, V.K. & Terebaev, A.I. (1989). Yaks. In: Dmitriev N.G. and Emst, L.K. (ed), *Animal genetic resources of the USSR*. FAO Animal Production and Health Paper, No. 65, Rome. pp. 357-364.

Schaller, G.B. (1998). Wildlife of the Tibetan Steppe. University of Chicago Press.

Study group (Qiangtang) of Agriculture and Animal Husbandry Department of the Tibetan Autonomous Region (1978). The observation on wild animals on the Qiangtang grassland. *Scientific Research Materials Collection*, pp. 60-66.

TAHVS (Tianzhu Animal Husbandry and Veterinary Station) and DAS (Department of Animal Science of Gansu Agricultural University) (1985). *Breed criterion of the Tianzhu White yak in Gansu Province (Gan Q/NM4-85)*. Issued by Provincial Administration for Standardization on 2 January 1985 and effective 1 April 1985.

Wang Yuchang & Wang Yanhong (1994). Conservation and improvement of the Tianzhu White yak. Proceedings of the first international congress on yak. *Journal of Gansu Agricultural University* (Special issue June 1994) pp. 80-85.

Wen Yongli *et al.*, (1995). *Breed criterion of the Maiwa yak in Sichuan province (DB51/249-95)*.

Xie Chenxia (1985). *History of sheep and cattle husbandry (including deer) in China*. Beijing; China Agriculture Press. pp. 31-32.

Xu Guilin (1985). The differentiation of wild yak and domestic yak and the economic value of wild yak in breeding. *Journal of China Yak*, 1: 21-25.

Yan Ping, Lu Zhonglin & Lu Hongji (1994). Study on production and quality of hair for wild yak with domestic yak. Proceedings of the first international congress on yak. *Journal of Gansu Agricultural University* (Special issue June 1994) pp. 154-156.

Yan Shoudong (1998). Observation on the growth and development of crossbred wild yak. *Forage and Livestock*, Supplement: 46-47.

Yan Shoudong (2002). *A study on the improvement of yak reproductive performance by introducing wild yak blood*. Proceedings of the third international congress on yak, in Lhasa,China, 4-9 September 2000. ILRI (International Livestock Research Institute), Nairobi. Pp 324-327.

Yang, Rongzhen *et al.* (1997). *Report on growth and development of domestic yak progenies rejuvenated by wild yak*. Proceedings of the second international congress on yak, in Xining, China, 1-6 September 1997. Xining, China, Qinghai People's Publishing House. pp. 21-25.

Yang Rongzhen, Han Xingtai and Luo Xiaolin (1997a). *Yak production in the Central Asian highlands*. Proceedings of the second international congress on yak, in Xining, China, 1-6 September 1997. Xining, China. Qinghai People's Publishing House. 298 pp.

YRO (Yak Research Office) of Southwest Nationalities College and XLF (Xiangdong Livestock Farm of Sichuan Province) (1983). Experiment and its result analysis on improving productive performance of yak by using frozen semen of ordinary cattle for AI. *Journal of Southwest Nationalities College* (Animal Husbandry and Veterinary Sciences Edition), 2: 17.

YRO (Yak Research Office) of Southwest Nationalities College and GISP (Grassland Institute of Sichuan Province) (1984). The research on the interspecific cross combination between female yak and cattle bull. *In The research on the utilization and exploitation of grassland in the northwestern part of Sichuan province*. Chengdu, China, Sichuan Nationalities Press. pp. 107-103.

Zagdsuren, Yo (1994). *Some possibilities to increase meat and milk production of yak husbandry*. Proceedings of the first international congress on yak. *Journal of Gansu Agricultural University* (Special issue June 1994) pp. 113-118.

Zhang Haimin & Liang Yulin (1998). Survey on herd structure and management of Tianzhu White yak. *Forage and Livestock*, Supplement: 57-58.

Zhang Rongchang (1989). *China: the yak*. Gansu Scientific and Technology Press, Lanzhou, China. 386 pp.

Zhang Rongchang, Han Jianlin and Wu Jianping (1994). *Yak production in the Central Asian highlands*.Proceedings of the first international congress on yak, in Lanzhou, China. *Journal of Gansu Agricultural University* (Special issue June 1994). 345 pp.

Zhang Yun (1994). The relationship between season and age of stud yak bull in Damxung. Proceedings of the first international congress on yak. *Journal of Gansu Agricultural University* (Special issue June 1994) pp. 303-307.

Zhao Bingyao & Zhang Jianwen (1994). Present situation, problems and prospects of wild yak utilzation in Gansu. *Journal of Gansu Agricultural University* (Special issue June 1994) pp. 137-139.

Zhao Zhengrong (1957). *Animal husbandry in the middle part of Gansu province*. Beijing, Scientific Publishing House.

Zhong Guanghui (1998). Brief introduction to the research activities of the Department of Animal and Technology of the Southwest Nationalities College. *Forage and Livestock*, Supplement: 60-61.

Zhong Guanghui *et al.* (1995). *Breed criterion of the Jiulong yak in Sichuan Province (DB51/250-95)*.

Zhong Jincheng (1996). *Yak genetics and breeding*. Chengdu, China, Sichuan Scientific and Technology Press. 271 pp.

OVERVIEW

Yak have many characteristics and attributes that must be regarded as adaptations to many factors: extreme cold; high altitude with low oxygen content of the air and high solar radiation; difficult, often treacherous terrain; and cyclical nutrition with short growing seasons for grazing herbage as well as a variety of herbage.

In general, temperature is the single most important factor determining the distribution, stocking density and, indirectly, the growth rate of yak. Yak survive and perform adequately if the annual mean temperature is below $5^{o}C$ and the average in the hottest month is not above $13^{o}C$. They can also survive satisfactorily at ambient temperatures down to $-40^{o}C$. Altitude, as such, is of lesser importance. The further north (of the equator) yak live, the lower, in general, the altitude at which they are found. Yak in North America and in animal and zoological parks in several parts of the world, may again have re-adapted, over time, to life in these, for them, non-normal situations.

Yak cope with cold by conserving heat, rather than by generating it – which would require food that may not be available. Heat conservation is effected by a compact conformation, a thick fleece of coarse outer hair and an undercoat of fine down. The proportion of down in the coat increases greatly before the onset of winter. Young calves have a fleece composed exclusively of down fibre. Normally, yak accumulate a layer of subcutaneous fat prior to winter. This also helps heat conservation and provides an energy reserve. The skin is relatively thick. It contains sweat glands, though for the most part, these are not functional. This is one reason why yak are intolerant of high ambient temperature.

Adaptation to low oxygen content of the air arises from yak having a large chest (14 - 15 pairs of thoracic ribs), large lungs and a large heart relative to their overall body size. The haemoglobin content may not be exceptionally high relative to cattle at sea level, although the content increases with altitude, but the haemoglobin of yak blood has a high affinity for oxygen. Also, anatomically, the yak is designed to be capable of breathing rapidly and take in large amounts of air.

The skin is highly pigmented and the predominant hair colour is black. Both of these attributes help to resist the effects of solar radiation. White yak exist because herdsmen in some localities prefer them.

The large rumen volume of yak relative to body size may be a useful adaptation to foraging herbage under rough grazing conditions. Yak are adapted to grazing a wide variety of plant species: grass, coarse plants and sedges and some shrubs. Yak can graze long grass using their tongues, as is common for cattle, but they can also graze very short herbage, after the manner of sheep, by using their incisor teeth and lips. When ground is covered with snow and ice, they break through the cover to the wilted grass beneath, using their hooves and heads. Yak also graze rapidly and for long hours.

To cope with precipitous terrain, yak have developed particularly suitable hooves and a temperament that is suited to potentially dangerous situations, such as marshy ground. Yak prefer to group in large herds for protection, particularly against wolves, but they are also nervous of wild animals and man and, if startled, will readily take flight.

Introduction

Features common to the environment in which yak live are extreme cold, mountainous terrain, high altitudes with reduced oxygen in the air, high solar radiation and short growing seasons for herbage and a variable assortment of herbage, sparse in some areas. Plant growing seasons vary from 120 to 180 days, but the periods of relatively vigorous plant growth are even shorter than that. Wilted herbage provides some sustenance for the yak at other times of year, but not in sufficient quantity for their requirements. There is, of course, some variation in these features. Some "compensatory" factors have also to be taken into account. For example, the more northerly the latitude at which the yak are found, and hence, in general, the colder the climate, the lower the altitudes at which the yak will live. These points will be discussed in more detail later in this chapter. Many of the characteristics of the yak can be regarded as adaptations to these conditions, in which cattle of other species have difficulty in surviving.

Distribution in relation to environmental factors

Several studies in China have analysed the distribution of the yak using multiple regression approaches with the stocking density of the yak, in selected areas, as the dependant variable and various factors of the environment as the independent variables. The factors most commonly included in these studies (for example, Wen Zhenzhong and Xie Zhonglun, 1985) are: altitude above sea level, yearly average air temperature, annual precipitation, average relative humidity, average annual sunshine and, in some studies, the type of plant cover.

These factors are not independent of each other. For example, altitude and air temperature are related, as are annual precipitation and annual sunshine, and all these factors impinge on the length of the growing season for plants and the type of plant cover likely to be found. With these limitations in mind, authors of various studies concluded that air temperature was of major importance for the distribution and body size of the yak and more important than altitude (Cai Li, 1992; Chen Zhihua, 2000). In analyses where the type of plant cover was also included as a variable (Huang Wenxiu and Wang Sufang, 1980; Dou Yaozong, et al. 1985) its importance ranked alongside temperature.

However, the quantity of available herbage itself must be strongly influenced by the climate of the area. Annual precipitation was generally of less importance to the distribution of the yak, and altitude, as such, of lesser importance still.

Some environmental factors in relation to areas of yak distribution are shown in Table 4.1. It can be seen that yak are found generally above 3 000 m above sea level (a.s.l.), with cold and semi-arid to semi-humid climate (yearly average temperature ranging from -5°C to 5.5°C, and average relative humidity from 50 percent to 65 percent). The main natural feeds are grass, sedges and forbs.

The effect of air temperature

In the native regions of yak in present times, the stocking density of yak declines as average annual temperature increases. The greatest concentrations of yak are found at average annual air temperatures between -3°C and $+3^{o}$C. In Qinghai province, the yak are concentrated in areas with annual mean temperatures between -3°C and -4°C; those in Tibet are densest at the range of -3°C to -5°C; and in Sichuan province between -1.6^{o}C and $+3.4^{o}$C (Table 4.1).

Table 4.1 Environmental factors in yak distribution areas

Areas	Altitude (m a.s.l.)	Yearly average temp (°C)	Annual precipitation (mm)	Type of plant cover	Sources
Tibet	4 500 - 5 500	-3 - -5	600 - 700	Grass, sedges and forbs	Lu Zhonglin, 1999
Qinghai	4 000 - 4 500	-3 - -4	500 - 600	Grass and sedges	Cai Li, 1994
Southern Gansu	3 000 - 4 500	1.4 - 3.2	300 - 860	Grass and sedges	Lu Zhonglin, 1999
Western Sichuan	3 000 - 5 000	-1 - 5	600 - 800	Grass, sedges and forbs	Cai Li, 1989
Zhong Dian, Yunnan	3 000 - 4 000	5.2 - 5.5	500 - 700	Grass and sedges	He Shaoyu *et al.*, 1997
Bazhou, Xinjiang	2 400 - 4 000	-4.7	Around 284.6	Grass and shrubs	Lu Zhonglin, 1999
Bhutan	3 600 - 4 600	5.5	Below 650	Grass and sedges	Tshering *et al.*, 1996
India	4 000 - 5 000			Grass and forbs	Pal *et al.*, 1996
Mongolia	3 000 - 5 000		350 - 500	Grass and shrubs	Davaa, 1996
Nepal	3 000 - 5 000			Grass and sedges	Sherchand *et al.*, 1996

Li Shihong *et al.* (1981) reported that above an ambient temperature of 13°C the respiration rate of the yak starts to rise, and at 16°C the heart rate and body temperature start to rise. When environmental temperatures reach 20°C, yak will stand near water or in shade, if available, without moving, grazing, drinking or ruminating. At the other extreme, yak can feed and move normally on grasslands with air temperatures ranging as low as -30°C to -40°C, or even lower as in the Tibetan Naqu area where a minimum air temperature in the cold season was recorded as -42°C. The lowest temperature that yak can tolerate has not been recorded.

It appears from these studies that air temperature is the single most important environmental factor influencing the distribution of the yak. Yak survive and perform adequately provided the annual mean temperature is below 5°C and the average in the hottest month does not exceed 13°C, though daily maximum temperatures can rise in the summer to much higher levels before falling again at night. (Nonetheless, yak kept commercially in North America and those in zoological and wild animal parks in many countries appear to have adapted to different sets of conditions – see Chapter 11, part 3). It is a matter of observation that the farther north of the equator that yak live, the lower is, on average, the altitude of the terrain on which they are found because average temperature declines with increasing latitude (cf. Table 4.2).

Air temperature has also been reported as the most important environmental factor influencing the growth and body size of yak (Cai Li, 1992; Yao Yubi and Li Yuqing, 1995; Chen Zhihua *et al.*, 2000). Yao Yubi and Li Yuqing, (1995) derived an equation of meat production from its relation with air temperature by using multiply regression as follows: $\hat{y} = 2.452 + 7.166T_7 + 1.726 R_2$ (r=*0.907,* P<0.01). Where $\hat{y}$ is average carcass weight of yak, T is the average temperature of the mid-ten days in July and R is the precipitation in February.

The effect of altitude

Subject to the availability of adequate grazing, the distribution and stocking density of yak increases with altitude, but as already noted, this is also dependent on latitude. Thus, at the more southerly latitudes as, for example, Qinghai province, yak seek out higher altitudes than in more northerly areas, such as Mongolia. The few yak introduced to Canada and Alaska in far northern latitudes existed at relatively low altitudes (see Chapter 11, part 3). It is likely that, as previously suggested, the relationship between altitude and latitude is mediated through air temperature.

The highest altitude where yak live normally is at 5 500 m in the Tibetan Rongbusi region in the lower ranges of the Himalayas. Yak steers used as pack animals are quite capable of traversing terrain at 7 200 m. Low oxygen content of air and high solar radiation are not therefore barriers to the yak's survival.

The effect of precipitation and relative humidity

Yak live in two distinct zones. One is semi-arid with an annual precipitation of 500 - 600 mm and a relative humidity of 50 - 60 percent. In these areas the potential for evaporation tends to exceed the level of precipitation (e.g. Qinghai and much of Tibet). The other zone has an average annual rainfall of 600 - 700 mm and a relative humidity of 60 - 65 percent and is described as semi-humid (e.g. eastern Tibet and southwest Sichuan). The two zones differ in the predominant types of vegetation found and, as noted in Chapter 2, the two zones are associated with different types of yak.

The effect of sunshine

In general, yak live in areas with more than 2 000 hours of annual sunshine. In Qinghai province, the highest densities of yak are in areas with between 2 500 and 2 700 hours sunshine (Wen Zhengzhong and Xie Zhonglun, 1985), while in Sichuan province the greatest density of yak is in the districts with between 2 000 and 2 200 hours of sunshine per year.

Adaptive characteristics

The ability of the yak to live in conditions in which other bovines will not survive, or, at least, not thrive, suggests that the yak has developed specially adapted characteristics. These are described in the following sections.

Resistance to cold

Conformation

The yak's body is compact with short neck, short limbs, no dewlap, small ears and a short tail. (The limb length index, defined as {[height at withers-chest depth]/height at withers} x 100, is small at 40 - 42 percent, relative to other cattle in the region.) The scrotum of the male is small, compact and hairy, and the udder of the female small and also hairy. The skin has few wrinkles, and the surface area of the yak is relatively small per unit of bodyweight (0.016 sq m per kg [Li Shihong *et al.* 1984]). The yak has only a few functional sweat glands (see section, Skin thickness and sweat glands). All these factors result in a minimized dissipation of body heat.

In addition in terms of appearance though not relevant to heat dissipation, yak can be either horned or polled. The distribution of these two forms appears to depend on the regional preferences of the herdsmen. Thus, yak in Mongolia, for example, are predominantly polled (or dehorned) while those of Tibet or Nepal are nearly all horned. The distribution of the horn types is shown in Table 4.2.

Coat of the yak

Heat conservation is enhanced by a thick fleece on the whole body, composed of an outer coat of long hair and an undercoat of a dense layer of fine down fibres that appear in the colder season. As already noted, hair colours vary from black and brown through variegation to white. Since white absorbs less heat, the existence of this colour must be attributed to herders' preference rather than to adaptive usefulness. It is significant, however, that white yak are more prevalent at more northerly latitudes. In such areas, solar radiation is not as intense as in the more southerly latitudes, or at the higher elevations where black is the predominant colour (see Table 4.2). Hair production of white yak is higher than that of the black and brown ones (Wang Yuchang, 1995). The thick and dense coat of white yak may partly compensate for less heat absorption of the white colour in winter.

Details of fleece production and physical and structural properties of the fibres are given in Chapter 6. The purpose here is to discuss the coat as a feature of the adaptation of the yak to its environment.

In general, the coat of the yak seems well suited to insulating the animal from cold, protecting it from heat and repelling moisture. All these factors are important to survival in the prevailing climate. As Yousef (1985) noted, a thick winter coat is a general adaptation of animals living in extreme cold, e.g. arctic mammals. Thus, conservation of heat takes precedence over extra generation of heat. To generate extra heat would ultimately require additional feed, which is in short supply throughout the winter. It is of interest in the present context to observe that one of the most successful of all the yak breeds, the Jiulong yak of Sichuan province, has a fibre strain that produces, on average, between three and five times as much fleece as other types of yak. This strain also inhabits one of the coldest, dampest and most fog-bound areas of all yak territory. It is probable that it is the dense, heavy coat that has helped the Jiulong yak to survive in these conditions.

Insulation from the fleece

The coat consists of three types of fibre: coarse, long fibres with a diameter in excess of 52 μ, down fibre with a diameter below 25 μ and mid-type hairs with diameters between these two values. The down fibre is a particular attribute of the winter coat of the yak to provide the additional insulation then required. Coats with a mixture of fibre types have been shown to maintain a stable air temperature within the coat. Ouyang Xi and Wang Qianfei. (1984) measured temperatures at the skin surface and at the middle and top of the staples of various parts of the yak body, namely the ear, forehead, sides of neck, shoulder, rump, the back, belly, tail and legs. Measurements were made on ten animals on three successive days in the cold season in February (mean ambient temperature $-18\,^{\circ}C$) and on nine animals on three days in the warm season at the end of May (mean daytime ambient temperature $22\,^{\circ}C$ – though somewhat windier at that time than in February). Figures 4.1 and 4.2 show the measurements.

The results (Figures 4.1 and 4.2) show that the gradient in temperature between the skin surface and the top of the staple is far greater in winter than in summer for parts of the body trunk, such as the shoulder, rump and belly.

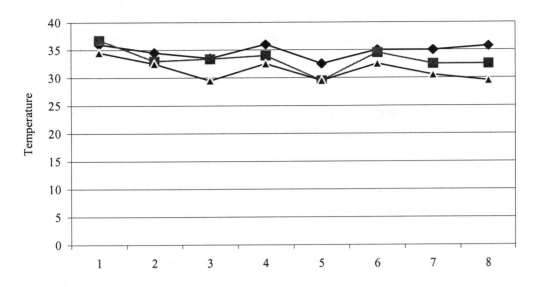

Figure 4.1 Temperature °C in **summer** (mean daytime ambient temperature 22°C) at the skin surface (blue), mid-staple (purple), and top staple (yellow) of various body parts: *1 back, 2 ear, 3 neck, 4 forehead, 5 tail, 6 shoulder, 7 rump, 8 belly* [Source: Ouyang Xi *et al.*, 1985]

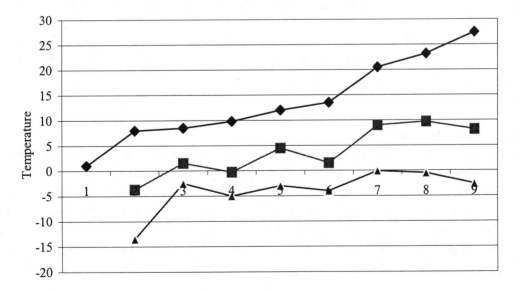

Figure 4.2 Temperature °C in **winter** (mean ambient temperature -18°C) at skin surface (blue), mid-staple (purple), and top staple (yellow) of various body parts: *1 leg, 2 back, 3 ear, 4 neck, 5 forehead, 6 tail, 7 shoulder, 8 rump, 9 belly* [Source: Ouyang Xi *et al.*, 1985]

However, the seasonal difference in the temperature gradient from skin surface to top of staple is much less at extremities of the body, such as the ears, where vasoconstriction occurs during cold. For this reason, temperature varies at the skin surface, during the cold season, between the different parts of the body, as shown in Figure 4.1. The results also show clearly the insulation from cold provided by the fleece (though these features are not unique to the yak; the effect of fleece on heat regulation, and consequently on the energy metabolism of the animal, have been demonstrated, e.g. in relation to sheep by Blaxter, *et al.* 1959). No case of frostbite has been recorded in the yak, even at the extremities of its body.

The function of the coat in helping yak to survive in very cold and wet conditions is enhanced by the low water absorption of the coat (Xue Jiying and Yu Zhengfeng, 1981).

The *arectores pilorum* muscles are highly developed in the dermis of the yak (Ouyang Xi and Wang Qianfei, 1984). Their contraction makes fibres stand up and effectively increase the depth of the coat and reduce heat loss under stress from cold.

Seasonal changes

Hair growth and the composition of the coat change with season. As air temperature falls with the approach of winter, down fibres grow densely among the coarser hairs, especially on the shoulder, back and rump. Ouyang Xi *et al.* (1983) found in a herd studied both in summer and in winter that the proportion of down fibre increased by between 17.5 percent and 30 percent in winter, through the activation of down follicles that had lain dormant. The proportion of coarse hairs correspondingly decreased. As air temperature rises with the onset of the warm season, down fibres begin to be shed from the fleece (see Chapter 6).

As a consequence of the abundant grazing in summer and early autumn, yak are normally able to develop a layer of subcutaneous fat that also provides them with insulation from cold as well as an energy reserve during the period of nutritional deprivation over winter and spring.

Breed and location differences

The amount of down fibre on the yak's back may vary with breed. From different studies it appears that down fibre is more than twice as dense in Tianzhu White yak in Gansu province as in Luqu yak of southern Gansu, with the Maiwa yak of Sichuan province somewhat intermediate (Zhang Rongchang, 1977; Lu Zhongling *et al.*, 1982; Wang Jie *et al.*, 1984). However, here again, breed type is confounded with the area in which the different breeds are kept. To establish that it is breed and not location that is responsible for the differences would require a comparison of the different breeds at the same location.

Studies also indicate that fibre density declines when yak are moved to areas with warmer summers and longer frost-free periods. Thus, yak introduced in the 1970s to the Jingbei Plateau of northern Weichang county of Hebei province had an average density of fibres of 3 167 per sq cm at that time. The density subsequently declined to 1 870 fibres per sq cm.

The changes occurred through a decrease in the density of down fibre in particular, but the coarse hairs decreased in length. These changes allowed better heat dissipation at the warmer times of the year and can be assumed to have occurred in response to the environmental changes directly affecting the animal rather than due to selection among the yak.

Age effects

In calves younger than six months, the coat consists almost entirely of down fibre. Thereafter, the proportion (by weight) declines to 62 percent at one year old and 52 percent by year two, 44 percent at year three and 43 percent at four and five years old (Zhang Yingsong *et al.*, 1982). There is a corresponding increase in the deposition of subcutaneous fat as the animals grew older.

Skin thickness and sweat glands

Xiao Wangji *et al.* (1997) found Zhongdian yak produced more hide and possessed a higher proportion of skin to body weight (P<0.01), when compared with Zhongdian cattle and yak-cattle hybrids. Skin thickness is greater on the back of the yak than on other parts of the body. This is associated with the fact that the back is the part of the animal most exposed to wind, rain and snow. Li Shihong *et al.* (1984) measured skin thickness on the shoulder blade, the back and the knee of 70 live female yak and found the average thickness at the three positions to be 5.6 ± 0.36, 7.5 ± 0.83 and 5.6 ± 0.40 mm, respectively. Ouyang Xi *et al.* (1984), using histological sections, measured thickness of epidermis and dermis combined. Again, the back had the thickest skin (average 5.13 mm) and the densely haired parts had a thickness of as little as 2.36 mm. Averaged over the different parts of the body, the skin thickness was 3.37 ± 1.38 mm, but the epidermis itself was very thin at 0.044 ± 0.019 mm.

Sweat glands are distributed in the skin over the whole body and are of the apocrine type. Density per sq cm was found to be greatest on the forehead (891 sq cm) and least on the rump (138 sq cm), with an overall average of 399 ± 251 sq cm (Li Shihong *et al.*, 1984; Ouyang Xi and Wang Qianfei, 1984). However, the function of the sweat glands is poorly developed. Tests made by these authors, using different methods, agree in detecting sweat secretions only on the muzzle and not on other parts of the body. The absence of sweating in the yak assists cold tolerance but helps make the yak intolerant to heat.

Energy metabolism

Hu Linghao (1994) studied the energy metabolism of growing yak at three different ages (one, two and three years old) and compared it with that of yellow cattle, both kept at three different altitudes (2 261 m, 3 250 m and 4 271 m). He reported that the fasting heat production of the yak remained fairly constant irrespective of altitude, whereas that of the yellow cattle rose markedly. This could well point to an adaptive response of the yak to life at high altitude and to the nutritional deprivation that yak experience in winter and early spring.

At the lowest of the three elevations in the trials conducted by Hu Linghao, the absolute fasting heat production of the yak was higher than that of the yellow cattle, but not so at the higher altitudes. In another experiment by Hu Linghao, the yak generated a little more heat in the course of walking than did the somewhat larger yellow cattle. The author attributes the difference in heat production to the difference in body size, as smaller animals are expected to generate more heat. Clearly, these and similar experiments are important for understanding the factors that lead to adaptation and may, in due course, provide a means for devising improved grazing and management strategies.

Adaptation to low atmospheric oxygen and high solar radiation

At elevations of 3 500 m above sea level, where most yak live, the oxygen content of the air is some 35 percent lower than at sea level. On even higher grazing pastures, at an altitude of 5 000 m, the oxygen content is halved. Also, in most of the areas there is more than 2 000 hours of sunshine and levels of solar radiation are between 130 and 165 kcal per sq cm (540 - 690 kJ per sq cm) annually, depending on elevation.

The yak has adapted to these conditions: It is considered to take in larger volumes of air than most other cattle, to retain a higher proportion of the oxygen breathed in and to be protected against harmful effects of solar radiation by the colour of its coat and skin.

Vertebrae, thorax, heart and lungs

Vertebrae. Yak have 14 thoracic vertebrae and 14 pairs of ribs – one more than in other cattle – although several authors report 15 ribs, two more than in other cattle. This gives the yak a larger chest capacity. There are five lumbar vertebrae, one less than in other cattle. The number of coccygeal vertebrae is variable in the range from 12 - 16 (other cattle have 16). The yak has five sacral vertebrae and seven cervical ones, the same as for other cattle. The total number of vertebrae are thus fewer than for other species of cattle.

*Thorax and organs.*Yak ribs are narrow and long with a relatively large distance between them. There is also a good development of muscle between them. Relative to local cattle, the yak has a large thorax (heart girth index = 150 [heart girth x 100/height at withers]), allowing the development of large lungs and a large heart. For example, according to Xiao Wangji *et al.* (1997), the lung of Zhongdian yak (n=12) weighs 3.7 ± 0.54 kg, more (P<0.05 than that of Zhongdian cattle 1.8 ± 0.57 kg (n=5) and yak-cattle hybrids 2.5 ± 0.39 kg (n=10). Similarly, these authors recorded the heart of Zhongdian yak, weighing on average 1.3 ± 0.29 kg, heavier (P<0.01) than the cattle heart (0.87 ± 0.24 kg) or the yak-cattle hybrids heart (0.84 ± 0.11 kg). The larger sizes of these organs help the yak to achieve adequate intake and circulation of oxygen in conditions where the supply is low. Lung weights of the Chinese yak vary among the different breeds, from 1.1 percent to 1.5 percent of body weight, and heart weights vary between 0.5 percent and 0.78 percent of body weight (Li Shihong *et al.*, 1984; Zhang Rongchang, 1985).

Denisov (1958) found that the alveolar area occupied 59 percent of the cross-sectional area of the yak lungs, compared with 40 percent for Jargas cattle located nearby. This suggests that the yak lung also has a relatively large surface area from which to absorb air in order to compensate for the lower oxygen content of the air.

The trachea of the yak is also particularly large to allow a high rate of intake of air. Zhang Rongchang et al. (1994) stated that the trachea length in Tianzhu White yak is shorter than in other cattle but that the diameter is appreciably greater. Wang Yuchang (1995) confirmed that finding and also referred to large nostrils in the yak that further assist air intake. Li Shihong et al. (1984) measured five females and reported 43 cm for the length of the trachea and 5.5 cm for the diameter. Apart from variation in the trachea dimensions among individual animals, the size of the trachea varies with the general body size of the yak, as affected by breed and location. The annular cartilage of the trachea was found to be narrow and adjacent cartilages of the trachea to be about 4 cm apart. This allows the yak to breathe rapidly and to quickly increase air intake into the lungs when conditions demand it.

Circulation and oxygen intake and absorption
Heart and pulmonary pressure. A study of five yak at high altitude (Ladakh, India, 4 500 m) and six yak at low altitude (Whipsnade Park, England, 150 m) by Anand et al. (1986) found that the pulmonary arterial pressure was not significantly different in the two groups. But the pulmonary arterial resistance was slightly higher in the yak at high altitude than in those at virtually sea level (0.58 vs. 0.34 mm Hg l^{-1} min). A higher resistance would be expected if vasoconstriction has occurred in the pulmonary arterial system.

Vasoconstriction commonly occurs in order to reduce blood supply to under-ventilated areas of the lung and maintain homeostasis in other respects (Anand et al. 1986).

For example, in an animal with a pneumonic lung, the vasoconstriction reflex will shut off oxygen to the damaged area even at low altitude, making more oxygen available to the functional areas of the lung. At high altitude, as Anand et al. (1986) argued, such vasoconstriction would not be a good long-term response to permanently hypoxic conditions. Because the whole lung becomes a low-oxygenated area at high altitudes, the vasoconstriction reflex would be very damaging, as it would then affect the whole lung. As shown by these authors from comparisons of yak with cattle, it seems the yak has adapted to prevent this vasoconstriction happening to all but a very small extent.

Thus, when comparing yak with Himalayan (hill) cattle and hybrids of these with yak, all at the high altitude, Anand et al. (1986) found that while arterial pulmonary pressure in the cattle was somewhat higher than in the yak, the pulmonary arterial resistance was more than three-fold greater. In these respects, the first-generation hybrids of the yak with these cattle were intermediate in their pulmonary haemodynamics, but considerably closer to the yak. Backcrosses to cattle (three quarter cattle, one quarter yak), however, had a bi-modal distribution - with some animals closer to cattle and others closer to yak, especially in respect to the resistance trait. Anand et al. (1986) concluded from this study that there was an inherited basis to pulmonary arterial resistance and that the yak had gone a long way towards eliminating the vasoconstrictor response to high-altitude-low-oxygen living.

Anand *et al.* (1986) provided a cautionary comment to their conclusions by saying that they cannot be certain to what extent the differences in resistance between the hill cattle and the yak are an expression of the differences in the size of the animals (the cattle were much smaller). If the results are confirmed, a genetically attenuated vasoconstrictor response to low-oxygen conditions is clearly an adaptation of importance.

In an effort to explore the subject further, Anand *et al.* (1988) did another study in which sheep and goats were also included. Their later results supported the earlier thesis, in relation to the reduced vasoconstriction response in the yak, and also added data (albeit from only one yak), suggesting that the yak has a relatively larger right ventricle of the heart than what is found in hybrids of yak with cattle. Moreover, the yak, unlike the cattle, had a smaller medial thickness of the small pulmonary arteries (further suggesting a reduced capacity for vasoconstriction).

Belkin *et al.* (1985) reported, on the basis of a study of 40 hearts from mature yak, that there was a higher degree of capillarization of the right ventricle of the heart compared with the left. This suggests a further adaptive response of the yak to high altitude conditions that require the right ventricle to cope with increased loading.

Respiration. Cai Li *et al.* (1975) observed 48 adult female yak at pasture at an altitude of 3 450 m in July and August. Respiration rate was between 20 and 30 per minute when the air temperature was below 13°C, but above that temperature the respiration rate rose rapidly. Respiration rate was significantly higher in the evening than in the morning, but was not significantly correlated with humidity, wind speed or the prevailing weather. Zhang Rongchang (1989) reported a respiration rate in adult yak of 80 per minute at 28°C, 49 per minute at 10°C and 25 per minute at 5°C. For one-year-old yak, the respiration rate at the high temperature was as high as 130 per minute but declined to 7 - 15 breaths per minute at -6°C. A study by Wang Yuchang (1995) on Tianzhu White yak found both respiration rates and pulse rates to be higher in the females than in males.

As expected, respiration rate was also found to be higher during periods of activity than during inactivity.

Zhao Bingyao (1982) examined seasonal differences in the respiration rate in five adult female yak at an altitude of 3 400 m on cold grassland. Over a period of a year, the animals were observed each day between 0600 hrs and 0800 hrs and again between 1800 hrs and 2000 hrs. The respiration rate was found to be highest in August and pulse rate highest in June. Both rates declined gradually after the warm season ended and were at their lowest in March. Body temperature was virtually unaffected by season and averaged 37.6°C in the morning and 38.5°C in the evening. All of this suggests that yak alter their respiration rate not only in response to a changing need for oxygen, but also to regulate body temperature.

The yak, with its thick skin, absence of sweating and a heavy coat, has few means at its disposal for heat dissipation, other than respiration rate. The lowest pulse rate in March corresponds to the time of year when yak are in their poorest condition and often at a point of exhaustion. At this time, they have a low metabolic rate due to the prolonged period of a shortage of feed over winter that leads to near starvation.

Blood cells and haemoglobin. The capacity to take in sufficient air by virtue of anatomical features, respiration rate and physiological response is clearly an important aspect of yak adaptation to life at high altitudes. It is also important that absorption and retention of oxygen from the air should be adequate for the need. This, too, may be specially adapted in the yak. In this regard, the evidence from red blood cells and haemoglobin (Hb) content is not totally conclusive. Data from 21 different sources are presented in Table 4.3. These results suggest that, relative to adult cattle (*Bos taurus*) at or around sea level, the yak in these various studies do not have exceptionally high numbers of erythrocytes per unit volume of blood. The values range from 5.2 to 10.3, with an average of 6.9 (10^{12} per l) for the 16 mean values shown. This compares with a mean of 7.0, and a range from 5.0 to 9.0, given as normal values for other cattle in a review article by Doxey (1977).

The overall average of the 21 Hb values (g per dl) in Table 4.3 is 11.8 (range of averages from 8.3 to 18.4). These values are only slightly higher than the overall average of 11.0 (8.0 - 14.0) given as the normal values by Doxey – and the mean values of only two of the groups of yak fall outside the range for the cattle examined. The data in Table 4.3 indicate that the haemoglobin concentration in blood increases, in general, with increasing altitude, particularly if only the data from yak at the several highest altitudes are considered. Interestingly, the values for yak at Whipsnade Park, a little above sea level, were similar to the values for yak from China, Bhutan and India. Taking account of the altitude effect, it seems that yak are not exceptional relative to cattle. (There is no particular explanation for the fact that two of the values quoted by Zhang Rongchang *et al.*, 1994, for yak in Tibet at altitudes of 4 366 m and 4 500 m, are markedly higher than the other values from that area. Sampling errors cannot be ruled out because the number of animals involved is not given). Only a few authors provide data on packed cell volume (PCV). These are, on average, higher than the normal mean given in the article by Doxey, previously mentioned. None are outside the range he quotes. A useful parameter, which can be derived from a combination of PCV and red-cell count, is the mean corpuscular volume (MCV), which provides an indication of red-cell size. The average of the seven estimates available is 59.8 and puts this at the top of the range quoted by Doxey for cattle. This, then, may indicate that yak have larger red cells with a greater surface area and a higher capacity for the retention of oxygen. (Larrick and Burck, 1986, in a general article on yak in Tibet, give a contradictory view by suggesting that yak have very small red cells in relation to sea-level bovines but have vastly more cells per unit volume of blood; unfortunately no actual data or references are provided to verify this claim.)

An intriguing paper by Lalthantluanga, *et al.* (1985) showed that two types of α and two types of β chains are found in the yak haemoglobin, and that there has been a substitution of valine at position 135 of the β^{II}-chain, in place of the more usual alanine. This was considered by the authors to be the reason for the intrinsically higher oxygen affinity of yak haemoglobin, compared to that of lowland cattle, which is quoted by them and other authors as an established finding in the yak.

It seems, therefore, that factors concerned with air intake, combined with a high oxygen affinity of yak haemoglobin, provide the basis for the yak's adaptation to life at high altitudes.

One final note regarding Table 4.3: Attention is drawn to the difference in blood values at Whipsnade Park between yak manually restrained and those sedated with xylazine. The act of struggling by the animals in the course of manual restraint was shown by Hawkey *et al.* (1983) to release reserves of red cells from the spleen and hence raise the values of several of the blood parameters above those of sedated animals. This point was noted by Winter *et al.* (1989) who also sedated their animals. It has to be assumed, in the absence of information to the contrary, that all the other estimates presented in Table 4.3 are based on manually restrained animals. Therefore, the values from the majority of the sources are likely to be higher than they would have been from sedated animals. It seems possible that the degree of struggling by the animal in the course of restraint may also affect the results, though there are no data presented on that point.

Seasonal variation in Hb content. There is some seasonal variation in the Hb content of yak blood. It is relatively low in May (10.5 g per dl) and higher in October, after the end of the summer grazing season (14.6 g per dl, based on some observations of female yak in Menyuan county of Qinghai province (Research Co-operative Group, 1980 - 1987). Similar observations were made on yak in parts of Siberia by Belyyar (1980), who recorded an Hb content of 10.2 g per dl in the spring and 12.8 g per dl in the autumn of the same year. He also noted that the diameter of the erythrocytes in these yak was 4.83 μ, which was larger than for contemporary Yakut cattle (4.38 μ) in the same area.

Cai Li *et al.* (1975) also provided some evidence on age differences and the difference between lactating and dry adult females. Age effects were not significant on the numbers involved (groups of 17 to 58 for female yak). However, lactating yak had lower red cell counts than dry cows (as shown in Table 4.3 for data from Ruoergai).

Table 4.2 External characteristics of yak at different locations varying in altitude

Area	Location* Latitude (N)	Location* Longitude (E)	Altitude (m)	No. observed	Polled (%)	Black/ brown (%)	Black with white patches (%)	Varie- gated (%)	White (%)
Tibet, Pali	27.5	89.0	4 300	529	few	89.0	11.0		
Yunnan, Zhongdian	28.0	99.5	3 300	946	0.0	62.4	37.6		
Sichuan, Muli	28.5	101.0	3 500	772	0.0	9.5	90.5		
Sichuan, Jiulong	29.0	101.5	3 800	337	0.0	75.4	24.6		
Sichuan, Liuba	29.5	101.5	3 800	4455	0.5	50.6	49.2	0.1	
Tibet, Pengbuo	30.0	91.5	4 000	96	Few	75.0	15.6	9.4	
Tibet, Dangxiong	30.5	91.0	4 400	591	0.0	91.9	8.1		
Tibet, Jiali	31.0	93.5	4 500	241	17.0	41.0	50.0	9.0	
Sichuan, Shachong	31.0	101.0	3 200	486	1.6	78.1	21.9		
Sichuan, Ganzi	31.5	100.0	3 800	330	3.0	66.0	31.0	3.0	
Tibet, Naqu	31.5	91.7	4 570	795	9.2	78.4	16.1	5.1	0.4
Sichuan, Seda	32.5	100.5	3 893	245	11.8	75.1	21.6	2.5	0.8
Sichuan, Hongyuan	33.0	103.0	3 500	782`	7.4	69.4	22.1	8.1	0.4
Gansu, Gannan	34.0	103.0	3 400	957	57.1	78.2	15.8	6.0	0.1
Qinghai, Tongde	35.0	100.5	3 300	580	80.0	81.7	14.1	4.1	
Qinghai, Haiyan	37.0	101.0	3 500	1065	80.0	60.7	25.7	12.7	0.9
Qinghai, Menyuan	37.5	101.5	3 300	1383	43.6	58.2	23.1	7.8	10.9
Qinghai, Gongda	37.5	100.0	3 500	2576	60.6	73.7	16.1	8.1	2.1
Gansu, Shandan	38.5	101.5	3 000	463** 109	46.2	71.6	22.0	5.5	0.9
Xinjiang, Bazhou	40.0	84.0	2 500	280	22.7	57.9	17.5	19.3	5.3

* Median latitude and longitude for the area in question

** 463 observed for horned/polled, 109 for hair colour

Table 4.3 Red cell counts, haemoglobin (Hb) concentration, packed cell volume (PCV), and estimated mean corpuscular volume (MCV) in adult yak from various sources

Area	Altitude (m)	No.	Red cell count [10¹²/l] Mean	[SD]	Hb count [g/dl] Mean	[SD]	PCV [l/l] Mean	[SD]	MCV [fl]	Note	Source
UK, Whipsnade Park	150	7	6.4	0.39	13.7	1.7	0.38	0.04	59.3	(m)	Hawkey et al., 1983
UK, Whipsnade Park	150	18	5.4	0.7	10.9	0.9	0.31	0.04	57.4	(s)	Hawkey et al., 1983
USSR, Yakutia	650	26	5.8	0.1	11.5	0.34	0.38	0.014	65.0		Zhang Rongchang et al., 1989 [quote]
Mongolia	1 500				10.0	1.0					Katzina, 1997 [quote]
Xinjiang, Bazhou	2 500	5	7.3		8.3						CCOYSR, 1982
India, Dirang	2 750	6	5.2	0.2	10.7	0.4	0.28	0.012	53.5		Mondal et al., 1997
Gansu, Tianzhu	3 000	35	6.6	0.9	8.6	1.2	0.33	0.03	50.4		Zhang Dasou et al., 1985
Tibet, Linzhi	3 000	??			11.3						Zhang Rongchang, 1994 [quote]
Yunnan, Zhongdian	3 300	11	6.6		10.0						CCOYSR, 1982
India, Sikkim	3 300	10	6.1	0.4	13.2	0.2	0.39	0.05	58.0		Sahu et al., 1981
Qinghai, Gonda	3 400	57	6.9		10.3						Li Jinxuan, 1984
Sichuan, Ruoergai	3 450	56	10.3	1.1	12.9	0.9				dry	Cai Li et al., 1975
Sichuan, Ruoergai	3 450	52	7.5	0.9	12.7	0.7				lact	Cai Li et al., 1975
Sichuan, Hongyuan	3 500	5	7.6		10.7						Liu Qibui, 1983
Bhutan, (east)	4 000	13			13.5	1.3	0.39	0.04		(s)	Winter et al., 1989

* Number of yak is 40.

** Number of yak is 70. (S) = Sedated with xylazine; (m) = manually restrained; others: form of restraint not specified, manual restraint assumed; dry = dry adult females; lact = lactating adult females.

(continues)

Table 4.3 (continued) Red cell counts,haemoglobin (Hb) concentration, packed cell volume (PCV), and estimated mean corpuscular volume (MCV) in adult yak from various sources

Area	Altitude (m)	No.	Red cell count [10^{12}/l] Mean	[SD]	Hb count [g/dl] Mean	[SD]	PCV [l/l] Mean	[SD]	MCV [fl]	Note	Source
Qinghai, Huzhu	2700 - 4100	43	6.0	0.93	10.3 (40)*	2.2	0.32 (70)**	0.06			Ma Sen, 1997
Qinghai, Darri	4200	38	6.9		10.8						Xu Rongchan & Wu Zhiqiang, 1984
Tibet, Naqu	4366	??			15.4						Zhang Rongchang *et al.*, 1994 [quote]
Tibet, Dangxiong	4400	30	7.4		11.6						Tang Zenyu *et al.* 1982
Tibet, Longzhi	4500	??			18.4						Zhang Rongchang *et al.*, 1994 [quote]
Tibet, Yagao	4700	10	7.6		13.6						Huang Wenxiu & Wang Sufang, 1980

* Number of yak is 40.

** Number of yak is 70. (S) = Sedated with xylazine; (m) = manually restrained; others: form of restraint not specified, manual restraint assumed; dry = dry adult females; lact = lactating adult females.

Other blood cells and constituents
Most of the papers quoted in Table 4.3 also provide values for white-cell content of the blood. They average 10.2 (10^6 per litre) (8.6 - 12.5), suggesting that the animals were in normal health at the time of bleeding. White cell content of the blood of Tianzhu White yak is about 9.1 - 12.5 (10^6 per litre), higher than that of local cattle, 7.6 (10^6 per litre), according to Zhang Rongchang's report (1989)

Cai Li *et al.* (1975) showed (Table 4.2) that, as expected, lactating females had significantly lower blood glucose levels than dry females (61.5 vs. 66.5 mg per dl). Blood calcium and phosphorus concentrations (mg per dl) for the different groups of females in this study ranged from 8.7 for dry adult cows to 9.5 for calves (for Ca) and from 5.5 for the dry cows to 7.4 for the calves (for P). The blood pH was 7.0, on average, in these data.

Colour of coat and skin
The predominantly dark coat colours of the yak (see Chapter 2) help to protect it against the effects of solar radiation, which is particularly intense at the southern latitudes. The lighter colours and white yak are found farther north and at lower altitudes where solar radiation is less intense. However, were it not for selection and colour preferences by man, it is unlikely that the lighter shades, and white yak in particular, would exist. These light shades are not generally found among wild yak where these would be expected to be at a disadvantage in terms of natural selection. Hair colours of yak, in different areas at different elevations, are shown in Table 4.2.

The cells of the epidermis of the yak contain many pigmented granules, especially in the cells of the *stratum basale*. These pigmented granules can help to prevent injury from ultraviolet light in the deeper layers of the skin. Yak with white faces generally have eyes surrounded by black hair. The black eye sockets of Maiwa yak of Sichuan province are accepted as a breed characteristic. Also, the hair on the yak's forehead is well developed and can cover the eyes. No specific research appears to have been done on the possible protection against solar radiation afforded to the eyes and face by this forehead hair, but it is reasonable to assume that the hair has such a function.

Adaptive characteristics related to grazing conditions

The cold pastures on which yak graze have predominantly short grass in some areas and rough grazing conditions with sedges and shrubby plants in others. Yak have developed organs for food intake and a grazing behaviour peculiarly suited to this environment.

Grazing procedure and grazing behaviour
Mouth. Yak have broad mouths, small muzzles and thin flexible lips. The front (incisor) teeth are hard and broad and have a flat grinding surface. The tip of the tongue is also broad and blunt and the filamentous papillae on the surface of the tongue are highly developed and cutinized. The surface of the tongue feels rough and "thorny".

Grazing habit. Yak can graze long grass, using their tongue as do other cattle, but they can also graze in the manner of sheep, using incisor teeth and lips to graze short grass and creeping stems, and roots of grass. Yak will also take tender branches of shrubs in alpine bush meadow. Under most normal conditions, yak have learned to avoid poisonous or thorny plants as recorded instances of poisoning are very rare. However, there are reports of extensive pyrrolizidine alkaloid poisoning in Merak Sakten, a part of Bhutan (Winter *et al.*, 1992). This was thought to be due principally to grazing of *Senecio raphanifolius* (although other plants may also have been involved) (Winter *et al.*, 1994). This plant, as pointed out by the authors, was almost certainly eaten by the yak because of overstocking of the pastures concerned, leading to overgrazing. Otherwise, with a more plentiful supply of feed, the yak would have avoided these plants.

Yak will also readily graze the rough stems and leaves of sedges in low-lying marshy areas. Zhou Shourong (1984) recorded more than 60 species of grasses in the diet of yak on alpine, subalpine marsh and semi-marsh meadow (see also Chapter 13). When the ground is covered with snow, as it typically is for long periods, yak will paw through quite thick snow layers, using both head and face to help them to gain access to the wilted vegetation underneath.

Yak will reduce grass with a height of 15 cm to between 2.6 cm and 5.2 cm (Ren Jizhou and Jing Juhe, 1956). In the spring, yak will graze green shoots no more than 2-3 cm above the ground – though it would be surprising if they could not graze more closely than that if necessary (as sheep in Scotland, for example, are known to do). In addition, the yak take stems and leaves from the residual wilted grass still available in the spring.

The grazing time of yak is affected by season, weather, type and quality of grazing and the structure of the herd in terms of age and sex. This has been studied by many researchers (e.g. Ren Jizhou and Jin Juhe, 1956; Cai Li, *et al.* 1960; Zhang Rongchang *et al.*, 1982; Qi Guangyong, 1984; Lei Huanzhang *et al.*, 1985; and Zhang Hongwu, *et al.,* 1985).

The general conclusions are that the intake time varies between 34 percent and 80 percent of the total time available for grazing. The rest of the time is used for walking, resting and drinking. Normally, lactating yak herds spend more time grazing than do mixed herds – as also found in other grazing cattle. However, in herds of mixed age, where females have young calves at foot, the grazing rhythm is disturbed as the calves suckle and also learn to graze. Under such conditions, the intake time may be curtailed.

The speed with which the yak moves over the pasture varies with season and pasture conditions, but it is usually faster at the start of the day than later on, and it is also more rapid in the cold season than in warm weather. With the approach of snow or hail storms, yak can be seen to run over the pasture, in bursts of speed up to 57 m per minute – up to four times the normal speed at the start of the day.

There is relatively little variation in the bite rate – around 0.8 - 1.1 mouthfuls per second, but intake varies with season, sward height and other factors. Intake ranges from around 28 kg to 38 kg herbage over a period of ten hours in the summer to only 13 kg or less in the same period when grazing wilted grass in the cold season. The energy and protein intakes are adequate to meet maintenance, work and production, but in the later parts of the winter and the early spring they fall below the requirements. Yak then lose weight and condition.

Rumen volume
Xiao Wangji *et al.* (1997) reported that the rumen volume of Zhongdian yak relative to their body size was larger than in the local cattle (P<0.01). And the report from Zhang Rongchang (1989), see Table 4.4, showed that the rumen of yak was better developed than that of the cattle, based on the proportion of the weight of different parts to the total stomach. A large rumen may be a useful adaptation to forage roughage achieved by natural selection under the particularly rough grazing conditions prevailing in the yak territories.

Table 4.4 Proportion of each part as a percentage of the total stomach of yak and cattle [Source: adapted from Zhang Rongchang, 1989) (n=6, ±SD]

Stomach part	Tianzhu white yak	Kirgizia yak	Kirghiz cattle
Rumen	72.2 ± 4.2	64.0	51.9
Reticulum	5.6 ± 1.0	7.5	13.1
Omasum	10.4 ± 1.3	17.5	27.2
Abomasum	11.8 ± 1.7	11.0	7.8

Rumination
Under normal conditions, when grass is abundant in summer, yak have four periods of rumination each day. The first of these is generally two hours after the start of morning grazing. A second period is around noon, when the ambient temperature is high and yak stop grazing. A third period of rumination occurs about two hours before the animals are driven from the pasture back to the campsite. A fourth period is in the evening. Rumination periods generally last between 0.8 and 1.9 hours.

If yak are allowed to graze at night, as well as during the day, the periods of rumination are different. In yak used for work, the periods of rumination fit in with the timing and intensity of the work being performed. Occasionally yak will ruminate at night, but usually they lie in a state of light sleep.

Contractions of the rumen reticulum was studied in 48 yak over a three-day period (in Rouergai county, Sichuan) and showed contractions at the rate of 8.7 ± 1.6 (mean and SD) per five minutes immediately before grazing, and almost the same (9.0 ± 1.2) after grazing. Similar results were obtained at other locations.

In other types of cattle, the frequency of contractions when the animal is resting or ruminating may be only half the rate during feeding (Phillipson, 1970). It is possible therefore that the results on yak suggest a different behaviour, which could reflect an adaptation to the grazing conditions.

Sure-footedness

Yak can walk freely in precipitous places at high altitudes, which cannot be reached by horse or sheep (very few domestic goats are found in these areas) and they can cope well with marshy ground. As described by Phillips *et al.* (1946), yak, if in danger of sinking in a marsh, will spread out their legs and use the underside of their bodies to prevent themselves from sinking. They will plod on with a swimming-kind of motion rather than panic and thrash around as a horse might. Yak can swim across rapids and are at ease trekking through snow. They can even be used to make tracks through the snow to clear paths for people – a sort of "biological snow plough".

To help in meeting the challenges of difficult terrain and inclement climate, yak have strong limbs and small hooves of compact texture, with a narrow and sharp hoof tip, hard hoof edges and a close hoof fork. There is an area of soft cutis on the sole.

As noted by Zhang Rongchang (1985), the characteristics of the yak hoof make deep imprints in the ground that allow the yak to control its momentum when going downhill – an important component of its aptitude to move freely in difficult, precipitous terrain.

Adaptation of reproduction

Zhang Rongchang *et al.* (1994) argued that two aspects of yak reproductive characteristics (see Chapter 5) are also adaptive responses to the environment. First, the higher the altitude where the yak live, the more delayed is the breeding season. (For example, according to these authors, it begins 29 May at 1 400 m a.s.l., 10 - 15 June at 2 100 - 2 400 m a.s.l., 19 - 22 June at 2 700 m a.s.l., 25 June at 3 000 - 3 800 m a.s.l. and the beginning of July at 4 570 m a.s.l.). This allows calves to be born in somewhat warmer weather or closer to the onset of such weather and during, rather than before, the start of significant grass growth in the following warm season. From that point of view, a delay in the ability to breed must be regarded as a sensible adaptive response. Nonetheless, one must question whether nature, in this case, has not chosen a second-best strategy because yak that are mated late in the season have less chance of being re-mated that year, should conception have failed, than females mated earlier in the season. Also, calves that are born late in the year have insufficient time to get into good body condition to improve their chances of surviving the rigours of their first winter.

A second adaptive response claimed by these authors is the short gestation length of yak females (258 days on average; see Chapter 5) relative to other species of cattle. Short gestation, with consequently smaller calves, leads to a less stressful and quicker parturition, a lower oxygen requirement by the calf and less body-weight loss by the cow.

These factors must be of some importance in the yak environment, especially in the face of danger from wolves. However, it could be debated that the consequent, relatively low birth weight of the calf may be a disadvantage to the calf.

Another aspect of reproduction in the yak that might be regarded as an adaptation to its environment is that many yak females show only one oestrus in a breeding season and, if not then pregnant, the next occurrence of oestrus will be delayed to the following year (see Chapter 5). It is thought, though hard evidence is not presented, that priority is given by the yak to the deposition of internal fat reserves late in the breeding season rather than to conception. This helps the animal survive the ensuing harsh winter and spring when feed becomes in such short supply as to leave the yak starving. (Under more favourable feeding conditions and in some countries, however, as discussed in Chapter 5, yak regularly come into oestrus several times in one season).

General behaviour in relation to adaptation

Behaviourally, the yak is active and easily excited and can have a ferocious temper. Its conditioned reflexes make it respond rapidly to danger and external forces. In the grazing situation, yak will often jump and run, pursuing each other with tail in the air. Yak can gallop like a horse – an attribute that is enjoyed by herdsmen who organize annual races. Yak can also roll over on pastures as horses do – but unlike other bovines.

Yak have the ability to be readily trained. This ability helps the herdsmen in the feeding and management of the yak, especially as most yak graze year round and are not housed and not usually fenced in or tethered, except for milking. In some pastoral/agricultural areas of Mongolia, housing is sometimes practised (see Chapter 11, part 2). The yak are trained by the herdsmen to return to the campsite by the call of their names, or by special cries or singing. Yak are also readily tamed and trained for use as pack animals or for riding. Once trained, yak retain their acquired behaviour.

Yak are easily frightened and vigilant to attack by wild animals, wolves in particular. The yak will form a defensive position and fight off aggressors. It is often reported, for example from the grasslands of western Sichuan province, that male yak have killed wolves with their horns.

Yak are very gregarious. In herds of 100 or more, it is highly unusual to lose an animal from attack by wild animals, as the yak protect each other. When grazing, they are never far apart from each other. Yak can get very frightened if attacked suddenly while resting and not on guard. In such a case, they will flee from the herd and may then be killed by wild predators. Also, when startled on a hillside from above, by either human disturbance or by cries from wild beasts, they can panic and slip or roll down a hill and die in the fall. Dong Baosen (1985) reported that 312 yak died after rolling downhill in four separate instances in Gen county of Xinjiang – three of these due to incorrect driving of the yak by the people involved.

In ones or twos, yak are difficult to drive or manage, although some yak steers trained as pack animals will work individually, as will yak trained for ploughing. Yak will even find their way back to the campsite without a herder – if it is not too far away. Groups of ten or more yak steers trained as pack animals, however, can be easily managed as a group.

References

Anand, I.S. *et al.* (1986). Pulmonary haemodynamics of the yak, cattle and crossbreeds at high altitude. *Thorax*, 41, 696-700.

Anand, I. *et al.* (1988). The pulmonary circulation of some domestic animals at high altitude. *International Journal of Biometeorology*, 32, 56-64.

Blaxter, K.L., Graham, N. McC. & Wainman, F.W. (1959). The environmental temperature, energy metabolism and heat regulation in sheep. III. The metabolism and thermal exchanges of sheep with fleeces. *Journal of Agricultural Science (Cambridge)*, 52,41-49.

Belkin, V.Sh., Astakhov, O.B., Gutorov, S.L. (1985). [Capillarization of myocardium in the yak.] Arkh. Anat. *Gristol. Embriol.*, 88, 53-57.

Belyyar, D.K. (1980). Domestication of Yakutsk. Siberian Publication House.

Cai Li, Hu Angang & Du Shaodeng, (1960). The experiment of improving feeding and management to increase milk yield of yak and Pian Niu. Journal of Animal Husbandry and Veterinary Medicine of China, 1960 (3): 16-20.

Cai Li *et al.* (1975). Determination of physiological and biochemical indexes in yak. *Journal of Chinese Animal Science*, 1975 (6), 29-31.

Cai Li (1989). *Sichuan Yak.* Chengdu, Sichuan Publication House.

Cai Li (1992). *China Yak.* Beijing,. Agricultural Publishing Company.

Cai Li (1994). The type and distribution of Chinese yak. Proceedings of the First International Congress on Yak. *Journal of Gansu Agricultural University* (Special issue, June, 1994) pp. 48-52.

CCOYSR (1982). Summary report of two-year's work of Chinese cooperative organization of yak scientific research (CCOYSR). *Journal of China Yak.* 1: 3-9.

Chen Zhihua *et. al.* (2000). The Relationship between yak body size and ecological factors. *Journal of Southwest Nationalities College* (Natural Science Edition), Vol. 24 (4): 403-406.

Davva Myadag (1996). Conservation and management of domestic yak genetic diversity in Mongolia. *In* Miller, D.G., Craig S.R., & Rana, G.M. (eds). *Proceedings of a workshop on Conservation and Management of Yak Genetic Diversity* held at ICIMOD, Kathmandu, Nepal 29-31 October 1996. ICIMOD (International Centre for Integrated Mountain Development), Kathmandu. pp. 41-46.

Denisov, V.F. (1958). Domestic Yak and Their Hybrids, Selkhozgiz: Moscow. 116 pp.

Dong Baosen (1985). A preliminary study on the yaks that died from falling off a slope. *Journal of China Yak,* 1985 (3), 51-53.

Dou Yaozong, Yang Zai & Xue Zengya (1985). Studies on the geographic ecology and population ecology of the yak in Tibet. *Journal of Southwest Nationalities College* (Animal Husbandry and Veterinary Sciences Edition), 1985(2), 29-33.

Doxey, D.L. (1977). Haematology of the ox. *In* Comparative Clinical Haematology (eds. R.K. archer & L.B. Jeffcott). Oxford, Blackwell Scientific Publications.

Hawkey *et al.* (1983). Normal and clinical haematology in the yak (Bos grunniens). *Research in Veterinary Science*, 34, 31-36.

He Shaoyu *et al.* (1997). Zhongdian Yak. *Journal of China Yak*. 1997 (1): 1-5.

Hu Linghao (1994). Study of energy metabolism and rumenal metabolism in growing yaks. *Journal of the Gansu Agricultural University* (Special issue, June 1994), pp. 188-195.

Huang Wenxiu & Wang Sufang (1980). A research on the character and regulation of ecological distribution of livestock on the Tibet Plateau. *Journal of Natural Resource*, 1980 (2).

Katzina, E. V. (1997). Comparative analysis of blood morphology in yaks and two strains of cattle. *Proceedings of the Second International Congress on Yak* in Xining, China, 1-6 September 1997. Xining, China, Qinghai Publishing House. pp. 201-203.

Lalthantluanga, R., Wiesner, H. & Braunitzer, G. (1985). Studies on yak haemoglobin (Bos grunniens, bovidae): Structural basis for high intrinsic oxygen affinity. *Biol. Chem. Hoppe-Seyler,* 366, 63-68.

Larrick, J.W. & Burck, K.B. (1986). Tibet's all-purpose beast of burden. *Natural history*, 95, 56-65.

Lei Huanzhang et al. (1985). Studies on the ecological reaction of criss-cross grazing of yak and its hybrid in the cold and warm seasons. *Journal of China Yak*. 1985 (2), 13-23.

Li Shihong *et al.* (1981). The preliminary observation on yak's heat resistance. *Journal of China Yak,* (2). 1-4.

Li Shihong *et al.* (1984). The observation on yak's heat resistance. A research on the utilization and exploitation of grassland in the northwestern part of Sichuan province, Sichuan National Publishing House, pp. 171-174.

Liu Jinxuan (1984). The projects of Chinese yak scientific research co-operative group during 1984-1985. *Journal of China Yak*. Total14: 15-20.

Liu Qibui (1984). Summary of the research work on improving the production on yak during 1982-1983. *Journal of China Yak*. Total 14:21-33.

Lu Zhongling *et al.* (1982). The hair quality of Luqu yak. *Journal of Southwest Nationalities College* (Animal Husbandry and Veterinary Sciences Edition), 1982 (1), 17-20.

Lu Zhonglin (1999). China yak resource. China Herbivore Vol. 1 (2): 42-46.

Ma Sen (1997). Physiological and biochemical parameters and potassium phenotype in the blood of Qinghai white yak. *Proceedings of the Second International Congress on Yak* in Xining, China, 1-6 September 1997. Xining, China, Qinghai Publishing House. pp. 210-212.

Mondal, D. *et al.* (1997). Effect on normal hemato-physiology due to pack on yaks: a preliminary study. *Proceedings of the Second International Congress on Yak* in Xining, China, 1-6 September 1997. Xining, China, Qinghai Publishing House. pp. 204-207.

Ouyang Xi *et al.* (1983). Effects of seasonal change of natural ecological conditions on yak's hair-coat. *Journal of Southwest Nationalities* College (Animal Husbandry and Veterinary Sciences Edition), 1983(4), 1-5.

Ouyang Xi & Wang Qianfei. (1984). An observation on adaptation of calf yak. A research on utilization and exploitation of grassland in the northwestern part of Sichuan province, Sichuan National Publishing House, pp. 159-161.

Ouyang Xi *et al.* (1985). Studies on the cold resistance of yak. *Journal of Nationalities College* (Animal Husbandry and Veterinary Sciences Edition), 1985(4), 28-34.

Pal, R. N., & Moti Lal Madan (1996). Yak production in India. *In* Miller, D.G., Craig S.R. & Rana, G.M. (eds). *Proceedings of a workshop on Conservation and Management of Yak Genetic Diversity* held at ICIMOD, Kathmandu 29-31 October 1996. ICIMOD (International Centre for Integrated Mountain Development), Kathmandu. pp. 29-39

Phillips, R.W., Tolstoy, I.A. & Johnson, R.G. (1946). Yaks and yak-cattle hybrids in Asia. *Journal of Heredity*, pp. 37, 163-170, 207-215.

Phillipson, A.T. (1970). Ruminant digestion. *In* Dukes' Physiology of Domestic Animals. Cornell University Press. 8th ed. pp. 424-483.

Qi Guangyong (1984). The behaviour of young calf yak. A research on utilization and exploitation of grassland in the northwestern part of Sichuan province. Sichuan National Publishing House, pp. 162-170.

Ren Jizhou & Jing Juhe (1956). The observation on grazing habit of yak herd. *Journal of Animal Husbandry and Veterinary Medicine of China*, 2.

Research Co-operative Group for China Yak (1980-87). The 30 investigation reports on China yak resource. *Journal of China Yak.* 26:1-26

Sahu, R.N., Katutyar, R.D. & Kheta, R.C. (1981). Blood studies in yaks of Sikkim. *Indian Veterinary Journal,* pp. 58, 614-616.

Sherchand, L. & Neel Prakash Singh Karki (1996). Conservation and management of yak genetic diversity in Nepal. In: Miller, D.G., Craig S.R., & Rana, G.M. (eds). *Proceedings of a workshop on Conservation and Management of Yak Genetic Diversity* held at ICIMOD, Kathmandu 29-31 October 1996. ICIMOD (International Centre for Integrated Mountain Development), Kathmandu. pp. 47-56

Tang Zenyu, *et al.* (1982) Resources investigation of Dangxiong yak in Tibet Autonomous region. *Journal of China Yak*, 2:71-77.

Tshering, L., Pema Gyamtsho & Tshering Gyeltshen (1996). Yak in Bhutan. In: Miller, D.G., Craig S.R., & Rana, G.M. (eds). *Proceedings of a workshop on Conservation and Management of Yak Genetic Diversity* at ICIMOD, Kathmandu 29-31 October 1996. ICIMOD (International Centre for Integrated Mountain Development), Kathmandu. pp. 13-24.

Wang Jie *et al.* (1984). The physical properties of the hair of yak. *Journal of Southwest Nationalities College* (Animal Husbandry and Veterinary Sciences Edition) (1): 25-29.

Wang Yuchang (1995). Tianzhu White yak of China. *Journal of China yak.* 1995(3):2-4.

Wen Zhenzhong & Xie Zhonglun (1985). The relationship between the distribution and ecological environment of yak, sheep and goat in Qinghai Province. *Journal of Southwest Nationalities College* (Animal Husbandry and Veterinary Sciences Edition), 1985(2), 34-46.

Winter, H. *et al.* (1989). Haemoglobin and packed cell volume of yaks at high altitude. *Australian Veterinary Journal,* 66, 299-301.

Winter, H. *et al.* (1992). Pyrrolizidine alkaloid poisoning of yaks (Bos grunniens) and confirmation by recovery of pyloric metabolites from formalin-fixed liver tissue. *Research in Veterinary Science*, pp. 52, 187-194.

Winter, H. *et al.* (1994). Pyrrolizidine alkaloid poisoning of yaks: identification of the plants involved. *The Veterinary Record*, pp. 134, 135-139.

Xiao Wangji, Tian Yunbo & Ge Changrong (1997). Study on slaughter performance of Zhongdian yak. *Journal of Yunnan Animal and Veterinary Science.* 1997(3):36-37.

Xu Rongchan & Wu Zhiqiang (1984). A test report about physiologic indices of yaks in Dari area. *Journal of China Yak*. (3):18-24

Xue Jiying & Yu Zhengfeng (1981). The property and utilization of yak's down hair. *Journal of China Yak*, 1981(1), 1-5.

Yao Yubi and Li Yuqing (1995). Analysis on the effect of climatic factors on meat production of yak. *Journal of China Animal Husbandry*. 1995(1): 33-34.

Yousef, M. K. (1985). Physiological adaptations of less well-known types of livestock in cold regions: yak and reindeer. In: *Stress Physiology in Livestock*. Vol. II. Ungulates (ed. M. K. Yousef). Boca Raton, Florida, CRC Press Inc. pp. 142-148.

Zhao Bingyao (1982). Study on the three physiological indexes of yak. *Journal of China Yak*, 1982 (4), 24-30.

Zhang Hongwu, Zhao Yibin & Lei Huangzhang (1985). Studies on ecological reaction of yak and its hybrid during pasturing in cold season. *Journal of China yak*, 1985 (3), 15-21.

Zhang Deshou (1985). Indexes of physiology guideline and biochemistry in blood of Tianzhu white yak (adult cows). *Gansu Animal and Veterinary Science*. (1) 8-9.

Zhang Rongchang et al. (1982). Observation on grazing habits of yak and steers of inter-specific hybrid. *Journal of China Yak*, 1982(4). 5-12.

Zhang Rongchang (1985). China: the yak. *World Animal Review* (FAO) No. 54, 24-29.

Zhang Rongchang (1989). Yak of China. Lanzhou: Gansu Science and Technology Publishing House. 75-194.

Zhang Rongchang *et al.* (1994). Anatomical physiology of yak adapting to the low oxygen content on the high plateau. Proceedings of the first international congress on yak. *Journal of Gansu Agricultural University* (Special issue, June 1994) pp. 236-240.

Zhang Rongchang (1977). The hair quality of white yak on Zhuaxixiulong grassland of Tianzhu County. *Journal of Gansu Agricultural University*, 1977(2).

Zhang Yingsong, *et al.* (1982). Investigation report of yak resources in Menyuan county in Qinghai province. *Journal of China Yak*. 3:61-65.

Zhou Shourong (1984). Study on the forage and feeding habits of yak. A research on the utilization and exploitation of grassland in the northwestern part of Sichuan province. Sichuan National Publishing House, pp. 134-137.

OVERVIEW

In general, the reproductive rate of the yak is low under the normal grazing and rearing conditions of the principal yak territories. Female calves born early in the year may show oestrous for the first time when 16 - 18 months old. But those born later in the season will not show oestrous until they are more than two years old. Yak are seasonal breeders with mating and conception restricted to the warm part of the year. In a few areas, under favourable conditions some of the yak may be mated for the first time after they have reached the age of two years or, very exceptionally, even a year earlier. Normally and in most places, yak are not mated for the first time until they are three years old, and often not until four years. Thereafter, female yak are most likely to calve once every two years or twice in three years – producing, on average, perhaps four to five calves in a lifetime. Many yak cows will have only one annual oestrous, irrespective of whether they calved in that year or not. The next oestrous will often not occur until the following year. Under better conditions, in some areas and some countries, yak cows do show oestrous up to three or four times in a season, if they are not already pregnant. Statistics for Hongyuan county of Sichuan province, over the period 1976 - 1980, showed that from nearly half a million female yak of breeding age, 43.8 percent produced calves, which also survived, in any one year. Some breeds, such as Jiulong yak, may do better, and so will yak in areas where improved husbandry is practised. Clearly, the seasonal and general environmental conditions affect the reproductive rate markedly. In exceptionally harsh years, mortality rates of cows and calves can be very high.

Behavioural changes in the yak cow resulting from oestrous are not usually as clear as in other domestic cattle. The duration of oestrous is normally less than a day, although some reports give longer averages, and the range for individual animals is much greater. The average length of the oestrous cycle is approximately 20 days. Gestation length on average is around 258 days, shorter than in other cattle. It is longer when male calves are carried by the dam than it is with female calves. Also, the gestation length is longer, by as much as 20 days on average, when the yak female carries an F1 hybrid calf (having been mated to a bull, or inseminated with semen, of another species of cattle). Abortions and other causes of premature termination of pregnancy are between 5 percent and 10 percent when yak are bred pure, but higher in interspecies hybridization when the calves born are much heavier.

Physiological parameters in oestrous and gestation are similar to those in other types of domestic cattle. Hormonal treatment can be used to induce oestrous and can increase reproductive rate, though the evidence on conception rates following such induction is somewhat conflicting. Conception rates are nearly always much better following natural mating than after artificial insemination.

There is sufficient evidence to suggest that the reproductive rate of yak can be increased by a variety of improvements in management and feeding and by techniques to increase oestrous frequency and the conception rate. Successful detection of first oestrous and good timing of mating can be useful aids particularly when mating is artificially controlled or assisted. Whether the economic rewards from such improvements are a sufficient incentive to incur the costs involved is a separate question.

Male yak start to show mounting behaviour around the age of six months, but sperm have not been found in the ejaculates of yak males before the age of two years. Bulls usually start to mate at three or four years old but then have to establish their position in the mating hierarchy of the herd. Bulls reach the peak of their mating ability around the age of six to seven years. Bulls fight with each other for possession of females, and the dominant bulls have the most mates.

When left to their own devices, yak cows will not allow a bull of another cattle species to approach them, and such a bull has no chance of mating when in competition with a yak bull. In the same way, yak bulls prefer females of their own species. Wild yak bulls, however, will readily mate with domestic yak. All matings of yak cows with *Bos taurus* or *Bos indicus* bulls have to be assisted by people, either through keeping yak bulls away from the females or, more often, through restraint of the cow followed by use of a bull or artificial insemination.

Introduction

The survival and spread of the yak species over the centuries testify to an adequate level of reproduction for this purpose – in the face of an adverse environment. In the context of livestock improvement, however, it is important to consider the limits set by reproductive rate. The reproductive rate affects the opportunities for selection of improved pure-bred stock and also the opportunities for hybridization systems where the yak cow is the dam, which normally depend on "surplus" numbers of pure-bred yak available to sustain hybridization. The reproductive rate also affects the economics of yak production. The purpose of this chapter is, therefore, to document the reproductive performance of the yak under various sets of circumstances. Consideration will also be given to components of the reproductive process, in order to indicate which of these is the most limiting, or most amenable to change in the yak.

The information is derived from investigations on experimental stations or in herds to which the investigators have been given access. Because farms or herds involved in investigations are, in that sense, exceptional, it cannot be known with certainty whether the results obtained are fully representative of those applicable to ordinary herds in remote areas. This problem is not unique to yak but needs to be considered in assessing the results. In situations where the taking of observations and records is not usual, the act of doing so might have led to some improvement in performance.

Some results are also provided on anatomical features and physiological parameters of the yak in relation to reproduction. Male reproduction will be considered in a separate section from the reproduction of females.

Reproduction in the female

Female organs

The structure of the reproductive organs of the yak differs in some respects from those of dairy cattle of the *Bos taurus* type. In order to facilitate and improve techniques for artificial insemination, Cai Li (1980a) dissected the reproductive tracts of 38 female Jiulong yak over the years 1976 - 1980 and found that:

- The cervix has three transverse circles (a very small number of yak have four).
- Each circle consists of many small, tight folds (19 on the outer circle, 13 - 15 on the middle circle and nine to ten on the inner circle).
- The cervix is less than 30 cm from the vulva.
- The cervix is 5.0 ± 0.9 cm long and 3.2 ± 0.7 cm in diameter.
- The *corpus uteri* is relatively short, with a length of 2.1 ± 0.8 cm.
- A long and distinct septum (approximate 6 cm long) extends downward from the bifurcation of the uterine horns towards the *corpus uteri* (and is part of the wall separating the horns).

Cui and Yu (1999) published a study detailing a number of the anatomical features of the reproductive tract of female yak at age one month, one year, two years and seven to ten years old (using a total of 45 animals). Included in their study are the size and weight of the ovaries (on average only a little more than 2 g in weight in the oldest group of 14 cows), the numbers of follicles exposed (on average between three and seven on each ovary but for some reason significantly lower in the two-year old females), and various dimensions of the uterus and uterine horns, oviducts and cervix. The cervix length and diameter (width) recorded by these authors was less than noted previously from the results of Cai Li – possibly because it involved a different type of yak (the Gannan yak) from a different location.

When using artificial insemination, the short *corpus* and the long septum make it reasonably easy to deposit semen in optimal positions, such as the *corpus uteri*, uterine horn or its tip, especially as the cervix is relatively free within the pelvic cavity and can be readily held.

Nonetheless, deep insemination of female yak, using a recto-vaginal technique, is more difficult in the yak than in ordinary dairy cows. The histological structure of the reproductive organs of the yak is similar to that in dairy cattle (Qiu Zhongquan and Zhu Qimin, 1981).

Oestrous of the female yak

Puberty

Generally, first oestrous occurs in the second or third warm season (summer and autumn) following birth, at ages between 13 and 30 months. Generally, puberty occurs earlier in yak with larger body size under better nutritional conditions (Zhang Rongchang, 1989). Magash (1991a) made a detailed study of 104 female yak in Mongolia. The distribution of first oestrous in his study is shown in Figure 5.1. As noted already, oestrous occurred only in the warm season.

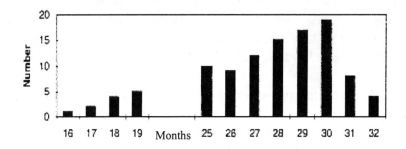

Figure 5.1 Frequency distribution of first oestrous in 104 female yak in Mongolia, by age [Source: Magash, 1991a]

The results of Magash (1991a) show that little more than 10 percent of the female yak came into oestrous for the first time in the second summer of their life, and that most females did not show oestrous for the first time until their third summer, when they were more than two years old. Magash pointed out that the 12 females that showed first oestrous when they were 16 - 19 months old had all been born in March or April of the previous year – and had managed to make more growth before the onset of winter than those born later in the season. Those not born until May or June had first oestrous delayed for a year, when they were 25 months old, or older. Magash concluded that the onset of first oestrous was determined more by body development at the beginning of the breeding season than by age. Very similar results, based on observations on yak in the (then) Tuva autonomous republic, were reported by Katzina and Maturova (1989). Yu and Li (2001) found, in 60 yak heifers in Gansu, that the sexual maturity in terms of cyclic activity came when the animals were 33 ± 6.7 months old.

In China, the majority of yak are mated for the first time at the age of three years – in the fourth warm season following birth, but under favourable conditions some yak may be mated a year earlier. Such conditions prevailed among 197 primaparous Jiulong yak cows in Sichuan province studied by Cai Li *et al.* (GAAHB and YRO, 1980): 32.5 percent of them calved first at three years old, 59.9 percent at four years, 6.1 percent at five years and the remaining 1.5 percent (three yak) at six years old. As shown in the next chapter, the three-year-old Juilong yak had reached about 78 percent their mature body weight (here the weight at six years old) (see Table 6.8).

In this context, Katzina and Maturova (1989) noted that in the Tuva autonomous republic (an area at more northern latitudes, but an elevation of only 1 500 - 2 500 m) female yak reached fertile oestrous at approximately 90 percent of mature body weight compared with 60 percent for *Bos taurus* cattle in that region. First mating at the age of two years, though it also occurs in China, is more common among yak in some other countries (see Chapter 11, parts 2 and 3).

Breeding season

Yak are seasonal breeders. The onset and end of the period in the year when female yak come into oestrous is affected by climatic factors, grass growth and both latitude and altitude. When temperature and humidity start to rise, the ground begins to thaw and grass starts to grow. The female yak then improve in body condition and gain weight – following their long period of deprivation and weight loss over the winter – and they come into season. On the northwestern grasslands of Sichuan this occurs around June (Hu Angang *et al.*, 1960). At the higher elevation of Nakchu prefecture in Tibet, the breeding season may not start until July. Similar observations are reported from Kyrgyz where it was noted, rather precisely, that the annual onset of the breeding season started on 25 May at an elevation of 1 400 m and became progressively later until at the altitude of 2 700 m oestrous started on or after 22 June (Denisov, 1958) – though it would be surprising if these precise dates applied to every year.

Zhang Rongchang (1989) summarized information from different sources on the effect of elevation on the time of onset of oestrus in yak. For example, at an elevation of 1 400 m yak started to show oestrus around 29 May; at 2 100 - 2 400 m it started 10 - 15 June; at 2 700 m it started 19 - 22 June; and at 3 000 - 3 800 m it started on 25 June. In Nakchu, Tibet, at an elevation around 4 570 m the yak only came to oestrus in early July.

The breeding season reaches its peak in July and August when temperature is at its highest and grass growth at its best. Thereafter, yak oestrous decreases in frequency and stops around November. Two sets of data on the onset of oestrous by month of year are summarized in Table 5.1; one set derived from the Datong Yak Farm in Qinghai province and the other from the Chovosol district in Mongolia.

Table 5.1 Oestrous in female yak according to month of year

Location	Percentage in oestrous from June to November[month]							
	[6]	[7]	[8]	[9]	[10]	[11]	No.	Source
Qinghai	3.5	21.7	28.7	18.3	15.6	12.2	115	Zhang Rongchang, 1979
Mongolia	5.5	12.1	41.2	14.3	6.7		342	Magash, 1990

The type of distribution shown in Table 5.1 is fairly typical of the general situation. Accordingly, if mating and conception do not occur, some yak may not return to oestrous in that season. Yak showing only a single oestrous in a season are not uncommon.

The vast majority of all mating takes place naturally between bull and cow at pasture (several bulls competing for the privilege – see section, Puberty and mating). For mating to other species of cattle, the yak cows are normally restrained (as they are also in some areas for mating to yak bulls). For mating to "improved" breeds of cattle (e.g. Holstein or Simmental), artificial insemination is now always used (as the bulls of these breeds do not adapt to the climate and altitude).

Signs of oestrous

Changes in the appearance of the reproductive organs are more obvious than behavioural changes, although these also occur (Luosang Jiangcuo and Chen Yu, 1987; Zhang Zhaowang *et al.*, 1997). The vulva becomes swollen and the vagina reddens. Mucus is discharged from the vulva in a majority of females in oestrous, but a substantial minority show no such discharge. Vagina and cervix dilate, and the female tends to raise her tail and urinate frequently. As in other cattle, female yak in heat search out and ride other females and like to be approached by male yak – but these signs are less pronounced than in *Bos taurus* cattle. When a specific mating is required by the herder and mass mating is not practised, heat detection usually requires the use of a teaser bull. It is thought that the use of a teaser bull, on female yak in heat, will increase pregnancy rate following either natural mating or artificial insemination. Katzina and Maturova (1989) also make the point that signs of heat in yak are less obvious than in other cattle, and detection by herdsmen is unreliable.

Daily milk yield shows a dip during oestrous although this could not, on its own, be used to accurately indicate the presence of oestrous (Cai Li, 1989b). However, Yu *et al.* (1993b) have reported that the pre-ovulatory peak of oestradiol 17β and the progesterone profiles in both blood and milk are similar in yak to those observed in dairy cattle. Magash (1991a) has similar findings.

Time of day of oestrous

Most yak start their oestrous in the early morning or in the evening and only rarely at other times of day. Among 633 female yak on the Xiangdong Livestock Farm, Cai Li (1989a) observed that two thirds of the animals started to show heat before 0900 hours when they had started grazing, and most of the remaining third started after 1900 hours when grazing had ended for the day. Similar observations were reported by Lei Huanzhang *et al.* (1964). Magash (1991a) with records on 73 yak in Mongolia found, by contrast, that only 38 percent came on heat between 0200 and 0800 hours, and 34 percent between 1600 and 2200 hours. This still left a substantial remainder to show oestrous outside those hours – mostly between 2200 and 0200 hours.

Table 5.2, from yet another set of data, shows the distribution of oestrous of yak cows on the Datong Yak Farm. It is difficult not to conclude, from these various studies, that the location of the herd or other environmental factors help to determine the time of day at which oestrus starts.

Table 5.2 Distribution of oestrous according to time of day
[Source: Zhang Rongchang, 1989]

	Time of day				
	0600-0900 hrs	1000-1200 hrs	1300-1800 hrs	1900-2200 hrs	Total
Number	35	6	14	20	75
%	46.7	8.0	18.6	26.7	100

Length of oestrous cycle

There is some variation in the length of the oestrous cycle from year to year. For example, the 1 184 observations by Liu Wulin and Liu Shengyu (1982) included in Table 5.3 were collected over a period of five years and showed that the annual mean length of the oestrous cycles varied from 19.2 to 21.6 days.

A feature of all the studies summarized in Table 5.3, except that of Yu *et al.* (1993a), is the large amount of variation among individuals. The coefficient of variation among these studies ranged from 16 percent to 41 percent. The reason for this is that oestrous in the yak is greatly affected by the environment. When the weather is unfavourable, the onset of oestrous is delayed; while in favourable circumstances, the onset of oestrous in female yak is advanced. The interval between heat periods can vary up to three-fold.

However, in different production systems there are reports of female yak capable of showing oestrous up to three to four times in the same season, as in the report of Katzina and Maturova (1989) for yak in the Tuva region, and Magash (1990) for yak in Mongolia, both referred to earlier.

Duration of oestrous

The duration of the oestrous period is not easily determined in the yak because the symptoms of oestrous are not always clear. Estimates from northwestern Sichuan suggest 12 - 16 hours (Cai Li, 1989a, b), while a report from yak in Shandan, Gansu province suggests 1.6 ± 0.8 days (Liu Wulin and Liu Shengyu, 1982). In a very small proportion of yak, oestrous may last four to five days, but one to two days is not unusual. Thus, a study with 41 well-fed and closely monitored female yak showed that 26 of them had an oestrous lasting 24 hours or less and three yak had oestrous up to 72 hours. More than 80 percent of these animals ovulated within 24 hours after the end of oestrous (Yu *et al.*, 1993a).

Table 5.3 Various estimates of the length of the oestrous cycle (days)

Number of observations	Mean	[SD]	Source
1 184	20.5	5.4	Liu Wulin and Liu Shengyu, 1982
308	20.1	8.2	Liu Wulin and Liu Shengyu, 1982
53	22.5	5.4	Zhang Rongchang *et al.*, 1979
12	18.3	6.1	TLRI, 1978
35	20.4	1.6	Yu *et al.*, 1993a
90	19.1	(10 - 28)*	Katzina and Maturova, 1989
54	20.0	4.0	Purevzav and Beshlebnov, 1967
74	19.8	(10 - 27)*	Magash, 1991a

*Range

Zhang Zhaowang *et al.* (1997) reported a duration of oestrus of 12 - 48 hours for Tianzhu White yak. There is a tendency for the proportion of yak with heat periods of one to two days to increase later in the breeding season (August/September) when air temperature begins to decline. Katzina and Maturova (1989) reported an unusually long average duration of 3.7 days (from a range of 1 to 6 days) for yak in the Tuva region. In this context, it is interesting that the majority of their yak conceived in September. By contrast, Purevzav and Beshlebnov (1967) recorded substantially shorter heat periods in Mongolia. Among 54 Mongolian yak, 26 were noted to be in heat between only 0.5 and 6.5 hours, 17 yak in heat between 6.5 and 12.5 hours, 7 between 12.5 and 18.5 hours and only 4 yak with a longer oestrous duration. To account for some of the differences between the different studies, it is difficult not to conclude that the observational criteria of what constitutes the length of oestrous must vary among the studies.

Postpartum anoestrous

The average duration of postpartum anoestrous at the Xiangdong Livestock Farm in Sichuan province was found to be 125 days. That figure, however, was subject to much variation. At this farm, females that had calved did not usually show oestrous again in the year of calving (Cai Li, 1989b). The exceptions were cows, which had calved early in the season – before June – and which had acquired good body condition and good fat deposits over the summer. Postpartum anoestrous periods were found to be much shorter (70.5 [SD 18.5] days) for yak in good body condition than for those in a poorer body condition (122.3 [SD 11.8] days) (Liu Wulin and Liu Shengyu, 1982).

The anoestrous period following calving has been reported as related to the month of calving: 131 days, 124 days, 90 days and 75 days for females calving in March, April, May and June, respectively. (As reported earlier, only a few of the yak calving later in the season return on heat in the same year.)

Magash (1990) provided results on the interval between calving and first postpartum oestrous for female yak in Mongolia. These show clearly a relationship with month of calving – the earlier the calving, the longer the interval. However, in these results there was a considerable amount of variation around the average intervals. The results of Magash are shown in Table 5.4.

Table 5.4 Interval between calving and first postpartum oestrous in yak according to month of calving [Source: Magash, 1990]

Month of calving	Number of animals	Interval (days)		
		Mean	Range	SD
March	38	120.5	69 - 188	25.3
April	87	96.1	59 - 172	36.3
May	69	75.4	40 - 145	29.1
June	21	53.6	30 - 106	21.6
Overall	215	90.2	30 - 188	34.9

In the same study, Magash (1990) reported that, as might be expected, the service period following calving (on average only eight days longer than the oestrous interval) showed a very similar seasonal pattern to that seen in Table 5.4 for the interval between calving and first postpartum oestrous. Magash (1990) also showed for Mongolian yak that the interval between calving and the first postpartum oestrous was longest in cows that had calved only once (around 120 days) and that it then declined to its lowest interval in females between fifth and seventh calving (around 85 days) and increased again thereafter for older cows. Wang Minqiang *et al.* (1997) reported a calving interval of 459 days in a study of 439 parities of 161 cows on the Datong Yak Farm. This interval, they observed, was 25 - 48 days shorter among the cows of third to sixth parities than the interval for cows of both the earlier and later parities.

Erdenebaatar *et al.* (1997) attempted to shorten the interval to postpartum oestrous in the cows that had calved early in the year (from May to June) by various hormone treatments given early in the postpartum period (around 24 - 32 days after calving). But the results were not as expected, possibly due to failure, it was thought, of the activating hypothalamic-pituitary axis to support follicle development.

Proportion of cows in oestrous and calving
The proportion of female yak that come into oestrous in any one season depends on the previous calving history of the females as well as on their individual body condition. Female yak of reproductive age can be divided into three categories: those that have calved in the current year and are lactating and suckling a calf ("full-lactating yak"); those that calved in the previous year, are not pregnant but may or may not be still suckling their last calf (*Yama* or "half-lactating yak"); and those that previously had a calf but not for at least two years and are not lactating (*Ganba*).

95

On the Xiangdong Livestock Farm (from June to mid-September), *Yama* had the highest proportion of females in oestrous during that period (112/161), *Ganba* came next (217/408) and "full-lactating cows" had the lowest proportion (90/629) (YRO and XLF, 1983; Cai Li, 1989a). Similar observations were made by Zhang Rongchang (1979) in a study at the Datong Yak Farm in Qinghai (84.3 percent of *Yama*, and 36.6 percent of cows suckling a calf of the current year). Relative to the full-lactating cows with a calf at foot, the *Yama* and *Ganba* classes have had a better opportunity to recover from the drain on their body resources, consequent on calving and lactation, and more than 95 percent of them show oestrous (Ling Chenbang *et al.*, 1982).

In ordinary production herds in the mountainous regions of China, a general average figure is that 50 - 70 percent of yak cows of suitable age show oestrous in any one year and that such female yak are mated and calve twice in three years, or once every second year. In one study, Cai Bolin (1981) found that 28.8 percent of Maiwa yak cows of reproductive age gave birth every year, 51.3 percent every second year and the rest, 19.8 percent, every third year. In another survey, by Lu Caijie (1982) in Tongren county, Qinghai, only 11 percent of yak cows gave birth every year, 75 percent twice in three years and 14 percent in every second year. The majority of yak in Damxung, Tibet calved every second year (Tang Zhenyu *et al.*, 1982).

Use of hormones to induce oestrous

Various studies have shown that oestrous can be induced in yak and that the reproductive rate can be increased by that means. For example, at the Xiangdong Livestock Farm, Cai Li (1980b) gave an intramuscular injection of an analogue of LRH early in August – approximately one month after calving had ended – to induce oestrous in yak cows that had calved and were nursing a calf. Table 5.5 provides a summary of the results from the three-year investigation.

Table 5.5 Reproductive rate of yak cows with induced oestrous and normally occurring oestrous (control) [Source: Cai Li, 1980b]

Group	Year	No.	Calved next year (%)	Calved and surviving (%)
Induced	1976	120	30.0	30.0
	1977	120	90.0	84.2
	1978	110	73.6	73.0
Control	1976	722	42.8	40.0
	1977	871	45.2	44.9
	1978	914	53.4	53.3

The results from Table 5.5 show that the induction of oestrous by hormonal treatment, followed by mating, was not very successful in terms of calves born in the first year of the trial (1976). But the proportion of cows in which oestrous had been induced that then calved and the number of calves that survived to the end of the year had improved markedly in 1977 and 1978. (Calf survival was not, apparently, reduced by the increase in calving rate). Results of a study by Magash (1991a) with yak in Mongolia agree in showing, albeit on much smaller numbers of animals, that the oestrous rate in female yak can be increased by hormonal induction, compared with untreated controls. But, in his trial, there was, generally, a reduced conception rate following artificial induction of oestrous (similar to the result in 1976 of Table 5.5). Thus, following a single hormonal treatment, the conception rate recorded by Magash was around 56 percent compared to 75 percent in the controls. Following two hormonal treatments, the conception rates in the treated and control groups were 78 percent and 86 percent, respectively. In another report, Magash (1991b) noted also that the success of oestrous induction increased from June to August, approximately doubling over that period (the actual oestrous rates depending on the method of induction). This is analogous to the increase in oestrous rate, which occurs naturally over that period, as was noted earlier (Erdenebaatar et al. 1997).

Other researchers at various locations in China have used different hormonal treatments to induce oestrous in the yak. These trials have shown, for the most part, that the onset and timing of oestrous can be controlled in the yak, as in ordinary cattle species (e.g. Shao Binquan and Zhao Yanben, 1984; Yang Tingyou, 1984; Liu Zhiyao and Shuai Weiwen, 1985; Shao Binquan et al., 1986; Yu and Liu, 1996). The use of triple hormone injections was usually the most effective in these experimental situations. In one set of trials, Chinese traditional medicine ["injecting Herba Epimedii compound"] (Ma Tianfu, 1983) produced an increase in the number of animals on oestrous compared with the control group (44 percent vs. 18 percent).

Zhang Yun (2002) reported that among 80 yak cows synchronized for oestrus by different hormonal treatments, 62 showed oestrus within seven days. Seventy-six of these cows were inseminated by A.I. and 54 of them (71 percent) became pregnant, though only 44 of them calved. From a study in Mongolia, Magash (1997) reported that oestrus synchronization was achieved by using the PGF2-α alone. Davaa et al. (2002) used four different treatments to induce oestrous: PGF2-α, progesterone sponge, PMSG and FSH – but with only small numbers for the last two. Overall, 28 (53 percent) of the 53 cows and 8 (31 percent) of the 26 heifers showed synchronized oestrus. These authors also pointed out that the success of synchronization and of subsequent conception were both markedly affected by the body condition of the animals – the better the condition, the better the success of the treatment. Other factors, such as age of cow, interval after calving and the type of hormone preparation, also influenced oestrus induction. (In this trial, the FSH treatment [four cows and four heifers] appeared to be the least successful of the four treatments.)

A general comment on reproduction in yak

From the evidence just presented, the conclusion might be drawn that the yak is reproductively poor – calving relatively late for the first time and not regularly thereafter. This, however, is entirely a description of the situation prevailing in the high mountainous regions and the high mountain plateau where the vast majority of the world's yak are found. It has to be borne in mind that in these regions, with a short summer growing season followed by a harsh, prolonged winter, there is a severe shortage of feed for the animals over several months, coinciding with the time when cows should be pregnant. The lack of sufficient feed over winter leads to loss of weight and body condition, both often severe, in the female yak. These substantial losses are only made up over the next summer season – provided that the summer is not marred by lack of rain. It is highly likely therefore that the principal reason for variation in the age of the first onset of calving and the subsequent frequency of calving is due to variation in the nutrition of yak cows over the winter period. Evidence from the effects of supplementary feeding trials supports this. Further evidence is deduced from the reported reproductive rate of yak in North America (see Chapter 11, part 3). The yak there, although a relatively small population, are given sufficient hay and other feed throughout the winter to eliminate weight loss. The majority of such female yak will then breed for the first time a year earlier than in traditional yak territories and thereafter calve annually. Under the conditions of the traditional yak regions, such supplementary feed may, of course, be neither available nor cost effective, even if it can be procured (but see also Chapters 8 and 14). The point needs to be made that the relatively poor reproductive record of the yak, compared to, for example, dairy or beef cattle elsewhere, is not a consequence of heredity but of environment. The ability to induce oestrus by hormonal treatment, as shown by the results presented earlier, is clearly of interest. As also shown, however, body condition affects those results. More investigation is certainly needed to discover whether conceptions thus induced, in the absence of adequate winter nutrition, might not further exacerbate the problems of yak reproduction in subsequent years.

Gestation and parturition

Pregnancy rates
Conception following mating at first oestrous of the season is generally high. Among 68 female yak on heat, Cai Li (1989a) found by rectal palpation that 53 of them had well-developed follicles and 15 did not, due to diseased reproductive organs. In a trial (Liu Zhengkui, 1981) with 265 yak that had calved previously, 72.4 percent became pregnant following the first oestrous of the season, another 23.4 percent following the second, and 3.4 percent and 0.8 percent following the third and fourth cycles, respectively. Zhang Zhaowang et al. (1997) observed a 76.5 percent (727/950) conception rate to a single service in Tianzhu White yak. In an investigation with 342 yak in Mongolia, Magash (1990) found that 70.5 percent were pregnant after a first service, 19.3 percent conceived to a second and 4.6 percent to a third service, giving an overall pregnancy rate of 94.4 percent. It appears in that part of Mongolia, at least, that yak which do not become

pregnant at a first service are able to return to oestrous up to three times in the same season, as already referred to earlier. Conception to first service improved as the breeding season advanced, and was best in September.

In one particularly well-maintained group of yak on grassland in Gansu province where the yak had also been given some supplementary feed in late winter and early spring, a conception rate of 94.3 percent was achieved (Yu *et al.*, 1993a). A pregnancy rate of 74.9 percent, following insemination with frozen semen at first oestrous of the season, has also been recorded by Cai Li (1989b) in trials with 621 yak.

Many studies, in addition to those quoted, have shown that once mating has occurred, whether naturally or by artificial insemination, pregnancy rates above 70 percent in female yak are not uncommon, provided matings have been to yak bulls (Table 5.6 and also: NIAVS and Datong Yak Farm, 1965; Du Fusheng, 1981, 1987a, b; TLRI, 1978; Luosang Jiangcuo and Chen Yu, 1987). There is, however, a marked difference between pregnancy rates resulting from pure-breeding of yak and those from hybridization. When the yak female is inseminated with semen (or mated by a bull) of other species of cattle, antagonisms appear to arise and the pregnancy rate falls. As apparent from Table 5.6, the proportion of calves born and surviving was more than halved when yak cows were mated to *Bos taurus* bulls. The situation was even worse, and dramatically so, when A.I. was used with semen from such bulls – only three calves survived from the 217 such cows initially available for service. A combination of circumstances led to this disappointing result, including in this particular situation poor detection or occurrence of oestrous, poor conception rate and high loss of foetuses from the few pregnant cows. It is possible that advances in methods and AI technology (Zhang Rongchang, 1979; Ling Chenbang *et al.*, 1982; Li Shihong, 1985), developed since the time when the trial recorded in Table 5.6 was conducted, might have led to an improvement on that situation.

Data from the Datong Yak Farm in Qinghai province where semen from Hereford bulls was used by A.I. to inseminate 117 yak showed a conception rate of 43.6 percent from 1975 to 1978 (Zhang Rongchang, 1989). Similarly, frozen semen of cattle was used for A.I. with yak in Hongyuan county of Sichuan province and the average conception rate was 44.9 percent (12 526 yak) with some variation over the years and, on average, 25 percent of the cows mated ended up with a surviving calf (Table 5.7).

Table 5.6 Effect on success of mating, conception and calving in yak cows of different types of mating [Source: YRO and XLF, 1983, 1984]

Mating of yak female*	No. females of breeding age available	Mated (%)	Conceived of those mated (%)	Foetuses lost of those pregnant (%)	Calving of those pregnant (%)	Cow with surviving calves of those pregnant *** (%)
Yak male – natural service	323	51.1	87.3	11.1	88.9	36.8
Bos Taurus male – natural service	59	52.5	54.8	41.2	58.8	16.9
Bos taurus male – A.I.	217	22.1	25.0	66.7	33.3	1.4
Yak male – natural service after failure of A.I.**	205	47.3	93.8	3.3	96.7	39.5

* Natural mating to yak bulls: July-October; A.I. with *Bos taurus* semen: July-August; re-mating, to yak bulls, of cows which failed to conceive to A.I.: September-October.

** Note months of re-mating (see above).

***Calves surviving to six months of age.

Table 5.7 Conception and calving in yak cows serviced by A.I. with frozen cattle semen in Hongyuan county of Sichuan [Source: adapted from Liu Shenqing, 1989]

Year	No. of females mated	Conceived of those mated (%)	Foetuses lost of those pregnant (%)	Calving of those pregnant (%)	Cows with surviving calves of those pregnant (%)
1976	275	48.0	21.2	67.4	65.2
1977	798	45.5	22.3	77.7	69.1
1978	3 774	39.9	17.6	81.0	69.6
1979	2 841	44.8	23.0	82.4	77.6
1980	3 212	51.9	26.3	73.6	68.5
1981	1 626	46.2	16.1	77.0	69.2
Total	**12 526**	**44.9**	**20.7**	**78.0**	**71.6**

Effect of age and physiological state

The three types of female categorized in terms of their current and previous calving history differ in pregnancy rate (see Table 5.8 and also: Ling Chenbang *et al.*, 1982; Cai Li, 1989a). The age of the female also has an effect, with five- to six-year-old females being the best, on average, although not by a large margin. By the age of nine to ten years the conception rate starts to fall away. Some results are shown in Table 5.8.

(An explanation is required in respect of the youngest age group – the yak females aged three to four years old [this includes the summer following their fourth birthday when, strictly, the females may be four and a half years old]. Some of these animals will have calved previously at two or three years of age – that is the relatively small proportion of yak females that had achieved this because of particularly good body condition and other favourable circumstances earlier in their life. If they had not become pregnant again after their first calving, they were also categorized as *Yama* or *Ganba*, even though they were only three to four years old.)

Table 5.8 Conception rate of three types of yak female according to age

Type of female	3 - 4 years		5 - 6 years		7 - 8 years		> 9 years	
	No.	%	No.	%	No.	%	No.	%
Yak cow with calf*	11	9.1	27	11.1	39	7.7	15	13.3
Yama**	52	30.8	135	39.3	117	45.3	82	40.2
Ganba***	53	22.6	436	22.2	537	18.8	308	14.6

* Yak cow nursing calf born in current year.

** Yama = cow calved in previous year – with or without calf.

*** Ganba = cow that has calved, but not for at least two years.

The gravid uterus

Cai Li (1980a) dissected the reproductive organs of 38 female yak on the Xiangdong Livestock Farm (Sichuan), 17 of which had been pregnant between one and four months. Eleven of these 17 had the foetus implanted in the left uterine horn and six in the right. The size of the ovary and the oviduct on the side of the gravid horn was substantially larger. However, the maternal caruncles and cotyledons were about equally developed in both uterine horns. Up to one and a half months after conception, the gravid and empty horns had the same diameter; and up to that time the foetal placenta can invade both horns equally. Thereafter, the septum dividing the horns becomes indistinct and disappears as the foetus grows. The gravid horn sinks below the pelvic brim after two months of pregnancy. In early pregnancy, diagnosis of pregnancy by rectal palpation depended mainly on the size and shape of the two ovaries and on changes in the shape of the septum.

Mohanty *et al.* (2002) at the National Research Centre on Yak in India examined 16 placentas immediately after their expulsion following the birth of the calf and found that the average placental weight was 1.6 ± 0.5 kg and the total numbers of cotyledons in pregnant and nonpregnant horns were 45.0 ± 7.1 kg and 27.3 ± 4.1 kg, receptively. Total cotyledon area was 1494 ± 327 sq cm and the average calf birth weight was only 12.4 kg, giving a ratio of total cotyledon area to birth weight of calf of 123.0 ± 23 sq cm per kg. The authors suggested that malnutrition in the third trimester of pregnancy seems to be the major cause of low calf birth weight and low placental weight.

As in other cattle species, the progesterone level in milk increases during gestation, but in mid-cycle it falls greatly in barren cows (see Figure 5.2). Progesterone level can therefore be used in pregnancy diagnosis in yak and with a high degree of accuracy between about days 18 and 24 after mating (Xue Liqun, 1983; Magash, 1991b). Yu *et al.* (1993c) confirmed a rapid rise of progesterone levels both in blood and milk of yak starting around day two of pregnancy.

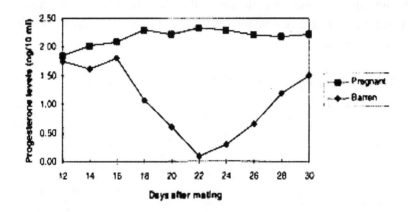

Figure 5.2 Progesterone levels in milk of 15 pregnant and 8 barren yak females between 12 and 30 days after mating [Source: Xue Liqun, 1983]

Gestation length

The gestation length of female yak is shorter than that of *Bos taurus* cattle, particularly when a pure yak calf is carried. Female yak bred pure have, on average, a shorter gestation length than when carrying a F1 hybrid calf. For yak with pure-bred calves, Denisov (1938) reported an average gestation length of 258 days; Lei Huanzhang *et al.* (1964) recorded an average gestation length in 36 yak of 260 days (range 253 - 278 days) for those carrying male calves and 250 (226 - 283) days for those with female calves on the Datong Yak Farm. Dubrovin (1992) reported an average gestation length of 258 days for 800 yak cows in the Caucasus; Katzina and Maturova (1989) noted an average gestation of 259 days (228 - 280 days) for yak in the Tuva region; and Yu *et al.* (1993) reported an average of 254 days [SD 2.7 days, a range of 248 - 258 days] for yak in Gansu province. Joshi *et al.* (1994) gave an average of 258 days for the gestation length of yak in Nepal.

The average gestation length of yak cows with F1 calves (cattle bull mated with yak cow) was found by Cai Li (1989a) to be around 270 days (273.2 with a SD of 12.7 days for 371 cows with male F1 calves and 268.6 with a SD of 10.2 days for cows with female F1 calves). In Cai Li's study, the breed of bull used also appeared to affect gestation length.

This also was noted by Zagdsuren (1994) for yak in Mongolia. Denisov (1938) recorded an average gestation length of 276.2 days for female yak mated to Schwyz cattle.

On the Datong Yak Farm, the average gestation lengths of yak cows carrying male and female hybrid calves sired by the Hereford were 277 ± 6.2 days and 261 ± 7.6 days, respectively (Zhang Rongchang, 1989) and longer for yak cows with pure yak calves (260 days on the Datong Yak Farm; Lei Huanzhang et al., 1964). The longer gestation lengths for the hybrid calves are associated with substantially higher birth weights relative to pure yak calves (cf. Li Kongliang et al., 1989) and this, in turn is a cause of an increase in dystokia when yak cows carry hybrid calves (see the parturition section that follows).

The wide range of gestation lengths quoted by some authors seems surprising, as do some of the differences among studies. The wide ranges, when not otherwise stated, will include the differences in gestation length attributable to sex of calf and any differences that may be associated with age of dam (though none such are reported). It is also possible that there are differences attributable to breed of yak, which would be, in these circumstances, usually confounded with location (although, again, there are no specific reports of breed differences in gestation length for the yak, though such differences are documented for other types of cattle). In order to explain some of the more protracted gestation lengths, one must perhaps wonder whether both females with yak calves and those bearing inter-species hybrid calves are included together in the ranges, although this is not apparent from the reports. These considerations would still leave unexplained the very short gestation lengths reported at the lower end of the range. The problem with the ranges quoted is that they provide no clue to whether the extreme values are isolated cases and might include premature parturition.

Parturition
Almost all births take place during the day and only very few occur at night when the yak cows are normally at the herders' campsite. When the time for parturition approaches, the female yak looks for a sheltered spot, such as a depression in the ground or a ditch, at a distance from the herd. Typical behaviour of the yak during labour includes lying on her side and standing up again for delivery when a pure yak calf is carried. When a hybrid calf is carried, the female will deliver the calf while lying on her side – presumably on account of the larger size of the calf and the longer time needed for the delivery (Cai Li, 1989b).

Dystokia is a rare occurrence in female yak with pure-bred calves; for example, in Gannan, Gansu, it was only 1.8 percent among 1 929 yak cows (Lu Huaijiang, 1995). Normally, herdsmen offer no assistance. The umbilical chord is broken by the act of mechanical stretching as the cow gets up or the calf falls down after delivery. Inflammation of the chord is rare. Yak cows with hybrid calves, however, require help for delivery and dystokia occurs to some extent. For example, there were 28 cases among 861 such calvings (3.3 percent) over a period of ten years in one study in Sichuan. In another study, Yuan (1991) reported that 20 out of 63 yak cows that were carrying Holstein hybrid calves retained their afterbirth, whereas normally such retention is less than 5 percent in yak.

Zhang Rongchang (1989) suggested that to reduce the incidence of dystokia it might be helpful, when producing hybrids, to use the yak cows of larger body size, with well-developed rump, which had already calved in previous years. As found in studies with cattle elsewhere, it appears that the relationship of calf size at birth to maternal size may be a critical factor in dystokia.

Twins are rare in yak; in general, they account for about 0.5 percent of all births, though higher rates have been recorded occasionally.

Behaviour

The dam generally licks the newborn calf for about ten minutes, after which the calf attempts to stand up and suck. Again, differences in behaviour have been observed between dams delivering pure-bred yak and F1 calves. Some results are presented in Table 5.9. They show that time intervals are markedly longer when a F1 calf is involved than when pure yak calves are born.

Table 5.9 Intervals between successive events at parturition according to type of calf [Source: Qi Guangyong, 1984]

Nature of events	Interval (range in ' minutes and " seconds) between events	
	Pure yak calf	F1 hybrid calf
Appearance of calf to end of parturition	3' - 6'	45' - 107' (with help)
Calf out to calf being licked	0'2" - 0'5"	0'3" - 0'7"
Calf out to calf starting to stand up	14'2" - 21'30"	60'0" - 99'14"
Calf out to first sucking	15' - 22'	74' - 103'
Duration of first sucking	3'0" - 5'30"	5'32" - 11'21"

In a more recent study, Zhang Zhaowang *et al.* (1997) found in Tianzhu White cows that parturition was completed in 3 - 40 minutes and that the newborn calves stood up for suckling after about 20 - 30 minutes – both periods somewhat longer than in the study shown in Table 5.9. The placenta is ejected usually between half an hour and six hours after parturition

In the period shortly after birth, the dam is intensely protective of her calf and will attack any person coming close. She may not, however, do so directly. For example, the dam may retreat, as though afraid of the person, and then attack from the side or from behind. This is a time for people to take special care! (Cai Li, 1989b)

Bonding of dam and calf depends mainly on smelling and licking. Longer times of parturition and dystokia militate against such bonding and thus place F1 calves at a disadvantage to pure yak calves – at least on average. Yak cows can distinguish their calves by smell from among quite large groups of calves.

Calving season

The calving season is obviously connected with the time in the previous year when oestrous and mating occurred and is therefore prone to the same environmental and physiological constraints. Table 5.10 shows the distribution of calving from March to August at various locations.

On the basis of the distribution of the month in which yak cows in Mongolia were mated, as Magash reported by (1990), it can be estimated that a small proportion of the yak cows calved in March, probably around 25 percent in April, many more than that in May, the peak month, and a declining number in June and July.

Table 5.10 Percentage distribution of calving in different months of the year at different locations

Location [source]	No.	Mar	Apr	May	Jun	Jul	Aug
Qinghai – Datong [1]	155	12.3	39.3	24.5	15.5	8.4*	
Qinghai – Datong [2]	137	4.4	39.4	33.6	18.2	2.9	1.5
Gansu – Zhangxian [3]	98	20.4	24.5	27.6	21.4	6.1	
Sichuan – Ganzi [4]	34		17.6	35.3	41.2	5.9	
Yunnan – Zhongdian [5]	34		8.8	26.5	38.2	23.5	2.9

*Including August.

Sources: [1] Lei Huanzhang *et al.*, 1964; [2] Liu Zhengkui, 1981; [3] Xiong Zaiyue, 1982; [4] Hu Angang *et al.*, 1960; [5] Jiang Ruisheng and Bai Yinhua, 1985.

Denisov (1958) reports from (what was then known as) "Kirgizia" that the calving season for a herd of 597 yak extended from February to December but with only five calves born in February, rising to 116 in March, 253 (42.4 percent) in April and 113 in May, with numbers tailing off rapidly thereafter.

When hybridizing yak to produce F1, it is common practice to attempt the hybridization – irrespective of whether by natural mating or A.I. – in the first half of the breeding season and to follow this by the use of yak bulls, to catch cows that have not conceived and have returned on heat. Thus, it is not unusual for the hybrid calves to be born earlier in the season than the pure-bred ones.

Calf survival – prenatal and postnatal

Abortions and other causes of premature termination of pregnancies account for perhaps 5-10 percent of all pregnancies, as was shown in Table 5.6 with observations from Sichuan. A similar incidence was reported from observations on 971 female yak in Nagqu, Tibet with an abortion rate of 5.4 percent, and a rate of 5.2 percent among 1 929 yak cows in Luqu, Gansu (Lu Huaijiang, 1995). On the Datong Yak Farm, Qinghai, 85.9 percent of 2357 pregnant yak cows calved normally (NIAVS and Datong Yak Farm, 1965).

As already indicated, the normal calving rate is lower when interspecies hybridization is carried out. Among 1 348 such yak cows (carrying hybrid calves) in northwestern Sichuan, 20 percent lost their calves during pregnancy and, in another study with 158 young pregnant yak females, 14 lost their hybrid calves before normal parturition (Ling Chenbang *et al.*, 1982). Calf survival is generally high when the calves are allowed to suckle and the dams are not milked, but survival can fall greatly when the cows are also milked, as shown in Table 5.11.

Table 5.11 Survival of calves according to rearing method
[Source: Wu Derun and Ma Juru, 1985]

Rearing Method	No. of cows	Calves born (%)	Calves surviving of those born *** (%)	Reproduction rate *** (%)
Dam milked*	1 366	66.0	57.9	38.2
Dam not milked**	2 542	81.1	93.7	76.0

Year of records: *1975 - 1976
 **1977 - 1979
 ***of cows mated with calf surviving to six months old

Since the two rearing methods were conducted in different years (Table 5.11), it is possible that a year effect might have affected the results. The apparent difference between the groups in the proportion of calves born is difficult to explain unless it is a "random" year effect, or unless it is a carry-over effect from the previous year. Such an effect could have arisen if the herder's decision to milk or not to milk is repeated across years so that cows milked in the current year were also those milked in the preceding year, and those not milked were also not milked in the year before (information on this point is not given). It would be surprising if a year effect negated the large rearing effect on calf survival after birth, as similar results to those shown in Table 5.11 have also been obtained in other sets of observations (NIAVS and Datong Yak Farm, 1965; GAAHB and YRO, 1980).

A 90 percent survival rate is typical for pure-bred calves, e.g. 1 328 out of 1 470 calves surviving among Jiulong yak in Sichuan (Cai Li, 1989b), and 1 818 out of 2 025 pure-bred calves on the Datong Yak Farm, Qinghai (NIAVS and Datong Yak Farm, 1965). In contrast to the greater problems before and during parturition experienced with F1 calves, the hybrid calves, once delivered, have a slightly better survival rate after birth than pure yak calves. Results at the same locations showed survival for F1 calves to be about 2 percent better than for the pure-bred calves.

Detailed observations (Ouyang Xi *et al.*, 1984) on 20 yak calves on a farm at an elevation of 3 500 - 4 100 m showed that neonatal survival was also related to the maintenance of body temperature in the calf. The fall in temperature in the first hour after birth (average fall 0.38°C) was significantly correlated (r 0.69) with birth weight (the greater the weight, the less the temperature loss) but much less strongly correlated with ambient temperature. Thus, the body condition of the dam during pregnancy affected calf survival through its effect on birth weight. The body temperature of the calves returned to normal, after three hours on average.

To maintain the temperature of cows and newborn, a simple greenhouse made from clear plastic sheeting has been introduced to yak-raising areas in Gansu, Qinghai and Tibet to keep the animals inside during the colder times of the day.

Other factors influencing reproductive efficiency and calf survival

Inbreeding effects

Chen Youkang *et al.* (1994a) studied the effect of inbreeding on reproductive efficiency in 70 yak cows. They found that in this experimental herd, the inbreeding coefficient went up from the base generation (taken as zero inbreeding) to 0.11 in generation 1 and 0.19 in generation two. The interval between generations zero and one was 1.82 years and that between generations one and two was 2.61 years. At the same time, calf survival went down from 94 percent to 81 percent respectively for the two generations. The decline in conception rate and increase in calf mortality, which together were responsible for a marked reduction in reproductive efficiency, was attributed to the increasing inbreeding. Inevitably, different generations are born in different years. Unless special measures are taken to create an overlap of generations within year, a year effect could be confounded with the inbreeding effect. The inbreeding effect, showing a decline in reproductive efficiency is, however, in the direction expected (see Chapter 3).

Supplementary feeding

Yak cows given supplementary feed during pregnancy showed a small increase in the number of calves born, probably through reduced embryonic loss, and a somewhat greater increase in calf survival. This result is derived from an experiment conducted at Longri Farm in Aba county of Sichuan (part of a project undertaken by the Southwest Nationalities College [now University] with support from United Nations Development Programme and FAO). Results from this trial will also be referred to in Chapter 6, in relation to growth and milk yield; the design is described here only in outline.

Three groups of females, equivalent to each other in all respects and which had previously had normal opportunities to mate, were allocated to three feeding regimes. One group was given hay from mid-December to the end of April. The amount eaten by the cows in mid-winter varied around 4 kg per animal per day, but the intake fell to less than 1 kg, on average, in April. This treatment was repeated for two years. A second form of supplementation was practised in the first of the two years by allowing a group of cows access to grass paddocks that had been closed off in the autumn. The yak in this group were allowed into these paddocks with standing wilted grass for 45 days from the beginning of April – the latter part of pregnancy for most of the animals. The third group of yak cows received no supplementary feeding and were subjected to the management normal for the area. This group acted as the control. The results, in respect to the number of calves born and calf survival, are shown in Table 5.12.

Table 5.12 Percentage of Maiwa yak cows calving and calf survival from three groups of cows [Source: Wen Yongli *et al.*, 1993]

Year	Treatment group*	No. cows	Calving (%)	Calf survival (%)	Calves surviving Per 100 cows mated
1989/90	Hay	75	58.7	93.2	54.7
	Paddock grass	75	56.0	90.5	50.7
	Control	148	55.4	85.4	47.3
1990/91	Hay	58	64.4	92.1	59.3
	Control	150	60.0	85.6	51.3

*For details, see text.

a) fed hay from mid-December to end of April;

b) allowed access to conserved grass paddocks from 1 April for 45 days; and

3) unsupplemented, control group

In relation to the results in Table 5.12, it is tempting to suggest that the provision of hay may have stopped before the final stage of pregnancy, when foetal growth is at its most rapid. However, as indicated earlier, the cows began to eat less in the latter part of the feeding period as the first green shoots of grass started to appear on the pastures. Of course, the overall effect of feed supplementation cannot be judged by only the small increase, about 8 percent, in the proportion of surviving calves per 100 cows mated. Other effects, shown in Chapter 6, need to be considered. Unfortunately there is no information available on possible carry-over effects on the subsequent conception rate of the supplemented and control groups of cows. Results presented in Chapter 14 (Table 14.17) provide further evidence on the positive effects of supplementary feeding on reproductive rate and other aspects of performance.

Length of reproductive life

Exceptional female yak may live to an age of about 24 years, but 15 - 16 years is the normal upper limit for reproductive activity. The peak reproductive ability is considered to be between the fifth and the ninth year of life. Maiwa yak females reproduce normally for about ten years with a total of five to seven calvings (Cai Bolin, 1981) and Zhongdian yak cows showed their best reproductive performance between the ages of five and 11 years (Duan Zhongxuan and Huang Fenying, 1982). In one study by Ding and Chen (1994) 82 percent of females of reproductive age were ten years old or younger. Chen Youkang *et al.* (1994b) found five cows older than 20 years among 437 yak cows giving birth on the Xiaman Farm in Sichuan, but the survival of their calves was poor. Zhang Zhaowang *et al.* (1997) noted that the normal practice among herders of Tianzhu White yak is to use them for breeding up to the age of 15 years (see also Chapter 11, part 1).

Reproduction in the male

Male organs

The anatomical and histological structures of the genitalia of the yak bull are virtually the same as those of other bovine species, apart from the small, hairy scrotum – an adaptation to the cold environment (Qing Fufang *et al.*, 1990, 1993; Xu Kangzhu *et al.*, 1991). Pan Heping and Yan Ping (1997), Yan Ping *et al.* (1997) and Doyoddorji and Batbayar (1997) showed variously that the sizes and weights of testes and epididymis, as indicators of spermatogenesis, increased greatly from a young age right up to five years old. Doyoddorji and Batbayar (1997), for example, recorded that the weights of the right and left testes of 14 two-year-old Mongolian yak were 44.9 ± 3.6 g and 48.9 ± 2.9 g, respectively (similar to the weights of testes of 18-month-old yak in Pan Heping and Yan Ping's survey.). By the age of five years, the testis weights (from three bulls) were almost four times greater, and the epididymis weights had doubled. The Pan Heping and Yan Ping studies also included crosses between domestic and wild yak, but in terms of the sizes of testes and epididymis, or the increases in size, there was relatively little difference between the crossbred and the pure-bred males.

Puberty and mating

Age
Yak males start to show mounting behaviour around the age of six months, towards the end of the first warm season in the year of their birth. In the following year, this behaviour continues and intensifies to include searching for female yak and mounting them. No sperm were found in the epididymal fluid of yak bulls before the age of two years in a study by Wang Xiaoxin (personal communication, based on a research report of a former Northwest Animal Husbandry Institute, 1964). Thus, puberty normally occurs in the third warm season following birth, when the male is more than two years old. In practice, bulls start to mate from the age of three years or, more usually, four years onward, reaching their peak ability at around six to seven years old – after establishing their position in the mating hierarchy after four years in the same herd. After the age of eight years, yak bulls start to lose to younger bulls in the competition for females (see section, Breeding season). Cai Bolin (1981) noted that Maiwa yak bulls were used for mating from three years old onward and that their peak ability came around four to nine years old. Zhongdian yak bulls started to be used for mating when four years old and showed peak capacity between the ages of 5 and 11 years (Duan Zhonxuan and Huang Fenying, 1982).

A study of 38 yak bulls at an A.I. stud in Tibet (elevation 4 300 m) supported the belief that the sexually productive life expectancy for a yak bull does not exceed ten years. The Tibet study showed that the ejaculate volume and the concentration and motility of sperm in the semen rose steadily from the age of three to nine years and then declined (Zhang Yun, 1994).

A study by Magash (1990) provided interesting additional evidence from Mongolia on the changes in the mating activity of yak bulls in relation to their age. This is summarized in Table 5.13.

Table 5.13 Mating activity and success of yak bull in Mongolia according to age of bull [Source: Magash 1990]

Age of bulls (years)	Cows mated No.	(%)	No. of mounts per cow	Percentage of cows pregnant
7	61	(43)	1.5	72.1
6	43	(30)	1.8	83.7
5	27	(19)	2.1	92.6
3	11	(8)	2.3	90.9
Total/average	**142**	**(100)**	**1.8**	**80.9**

The results from the Mongolian yak study (Magash, 1990) presented in Table 5.13 indicate that the older the bull (within the age range shown), the more females the yak bull was able to serve – consistent with the courtship behaviour and dominance hierarchy of bulls. Interestingly, the results also show that the younger bulls, with fewer females at their disposal, mount their mates more often. Thus, the three-year-old bulls mounted their mates half as often again as the seven-year-old bulls. It is also interesting that fertilization seemed to be more dependent on the number of services than on the age of the bull, in line with the pregnancy results of the same Magash study quoted earlier, which showed that the overall pregnancy rate of females increased with the number of services.

Behaviour
Bulls stay with the herd only during the breeding season. They spend winter and spring alone. Bulls can pick up the scent of females on heat at a distance of several kilometres – even 10 km have been reported.

Courtship behaviour
When with a herd of females, bulls will fight each other to obtain possession. Only the strongest attain the dominant position in the herd and such bulls have the most mates (as the oldest but virile group did, shown in Table 5.13). However, other strong bulls will also get an opportunity to mate cows, though in smaller number. Old, feeble bulls retain no mating position in the hierarchy of the herd. They then no longer try to mate and leave the herd. Young bulls do not usually win a place in the competition for mates until they are four years old and then only after some experience of fighting in the previous year. (Yak bulls in Mongolia, as judged from the results in Table 5.13, are apparently more precocious and reach that stage a year sooner). Such competition among bulls, to the extent that it introduces an additional element of natural selection, must provide the yak with some advantages in surviving in an unfriendly environment. By also ensuring that old bulls are replaced, generally before their daughters in the herd have reached breeding age,

this competition for dominance may also have a role in reducing the chance for inbreeding to occur.

The extent to which inbreeding is avoided must be uncertain, as there is nothing other than human intervention to prevent bulls from mating their siblings or from bulls being succeeded in the herd by their sons.

Mating behaviour

Yak bulls get very excited sexually. Those that have won a mating position in the herd will mate several times a day. The bulls are so intent on mating that when in the process of doing so they will not attack other bulls, unless strongly provoked. It would be interesting to have information on the extent to which dominant bulls, which mate frequently, lose body condition as a result of their sexual activity over the mating season. This is known to occur in some wild animal populations (e.g. deer) and when it happens, it gives less dominant males the chance to mate.

Artificial insemination

Training

Yak bulls can readily be trained to provide semen for artificial insemination, and, once trained, they will retain this capacity into the next breeding season. The bulls can be taught, in as little as seven days, to mount dummy cows and supply semen into an artificial vagina (Du Fusheng, 1987a, b; Li Kongliang *et al.*, 1986; Zhang Yun, 1997). More detail is given in Chapter 8.

Semen quantity and quality

Volume and quality are generally considered good. In one trial with more than 14 collections (Du Fusheng, 1987), the average volume was 2.4 ± 0.9 ml with average sperm density of 2 680 ± 590 million per ml, motility of 0.82 ± 0.05 and a malformation rate of 8.3 percent (6.3 - 10.4 percent). The yak semen retains good fertility after diluting three-fold for fresh use and after pelleting and frozen storage.

Liu Hui *et al.* (1993) reported that the daily sperm yield in yak bulls is about $4.66 \pm 0.47 \times 10^9$. This is lower than reported for *Bos taurus* cattle but higher than for zebu cattle (*Bos indicus*).

The densities referred to above are more than twice those reported by Zhang Yun (1994) from a station in Tibet (at an elevation of 4 300 m) producing frozen semen from yak bulls (the density values shown are also higher than those usually quoted for bulls of the "improved" cattle breeds [300 - 2 000 million per ml according to a review by Setchell, 1993] although the volume of ejaculate in such bulls is usually greater than in the yak). The sperm concentrations (per ml) reported by Zhang Yun (1994) were in the range 740 - 1 210 million per ml depending on the month of year and the age of bull. Ejaculate volume in these bulls varied with month and age, from 1.2 ml (in March) to almost 3 ml (in August) and from 2 ml in three-year-old bulls to 3.3 ml in nine-year-old bulls. Semen quality was also at its best from the nine-year-old bulls, and in the month of August in that part of Tibet.

Relations with other cattle species

When left to their own devices, yak cows do not allow bulls of other cattle species to approach them, and yak bulls show no inclination to mate cows of other cattle species. The reluctance to mate across the species has been reported from a number of different regions, as, for example, by Bonnemaire and Teissier (1976) in their studies from Nepal.

When forced to graze in herds of mixed species, the antipathy of the yak to members of the opposite sex from the other species of cattle declines, though it may not disappear altogether. When bulls of both species are present at the same time in a herd, a yak cow on heat will only allow a yak bull to mate with her. Bulls of the other species do not win in any competition with yak bulls for yak females.

In situations where a yak cow has been mated by a bull of another species and is then served again by a yak bull in the same oestrous period, the calf is almost always pure yak and not a hybrid – suggesting a preferential fertility for the yak sperm. Thus, to obtain hybrid calves, the yak cows must be kept with the bulls of the other species, and access to yak bulls has to be prevented. One way of doing this, as referred to earlier, is to restrain the yak cow in a mating crate and then allow her to be served by the bull of choice or by artificial insemination.

As was noted in Chapter 3, wild yak bulls readily mate with domestic yak females and produce wild-with-domestic crosses. In this case, there is no preferential fertilization from domestic yak bulls when they are present in the same herd alongside the wild yak bulls.

References

Bonnemaire, J. & Teissier, J.H. (1976). Some aspects of breeding at high altitude in the central Himalayas: yaks, cattle, hybrids and crossbreds in the Langtang Valley (Nepal). *In Le Yak. Son role dans la vie materielle et culturelle des eleveurs d' Asie centrale. Ethnozootechie*, No.15, France. pp. 91-118.

Cai Bolin (1981). Introduction to the Maiwa yak. *Journal of China Yak*, 1: 33-36.

Cai Li (1980a). Study on the reproductive organs in female yak. *Journal of China Yak*, 3: 10-16.

Cai Li (1980b). Conception followed advanced breeding by luteinizing hormone 2 (LRH-A). *Chinese Journal of Animal Science*, 6: 18-20.

Cai Li (1989a). Reproductive performance of yak. *Journal of Southwest Nationalities College (Animal Husbandry and Veterinary Sciences Edition)*, 15 (2): 52-65.

Cai Li (1989b). Sichuan yak. Chengdu, China, Sichuan Nationality Press. 223 pp.

Chen Youkang, Huang Huaizhao & Yuan Youqing (1994a). Preliminary study on the effect of inbreeding on reproductive performances of yak cows. *Journal of China Yak*, 2: 14-17.

Chen Youkang *et al.* (1994b). Test of the reproductive capacity of yak cows on the Xiaman Farm. *Journal of China Yak*, 2: 23-25.

Cui, Y. & Yu, S.J. (1999). An anatomical study of the internal genital organs of the yak at different ages. *The Veterinary Journal*, 157: 192-196.

Davaa, M. *et al.* (2002). Experimental results of oestrus synchronisation in yak. *Proceedings of the third international congress on yak, in Lhasa, China, 4-9 September 2000*. International Livestock Research Institute (ILRI), Nairobi. Pp 346-348.

Denisov, V.F. (1938). Hybridization if the yak with Kirghiz cattle and the Schwyz. *Izv. Acad. Nauk. USSR (Otd. mat. est., Ser. boil)*, 863-878. (Cited from *CAB Animal Breeding Abstracts*, 7: 116-117.)

Denisov, V.F. (1958). *Domestic yak and their hybrids*. Selkhozgiz: Moscow. 116 pp.

Ding, X.T. & Chen, D.M. (1994). Preliminary study on the reproductive performance of yak, chauri and Ago cattle. Proceedings of the first international congress on yak. *Journal of Gansu Agricultural University* (Special issue, June 1994) pp. 307-309.

Doyoddorji, D. & Batbayar, T. (1997). Studies on dissection of genital organs of male (twinning) yak in Mongolia. *Proceedings of the second international congress on yak, in Xining, China, 1-6 September 1997*. Xining, China, Qinghai People's Publishing House. pp. 170-174.

Du Fusheng (1981). Production of frozen semen of yak. *Journal of China Yak*, 1: 6-11.

Du Fusheng (1987a). Preparation of frozen semen of Jiulong yak. *Journal of China Yak*, 1: 15-18.

Du Fusheng (1987b). Production of frozen semen of male yak. In: *The research on the utilization and exploitation of grassland in the northwestern part of Sichuan Province*. Chengdu, China, Sichuan Nationalities Press. pp. 151-156.

Duan Zhongxuan & Huang Fenying (1982). Report of survey on the Zhongdian yak. *Journal of China Yak*, 1: 75-82.

Dubrovin, A.T. (1992). Yak breeding in the northern Caucasus. Zootekhniya, No. 3-4: 18-20.

Erdenebaatar, B. *et al.* (1997). *Ovarian response to hormonal treatment in early postpartum female yaks*. Proceedings of the second international congress on yak, in Xining, China, 1-6 September 1997. Xining, China, Qinghai People's Publishing House. pp. 151-153.

GAAHB (Ganzi Agricultural and Animal Husbandry Bureau) and YRO (Yak Research Office of Southwest Nationalities College) (1980). The general survey and identification for Jiulong yak. *Journal of China Yak*, 3: 17-24.

Hu Angang, Cai Li & Du Shaodeng (1960). An investigation on yak in Ganzi county. *Journal of Southwest Nationalities College* (Animal Husbandry and Veterinary Sciences Edition), 4: 46-50.

Jiang Ruisheng & Bai Yinhua (1985). Investigation on the reproductive status of Zhongdian yak. *Journal of China Yak*, 3: 25-28.

Joshi, D.D., Lund, P.N., Miller, D.J. & Shrestha, S.K. (1994). Yak production in Nepal. Proceedings of the first international congress on yak. *Journal of Gansu Agricultural University* (Special issue, June 1994) pp. 132-136.

Katzina, E.V. & Maturova, E.T. (1989). The reproductive function of yak cows. *Doklady vsesoyuznoi ordena lenina akademii sel'skokhozyaistvennykh naukim V.I. Lenina*, 4: 26-29. (Cited from *CAB Animal Breeding Abstracts*, 58: 352.)

Lei Huanzhang *et al.* (1964). Observation on the reproductive physiology and features of yak. *Journal of Chinese Animal Sciences*, 7: 1-3.

Li Kongliang, *et al.* (1986). The experiment of taming the male yak containing half blood of wild yak, production of its frozen semen and A.I. *Journal of China Yak*, 1: 42-44.

Li Kongliang *et al.* (1989). Genetic improvement of yak in China. *In Chinese Yakology*. Chengdu, China, Sichuan Scientific and Technology Press. pp.206-252.

Li Shihong (1985). Discussion for the adaptation of yak. *Journal of China Yak*, 3: 22-25.

Ling Chenbang *et al.* (1982). The experiment to improve the reproductive and survival rate in yak's inter-specific cross. *Journal of China Yak*, 1: 38-40

Liu Hui, Wang Liqing & Xia Luojun (1993). Measurements of quantitative histology of daily sperm yield of yak testes. *Journal of China Yak*, 4: 34-35.

Liu Shenqing (1989). Reproduction of yak in China. *In Chinese Yakology*. Chengdu, China, Sichuan Scientific and Technology Press. pp. 188-205.

Liu Wulin & Liu Shengyu (1982). The observation and analyses of reproductive characters in female yak on the Shantan Farm. *Journal of China Yak*, 3: 27-28.

Liu Zhengkui (1981). Reproductive characteristics o Qinghai yak. *Journal of China Yak*, 4: 5-7.

Liu Zhiyao & Shuai Weiwen (1985). The study on yak's oestrus synchronization by using three combined hormones. *Journal of China Yak*, 2: 24-27.

Lu Caijie (1982). Survey on yak production in Tongren County, Qinghai. *Journal of China Yak*, 4: 44-48.

Lu Guanghui (1980). Experiments to improve reproduction rate of yak. *Journal of China Yak*, 1: 52-57.

Lu Huaijiang (1995). Survey on the reproductive difficulties of yak cows in Luqu. *Journal of China Yak*, 1: 37-40.

Luosang Jiangcuo & Chen Yu (1987). A report on the experiment of artificial insemination of yak in Shenzha county. *Journal of China Yak*, 3: 51-57.

Ma Tianfu (1983). The first report on induction of yak's oestrus with drugs. *Journal of China Yak*, 2: 16-18.

Magash, A. (1990). Statische Massmalen diagnostischer Zuchthygienemerkmale bei Yakkühen in der Mongolei. *Wiss. Zeitschift der Humboldt-Universität zu Berlin R.. Agrarwiss*, 39: 359-366.

Magash, A. (1991a). Ergebnisse von Untersuchungen über die Physiologie des Sexualzyklus beim weiblichen Yak. *Monatschefte für Veterinärmedicin*, 46: 520-522.

Magash, A. (1991b). Anwendung biotechnischer Verfahren bei der Reproduction des Yaks. *Monatschefte für Veterinärmedicin*, 46: 257-258.

Magash, A. *The use of biotechniques in yak reproduction*. Proceedings of the second international congress on yak, in Xining, China, 1-6 September 1997. Xining, China, Qinghai People's Publishing House. pp. 175-178.

Mohanty, T.K., Ansari, M.R. & Pal, R.N. (2002). *Anatomical characteristic of placenta and its relationship with calf birth weight in yak.* Proceedings of the third international congress on yak, in Lhasa, China, 4-9 September 2000. International Livestock Research Institute (ILRI), Nairobi. pp 404-407.

NIAVS (Northwest Institute of Animal and Veterinary Science, China) and Datong Yak Farm (1965). The observation on the improvement effect of hybrids from crossing yak with dairy cattle. *The Collection of Scientific Materials of Research and Investigation on Livestock* (1959-1962). Vol. 3 (Livestock): 347-374.

Ouyang Xi, *et al.* (1984). An observation on adaptation of yak calf. *In* The research on the utilization and exploitation of grassland in the northwestern part of Chengdu, China, *Sichuan Province.* Sichuan Nationalities Press. pp. 159-161.

Pan Heping & Yan Ping (1997). *Morphological observation on the testes and epididymis in hybrid of wild and domestic yaks during the growth periods.* Proceedings of the second international congress on yak, in Xining, China, 1-6 September 1997. Xining, China, Qinghai People's Publishing House. pp. 165-166.

Purevzav, Z. & Beshlebnov, A.V. (1967). Some data on the physiology of reproduction in the yak. *Zhivotnovodstvo Mask*, 29: 92-94. (Cited from *CAB Animal Breeding Abstracts*, 36: 302-303.)

Qi Guangyong (1984). The behavior of young yak calve. *In: The research on the utilization and exploitation of grassland in the northwestern part of Sichuan province.* Chengdu, China, Sichuan Nationalities Press. pp. 162-170.

Qing Fufang *et al.* (1990). Histological and histochemical studies on the thyroid of yak, cattle and their F1 hybrid. *Journal of China Yak*, 3: 46-48,45.

Qing Fufang *et al.* (1993). Electron microscopic observation of and stereoscopy study on the testes of yak and F1 hybrid. *Journal of China Yak*, 4: 9-11.

Qiu Zhongquan & Zhu Qimin (1981). Histological study on the genital organs of female yak. *Journal of China Yak*, 4: 25-28.

Setchell, B.P. (1993). Male reproduction. *In* King, G.J. (ed), *Reproduction in domesticated animals.* Amsterdam, Elsevier Science Publishers B.V.

Shao Binquan & Zhao Yanben (1984). Preliminary study on yak's synchronous oestrus. Journal of China Yak, 1: 81-88.

Shao Binquan *et al.* (1986). Experiment of oestrus synchronization of yak. The second report. *Journal of China Yak*, 2: 41-43.

Tang Zhenyu *et al.* (1981). Survey of the yak in Pali District of Yadong County in Tibet. *Journal of China Yak*, 2: 46-50.

TLRI (Tibetan Livestock Research Institute) (1978). Observation on the oestrus of yak. *Collection of Scientific Materials.* pp. 50-52.

Wang Minqiang, Li Pingli & Bo Jialin (1997). *Yak calving interval and calving efficiency.* Proceedings of the second international congress on yak, in Xining, China, 1-6 September 1997. Xining, China, Qinghai People's Publishing House. pp. 29-31.

Wen Yongli *et al.* (1993). Influences of two simple methods of supplement during the winter on the performances of female yak. *Journal of Southwest Nationalities College (Animal Husbandry and Veterinary Sciences Edition)*, 3: 263-241.

Wu Derun & Ma Juru (1985). Effects of milking and non-milking on reproductive and survival rate, growth and development of yak. *Journal of China Yak*, 3: 28-29.

Xiong Zaiyue (1982). Observation of yak introduced into Zhang county. *Journal of China Yak*, 2: 75-77.

Xu Zukang, *et al.* (1991). Study on the histology, anatomy and reproductive function of genital organs in yak and their F1 hybrids. *Journal of China Yak*, 3: 18-21.

Xue Liqun (1983). Concentrations of milk fat progesterone during estrous cycle and early pregnancy in yak. *Chinese Journal of Animal Science and Veterinary Science*, 14 (3): 193-196.

Yan Ping *et al.* (1997). *Quantitative histology studies on the testes in hybrid bull of wild and domestic yak.* Proceedings of the second international congress on yak, in Xining, China, 1-6 September 1997. Xining, China,Qinghai People's Publishing House. pp. 167-169.

Yang Tingyou (1984). The preliminary study on synchronization of yak's oestrus. *Journal of Southwest Nationalities College* (Animal Husbandry and Veterinary Sciences Edition), 3: 50-53.

YRO (Yak Research Office) of Southwest Nationalities College and XLF (Xiangdong Livestock Farm of Sichuan Province) (1983). Experiment and its result analysis on improving productive performance of yak by using frozen semen of ordinary cattle for AI. *Journal of Southwest Nationalities College* (Animal Husbandry and Veterinary Sciences Edition), 2: 17.

YRO (Yak Research Office) of Southwest Nationalities College and XLF (Xiangdong Livestock Farm of Sichuan Province) (1984). Analyses on effect of yak's improvement by using A.I. with the frozen semen of common bulls. *Journal of Sichuan Grassland*, 1: 39-48.

Yu, S.J. & Li, F.D. (2001). Profiles of plasma progesterone before and at the onset of puberty in yak heifers. *Animal Reproduction Science*, 31: 67-73.

Yu, S.J., Huang, Y.M. & Chen, B.X. (1993a). Reproductive patterns of the yak. I. Reproductive phenomena of the female yak. *British Veterinary Journal*, 149: 579-583.

Yu, S.J., Huang, Y.M. & Chen, B.X. (1993b). Reproductive patterns of the yak. II. Progesterone and oestradiol-17 beta levels in plasma and milk just before the breeding season; also during normal and short oestrus cycles. *British Veterinary Journal*, 149: 585-593.

Yu, S.J., Huang, Y.M. & Chen, B.X. (1993c). Reproductive patterns of the yak. III. Levels of progesterone and oestradiol-17 beta during pregnancy and the peri-parturient period. *British Veterinary Journal*, 149: 595-602.

Yu, S.J. & Liu Z.P. (1996). Use of exogenous hormones to induce oestrus in yak. *International Yak Newsletter*, 2: 31-34.

Yuan, Y.Q. (1991) A case of treatment for total prolapse of the uterus and eight cases of artificial separation of retained placenta afterbirth in yak. *Journal of China Yak*, 3:50

Zagdsuren, Yo. (1994). Some possibilities to increase meat and milk production of yak husbandry. Proceedings of the first international congress on yak. *Journal of Gansu Agricultural University* (Special issue June 1994) pp. 113-118.

Zhang Rongchang (1979). The reproductive characters of yak. *Journal of China Yak*, 4: 63-71.

Zhang Rongchang (1989). *China: the yak.* Lanzhou, China, Gansu Scientific and Technology Press. 386 pp.

Zhang Yun (1994). The relationship between season and age of stud yak bull in Damxung. Proceedings of the first international congress on yak. *Journal of Gansu Agricultural University* (Special issue June 1994) pp. 303-307.

Zhang Yun (1997). Taming of the stud yak bulls for producing frozen semen. *Proceedings of the second international congress on yak, in Xining, China, 1-6 September 1997.* Xining, China, Qinghai People's Publishing House. pp. 163-164.

Zhang Yun (2002). *Experiment on oestrous synchronization for artificial insemination with frozen semen in yak.* Proceedings of the third international congress on yak, in Lhasa, China, 4-9 September 2000. International Livestock Research Institute (ILRI), Nairobi. pp 349-352.

Zhang Zhaowang *et al.* (1997). *Observation of oestrous and parturition characteristics in Tianzhu White yak.* Proceedings of the second international congress on yak, in Xining, China, 1-6 September 1997. Xining, China, Qinghai People's Publishing House. pp. 189-192.

OVERVIEW

Growth

Rapid growth of the yak calf in the first few months of its life is a prerequisite for survival over the first winter and for a good start to its continuing growth in the following year. Thus, animals that are born early in the warm season have a better chance than those born later. Calves with exclusive access to the milk of their dams have the best opportunity for growth, especially if they are allowed to graze at night alongside their dams – but such night grazing is not common practice. Calves with dams that are milked once daily generally grow appreciably better than those with dams milked twice daily, not only because they have a somewhat greater milk intake but because they have perhaps an extra four to five hours daily available for grazing alongside their dam. Males become heavier than females, but they grow relatively more slowly in the early years of life and continue to grow for longer. Typically, in China, males are brought into the adult herd at six years old and females at four years; but in some other countries this occurs a year earlier. Breeds of yak appear to differ in size and growth rate, though this observation is usually confounded with differences in location. There is much seasonal variation in body weight.

Heavy losses in weight over winter and spring are recovered during the following warm season, when young animals recover what they have lost and make all their additional growth. This pattern is repeated each year. Approximately 25 percent of the weight at the end of the warm season normally is lost over the succeeding winter and spring – except in the first year of life when that loss is only about 12 percent. Linear body dimensions of the animals reach their final size at an earlier age than does body weight – although there are differences among the dimensions in age at maturity. As must be expected, the linear body dimensions show less seasonal variation than does body weight.

Milk production

Milk yield in yak is low and seasonal. The amount produced is only what would normally be needed for the good development of the calf. However, as milk is an important product for the herdsmen, milking is done at the expense of the calf – though once-a-day milking has relatively little adverse effect on calf growth compared with twice-a-day milking. There are reported differences in milk yield among breeds, but these are breeds kept at different locations. There are no specialized milk strains of yak. Though the milk yield is low, the solid content, and fat in particular, is high (6.5 percent is not uncommon).

The single most important factor influencing milk yield is the supply and quality of grass in the warm season of the year. Daily yield most often reaches its peak in August. Supplementary feeding, though effective in maintaining yield out of season, is not practical or economic under most present conditions.

Yak do not dry off when milking ceases at the end of the warm season, and the calf, when present, continues to take some milk. Lactation can continue into a second year without pregnancy recurring and reach between one half and two thirds of the yield in the year of calving. The yak does not readily let down its milk without stimulation from the calf, and milking is quite strenuous because of the strong sphincter muscles in small teats.

Meat production
Yak meat is obtained mostly from animals that are surplus to other requirements. Surplus males are castrated – usually at a fairly mature age – and slaughtered as steers. Meat quantity is determined largely by body weight. Animals are normally slaughtered in September or October when they are in the best and fattest condition.

Dressing percentages commonly range from around 45 percent to 58 percent, the ratio of lean to bone from as little as 3:1 to as high as 6:1, depending on the source and condition of the animal. The fat content of the carcass and the fat content within the meat are generally low.

Fibre production
Hair is an important by-product of the yak. Quantity produced varies with the age and size of the animal, with breed and sex and with the method of harvesting. There are two distinct types of fibre – down fibre and coarse hair – differing in diameter, length, degree of medullation and other properties; there is also an intermediate "mid-type" hair. The proportions of the different types of hair vary on different parts of the yak body. The proportion of down fibre is high in calves and declines as the animal gets older. Down fibre grows as additional protection for the yak over winter and has to be harvested prior to being shed in the early summer. The down fibre is much valued for textiles.

Hides
Large numbers of hides are produced and processed, but quality is not regarded as good as from other cattle. Weights of hides vary with but represent around 6 percent of live weight. Thickness of skin varies with the age of the animal and the part of the body.

Draught performance
Yak steers are used widely for carrying packs, for riding and, in some areas for cultivating land. Yak have high endurance for work and can carry heavy loads in relation to their own body weight. They are particularly valued for their ability as pack animals to cope with dangerous terrain and marshy land at high elevations.

Improvements in production

Interventions in breeding, animal and herd management, feeding, housing and pasture management can all be used to try to improve output. However, it is important to ensure the cost-effectiveness of such measures.

Introduction

The yak is a multi-purpose animal, providing its owners with milk (and the resultant milk products), meat, hair and wool, hide, work as a draught animal (packing, riding, ploughing) and faeces – important as fuel in the absence of trees, but also as manure and as a building material. As noted from earlier chapters, the harsh but varied environment greatly affects the performance of the animals and the output of the various products. There are also differences among types and breeds of yak, though these differences are usually confounded with differences among the areas where these types and breeds are located.

This chapter will look, in turn, at each of the main performance characteristics of yak. Discussion of yak management and of the harvesting and utilization of the products appears in later chapters.

Growth

As would be expected, growth and development of the yak is highly influenced by the seasons, which, along with the location, largely determine pasture growth and hence the feed supply. Age, sex, type or breed of yak and herd management are among the other main causes of variation.

Body weight

Birth weight

In general, birth weight is low, ranging from 10 kg to 16 kg and representing about 3 to 7 percent of adult weight. The relatively low birth weight is a consequence of a relatively short gestation length (see Chapter 5) and the fact that in mid- and late pregnancy the yak, typically, has to exist on ground that is frozen and covered with ice and snow. Also, the yak does not normally have the benefit of supplementary feeding. For these nutritional reasons, the physical condition of the female yak is at its lowest in late pregnancy thus leading to nutrient deficiency for the foetus at the very time when the foetus is at its most demanding. The consequence is relatively poor foetal development. Table 6.1 provides some results from different sources and breeds – showing the Jiulong yak of Sichuan province with the highest absolute birth weights and the "Pengbo" yak in Tibet with the lowest.

Table 6.1 Birth weights of male and female yak of different breeds at different locations in China.

Province	Breed or local yak*	Male			Female			Source (first author *et al.*)
		No.	Weight (kg)	Proportion of adult weight (%) ***	No.	Weight (kg)	Proportion of adult weight (%) ***	
Sichuan	Jiulong	27	15.9	2.9	24	15.5	5.8	Cai Li *et al.*, 1980a
Sichuan	Maiwa	77	13.4	3.2	71	11.9	6.5	Chen Xiafei *et al.*, 1981
Sichuan	Maiwa	35	14.7	3.6	60	13.0	5.8	Longri Breeding Farm, 1993
Yunnan	Zhongdian	11	14.5		14	12.8		Duan Zhongxuan and Huang Fengying, 1982
Gansu	Tianzhu White	25	12.7		24	10.9		Research Co-operative Group, 1980 - 1987
Gansu	Maqu#	45	14.6		46	13.5		Zhao Bingyao *et al.*, 1984
Qinghai	Plateau	11	13.4		11	13.1		Lei Huanzhang *et al.*, 1983
Qinghai	Datong#	52	13.2		59	11.8		NW China Animal Science Institute, 1960
Qinghai	Plateau (?)	37	13.2	3.1	37	11.8	3.5	Song Jianxin *et al.*, 1982
Qinghai	Guoluo	16	11.7		24	11.8		Li Quan *et al.*, 2000a
Tibet	Alpine	46	13.7		32	12.8		Research Co-operative Group 1980 - 1987
Tibet	Pengbo#**	(63)	(10.5)					Ma Zongxiang and Dou Yaozong, 1981
Xinjiang	Bazhou	8	15.8		17	14.3		Agri. Exploit. Acad. Of Xinjiang, 1984

*Jiulong, Maiwa, Tianzhu White and Alpine are "listed" Chinese yak breeds.   ** Number and average of male and female yak calves combined.
*** Birth weight as a proportion of adult weight.   # Yak name denotes locality or farm   ? breed or type assumed.

Although breed differences in birth weight may exist, it is not possible, as already mentioned, to differentiate between the effects of breed and those of location. Female calves are, on average, about 1 kg lighter at birth than the males.

Supplementary feeding of dam over winter. An experiment conducted at the Longri Breeding Farm examined the effect of two methods of supplementary feeding of the dams during pregnancy. (This experiment, conducted by the then Southwest Nationalities College [now University] with support from UNDP/FAO was described in Chapter 5 in the section on calf survival). Table 6.2 shows the effects of supplementary feeding of dams in winter or early spring on birth weight and the subsequent daily gain of the calves.

As seen in Table 6.2 the effects of supplementary feeding of the dams were small but positive both on birth weight and daily weight gain and may have reached statistical significance, according to the report of Wen Yongli *et al.* (1993). A feeding experiment conducted by Dong Shikui *et al.* (personal communication, 2000) on Tianzhu White yak showed that the birth weight was improved by nearly a third and weight gain of calves was doubled when the dams were supplemented with urea multinutritional molasses blocks (UMMB) from the start of December 1998 to the end of April 1999. In both experiments, the improved weight gain was likely to be attributable to the advantages of a higher birth weight and a slightly better milk yield of the supplemented dams (see also Tables 6.6 and 6.7 for the effects of rearing on calf growth). Any advantage in terms of body weight must also be viewed in conjunction with the small but positive effect of the winter feed supplementation on the number of calves born and reared (see Table 5.10). Further information on the effects of supplementary feeding is presented in Chapter 14.

Table 6.2 Birth weights and weight gain to 90 days of age of Maiwa yak calves from three groups of dams Least squares means and standard deviations
[Source: Wen Yongli *et al.* 1993]

Year	Treatment group	No. calves	Birth weight (kg)		No. calves	Daily weight gain (g/day) (90 days)	
			Mean	SD		Mean	SD
1989/90	Hay	36	16.2	2.2	32	300	83
	Paddock grass	41	16.0	2.2	36	298	54
	Control	81	14.5	2.5	66	279	51
1990/91	Hay	35	18.1	2.4	30	316	88
	Control	98	15.6	3.7	98	295	57

a) fed hay from mid-December to end of April, b) allowed access to conserved grass paddocks from 1 April for 45 days and c) unsupplemented, control.

Parity and age of cow. Both parity and age of yak dam have effects on the birth weight of their calves, as shown in Table 6.3 and as widely reported in studies on ordinary cattle elsewhere. Data are again taken from the Longri experiment involving trials of the effects of supplementary feeding during pregnancy. (Because supplementary feeding of the dams has affected calf weights in this experiment, the overall mean birth weight of all the calves is also somewhat higher than it would be without the inclusion of the feed-supplemented groups [the least squares mean for each treatment group were shown in Table 6.2]. Therefore, effects of parity and age of dam, shown in Table 6.3, are presented as deviations from the overall fitted mean of the data.)

Table 6.3 Effects of parity and of age of yak cow on the birth weight of her calf, shown as deviations from the least squares fitted mean [Source: Chen Zhihua *et al.*, 1994]

Parity of dam	No. of cows	Deviation of birth weight (kg)	Age of dam (years)	No. of cows	Deviation of birth weight (kg)
1	37	-0.02	4	33	-0.52
2	27	-0.34	5	9	-0.24
3	26	-0.26	6	3	-0.23
4	28	-0.90	7	20	0.62
5	20	0.81	8	21	0.25
6	18	0.71	9	32	0.54
			10	38	-0.42

It is apparent from the results of Chen Zhihua *et al.* (1994) shown in Table 6.3 that calves born in early parities are lighter in weight than those born to later-parity dams. However, unlike most results from "improved" cattle breeds, calves born to first-parity dams were not at great disadvantage. Similarly, the effects of age (as distinct from parity) show that young yak cows had calves slightly lighter in weight than those born to older cows – though the oldest age group started to show, as might be expected, a decline in the birth weight of its calves. The variation is not large (though statistically significant) and there are some estimates that disrupt a steady trend (e.g. the estimate of a relatively large negative effect of fourth parity). It is not clear, however, how accurately an analysis such as this can estimate the effects of parity and age of the dam when both factors are included at the same time, as the two are partially confounded. Some aberrant values are not surprising.

Body weight of cow. According to Zhang Rongchang's observations in Tianzhu White yak (personal communication, 2000), calf birth weight is highly related to the mother's body weight. In his study, yak dams weighing less than 200 kg produced young of around 15.2 kg at birth (n=27), while newborn from yak dams weighing 201 - 230 kg and those weighing above 231 kg had offspring of about 16.4 kg (n=41) and 16.9 kg (22), respectively.

Other effects on birth weight and growth

Month of calving. Most calves are born from April to July, with May the peak month. Birth weight varies to some extent with month of calving (Table 6.4), as shown by the experiment at the Longri Breeding Farm in Sichuan, mentioned previously. As in respect of Table 6.3, and for the same reason, the results in Table 6.4 are presented as deviations from the overall least squares mean.

Apart from the unexpectedly low birth weight of calves born in the first half of June, there is a steady increase in birth weight from the middle of April to the middle of July, with all birth weights after mid-June above average and those of calves born before that below average. The variation in birth weight attributable to date of birth (as defined) was shown by Chen Zhihua *et al.* (1994) to be statistically highly significant ($P<0.01$).

Variation in birth weight with month of calving was also noted by Cai Li in F1 (*Pian Niu*) calves (hybrids of yak and cattle) born at Xiangdong Yak Farm in Ruoergai county of Sichuan. Average birth weight rose from 21.7 kg, for calves born in April, to 24.3 kg, for those born in June.

Table 6.4 Effect of date of calving on birth weight shown as deviations from the least squares fitted mean (cf. Table 6.2). [Source: Chen Zhihua *et al.*, 1994]

Period of calving (day and month)	Number of calves	Deviation of birth weight (kg)
Prior to 15.4	6	-1.28
16.4 - 30.4	29	-1.67
1.5 - 15.5	26	-1.49
16.5 - 31.5	23	-0.77
1.6 - 15.6	30	-0.98
16.6 - 30.6	18	1.08
1.7 - 15.7	14	4.02
16.7 - 31.7	12	1.09

However, calves born early in the season, March or April, have a longer suckling period ahead of them than those born later in the season. For example, Ma Zongxiang and Dou Yaozong (1982) reported that calves born in March - April reached an average body weight of 45.6 kg by October of that year, while those born in June had attained only 34.2 kg, on average. The calf's growth in the first six months of its life is very important to its subsequent survival over the first winter. Calves born later in the season have a poorer chance of survival over winter than those born earlier.

Seasonal growth of yak. Typically, weight gain in a healthy calf reared by its dam is almost linear over the first six months of life, but declines with the approach of winter; this is followed by some loss in weight over the first winter and spring. Thereafter, in the second warm season, there is again a rapid gain in weight followed, once more, by a loss in weight over the next cold season.

Figure 6.1 illustrates growth from birth to 25 months old of 12 male and 12 female calves of the Plateau type born in April at Longri Breeding Farm of the Pasture Institute of Sichuan. Daily gain for the male calves was fairly constant over the first five months and declined rapidly thereafter. For female calves, weight gain for the first five months was somewhat more variable before declining over winter. In consequence, the weight of the calves increased linearly up to about five or six months of age before remaining more or less unchanged until the following warm season. In the second warm season after birth, weight gains from April/May to August/September were a little faster than in the first year, at between one third and one half kg per day. The third warm season started again with substantial gains in weight after the losses in the previous winter.

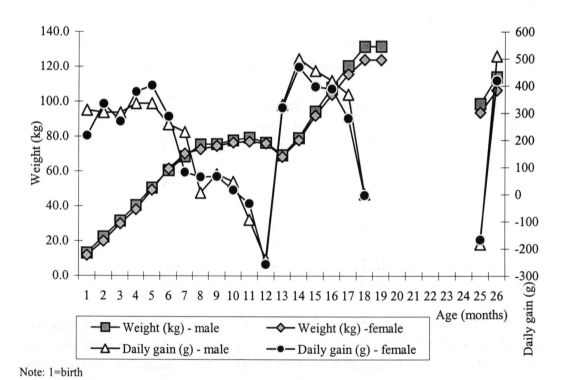

Note: 1=birth

Figure 6.1 (a) Body weights of 12 male and 12 female calves born in April at the Pasture Institute of Sichuan, from birth to 25 months old. (b) Daily gain of yak calves monthly from birth to 25 months old.

Similar results (Table 6.5) were obtained with calves of the Alpine type born in May at the Pengbo farm of Tibet (4 000 - 4 600 m a.s.l.), according to the report of Ma Zongxiang and Dou Yaozong (1981).

As shown in Table 6.5, the weight loss of calves over the first winter was around 12 - 15 percent of the weight before the onset of winter. Typically, over the following summer and autumn young yak regain their weight losses and may well double in weight before again losing, over the second winter of life, perhaps 25 percent of the maximum weight reached. The cycle of weight gain and weight loss continues throughout life. This is illustrated in Figure 6.2 by observations on 180 yak steers from birth to five years old (Lu Guanghui 1980). In fully adult yak, the weight loss in the cold season is roughly equal to the gain in the following warm season.

Table 6.5 Monthly change of live weight, monthly gain and daily gain (±SD) of calves (n=14) in cold and warm seasons in Tibet
[Source: adapted from Ma Zongxiang and Dou Yaozong, 1981]

Season	Month	Age of calf (months)	Live weight (kg)	Monthly gain (kg)	Daily gain (g)
Warm season	July	2	21.1 ± 1.5	-	-
	August	3	28.4 ± 2.0	6.3 ± 0.6	213.7 ± 21.1
	September	4	35.2 ± 2.6	5.1 ± 0.8	180.3 ± 19.4
Cold season	October	5	39.0 ± 3.1	5.2 ± 1.0	168.2 ± 11.7
	November	6	38.3 ± 1.8	-0.6 ± 0.3	-23.0 ± 5.1
	December	7	37.2 ± 2.7	-0.4 ± 0.3	-13.3 ± 3.0
	January	8	37.0 ± 4.0	-0.8 ± 0.4	-31.1 ± 1.2
	February	9	37.5 ± 2.3	0.5 ± 0.3	16.2 ± 2.4
	March	10	36.1 ± 1.4	-0.7 ± 0.4	-23.0 ± 3.0
	April	11	37.4 ± 1.3	0.5 ± 0.2	17.0 ± 4.0
Warm season	May	12	32.3 ± 2.4	-5.4 ± 0.2	-188.7 ± 24.1
	June	13	38.5 ± 3.0	8.0 ± 1.2	250.1 ± 25.0
	July	14	45.3 ± 3.4	5.3 ± 1.0	184.5 ± 14.2

Effect of type of rearing on weight gain. The manner in which the yak calf is reared profoundly affects its growth. The three main classes are: 1) to give the calf exclusive access to the milk of its dam (the dam is not milked), 2) to milk the dam once a day and allow the calf the remainder, and 3) to milk the dam twice a day and allow the calf what remains. An additional category (a subdivision of the first class) is that dams that are not milked may a) be allowed to graze at night or b) not be allowed to graze if kept restrained overnight with the yak females that are milked.

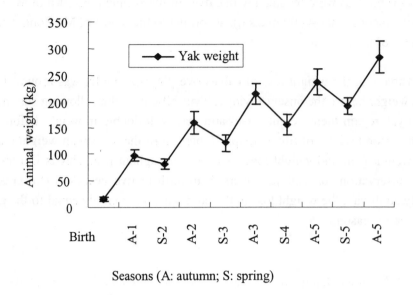

Seasons (A: autumn; S: spring)

Figure 6.2 Changes in the body weight of 180 yak steers from birth to five years old (the first weighting at the date of birth, then at the end of autumn and at the end of spring-start of warm season) [Source: modified from Lu Guanghui, 1980]

There are many studies on the effects of these rearing treatments on calf growth. There is generally a beneficial and quite large effect on calf growth when the calf has access to all the milk of its dam. Often, the largest difference is between calves allowed access to dams milked only once a day compared with those reared by dams milked twice daily. Weight gain under the former regime can be double that from the latter as in the study of Zhang Rongchang (1989) shown in Table 6.6. This is not, however, only a consequence of differences in milk intake by the calf (which are not recorded but estimated to be somewhat greater when the dam is milked only once a day). Normally, the calves are tethered when their dams are milked. When the dam is milked only once daily, the calf is tethered and kept apart from the dam for a relatively short time only and grazes and drinks water alongside the dam for most of the day. Calves with dams milked twice a day are tethered for much of the day and have perhaps only four to five hours of time during which they move around at pasture with their dams. In a similar study by Yang Rongzhen *et al.* (1997), the main difference in growth of calves was between those from dams not milked compared to those milked – with, unusually, no effect due to frequency of milking. In this study, calves at the age of 18 months weighed around one third less if their dams were milked than if they were not milked.

Table 6.6 Live weight and daily gain (±SD) of calves with different rearing methods
[Source: adapted from Zhang Rongchang, 1989]

Age (month)	Sex	No.	Not milked Live weight (kg)	Not milked Daily gain (g)	Milked once daily Live weight (kg)	Milked once daily Daily gain (g)	Milked twice daily Live weight (kg)	Milked twice daily Daily gain (g)
Birth	M	32	15.4 ± 3.5	-	15.9 ± 2.4	-	16.7 ± 1.3	-
	F	30	17.8 ± 2.9	-	17.3 ± 4.0	-	15.4 ± 2.4	-
6	M	32	120.1 ± 13.2	558.3 ± 33.2	100.4 ± 9.1	482.3 ± 21.4	55.9 ± 5.6	229.8 ± 12.5
	F	30	110.9 ± 10.2	533.1 ± 24.6	98.1 ± 5.6	456.9 ± 18.3	54.4 ± 3.4	215.2 ± 15.8
12	M	30	142.2 ± 7.8	349.9 ± 21.1	115.6 ± 7.7	287.2 ± 20.0	87.9 ± 7.2	194.2 ± 10.7
	F	30	125.3 ± 12.6	303.3 ± 19.3	110.0 ± 4.9	256.1 ± 14.3	84.3 ± 8.8	192.8 ± 15.4
18	M	30	256.1 ± 18.5	440.1 ± 22.4	233.6 ± 12.3	402.1 ± 23.9	160.1 ± 6.9	276.0 ± 20.1
	F	30	212.2 ± 14.3	383.4 ± 15.5	214.3 ± 10.2	366.1 ± 21.1	155.8 ± 9.7	255.6 ± 23.5

In another group trial conducted by Cai Li in Sichuan (at 3 450 m altitude), the six-month weight of calves from dams milked once a day was 93.1 kg compared with 48.5 kg for those with dams milked twice daily. At the Datong cattle farm in Qinghai, calves with dams that were not milked weighed 104.7 kg at six months old compared with 70.2 kg for those with dams milked once daily. Clearly, milking the dams and the associated separation of the calf from its dam adversely affected the weight gain of the calves.

Some calves suckle their dams for a second year and are not weaned until the end of the second warm season of their life. The dams lactating for that second season are those that have not calved again. Table 6.7 shows some results on a method of rearing on calf growth over a period of 92 days during their year of birth and then in the second year. (The results for the second year are all based on calves from dams that were milked once daily in the year in which their calf was born. In this trial, the females not milked were further divided into those that were confined at night along with their calves and those allowed to graze at night as well as during the day.)

It is seen that the additional grazing allowed to the dams and calves at night led to a substantial increase in the weight gain of the calves. Compared to the growth of calves confined at night along with their dams, milking of the dam once a day had no further detrimental effect at either age of calf – but milking twice a day and the attendant further restrictions on the calf reduced calf growth further (data for year of birth only). This seems to contrast with the larger effects of milking the dam, noted earlier, in the results of Zhang Rongchang (1989) and Cai Li (however, it is not explicitly stated for those studies whether the calves or their dams were confined at night or not). In view of the large, adverse effect of night confinement on calf growth shown in Table 6.7, it should be said that there are good reasons, apart from tradition, why it may not be possible everywhere to adopt a practice of night grazing for the calf alongside its dam. Thus, in many areas, yak calves need to be confined at night for reasons of safety and, if feasible, to provide their dams an undisturbed night's grazing prior to the morning milking.

Hand rearing of yak calves is restricted to situations where there is no alternative. Usually when a calf has lost its dam, it is fostered on a yak cow that has lost her calf (see Chapter 8). Data on the effects of artificial rearing on growth have not been obtained.

Breed and sex differences in growth. It is generally accepted that yak of the Alpine type, and especially the Jiulong breed (perhaps the best of the Alpine type), grow more rapidly than those of the Plateau type.

Table 6.7 Weight gain of yak calves in two successive years, according to rearing method [Source: Xu Guilin, 1985]

Dam	No.	Weight gain [92 days] (kg)
Year calf born (calf age 0 year)		
Not milked – dam and calf confined	14	29.0
Not milked but grazing at night	17	60.8
Milked once daily	26	28.1
Milked twice daily	29	20.2
Year after calf born* (calf age 1 year)		
Not milked – dam and calf confined	32	28.8
Not milked but grazing at night	9	49.8
Milked once daily	27	29.7

*The results are all based on calves from dams that were milked once daily in the year in which their calf was born.

The cautionary note has to be repeated that, normally, these different types and breeds are not at the same location at the same time and that yak type or breed are therefore confounded with location and the environmental differences implicit in that. This applies to the data shown in Table 6.8.

The greater growth of the Jiulong yak compared with the Maiwa yak (Table 6.8) appears to be a function not only of a larger final weight but also a faster early growth rate relative to that weight (since these results do not extend beyond the age of six and a half years, it is not known whether the weights at that stage are true mature weights although herdsmen usually regard the animals as "mature" by that age – see ensuing explanations).

By three to three and a half years old, the Jiulong males described in Table 6.8 had reached nearly 58 percent of their six- to six-and-a-half-year-old weight while the Maiwa had reached only 41 percent (for females the corresponding percentages are 78 percent and 70 percent, respectively). However, it is not known how these results may have been affected by the different environments in which the two breeds were kept. It is nonetheless apparent from Table 6.8 that for each breed the females grew faster relative to their final ("mature"?) weight in the early years of life than did the males. However, the growth of the females slowed after they reached the age of about four years. The males still continued to increase in weight quite markedly after that age – to reach a substantially greater final weight than the females. The growth differences between the sexes are reflected by the practice of the herdsmen to regard females as suitable for transfer to the adult herd at the age of four, whereas males are not regarded as "mature" (and at the height of their powers) until the age of six or seven.

Table 6.8 Estimated body weights* of Maiwa and Jiulong male and female yak (at separate locations) from birth to six and a half years old and weight at each age relative to final weight* (weights in October/November of each year).

[Sources: Maiwa - Chen Xaifei *et al.*, 1981; Jiulong - Cai Li *et al.*, 1980a]

| | Maiwa | | | | | | | | Jiulong | | | | | | | |
| | Male | | | | Female | | | | Male | | | | Female | | | |
Age (yrs)	No.	Wt (kg)	[SD]	% of final	No.	Wt (kg)	[SD]	% of final	No.	Wt (kg)	[SD]	% of final	No.	Wt (kg)	[SD]	% of final
Birth	77	13.4		3.2	71	11.9		5.4	27	15.9	2.3	3.6	24	15.0	2.5	5.0
1 - 1.5	84	65.9	2.2	15.9	82	67.0	11.3	30.2	34	145.3	20.8	30.7	35	124.9	25.2	40.2
2 - 2.5	33	120.1	19.7	29.0	35	119.6	28.5	53.9	18	208.6	25.5	44.0	21	189.6	29.4	61.0
3 - 3.5	30	170.7	25.8	41.3	61	154.8	28.5	69.8	3	272.6	25.6	57.5	11	243.1	23.2	78.3
4 - 4.5	15	302.3	49.5	73.1	73	181.9	21.2	82.0	11	312.5	19.2	65.9	26	269.7	18.3	86.8
5 - 5.5	10	375.3	69.8	90.7	40	188.7	42.6	85.1	7	386.0	20.1	81.4	9	283.1	33.9	91.1
6 - 6.5	17	413.8	67.0	100	21	221.8	25.9	100	38	474.1	38.8	100	10	310.6	26.9	100

*Final weight is that at 6 or 6.5 years old and is not necessarily the weight at full maturity.

The difficulty of interpreting data on size and other aspects of the performance of yak as presented here, and in the literature on the yak in general, rests on the fact, as already noted, that conditions under which yak are kept vary from locality to locality and between years and that these factors are also often confounded with the type or breed of yak and with the management system. This point is further exemplified by Sarbagishev *et al.* [1989] who note that yak in Kyrgyzstan are considerably larger than those in neighbouring Tajikistan because in the former country, yak are not milked but kept exclusively for meat production. Under good grazing conditions on state farms in Kyrgyzstan, the researchers recorded weight gains during 12-month fattening periods well in excess of 100 kg live weight per year. These gains were made both in the second year of life (107 kg for 248 yak) and the third year of life (126 kg for 87 yak) and they were only a little less in the year after that (92 kg for 11 animals). That these weight gains are markedly higher than those shown in Table 6.8 for Maiwa and Jiulong yak should occasion no surprise since the Maiwa and Jiulong were not specifically managed as "fattening" animals. The higher growth rates on the state farms in Kyrgyzstan illustrate, however, that yak do have a higher potential for growth than is sometimes realized in the predominantly harsh conditions in which they are normally kept.

Linear body dimensions

Height at withers, body length, chest and girth circumferences and the estimated body weight from linear body dimensions of adult male and female yak at different locations in China are presented in Table 6.9 (Zhang Rongchang, 1989). These data testify to the fact that the size and performance of yak vary with locations and the type or breed of yak kept at these locations. Generally, yak in Sichuan have the biggest body size and those in Tibet the smallest; and the yak of the Alpine type has a larger body size than that of the Plateau type.

Chen Zhihua *et al.* (2000) collated evidence on environmental factors and concluded that the annual average temperature and precipitation were the most important among the environmental (ecological) factors affecting growth of yak (see also Chapter 4). As evidence of the importance of the environmental factors on body size and growth, it is possible to point to differences in size and weight at similar ages of the same "breed" at different locations. This further reinforces the caution that must be attached to comparisons (such as breed comparisons) across locations. Correlations among the body dimensions were reported to be of the order of 0.3 - 0.5 and those of the linear dimensions with body weight in the range of 0.5 - 0.6 (P< 0.01) (Wen Yongli and Chen Zhihua, 1994).

Table 6.10 shows the increase in linear body dimensions over a period of years. As already noted in respect of body weight (cf. Table 6.8) the females mature earlier than the males, as apparent from the higher proportion of last observed size (four years old in this case) reached by each body dimension at each of the earlier ages.

Table 6.9 Linear body dimensions and body weight (±SD) of adult yaks of different types and breeds at different locations in China [Source: adapted from Zhang Rongchang, 1989]

Location	Breed	Sex	No.	Height at withers (cm)	Body length (cm)	Chest circumf. (cm)	Girth circumf. (cm)	Body weight* (kg)
Tibet	Alpine**	M	39	122.2 ± 3.5	142.0 ± 6.6	167.8 ± 6.4	18.9 ± 2.3	293.5 ± 20.4
		F	529	110.1 ± 4.8	125.1 ± 3.9	150.4 ± 4.8	15.4 ± 1.2	197.1 ± 16.4
	Plateau***	M	20	116.6 ± 7.9	141.3 ± 5.9	169.6 ± 5.9	18.4 ± 1.9	282.4 ± 23.8
		F	225	103.3 ± 5.5	126.1 ± 6.8	145.2 ± 9.1	15.2 ± 1.0	187.9 ± 19.0
Yunnan	Zhongdian	M	23	119.1 ± 8.1	126.9 ± 11.6	162.2 ± 10.8	17.6 ± 1.1	234.6 ± 35.8
		F	186	105.2 ± 5.3	117.1 ± 8.3	153.7 ± 22.9	16.1 ± 1.0	192.5 ± 27.5
Sichuan	Jiulong	M	15	137.5 ± 8.8	172.6 ± 13.4	218.6 ± 26.7	23.64 ± 1.5	593.5 ± 184.9
		F	708	116.6 ± 4.3	140.3 ± 7.8	178.5 ± 7.8	18.2 ± 1.3	314.4 ± 38.6
	Maiwa	M	17	126.0 ± 5.0	157.3 ± 10.4	193.4 ± 9.2	19.8 ± 0.8	413.8 ± 67.0
		F	219	106.2 ± 4.5	130.7 ± 7.3	154.6 ± 11.6	15.57 ± 1.0	221.8 ± 25.8
Qinghai	Plateau***	M	21	129.2 ± 6.2	150.6 ± 5.98	194.4 ± 7.7	20.10 ± 1.1	444.0 ± 54.7
		F	208	110.9 ± 4.9	131.9 ± 5.1	157.2 ± 6.3	15.8 ± 1.1	256.4 ± 81.2
	Huanhu	M	14	113.9 ± 6.5	143.7 ± 14.9	169.0 ± 15.3	18.3 ± 2.3	323.2 ± 100.6
		F	138	103.0 ± 0.3	123.8 ± 7.6	147.0 ± 6.9	15.4 ± 1.2	210.6 ± 34.5
Gansu	Tianzhu	M	17	120.8 ± 4.5	123.2 ± 4.7	163.8 ± 5.5	18.3 ± 1.1	264.1 ± 18.3
	White	F	88	108.1 ± 5.5	113.6 ± 5.2	153.7 ± 8.0	16.8 ± 1.8	189.7 ± 20.8
	Gannan	M	31	126.6 ± 6.4	141.0 ± 8.4	187.9 ± 10.8	21.3 ± 2.2	355.1 ± 35.7
		F	378	107.6 ± 5.6	118.8 ± 7.5	154.7 ± 6.9	16.3 ± 1.3	210.5 ± 26.4
Xingjiang	Bazhou	M	33	126.8 ± 6.2	140.1 ± 10.4	192.4 ± 11.8	20.7 ± 1.3	362.6 ± 22.6
		F	265	110.7 ± 2.5	123.5 ± 5.7	171.2 ± 9.1	16.3 ± 0.7	250.4 ± 21.3

*Estimated from body dimensions to avoid possible confusion over the breed nomenclature used in this Table.   **"Alpine" yak in southeastern Tibet normally regarded as home to the Jiali and Pali breeds.   *** "Plateau" yak in northwestern Tibet normally regarded as home to the Pali breed.

Table 6.10 Linear body dimensions (cm ±SD) of yak at different ages
[Source: Zhong Guanghui *et al.*, 1996a]

Sex	Age (yr)	No.	Height at withers	Chest depth	Chest width	Hip width	Heart girth	Cannon bone circumf.	Rump length	Body length
M	1	226	94.8 ± 20.7	44.4 ± 6.0	20.1 ± 2.7	23.8 ± 3.0	119.7 ± 12.9	13.7 ± 1.0	31.9 ± 3.5	99.8 ± 8.3
	2	155	104.4 ± 5.5	53.9 ± 5.4	23.9 ± 3.9	27.8 ± 3.3	138.5 ± 10.2	15.4 ± 1.1	36.1 ± 2.6	114.8 ± 7.9
	3	116	110.9 ± 5.7	58.6 ± 5.1	25.8 ± 3.5	30.4 ± 3.3	153.6 ± 13.0	16.5 ± 1.1	38.9 ± 3.8	124.5 ± 12.9
	4	91	122.4 ± 8.6	67.9 ± 7.8	32.3 ± 8.2	36.9 ± 6.8	177.6 ± 18.6	18.8 ± 1.9	45.0 ± 5.3	140.2 ± 12.6
F	1	220	91.5 ± 6.3	43.8 ± 5.3	20.2 ± 5.7	23.2 ± 3.0	117.4 ± 11.0	13.4 ± 1.0	30.4 ± 3.5	97.4 ± 8.7
	2	157	101.6 ± 5.3	51.6 ± 4.3	23.7 ± 4.4	27.6 ± 2.8	134.3 ± 13.7	14.7 ± 1.0	34.9 ± 3.9	111.4 ± 11.4
	3	181	107.1 ± 4.9	56.2 ± 3.7	24.5 ± 3.2	30.7 ± 3.6	147.6 ± 9.7	15.7 ± 0.9	37.5 ± 2.4	120.0 ± 6.7
	4	190	110.8 ± 6.3	58.9 ± 6.0	25.4 ± 5.2	32.2 ± 3.4	153.4 ± 11.7	16.1 ± 0.7	39.0 ± 2.2	126.1 ± 7.6
	5	160	112.1 ± 4.5	60.9 ± 3.2	25.8 ± 3.9	33.4 ± 3.4	158.1 ± 9.7	16.3 ± 0.6	40.3 ± 2.2	127.5 ± 11.2

Females at one year had reached between 5 percent and 10 percent more of their size at four years old than did the males. The results also show, as is well established in the literature, that some body parts such as height at withers and cannon-bone circumference, mature relatively earlier in life than do others such as chest depth and hip width (with body weight continuing to increase significantly even after the linear dimensions have virtually stopped growing).

Wen Yongli and Chen Zhihua (1994) published results on body dimensions of Maiwa yak that also show similar relative rates of maturity of the different body parts and of body weight and the relatively later maturity in males than in females.

In the yak, as in other bovines, the linear body dimensions show less seasonal variation in size than is found for body weight (a cubic measure of size). Results are shown in Table 6.11 – albeit over a period of only two years. Moreover, relatively early-maturing dimensions that are largely a function of skeletal size, such as height at withers, show less variability in size over the seasons (there was no decline in size over winter) than dimensions that mature later and also include, in the measurement, a greater proportion of muscle and fat (e.g. heart girth).

Table 6.11 Height at withers, body length, and heart girth of yak over a two-year period (measurements in cm. are given for the unweighted average of 12 male and 10 female animals) [Source: Sichuan Grassland Institute, 1982]

Age (month)	Height at withers	Body length	Heart girth
Birth	50.8	45.7	56.8
6	79.1	86.6	104.9
12	88.9	88.5	102.7
18	93.1	107.1	135.1
24	95.8	108.5	128.6

Milk production

General considerations

There is, at present, no breed or strain of yak developed especially for milk production. All breeds are kept, to a greater or lesser extent, to produce milk, in addition to their other uses and products. Milk yield is closely related to pasture growth and quality and, in general terms, the amount of milk produced by the yak cow is considered as no more than the amount needed for the normal growth and development of its calf. In this respect, the milk yield of yak is more akin to that of animals in the wild than to the milk yield of dairy cattle. Even though the milk may be taken from the yak cows at the expense of the calf, milk and milk products of yak are important for the herdsmen and their families, in China and in most other yak-keeping countries. In commercial terms, milk is perhaps the most important of the yak products. The F1 hybrids with other cattle produce substantially more milk than the pure yak – the actual amount depending on the cattle breed used to produce the hybrid. The F1 hybrid has, therefore, considerable value to the herdsmen in the right situation.

When considering estimates of the milk production of yak, account has to taken of the milk consumed by the calf – which can only be estimated – and the quantity extracted by the herders. As a rule, yak females are not milked for the first month after calving, though perhaps only the first two weeks in some areas. During that time, the calf takes all the available milk, including the colostrum, on the day or two days after calving. As in other cattle, the quality of the colostrum of yak cows is much better than the milk produced thereafter (Liu Haibo, 1989; Zhang Rongchang, 1989). Table 6.12 shows that the total solid content of the colostrum from yak is about twice that of the later milk, while milk protein content can be three times as high and fat content between two- and three-fold of that in the later milk.

Table 6.12 A comparison of composition between colostrum and normal milk in yak
[Source: adapted from Liu Haibo, 1989 and from Zhang Rongchang, 1989]

Species	No.	Milk type	Milk solid (%)	Fat (%)	Protein (%)	Lactose (%)	Ash (%)	Density kg/litre
Yak	17	Colostrum	32.0 - 34.5	13.2 - 15.8	15.1 - 17.1	1.7 - 1.9	0.9 - 1.1	1.03 - 1.07
Yak	33	Normal milk	16.9 - 17.7	5.5 - 7.2	4.9 - 5.3	4.5 - 5.0	0.8 - 0.9	1.03 - 1.04

After the initial period when the calf obtains all the milk provided by the dam, it is estimated that the calf takes about a third of the available milk if the yak cow is milked twice daily and about half the milk with once-a-day milking. Yak females produce about a third more milk, in total, if stimulated by milking twice daily compared with once a day (39 percent more in a study by Cai Li in Sichuan, and 26 percent more in an investigation in Qinghai (Lei Huanzhang *et al.*, 1983)).

There is no generally agreed upon method of assessing yak lactation milk yield. Production over a lactation period of 180 days has been proposed and estimated from the yield on three to five successive days and the use of coefficients based on the month in which the milk yield is measured. The coefficients, in turn, are based on the fact that yield is higher in months of high pasture growth than either at the beginning or end of the grass-growing season. To the estimate of yield derived from hand milking has to be added an estimate of milk consumed by the calf. Though such methods of estimating yield are attractive in principle, they suffer from the further difficulty that the coefficients for different months vary greatly for different locations and dates of calving; hence the absence of general agreement on the use of these methods.

Table 6.13 Milk yield and fat percentage of yak females of different breeds at various locations of China (± SD)

Province	Yak breed or yak location*	Month of measure-ment	No.	Average Daily yield (kg)	Estimated lactation yield (kg) (in days)	Fat (%)	Source
Gansu	Tianzhu White	5 - 10	223	2.3 ± 0.5	304 (135)	6.8 ± 1.3	Zhang Rongchang, 1989
Gansu	Plateau (in Shandan)*	5 - 11	21	2.6 ± 0.6	464 (180)	5.4 ± 1.5	Zhang Rongchang, 1989
Gansu	Gannan	5 - 10	15	1.8 ± 0.2	315 (177)	--	Research Co-operative Group, 1980-1987
Qinghai	Plateau	6 - 10	181	1.4 ± 0.3	214 (153)	5.6 ± 1.2	Research Cooperative Group, 1980-1987
Qinghai	Huanhu	6 - 10	96	3.0 ± 0.3	487 (153)	6.4 ± 1.4	Zhang Rongchang, 1989
Qinghai	Guoluo*	7 - 11	20	1.0 ± 0.2	162 (153)	6.6 ± 0.7	Li Quan et al., 2000b
Sichuan	Maiwa	4, 7	20	1.8	365 (150)	6.8	Chen Xiafei et al., 1981
Sichuan	Jiulong	7, 8	93	2.8 ± 0.2	414 (150)	5.7 ± 1.0	Cai Li et al., (1980a)
Tibet	"Plateau"*	7 - 9	19	2.7 ± 0.3	280 (105)	--	Zhang Rongchang, 1989
Tibet	Alpine*	8 - 10	41	0.92		6.4	Research Co-operative Group, 1980-1987
Tibet	Jiali **		48	0.8 ± 0.2	148 (180)	6.8 ± 1.3	Ji Qiumei et al., 2000a
Tibet	Pali **		25	1.0 ± 0.2	200 (180)	5.9 ± 0.7	Ji Qiumei et al., 2000a
Tibet	Sibu**		36	0.9 ± 0.1	180 (180)	7.5 ± 1.4	Ji Qiumei et al., 2000a
Yunnan	Zhongdian	5, 7, 11	81	1.1 ± 0.2	132-302 (180-210)	6.2 ± 1.6	Zhang Rongchang, 1989

* Location of yak within the province – for Tibet: "Plateau" here refers to Pali breed, Alpine to Jiali.
**Yields for these breeds are based on varying proportions of yak females in the lactation following calving and a lactation in a second year without calving again ("half lactation"). The "full lactation" yields for these breeds as shown in Table 11.5 (Chapter 11) are Jiali:192; Pali: 215; Sibu: 216.

Factors influencing milk yield

Breeding

Table 6.13 provides the estimated milk yields and fat content in milk of different yak breeds at various locations in China. These yields are the amounts milked by hand with an adjustment for milk taken by the calves. Table 6.13 indicates that, in general, the milk yield of the yak is low, but the fat content is relatively high. The results also suggest that the Huanhu yak in Qinghai had the highest milk yield and yak in Tibet had mostly the lowest.

Table 6.14 Milk production in crossbred* and domesticated yak
[Source: adapted from Jialin *et al.*, 1998a]

Month	Crossbred yak (n=20)					
	Daily milk yield (kg)		Fat content (g/kg)		Monthly milk yield (kg)	
	Mean	SD	Mean	SD	Mean	SD
May	1.1	0.02	47.5	3.6	32.9	6.0
June	1.7	1.2	53.5	8.7	49.8	6.7
July	2.1	0.17	49.4	4.9	60.4	5.2
August	2.3	0.28	57.7	5.4	68.9	8.5
	Significance					
Milk yield over 120 d (kg)	Mean = 212.2				SD = 20.2	
Mean daily milk yield (kg/d)	Mean = 1.7				SD = 0.16	
Mean fat content (g/kg)	Mean = 52.0				SD = 2.9	

Month	Crossbred yak (n=10)					
	Daily milk yield (kg)		Fat content (g/kg)		Monthly milk yield (kg)	
	Mean	SD	Mean	SD	Mean	SD
May	1.1	0.21	50.9	14.6	33.3	3.5
June	1.1	0.21	50.9	14.6	33.3	3.5
July	1.7	0.10	47.6	8.5	51.2	3.0
August	1.8	0.28	68.8	6.7	54.6	8.5
	Significance					
Milk yield over 120 d (kg)	Mean = 184.5				SD = 10.5	
Mean daily milk yield (kg/d)	Mean = 1.5				SD = 0.10	
Mean fat content (g/kg)	Mean = 53.5				SD = 4.1	

**Wild yak semen was used to inseminate domestic yak cows to produce the crossbred.

As stressed in respect of other breed comparisons in this book, some caution is needed in interpreting the variation in milk yield among the breeds: The "breed" differences may be associated with different herd sizes, forage availability, daily milking times (once a day or twice a day) and with differences in management among locations. Also, as noted elsewhere in this book, even estimates for the same breed can vary among different studies because different conditions apply to the observations.

Table 6.14 shows that a herd of crossbred yak (domestic yak dam crossed with wild yak sire), milked once daily after suckling of the calf, had a higher daily milk yield and total lactation milk yield than ordinary domestic yak, but there was no overall difference in the fat content of the milk.

Effects of age and parity
Lactation milk yield increases with the age of the female up to about 10 or 11 years old and also with the number of calvings (Zhang Rongchang *et al.*, 1983; Xu Guilin *et al.*, 1983) – although these two factors are rather closely associated with each other. Figure 6.3 shows seasonal changes in yield in six different lactations.

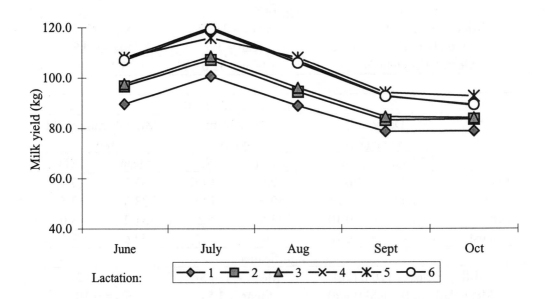

Figure 6.3 Milk yield of yak females in five (warm) months of the year in six separate lactations (Number females per lactation: 1:20; 2:20; 3:13; 4:10; 5:10; 6:18)

There appears to be no evidence to show that yak cows have a lactation peak in relation to calving date – as found in dairy cattle; an overriding effect on milk yield in the yak seems to be that of pasture growth, reflected by month, in each of the six lactations as seen in

Figure 6.3. Similar effects of parity and the month in which the cows lactate have also been shown for Jiulong yak (at an elevation of 3 200 m) in a substantial study by Wen Yongli *et al*. (1994) involving between 65 and 128 animals in each parity group.

Other correlations with milk yield

Lang Jie *et al*. (1999) reported that in breeding groups of Maiwa yak the correlation of milk production of mother and daughter was positive and linear (r=0.374, P<0.05) – of course, this does not provide an estimate of the heritability (the strength of inheritance) of milk production in yak. These authors also reported that the sizes of various linear body dimensions of yak in their first lactation are positively (and significantly) correlated with milk production (r in the range of 0.32 - 0.56). This shows a tendency for the better-grown females to yield more milk. This correlation was much weaker for female yak in later lactations.

Environmental factors affecting milk yield – the lactation curve

Herbage supply. As referred to earlier, one of the important factors influencing milk yield is pasture production – the quantity, growth status and nutritive value of the herbage. These are, in turn, affected by climate and season (cf. Chapter 13). All lactating yak, irrespective of age, parity or breed type and even location, tend to peak in yield in July and August when grass is at its best in terms of quality and quantity (cf. Figure 6.3). These months are known in yak-producing areas of China as the "golden age". Before July, though the grass has started to turn green and to grow, the amount of grass available is not high. After August, as air temperature falls, the nutritive value declines – as the grass produces seeds and then wilts, and the content of crude fibre of the grass is high. Table 6.15 provides some information on the composition of grass (but not on grass quantity) from samples taken on pastures at an elevation of 3 600 m in Hongyuan county of Sichuan province. The pasture samples were representative of the herbage grazed by the yak. (For more information on composition of different pasture species, see Chapter 13.)

Table 6.15 Percentage composition (on a dry-matter basis) of grass on meadow in different months over the warm season [Source: Sichuan Grassland Institute, 1982]

Date	Dry matter	Crude protein	Crude fibre	Ash	N-free extract	Calcium	Phosphorus
9 June	24	18.8	27.9	5.0	42.0	0.50	0.25
30 June	28	11.8	30.0	5.0	48.6	0.43	0.25
30 July	33	12.4	27.6	6.1	50.9	0.42	0.33
30 Aug.	38	10.0	30.8	8.2	48.9	0.61	0.26
29 Sept.	42	8.1	33.3	5.7	50.5	0.62	0.14
31 Oct.	62	4.8	34.8	5.0	53.5	0.53	0.16

Month of milking. In Hongyuan county, from where the data on grass composition in Table 6.15 were derived, the peak of monthly milk yield was in July for yak cows and in June for hybrids (both F1 [*Pian Niu*] and backcrosses to cattle [one quarter-bred yak]). The monthly yields and the fat percentage of the milk are shown in Table 6.16.

Table 6.16 Monthly milk yield and fat percentage of milk of yak, F1 (*Pian Niu**), and one quarter-bred yak** in Hongyuan county of Sichuan

		No.	June	July	Aug.	Sept.	Oct.	Nov.	Total
Yak	Milk yield (kg)	13	40.4	40.6	37.3	27.0	20.0	11.0	176.5
	Fat percent	6		5.6	6.6	6.5	7.6	7.8	6.8
(F1)	Milk yield (kg)	12	64.7	61.3	43.1	29.5	17.9	11.0	227.5
	Fat percent	5		5.1	5.4	5.8	6.8	6.6	5.9
¼-bred yak	Milk yield (kg)	10	48.5	40.9	40.9	29.5	19.4	6.7	185.9
	Fat percent	7		6.0	6.0	6.0	7.0	7.6	6.6

* The one half-bred yak from local *Bos taurus* (yellow cattle) bulls used for crossing with yak.
**The one quarter-bred yak are backcross offspring of the F1 (*Pian Niu*) dams mated to bulls of the yellow cattle.

The milk yields of the cows represented in Table 6.16 are lower than those represented in Figure 6.3, but both show the seasonal decline in milk production. It is also seen that, as found in dairy cattle, that the percentage of fat in the milk increases as the season advances and the quantity of milk declines.

Similar results to those presented on the period of peak lactation have been obtained from various locations, all showing that the supply of grass is the major factor influencing yield and that parity of cow has a much smaller effect. Another aspect of this, from a more northerly region (the Vostochnyi Sayan area of the Russia Federation), derives from a study of Katzina (1993). She reports that yak which had calved early in the year, in April, attained their maximum udder volume in the third month of the lactation, while those that did not calve until June attained their maximum udder volume of yak in the first month of lactation. Thus, both groups would have their largest udder volume around the same month of the year.

Month of calving. The study by Katzina (1993) also showed that yak that had calved in April had a maximum udder volume, which was far greater (two-and-a-half-fold) than that of yak that calved in June. The April-calving yak, in that part of the Russian Federation, lactated for six to seven months to produce around 360 kg milk while those that did not calve until June lactated for only four to five months to produce 150 kg of milk on average.

An interrelationship between the month of calving and the month of milking is shown particularly well in Table 6.17, with data from Mongolia. This re-affirms the month of milking as the most important variable for milk production – reflecting the importance of growth and quality of the available herbage.

Table 6.17 Monthly milk yield of adult cows (based on quantity milked plus amount of milk taken by calf) according to month of calving and month of milking [Source: State and Cooperative Farms: Bat-Erdene, 1993]

Month of milking*	Month of calving			
	March	April	May	June
1	65.2 (41 - 91)	70.1 (49 - 94)	70.1 (58 - 100)	112.6 (82 -128)
2	63.6 (47 - 85)	63.3 (48 - 81)	101.5 (67 - 154)	**118.3 (79 - 132)**
3	64.3 (41 - 90)	105.5 (71-130)	**108.5 (78 - 146)**	102.0 (71 - 111)
4	107.9 (76 -158)	**107.3 (93 - 132)**	109.3 (80 - 153)	87.2 (62 - 97)
5	**115.8 (87 - 174)**	99.8 (71 - 126)	82.0 (64 - 109)	65.6 (37 - 94)
6	104.7 (73 -151)	83.5 (68 - 107)	61.9 (44 - 90)	48.1 (27 - 84)
7	84.5 (59 - 119)	58.8 (40 - 84)	40.5 (25 - 90)	29.7 (16 - 31)
8	60.4 (42 - 90)	52.9 (25 - 73)	33.5 (16 - 48)	
9	44.7 (25 - 84)	31.3 (16 - 43)		
10	26.1 (16 - 45)			

*Month of milking counted from month of calving (e.g. calving in May, first month of milking is May, second month of milking is June etc.) **July**, as the month of milking, is shown in bold

Weather. Xu Guilin *et al.* (1983) recorded that the weather conditions on the day of milking affected yield on that day. Thus, in comparison with milk produced on a clear day, milk production on a cloudy day was 1.9 percent higher and on a rainy day 7.7 percent greater. Zhang Rongchang (personal communication, 2000) also found that variation of milk yield due to the weather condition can be up to around 8 percent. According to the Qinghai Provincial Meteorological Bureau, the optimum temperature for yak is around 5° - 13°C (Zeng Wenqun and Chen Yishi, 1980). Yak appear to produce less milk when the ambient temperature is too high especially when this is associated with strong solar radiation and a lack of wind on a clear day. Conversely, more milk is produced during cloudy or rainy conditions. It is not immediately obvious whether the small increases in milk production associated with the weather result from an increased intake of herbage or of water, or some other factors related to the environment – or from associated variation in the metabolic rates of the yak (the latter possibility being favoured by Zhang Rongchang, personal communication, 2002).

Effects of winter and cessation of milking. As air temperature starts to fall after October and winter approaches rapidly, hand milking of the yak females is normally stopped. As indicated earlier, a yak does not dry off in consequence of this and continues to secrete a little milk for its calf. This happens irrespective of whether a female yak is pregnant or not.

Only a cow that has lost her calf during the warm season will dry off when hand milking ceases. Similarly, a female that is pregnant but has been isolated from her previous calf will dry off when hand milking stops. Other pregnant females with a calf still at foot will not go dry until their one-year-old calf is removed prior to the next calving. Finally, a cow, even though not pregnant at the onset of winter but still suckling a calf, will continue to lactate through the following warm season and, normally, will be hand milked again. The "half-lactating" female yak (as it is called) will stop being milked at the end of her second warm season and will then go dry, irrespective of whether she is pregnant or not.

Supplementary feeding. Some trials have been conducted with supplementary feeding of conserved grass – silage, hay or straw – during winter months to study the effect on the subsequent lactation. In this context, Long *et al.* (1999a) reported a trial with 33 Tianzhu White yak cows at grazing that were given supplementary feeds of 1.0 - 1.5 kg highland barley straw or oat hay per animal per day, from the beginning of December to the end of April. This supplementation resulted in an increased lactation length (P<0.01) over the whole milking period, but there was no difference attributable to the type of straw used. Milk yield was also increased, but not significantly, perhaps because the supplementary feeding was stopped before calving began (see also Chapter 13 and Table 13.17).

Zhou Shourong (1984) conducted a trial with nine yak cows in Sichuan in the winter months. He found that supplements of 4 kg of silage per head per day led to a rise of milk output from 150 to 350 g per day, after only seven days of supplementary feeding and to 500 g of milk after 15 days of feeding.

However, the difficulties and costs involved in conserving grass as hay (other material is usually not available) may make supplementary feeding uneconomic over the winter and spring as a means of promoting milk production at that time of year. Silage, as used in the trial referred to above, is not a frequent option as it freezes solid in the cold winter conditions of the region if not very heavily and expensively protected. It is relevant to note in the context of supplementary feeding, that the yak cows are not in good condition during the winter and the additional strain of milk production may make matters worse for them. Also, herdsmen are reluctant to hand milk during the bitter cold of winter.

Nonetheless, there is at least one theoretical reason why supplementary feeding over winter is worth further consideration even if milk is not taken from the cows at that time. Interest centres on the possibility that such feeding may improve the condition of the cows and lead to improved calf production, reproductive rate and milk yield in the following warm season. The supplementary feeding carried out experimentally at the Longri Breeding Farm in Sichuan should be seen in that context (Table 6.18).

Table 6.18. Milk yield over a period of 184 days, fat percentage in milk, and weight loss over winter of Maiwa yak cows of three groups: a) fed hay from mid-December to end of April, b) allowed access to conserved grass paddocks from 1 April for 45 days, and c) unsupplemented, control. Least squares means and standard deviations)
(Source: Wen Yongli *et al.* 1993)

Year	Treatment group	No. cows	Milk yield (kg)		Fat (%)		No. cows	Weight loss (kg)	
			Mean	SD	Mean	SD		Mean	SD
1989/90	Hay	54	229.0	53.3	6.0	1.3	58	33.5	14.8
	Paddock grass	55	220.6	54.7	5.8	1.6	58	34.5	15.5
	Control	113	218.3	49.9	5.4	1.6	110	35.5	14.5
1990/91	Hay	50	235.4	53.6	5.9	1.3	59	39.9	18.0
	Control	137	224.1	47.6	5.4	1.2	150	42.7	17.4

As seen from Table 6.18, the supplementary feeding appears to have had small but positive effects on milk yield and, unexpectedly (because of the increase in milk yield), on the fat percentage of the milk which is reported to have increased by approximately 0.5 percent (from less than 5.5 percent to nearly 6.0 percent). The estimate of milk yield is derived from measured amounts milked three times per month and does not include, as far as is known, milk sucked by the calves.

The cows given supplements lost slightly less weight over winter than the unsupplemented controls (P<0.05). However, the weighing at the end of the winter period was delayed until the end of May, by which time the cows may have started to recover some of their condition, especially because, in 1990, pasture growth at this farm had started exceptionally early. Weight loss alone also does not fully reflect possible changes in body composition, fatness in particular.

Feeding of additive. An imbalance or deficiency of minerals in forages at pasture may limit milk yield of yak. Additives may therefore improve lactating performance of grazing yak. Table 6.19 shows the effect on milk production of a mineral mixture ($CuSO_4 \cdot 5H_2O$, $ZnSO_4 \cdot 7H_2O$, $CoCl_2 \cdot 6H_2O$, NaCl, KI, $NaSeO_3$, $CaHPO_4 \cdot 2H_2O$) (Yuan Youqing, 1994) given as a salt-lick block. The results of such addition during lactation indicate that milk yield of full-lactating yak cows (milking in the year of calving) was increased by 15.5 percent and that of half-lactating cows (those milking into a second season without calving again) by 14.8 percent.

Long Ruijun (1995) has suggested that inorganic phosphate (P) is adequate for grazing yak when a supplement of 0.5 - 1.0 kg of oat hay or highland barley straw was given per day during wintertime.

Data on the effects of individual minerals, including trace elements, on yak productivity are, at present, unavailable. With further investigation, specific trace elements or minerals (or combinations of them) may well be found limiting for yak production as has been found for animal production in other parts of the world.

Table 6.19 Effect of a mixture of mineral additives (provided as a salt block) on monthly milk yield (kg ± SD) of full-lactating and half-lactating cows in different months of the warm season [Source: Yuan Youqing *et al.*, 1994]

Lactating type	Treatment	No. cows	May	June	July	Aug.	Sept.	Oct.	Total
Full-lactating	Additive	10	35.0 ±4.2	45.9 ±4.0	60.4 ±4.2	48.9 ±4.3	44.3 ±4.0	36.4 ±4.1	272.1 ±20.2
	Control	10	31.6 ±3.9	41.0 ±4.5	53.7 ±4.0	41.1 ±4.1	36.8 ±4.2	30.5 ±4.0	235.7 ±17.2
	Significance		NS	*	**	**	**	**	**
Half-lactating	Additive	7	29.1 ±3.9	33.3 ±4.0	45.6 ±3.8	40.9 ±3.8	28.5 ±3.5	-	183.5 ±14.1
	Control	7	27.0 ±3.8	29.0 ±3.2	40.5 ±3.2	35.0 ±3.4	23.8 ±2.8	-	159.8 ±13.3
	Significance		NS	*	*	**	**		**

Protein deficiency in forage is potentially one of the most important limiting factors on yak production (especially milk production), and nitrogen supplementation can positively influence the milking performance of cows during lactation. An experiment conducted by Zhang Degang (1998) showed that urea molasses multinutrients block (UMMB) contained 10 percent urea, 0.1 percent mixed minerals and trace elements (Fe, Zn, Mg, Cu, etc.). Given as a supplementary feed (500 g per animal per day) during summertime, it significantly promoted milk yield of Tianzhu White yak and Gannan Black yak in Gansu (P<0.01), relative to control groups grazing only.

The yak with UMMB 500 g per day produced an extra 100 g and 160 g milk per day for Tianzhu White yak and Gannan Black yak, respectively. As an alternative protein source, many species of shrubsû leaf are ideal protein supplements for grazing yak due to their high contents in protein (25 - 35 percent) (Long *et al.*, 1999b; Dong Shikui *et al.*, 2002).

A general comment on the use of feed supplements for yak (already noted in respect of minerals and trace elements) may not be out of place. Many of the yak-rearing areas are remote and this not only increases the costs of supplying supplements (if not locally available) but also there may not be a ready market for extra produce. The main criteria for needing supplements will be unusually poor performance or ill health of the animals, and, when possible, a demonstration of a positive effect from using supplements in that particular situation. The further point about the need for cost-effectiveness has been made before. There is, however, also the other potential use of supplements (for example feed, blocks) as an insurance against the periodic snow disasters during which many yak can die.

Milk production in a second year without calving again

Many yak do not conceive again in the year of calving. It is thus common in yak for lactation to continue into a second year. The amount of milk given over the months from December to May is very low, declining to perhaps as little as 2-4 litres in the whole of April (in one set of observations). Yield then rises with the onset of grass growth and follows a monthly pattern similar to that already seen (cf. Figure 6.3 and Table 6.16), but the amount produced in the second year is approximately half that given in the year of calving (sometimes up to two thirds and sometimes less); hence the name "half-lactating" commonly given to females milking into a second season without calving again – in contrast to the "full-lactating yak" in the year of calving. Parity differences are maintained in the second season at the lower level of yield. The fat percentage in the milk during the second "half-lactating" season is correspondingly higher than in the first "full-lactating" season, in line with the negative correlation between milk yield (quantity) and the fat percentage in the milk.

Factors influencing milk composition

Yak milk is dense and sweetish and greatly liked by the local people. Although its composition varies slightly among different yak breeds at different locations, generally total milk solid (dry matter) content ranges around 15 - 18 percent, fat percentage around 5.5 - 7.0 percent (see also previous Tables), protein and lactose content each around 4 - 5.5 percent, and ash around 0.7 - 0.9 percent during the main lactating period (Table 6.20). The milk solid, fat and protein contents in milk of the yak and its hybrids are far higher than in other cattle, especially dairy breeds, and close to the levels in buffalo (Zhang Rongchang, 1989).

Typically, the proportion of essential to nonessential amino acids is 0.8:1 as observed in a full analysis of amino acids in the milk of the Tianzhu White yak (Zhang Rongchang *et al.*, 1986) and 0.79:1, 0.67:1 and 0.72:1 in the milk of the Jiali, Pali and Sibu yak (Ji Qiumei, 2000a).

Milk composition varies with seasonal grass growth and climate change as does milk yield. Milk solids, lactose, protein and amino acids in yak milk are at their highest in mid-lactation and fat percentage increases continuously into late lactation (corresponding also to the changes with season, as shown in Table 6.16). Some relevant results on the Tianzhu

White yak (Zhang Rongchang *et al.*, 1986) are given in Table 6.21. During the cold season, when milk yield of yak females may be only of the order of 100 g per day, the fat percentage of that milk can be as high as 14 percent. With the growth of forage, protein content in the swards declines from 115 g per kg DM (young grass) to 33g per kg DM (mature grass), and crude fibre in the swards increases correspondingly. The increased crude fibre can offer more acetic acid and butyric acid (the resources of fatty acid) for the mammary gland to synthesize more fat.

Table 6.20 Milk composition and milk yield of different breeds
(or yak of countries) at different locations

Breed or yak of country	No.	Milk solid (%)	Fat (%)	Protein (%)	Lactose (%)	Ash (%)	Milk yield** (kg _ SD)
Tianzhu White	17	16.9	5.5	5.2	5.4	0.77	141.7 _ 43.9
Jiulong	13	17.5	6.9	4.9	4.7	0.82	349.9 _ 131.9
Maiwa	24	17.5	6.3	4.9	5.4	0.82	176.5 _ 64.0
Jiali*	21	16.3	6.8	5.0	3.6	0.95	104.5 _ 31.7
Pali*	22	-	5.9	5.7	3.8	-	236.1 _ 74.9
Sibu*	19	-	7.5	5.3	3.5	-	---
Kyrgyzstan (country)	13	17.4	6.5	5.3	4.6	0.87	630
Nepal (country)	12	17.4	6.5	5.4	4.6	0.90	---
India (country)	14	17.9	6.5	5.9	4.7	0.87	238.4 _ 94.4

* Source from Ji Qiumei et al., 2000a and others from Zhong Guanghaui, 1996b.
**Source from Zhang Rongchang, 1989. (The number of animals shown for milk composition does not apply to milk yield.)

Table 6.21 Composition of milk of ten Tianzhu White yak in Gansu province
in three periods of lactation [Source: adapted from Zhang Rongchang *et al.*, 1986]

	Early lactation (12 June) (%)	Mid lactation (25 July) (%)	Late lactation (20 Sept.) (%)
Dry matter	16.1	17.8	16.3
Solids ñ not-fat	10.9	12.3	10.5
Fat	5.1	5.4	5.8
Protein	5.2	5.7	4.7
Lactose	4.9	5.9	5.0
Ash	0.79	0.75	0.77
Essential amino acid	10.7	11.6	8.1
Nonessential acid	13.7	14.8	9.8
Energy (MJ/kg)	3.5	3.6	3.8

The correlation between the total 184-day milk yield and the average fat percentage was shown to be very small (-0.04) and nonsignificant in a study on 184 Maiwa yak by Wen Yongli and Chen Zhihua (1994) (at the Longri Breeding Farm, referred to a number of times here). This is not a genetic correlation, but suggests nonetheless that if this lack of relationship is confirmed, that milk yield and fat percentage might be more readily improved simultaneously in the yak than is generally the case in dairy cattle.

The yak udder

Yak udders are small and, by the standards of dairy cattle, not well developed. Measurements in Sichuan showed an udder circumference in pluriparous females of 55 cm and an udder depth of between 2 and 3 cm. Sixty females measured in Qinghai (Zang Yinsong, 1985) had an udder circumference of 51.6 cm (SD 12.5), the mammary vein had a diameter of 0.94 cm (SD 0.38), and the teats were 2.2 - 2.3 cm in length and 1.1 - 1.2 cm in diameter. Usually (though not in all studies on the yak) the two rear quarters hold more milk than the two forequarters. The forequarters are generally reckoned to hold about 45 percent of the milk, but other ratios have been reported (e.g. 47.6 percent [Zhang Rongchang et al., 1983] and around 40 percent [Han Zhenkang and Lu Tianshui, 1980]).

The sphincter muscles of the yak's teats are strong and hard squeezing is needed to extract milk. The teats are normally squeezed between the fingers. Especially among Alpine-type yak, some one third of the females are found to have particularly "tense" teats.

In Jiulong county of Sichuan an average yield of 1.4 kg needed almost five minutes of milking time to extract the milk at 80 squeezes per minute – a rate of 0.28 kg per minute (Zhang Rongchang et al. [1983] reported a rate of 0.42 kg per min). When a trial with machine milking was conducted, a negative pressure of 400 mm Hg required to extract the yak milk.

Milk let-down

Normally, milk let-down does not immediately follow on squeezing the teats between the fingers, but requires the presence of the calf to jolt the udder and to suckle briefly. If the calf has died, herdsmen place the skin of the dead calf in front of the dam and allow her to smell and lick it, before milk let-down is achieved. Experimentally, the use of a hot towel to massage the udder has been found to stimulate let-down and even to increase yield (Hu Angang et al., 1960, unpublished).

The time required to stimulate the udder into let-down was found by Han Zhenkang and Lu Tianshui (1980) to be initially around one minute (SD 15 seconds), but a second, somewhat shorter, period of such stimulation was found usually to be needed in the course of the milking process before all the milk can be extracted. These authors also indicated that the amount of milk in the udder cistern of the yak accounted for only about 6.5 percent of the milk produced at a milking and that the milk produced as a reflex to milking accounted for around 80 percent – of which four fifths was let down as a result of the first stimulation of the udder and the remaining fifth after the second stimulation. Residual milk in the udder (that traditionally obtained by "stripping" in the hand-milking of dairy cattle) accounted for about 13 percent, but this is normally left by the herdsmen for the calf. These authors also found that proportion of milk stored in the udder cistern increased with the parity of the cow to around 10 percent by the fourth parity.

Meat Production

Meat from yak is derived from surplus males, often the castrated steers, and also from females, usually at the end of their useful reproductive life, or at the end of their time as milk-producers. In "efficiency" terms (meat output/feed input), the process of meat production in the yak cannot be regarded as "efficient" because, for the most part, the animals are not slaughtered until quite late in life after several cycles of weight gain and weight loss. Meat from the yak represents an important source of sustenance for the herders and their families and an additional source of income from sales. Also, there are circumstances when meat production from yak should be regarded as an efficient use of resources, at high altitudes, that might otherwise not be utilized at all. In this sense, Smirnov *et al.* (1990) pointed out that in a part of the Caucasus, the cost of a unit increase in live weight was ten times greater for beef cattle than for yak. (Yak in the Caucasus fatten on summer pastures at elevations of 3 500 - 4 000 m). In fact, it is claimed that the annual expenditure on keeping a yak was marginally less than that on a sheep. Similar claims of the "efficiency" of yak for meat production are made in other countries and referred to in Chapter 11, part 2.

Meat quantity

The major factor contributing to meat output is the body weight of the animal at the time of slaughter. Thus, the factors associated with variation in growth, discussed earlier in this chapter, all influence the amount of meat produced. Grass growth, as affected by season and location, is the major contributor, along with breed, age and sex of the animal. Seasonal changes in body weight, shown earlier in this chapter, clearly affect meat output. In practice, animals intended for meat are slaughtered, whenever possible, only in the autumn when they are in good, fat condition. Just as July-August are termed by herdsmen concerned with milk as the "golden age", local people regard October as the month of "best fatness" for meat production (in Tibet this is considered to be in September [Ma Zongxiang and Dou Yaozong, 1982]).

Breed and location

There is much variation in the meat properties of different breeds of yak at different locations (as noted earlier, these factors are generally confounded). Meat output in terms of dressing percentage, ratios of lean to bone and loin-eye area are thought to be better from Alpine – than from Plateau-type yak – though this impression may be derived largely from the superiority of the Jiulong breed in Sichuan province. Table 6.22 gives some of the results.

Live weights at slaughter varied with breed and location (and age at slaughter) from 116 - 576 kg. Dressing percentages ranged from 40 - 62 percent. In at least one case (Smirnov *et al.* 1990), the low dressing percentage was attributed to the slaughter of young male yak at what was considered the wrong age – two years old. There was also substantial variation in loin eye area. It should be noted, however, that in some instances the numbers on which the means are based are very small. Most of the information should be regarded as indicative of the range of values found in yak rather than definitive of the merits of any particular class or location of yak.

The question of stage of maturity at time of slaughter is clearly important (some of this information may be available in the source references shown in Table 6.22), but the main criterion for timing the slaughter of yak is usually to leave it to the end of the grass-growing season when the condition of the animals is at its best.

As referred to in Chapter 3, there is interest in the potential benefits of crossing domestic yak with wild yak (by the use of A.I.). Evidence, though not fully consistent across different studies, suggests that the first crosses and backcrosses are heavier and somewhat larger in body dimensions than the domestic yak. Jialin *et al.,* (1998b) reported that meat production of the first crossbred generation was assessed and carcass dissection was made of males. One group (n=14) was slaughtered at six months of age and the second (n=12) at 18 months. Crossbred yak in this study were significantly heavier (P<0.01) at 6 months and at 18 months than domesticated ones in the same herd and many of the associated carcass traits were larger in the crosses – but the dressing percentage was similar for both groups of animals (Table 6.23). It would be of interest to know whether the differences between the wild yak crosses and the domestic yak, in terms of meat production, would be maintained to the older slaughter ages more usual in herders' practice.

Effect of sex

As was seen in Table 6.22, there is a tendency for steer yak to have the higher live weights and carcass weights at slaughter relative to females and perhaps higher dressing percentages. However, there is not a consistent finding. Also, a report by Ji Qiumei *et al.* (2000b) indicated that in one of two groups (Jiali yak), dressing percentages and lean/bone ratio were similar in the two sexes and in the other group (Sibu yak) the females were the better in these traits.

Table 6.22 Meat production and carcass attributes of yak from different populations (animals at the age of 6.5 year or older unless otherwise indicated)

Province	Breed or Location#	Altitude (m)	Sex	No.	Live weight (kg.)	Carcass weight (kg.)	Viscera fat % of LW	Dressing percent*	Ratio Lean bone	Loin eye area (sq. cm)	Heart weight % of LW	Lung weight	Hide+hair weight	Source
Sichuan	Jiulong	3 500	Male	2	576	324	1.2	57.6	4.8	87.3	0.58	1.09	6.56	[1]
			Female	2	282	151	2.6	56.2	6.0	58.3	0.71	1.28	6.57	[1]
			Steer	12	496	253	1.8	55.7	4.2	86.7	0.61	1.37	6.53	[1]
	Kangdin-Liuba#	3 500	Steer	25	409	222	2.4	56.6	4.0	86.0	0.46	1.47	7.23	[pers com]
	Maiwa	3 500	Steer	2	372	208	2.8	58.6	3.0			1.68	7.21	[2]
			Steer**	4	116	59	1.3	52.1	3.9	31.7	0.59	1.42	6.59	[Cai Li]
Gansu	Tianzhu White	3 000	Male	2	288	146	1.3	52.0	2.7		0.63	1.29	8.28	[3]
			Steer	3	262	133	1.7	52.7	3.6	50.3	0.55	1.23	7.68	[3]
	Gannan	3 000	Steer	8	223	112	1.8	51.6	4.1		0.79	1.23	5.92	[4]
Qinghai	Plateau	3 700	Steer	12	368	194	1.6	53.2	4.1	60.6	0.47	1.25	5.88	[5]
	Huanhu	3 000	Steer	5	226	110	1.6	50.3	3.9	66.3	0.57	1.39	6.31	[5]
	Gangcha#	3 500	Female	11	362	154	1.4	43.9			0.51	1.19	6.26	[4]
			Steer	17	465	216	1.0	47.5			0.60		6.44	[4]
Caucasus (from Tuva)		3 500	Female	3	287	130	3.2	48.6	5.0					[6]
			Male''	3	205	81	0.8	40.3	3.9					[6]
Tibet	Laqu#	4 570	Steer	3	287	170	2.2	61.6			0.61	1.68	6.40	[7]
	Dangxiong#	4 400	Male	4	264	133	1.1	51.1			0.43	1.34	5.57	[4]
			Female	2	153	66	1.4	44.2			0.49	1.17	5.68	[4]
Xinjiang	Bazhou	2 500	Steer**	2	156	72	0.3	46.6	3.7	35.4	0.50	1.15	6.75	[8]
			Steer***	4	221	123	1.7	57.2	4.2					[8]
Yunnan	Zhongdian	3 000	Female	2	203	92		32.3	2.8		0.60	1.45	5.39	[9]
			Steer	8	309	179		45.7	4.3					[9]

* Viscera fat included in dressing percentage; ** sterrs of 16-17 months old; '' males 2 years old; *** steers 2.5 and 3.5 years old; # location of yak within province.

[Sources: (1) Cai Li *et al.*, 1980b; (2) Chen X. F. *et al.*, 1981; (3) Pu *et al.*, 1987; (4) Research Co-operative Group, 1980-87; (5) Lei, 1983; (6) Smirnov *et al.*, 1990; (7) Jia H. G, 1966; (8) Wei *et al.*, 1981; (9) He *et al.*, 1997]

Table 6.23 Weight and linear measurements of carcass components of crossbred (wild yak crossed with domestic yak) and domestic yak at 6 and 18 months of age [Source: adapted from Jialin *et al*, 1998b]

	6 months old					18 months old				
	Cross-bred		Domestic		Difference	Cross-bred		Domestic		Difference
	Mean	SD	Mean	SD		Mean	SD	Mean	SD	
Sex	4F, 3M		4F, 3M			3F, 3M		3F, 3M		
No.	7		7			6		6		
Live weight (kg)	74.7	10.4	59.8	10.2	14.9**	150.5	56.1	117.7	17.4	32.8**
Carcass weight (kg)	35.4	5.5	28.2	5.5	7.2*	71.2	3.0	54.3	8.9	17.0**
Dressing proportion	0.48	0.03	0.47	0.02	0.01	0.47	0.02	0.46	0.02	0.01
Meat weight (kg)	27.1	2.8	21.4	4.2	5.7*	56.1	2.2	42.3	7.5	13.8**
Bone weight (kg)	8.2	0.95	6.7	1.1	1.5*	14.6	0.32	12.3	0.11	2.3**
Meat: bone (1) ratio	3.3		3.2			3.6		3.4		
Eye-muscle area (mm²)	2 070	415	1 644	261	426*	2 914	134	2 520	172	394**
Carcass length (mm)	838	63	734	83	102**	894	46	846	41	49*
Carcass depth (mm)	430	56	377	43	53	582	23	495	31	87*
Carcass chest depth (mm)	453	57	403	49	50	537	18	416	55	120**
Chuck and dorsal meat (kg)	5.3	1.1	4.8	1.7	0.50	10.9	1.8	7.6	0.8	3.3***
Rib weight (kg)	4.3	1.2	3.2	0.39	1.1	4.7	1.4	3.2	1.1	1.5*
Brisket weight (kg)	1.7	0.57	1.1	0.25	0.60	5.7	1.4	4.8	0.90	0.90
Plate weight (kg)	1.7	0.39	1.5	0.48	0.20	3.0	0.68	2.1	0.44	0.90
Shank weight (kg)	2.8	0.20	2.5	0.65	0.30	8.5	1.1	6.7	0.26	1.8*
Loin weight (kg)	3.1	1.1	2.0	0.69	1.1*	8.9	1.6	6.8	3.0	2.1**
Rump weight (kg)	2.7	1.5	1.5	0.39	1.2*	6.7	1.1	4.9	1.3	1.8***
Round weight (kg)	5.5	1.7	4.8	1.5	1.7	9.0	0.86	6.5	1.1	2.5***
Prime cutting yield (kg)	12.3	2.1	9.3	2.4	3.0*	24.5	1.9	18.2	1.1	6.3***
Rate of prime cut	0.35		0.33		0.02	0.34		0.34		0.0

Significant differences: * P<0.05; ** P<0.01

153

Effect of age

In a trial in Sichuan province, entire male yak from the age of 1.5 - 4.5 years and thereafter, yak steers to the age of 20.5 years were chosen at random from yak herds in the same area and kept under year-round grazing without supplementary feeding. All the animals were slaughtered at the Animal Husbandry and Veterinary Station in Kangdin county of Sichuan at the end of autumn, in their fattest condition. In spite of the small number of animals involved, the trends shown in Table 6.24 indicate that the dressing percentage increased with age (and live weight) up to six and a half years and declined somewhat thereafter. However, the castration of males after the age of four and a half years and the subsequent switch to steers could be an important factor in the larger increase in dressing percentage noted between the ages of four and a half and five and a half years. Variation among the steers above the age of 16.5 years showed no clear trends (the data for these ages have been pooled).

Table 6.24 Dressing percentage (carcass weight/live weight) of yak males and steers, according to age at slaughter

Age (years)	Sex*	No.	Live weight (kg)	Dressing (%)
1.5	M	2	55	37.6
2.5	M	2	105	44.0
3.5	M	2	182	47.6
4.5	M	2	234	49.6
5.5	S	2	370	55.8
6.5	S	3	401	56.2
7.5	S	4	407	53.9
10.5	S	1	409	51.7
11.5	S	2	417	55.0
14.5	S	3	406	52.3
16.5-20.5**	S	10	413	53.4

*m=entire male s=castrated male (steer)

** Average for the older steers.

Composition of meat

Yak meat is fine textured and scarlet in colour. It is regarded as very palatable, but muscular marbling is poor. It is rich in myoglobins and has a flavour akin to game. Among local people yak meat has been prized above that of ordinary cattle since ancient times. Table 6.25 provides some evidence on composition of the meat for different locations, breeds and ages of yak steers (the rib sample from the Tianzhu White steers was unusually fat).

Table 6.25 Composition of yak steer meat (%) [+SD]

Province / country	Breed or Location	No.	Age (years)	Meat from:	Dry matter	Protein	Fat	Ash	Ca	P	Source
Sichuan	Maiwa	7	1.5	Rib 9-11*	25.8	21.5	3.3	1.04			Cai Li et al., 1984
Xingjiang	Bazhou	2	2.5	Rib 9-11*	24.7	21.2	2.0	1.07			Wei Ronglu et al., 1981
Gansu	Tianzhu White	3	4.5	Rib 9-10*	33.8	20.0	11.9	0.87	0.02	0.14	Pu Ruitang et al., 1987
				Loin eye	23.7	21.3	1.4	1.05	0.02	0.20	Pu Ruitang et al.,1987
Qinghai	Qinghai	?	4.5	Back, rib	25.9	22.1	2.1	1.61	0.03	0.20	Lei Huanzhang et al., 1983
			Over 6	Back, rib	26.8	22.3	2.8	1.68	0.02	0.24	Lei Huanzhang et al., 1983
	Domestic yak*	6	0.5	Rib 9-11	25.8	22.6 ± 1.4	3.3 ± 1.7	1.04 ± 0.6	-	-	Jialin et al., 1998b
	Wild yak x domestic yak crosses*	3	1.5	Rib 9-11	31.1	22.6 ± 1.9	7.9 ± 3.7	1.17 ± 0.2	-	-	Jialin et al., 1998b
		6	0.5	Rib 9-11	27.5	22.7 ± 1.1	3.6 ± 1.3	1.05 ± 0.1	-	-	Jialin et al., 1998b
Tibet		3	1.5	Rib 9-11	31.1	22.2 ± 2.2	5.9 ± 2.2	1.09 ± 0.2	-	-	Jialin et al., 1998b
	Pali	6	Adult	Rib 9-11*	44.1	17.8	25.3	0.84	0.020	-	Ji Qiumei et al., 2000c
				Loin eye	25.8	22.6	2.1	1.03	0.032	-	Ji Qiumei et al., 2000c
Mongolia	Mongolia	?	Adult	Rib 9-11*	27.2	18.8	5.0	0.92	-	-	Zhang Rongchang, 1989

*at Datong Yak Farm   ** Source: Research Co-operative Group (report), 1980 - 1987

Besides location, sex, age and breed (if it can be differentiated from location), the rearing treatment of the animals, which is reflected in body condition, must be expected to affect the meat composition of yak. Kirghiz literature cited by Zhang Rongchang (1989) indicates the relationship between rearing treatment and meat composition of yak (Table 6.26). It can be seen that dry matter, fat and energy in yak steer meat increased with the improved feeding level.

Table 6.26 Composition of yak steer meat (percent) under different rearing treatments in Kyrgyzstan [Source: Zhang Rongchang, 1989]

Group	Age (month)	No.	Live weight (kg)	Dressing (%)	Dry matter (%)	Protein (%)	Fat (%)	Ash (%)	Energy (MJ/kg)
I	19	22	234	44.0	26.8	23.0	2.4	1.1	4.9
II	19	22	258	46.3	27.4	22.8	3.6	1.1	5.3
III	19	22	275	49.8	28.9	22.2	5.7	1.0	6.0

* I: suckling the [milked] dam; II: milk with artificial rearing, III: milk with artificial rearing together with supplementation in the cold season.

The amino acid content of meat from different muscles of the yak has been analysed in a number of studies (for example, Zhong Guanghui *et al.*, 1993; Mkrtchyan *et al.*, 1993; Ji Qiumei *et al.*, 2000b, 2000c) The ratio of essential to nonessential amino acids was found to be between 0.6:1 and 0.8:1.

Fibre production and hides

Fibre

Yak produce two types of fibre: coarse outer hair and a fine down fibre, which grows prior to the onset of winter as additional protection for the yak against cold. The down fibre would be shed in early summer if not harvested. Since the 1970s, the down has been used extensively by the textile industry as an alternative to other fine animal fibres. Fabric made from yak down has better lustre than wool and handles well. It provides a high degree of heat insulation. The income the herder receives from yak fibre is, at present, small relative to the income that can be obtained from yak milk and meat. None the less, the economic value of the down is leading to consideration of developing strains of yak with improved fibre production.

The amount of fibre produced by individuals and the proportions of coarse hair and down varies with the region where the yak are kept and the associated climate, and with breed, sex, age and the season and method of harvesting the fibre.

Breed, sex and location

In general, yak of the Henduan Alpine type have a higher yield of fibre than those of the Plateau type. The highest amounts are obtained from a "fibre line" of Jiulong yak, especially selected for greater fibre production. Exceptional individuals of that breed are claimed to produce as much as 25 kg fibre, of which 50 percent is down fibre. This is ten-fold the yield of most ordinary yak (Cai Li *et al.*, 1980a). Table 6.27 provides some results from different breeds at different locations for adult male, female and steer yak.

The results in Table 6.27 suggest considerable differences in the amount of fibre harvested at the different locations. The hair was harvested, at all these locations, by first raking the fleece to extract down fibres and then shorn to harvest the remaining down and other hair. The conditions were not, however, uniform for all the animals and these are likely to contribute to some of the variation. The outstandingly high fibre yield of the Jiulong males is consistent with the yield expected from this line of Jiulong yak specially developed for fibre production. The yield from the same type of females, however, is lower not only on account of their smaller body size and other sex-related differences in hair growth, but also because, in common with all females coming into lactation, they start to lose quantities of fibre with the onset of lactation. Similarly, steers tend to lose fibre when used for work. The differences in yield between the sexes therefore reflect more what happens in practice than something solely attributable to biological causes.

A study by Chang Y. S. *et al.* (*in*: Research Co-operative Group, 1980 - 1987) (Table 6.28) showed that the total yield of fibre harvested increased as the animal became older and bigger. It showed, in particular, that the proportion of down in the fleece declined from nearly 70 percent in one-year-old male yak to less than 20 percent in those six years old. For females the reduction in the proportion of down fibre was less. Another study on Jiulong yak by Zhong Guanghui *et al.* (1996c) indicated that the hair production of male yak increased year by year until five years old and decreased thereafter, while in female yak the amount remained relatively constant up to three years old and declined after that. The fibre output did not differ between male and female yak when the animals were one to two years, but above the age of three years the males produced significantly more than the females.

Table 6.27 The total yield of fibre (coarse hair and down) (kg) in adult yak of different breeds at different locations according to sex of animal (conditions of harvesting not uniform)

Province	Breed or location	Male			Female			Steer			Source
		No.	Mean	SD	No.	Mean	SD	No.	Mean	SD	
Sichuan	Jiulong (selected fibre line)	19	13.9	2.4	16	1.8	0.7	10	4.3	0.9	Cai Li *et al.,* 1987*
Yunnan	Zhongdian	21	3.6	0.3	139	1.3	0.3				Duan Zhongxuan and Huang Fengying, 1982.
Tibet	Alpine	7	1.8		50	0.5		4	1.7		Research Co-operative Group, 1980-1987
Qinghai	Plateau				5	1.2	0.5	8	1.9	0.4	Lei Huanzhang *et al., 1983*
Qinghai	Menyuan (county)	4	3.6	0.7	11	1.6	0.6	15	2.6	0.6	Zhang Yinsong, *1985.*
Gansu	Tianzhu White	9	4.0		24	2.9		7	2.1		Zhang Rongchang, *1975*

* Cai Li's 1979 results, in a large report

158

Table 6.28 Total yield of fibre and proportion of down at different
ages of yak in Menyuan county of Qinghai province

[Source: Chang Y. S. *et al.*, in: Research Co-operative Group, 1980 - 1987]

Age (years)	No.	Male Total yield (kg) Mean	SD	Down (%)	No.	Female Total yield (kg) Mean	SD	Down (%)
1	2	0.80		68.8	7	1.10	0.25	60.0
2	20	1.84	0.64	48.9	27	1.47	0.38	54.4
3	13	1.97	0.61	40.6	24	1.50	0.52	46.7
4	15	1.99	0.68	43.2	11	1.39	0.58	43.2
5	3	2.65	0.38	21.9	11	1.60	0.58	53.1
6	4	3.60	0.70	18.6	8	[0.83]*	[0.32]*	*

* Only the down fibre was harvested in the milking females.

Method of harvesting

Combing out the down hair prior to shearing can increase the yield of down from the total fleece by about 10 percent compared with shearing alone. In one study (Wang Jie and Ouyang Xi, 1984), the percentage of down increased from about 50 percent with shearing to 61 percent with combing.

Melatonin (MT)

Melatonin is secreted by the pineal body gland and can promote hair and hide growth of the animals, such as goats and sheep. When it was injected into Menyuan yak, the length, speed of growth and the production of down hair were greatly increased (P<0.01), although the diameter of the down hair was not affected (Table 6.29).

Table 6.29 Effect of melatonin on growth of down hair of yak in Menyuan county of
Qinghai in the spring [Source: Xue Bai *et al.*, 1999]

Group	Length* (cm ± se)	Growth (cm/week)	Diameter (μ)	Production (kg ± se)
Treatment	10.0 ± 1.18a	0.39a	18 - 30	0.91 ± 0.16a
Control	7.3 ± 1.19b	0.01b	18 - 30	0.70 ± 0.06b

*Different letters (a or b) in the same column indicate significant difference /between means (P<0.01).

Fibres and staple properties

Fibre types have been examined in a number of studies (Wang Jie and Ouyang Xi, 1984; Wang Jie, 1984; Zhang Rongchang, 1975, 1977; Lù Zhonglin et al., 1982; Wu G. Y. et al., 1983; Xue Jiyin, 1981; as well as studies by Cai Li). The results can be summarized as follows:

Staple shape. This varies with the part of the yak body on which the fibre grows and differs between the coarser hair and the down.

- *Flat-topped type*. This is characteristic of down fibre of the best quality and is found especially in yak calves.
- *Micro-braid type*. The fibres are even in thickness and relatively fine but less so, and longer, than the flat-topped type. This is found mostly in one-year-old yak.
- *Sub-braid type*. The lower part of the staple is composed of down fibres and the upper part of mid-type and coarse hairs. This is seen often in the frontal parts of the body of one-year-old yak.
- *Braid type*. The staple is composed largely of coarse hair and is typical of the hair on the yak's belly.

Fibre types. The fibres of the yak can be divided into three main types: down, mid-type and coarse.

- *Down fibre*. Short, unmedullated fibres of less than 25 μ in diameter, with irregular crimps and a soft lustre.
- *Mid-type hair*. Diameter between 25μ and 52.5 μ. These hairs have a few large crimps. Some of the fibres have a latticed medulla. The hairs are longer than the down fibres and have a good lustre.
- *Coarse hair*. Diameter exceeds 52.5 μ. The hairs have no crimps and are long. A proportion of them are medullated (18 percent according to Lu Zhonglin *et al.*, 1982). They have strong lustre and poor textile quality.

(In practical production, there is often a dividing line drawn only between "down" hair, fibres of less than 35 μ diameter and "coarse" hair with a greater diameter.)

An analysis (Table 6.30) on the fibres of 60 Plateau yak by Zhao Longquan *et al.* (1994) indicate that the down content among fibres on shoulder, back and rump was much higher than on belly and foreleg (P<0.05). Down fibres also tended to be shorter and the other fibres longer on the belly and foreleg, but fibre diameters did not differ significantly among body parts.

Length of fibre. As shown in Table 6.30, there are considerable differences in the length of stretched fibres, depending on the type of fibre and the part of the body. Similar results have been reported by Zhang Rongchang (1989) with the length of coarse hair varying from 8.9 cm to 21.1 cm, and mid-type hair from 5.3 cm to 13 cm, with the longest in both cases on the belly and the shortest on the shoulder (and the fibres on the back intermediate in length). Down fibre length in Zhang Rongchang's report was slightly less (3.7 - 4.1 cm) than shown in Table 6.30, and in contrast to the results in that Table, the down fibres in Zhang Ronchang's study were longest from the belly and shortest from the back.

Table 6.30 Proportion, length and diameter of the different types of fibre on different parts of the body of 60 Plateau yak in Qinghai province [Source: Zhao Longquan *et al.*, 1994] (means ± SD)

Position	Coarse hair			Mid-type hair			Down fibre		
	Prop.	Length (cm)	Diameter (μ)	Prop.	Length (cm)	Diameter (μ)	Prop.	Length (cm)	Diameter (μ)
Shoulder	19.5	12.9 ± 1.5	79.3 ± 11.2	17.7	6.8 ± 1.1	41.7 ± 8.6	62.8	4.6 ± 0.75	17.7 ± 3.4
Back	21.1	13.3 ± 3.8	81.0 ± 12.4	15.0	8.8 ± 1.3	39.2 ± 8.2	63.9	4.6 ± 0.95	16.6 ± 3.4
Rump	20.4	17.9 ± 2.3	84.9 ± 12.1	18.9	9.6 ± 1.6	39.8 ± 9.2	60.7	4.2 ± 0.72	17.5 ± 3.8
Belly	63.6	19.0 ± 2.4	86.7 ± 12.5	29.5	10.2 ± 1.7	39.0 ± 8.9	6.9	3.8 ± 0.67	16.7 ± 3.4
Foreleg	60.3	19.3 ± 2.6	88.6 ± 13.7	33.9	10.1 ± 2.1	43.4 ± 9.1	5.7	3.8 ± 0.67	18.4 ± 3.2

Fibre diameter. Diameter varies greatly with type of fibre and with breed and sex of animal, but as shown in Table 6.30, for any given fibre type there were no significant differences in the diameter of these fibres among the various body parts.

Down fibres tend to be more uniform in diameter along their length than coarse hair fibres. In one study (Wang Jie and Ouyang Xi, 1984), the diameter was measured at the upper (outer end), middle and lower part of the fibre. Approximately 100 coarse hair fibres and a similar number of down fibres were examined from each of four yak. Results are shown in Table 6.31.

Table 6.31 Fibre diameter (μ) at different parts of the fibre*
[Source: Wang Jie and Ouyun Xi, 1984]

	Part of fibre	Mean	[SD]
Coarse	Upper	83	15.8
	Middle	75	16.6
	Lower	77	4.8
Down	Upper	21	3.3
	Middle	20	3.7
	Lower	20	3.1

*100 fibres from each of four yak

Fibre density. The density of fibres per unit area varies greatly with the position on the body of the yak. Some results are shown in Table 6.32. The density of down fibres per unit area is far higher than that of coarse hair. Particular note should also be taken of the high degree of variability in density among the 30 yak sampled. The coefficients of variation range from 23 to 64 percent.

Table 6.32 Fibre density of coarse hair and down hair on two different parts of the body of 30 adult yak [Source: Li Shihong *et al.*, 1985]

Position	Hair type	Density (fibres per sq cm of skin)	
		Mean	[SD]
Shoulder/back	Coarse	182	117
	Down	1468	473
Belly	Coarse	201	94
	Down	757	403

Fibre strength. One of the useful properties of both the coarse hair and the down from the yak is their strength. Results from a study by Xue Jiyin *et al.* (1981) were as follows: Down fibre (diameter 16.8 μ) strength (breaking load) dry 9.8 g, moist 6.9 g;

corresponding values for coarse hair (49.8 µ) were 32.8 g and 25.1 g, respectively. Wang Jie and Quyang Xi (1984) reported a breaking load of 12.9 g for down hair with a diameter of 22.7 µ. These breaking loads are remarkably high relative to those quoted for typical sheep wool (Ryder and Stephenson, 1968), if the methods used for determining the load are the same. Results from yak (Wang Jie and Quyang Xi, 1984) also suggest that the stretched length percentage of wet fibres (the limiting extension on the load extension curve; see Ryder and Stephenson, 1968) is of the order of 60 percent for both down and coarse hair fibres. This appears to be in the same range as sheep wool.

Other attributes of yak hair

Moisture retention. According to Wang Jie and Ouyangxi (1984), moisture retention in yak fibre increased with the air humidity as also found in sheep wool, shown for comparison in Table 6.33. Retention was higher in the coarse hair of yak than in its down fibre. The mid-type and down hair of the yak had a lower moisture retention than that of the local breeds of sheep.

Table 6.33 Moisture retention of yak fibre under different relative air humidity when air temperature equal to 20°C (13 yak sampled)
[Source: Wang Jie and Ouyang Xi, 1984]

Fibre type	Air humidity (%)	
	76	85
	Moisture retention* (%)	Moisture retention* (%)
Coarse hair of yak	11.3	12.3
Mid-type hair of yak	7.8	8.5
Down fibre of yak	7.4	7.7
Wool of Tibetan sheep	9.6	11.8
Wool of Xingjiang sheep	9.4	11.0

* The range of moisture retention was approximately 10 - 15 percent of their means.

Grease content. The lanolin content of yak hair is low. For Gannan yak this has been estimated as 2.7 percent and 1.7 percent of the shorn fleece for male and female yak respectively (Lu Zhonglin *et al.*, 1982). Another study (Wang Jie and Ouyang Xi, 1984) suggests that the grease content varies with the part of the body of the yak – 3.8 percent on the back, 2.2 percent on the rump, 1.5 percent on the belly, and only 0.3 percent for hair from the tail. The melting point of the lanolin ranges from 37° to 43° C (Xue Jiyin *et al.*, 1981).

Specific gravity. Specific gravity of yak down fibre is around 1.32 - 1.33 g per cu cm and coarse hair around 1.22 - 1.33 g per cu cm – similar to that of sheep wool (Xue Jiyin *et al.*, 1981).

Static electricity. Under similar conditions, the down fibres of the yak suffer less from static electricity disturbance than cashmere fibres from goats, thus giving yak fibres an advantage in processing (Xue Jiyin *et al.*, 1981).

Amino acid content. The strength and resilience of yak down fibre has been attributed to its content of high sulphur proteins. The total amino acid content of down fibre from female yak has been measured as 79.8 percent of dry weight, with cystine, proline and serine accounting for 19.4 percent – higher than the 15.9 percent of local sheep wool with which it was compared.

Other structural properties. The structural property of yak hair differs from that of sheep wool not only in respect of its greater strength. In the yak, the angle between scale and hair shaft, on the external surface of the fibre, is small so that the scale virtually sticks to the shaft – making the hair fibre relatively smooth. This gives yak hair poor felting qualities.

Shedding of fibres

Down fibres and mid-type hair begin to shed as the weather becomes warmer in the spring and early summer. Observations by Ouyang Xi *et al.* (1985) showed that shedding towards the end of May, in their locality, was greatest from the belly of the yak (nearly 20 percent) and less from the back and rump (just over 12 percent). Lactating females also start to shed fibres with the onset of lactation.

In July, when air temperature is at its highest, down fibre will twine around coarse hair or will fall on pasture and shrubs if not combed out or sheared. Shedding of the coarse hair has not been observed. As the length of coarse hair increases, the growth rate of the hair declines until it virtually stops.

Hides

Yak hide is a major source of raw hide in China – about one million yak hides are produced from the Qinghai-Tibetan Plateau per year.

Weight

Fresh hide weight varies with breed and sex of yak (Table 6.34) from 13.2 - 36.1 kg for adult yak, accounting for 5.5 - 5.8 percent of live weight. Average weights of hides per 100 kg body weight were 6.1 ± 0.5 kg for female yak, 6.6 ± 0.6 kg for steers and 6.8 ± 1.3

kg for entire males (Zhang Rongchang, 1989).

Size

The size of fresh hide of adult yak steers and males is reported to be about 0.11 sq m per kg and that of females around 0.19 - 0.21 sq m per kg (Zhang Rongchang, 1989).

Thickness

Skin thickness varies with the part of the yak body. It is thickest on the back and thinnest on the neck and belly. On average, the skin of three-month-old yak calves is reported to be about 2.7 mm thick and that of 9 - 12 years old yak around 3.9 mm.

Table 6.34 Hide production of adult yak (mean ± SD)
[Source: adapted from Zhang Rongchang, 1989]

Location	Breed or yak of country	Sex	No.	Fresh hide weight (kg)	Proportion of hide to live weight (%)
Tianzhu, Gansu	Tianzhu White	Steer	5	20.1 ± 3.6	7.7
		Female	7	14.8 ± 2.5	6.8
Ruoergai, Sichuan	Mawai	Steer	8	24.2 ± 3.9	6.6
(former) USSR	Kyrgyzstan	Male	7	36.1 ± 4.6	8.8
		Female	7	13.2 ± 2.5	5.6

Quality

The quality of yak hide is poorer than that of cattle. Factors affecting the hide quality include age, sex, live weight, nutritive status and environment where the yak lives (Zhang Rongchang, 1989) and including often extensive damage to hides from warble fly and from poor skinning and processing.

Draught performance

The yak is widely used for draught purposes at the high altitudes where it makes its home – and not only as the pack animal for much publicized Himalayan mountaineering expeditions, known world-wide. The yak has strong limbs, small, solid hooves with hard edges and a narrow hoof fork. These attributes help the yak to walk in dangerous places and over marshland and to climb over steep mountains. It can open up a path with its head and its hooves for people to follow, and it can swim across rapids. In difficult terrain it is said to be safer to ride on a yak than on a horse, as the yak will not readily panic, for example in swampy ground. Since ancient times, the yak has been known in the mountainous regions of China and surroundings as the "boat of the plateau".

Most of the yak used for draught are steers. Male F1 hybrids (yak-cattle) are also chosen (as they are sterile and cannot be used for breeding). The draught animals are used mainly for riding and as pack animals. Yak races are one of the games at folk festivals much loved by Tibetan people. In semi-agricultural areas yak are also used for ploughing and other cultivation.

Joshi (1982) also refers to the use of yak and hybrids for threshing grain in parts of Tibet by driving muzzled animals backward and forward over sheaves spread out on a hard floor.

Yak have great endurance; they will, for example, carry loads over long distances for two or three days without water or feed. In other circumstances, the yak may be required to carry loads during the day, with the opportunity to graze only at night, for as long as a month at a stretch.

Direct observations (Liu Qigui, *in*: Research Co-operative Group, 1980 – 1987) have shown the yak to walk 20 - 30 km per day carrying loads weighing 60 - 80 kg. In Sichuan, observations on Maiwa yak recorded 75 kg loads (18 percent of the body weight of the animal) carried over 30 km in 6.2 hours (4.84 km per hour).

Respiration rate, pulse rate and body temperature were found to have returned to the pre-work level within about 50 minutes of stopping work (Table 6.35).

Records from the grasslands of Qinghai province at an altitude of 4 100 m show pack weights up to a maximum of 300 kg (on top of a saddle weight of 11.5 kg), which is equal to 82 percent of the body weight of the animal (Lei Huanzhang *et al.*, 1985). Maiwa yak steers in medium condition weighing 480 kg have been recorded to carry as much as 390 kg for short periods.

Table 6.35 Carrying capacity of yak steer and F1 hybrid steer (mean ±SD)
[Source: adapted from Zhang Rongchang, 1989]

Breed	No.	Age (years)	Live weight (kg)	Load (kg)	Load/ live weight (%)	Distance (km)	Time (hr)	Recovery time (min)
Yak steer	4	6 - 11	408.1 ± 34.2	75	18.4 ± 3.5	30	7.2	50.0 ± 4.6
F1 steer	3	10 - 14	459.6 ± 40.2	75	16.3 ± 3.2	30	6.0	53.3 ± 3.7

Yak can be ridden by the herders on the high plateau. A study by Lei Huanzhang *et al.*, (1985) showed three Plateau-type yak were ridden on fairly even grassland at an elevation of 4 400 m for 500 m in 2.13 minutes. Their respiration, pulse and body temperature recovered in just over 25 minutes.

A small study by Zhang Rongzhang (1989) with two mature yak steers and two F1 steers provided an indication of the order of magnitude of maximum pulling power attained during ploughing. For the yak steers it was around 390 kg (96 percent of their live weight) and for the two hybrid animals it was higher at 550 kg (120 percent of their live weight).

Opportunities for improving the production

The results on the various aspects of performance of yak presented in this chapter indicate the kind of production levels relevant to a variety of conditions. There are few circumstances, however, where productivity could not be improved. Improvements might be produced by changes to breeding practice, changes in animal management and feeding, by the optimization of herd structure and by environmental interventions, such as changes to pasture and range management, provision of shelter, and so on. Such measures are dealt with in other chapters of this book.

Not all changes, however, result in improvements in productivity, or, even if they do, they are not necessarily cost effective. For example, hybridization by mating yak to "improved" breeds of dairy cattle like the Holstein, can lead to dramatic increases in the milk output by the hybrids, compared to the pure yak – but at the expense of a lower fat content of the milk and much higher feed and management costs, in addition to a more complicated breeding strategy (see Chapter 3). In the same way, the costs of changes, whether in management (Chapter 8), feeding (Chapters 8 and 14), the use of feed supplements referred to earlier, or by changes in range and grassland management (Chapter 13), should be more than offset by the value of any additional outputs, if such changes are to be worth making. Also, as discussed in Chapter 12, the social and cultural context of yak keeping, as much as the economic conditions, will influence what is appropriate in particular circumstances and what is not.

References

Agricultural. Exploitation Academy of Xinjiang (1984). Report on the result of yak's inter-specific hybridization. *Journal of China Yak*, 1: 71-75.

Cai Li *et al.* (1980a). [Agriculture and Livestock Bureau of Ganzi Tibetan Autonomous prefecture of Sichuan province and Southwest Nationalities College]. The good meat-purpose yak – the investigation and study of Jiulong Yak. *Journal of China Yak*, 1: 14-33.

Cai Li *et al.* (1980b). [Agricultural and Livestock Bureau of Ganzi Tibetan Autonomous prefecture of Sichuan province and Southwest Nationalities College] The general survey and identification for Jiulong yak. *Journal of China Yak*, 3:17-24.

Cai Li *et al.* (1984). [Yak Research Office of Southwest Nationalities College and Sichuan Grassland Institute] The research on the inter-specific cross combination between female yak and common bull. *The research on the utilization and exploitation of grassland in the northwestern part of Sichuan province*. National Publishing House of Sichuan province, Chengdu, China. pp. 107-113.

Cai Li *et al.* (eds) (1987). [Editorial Committee of Fauna of livestock and Poultry Breeds in Sichuan.] *Fauna of Livestock and Poultry Breeds in Sichuan*. Sichuan Science and Technology Publishing House, Chengdu, China.

Chen Xiafei *et al.* (1981). Investigation on Maiwa yak. Investigative reports on the resources of livestock and poultry breeds in Aba Tibetan Autonomous prefecture, Sichuan, China.

Chen Zhihua, Wen Yongli & Cai Li (1994). The systematic analysis of influence factors on the newborn weight of yak. *Journal of Southwest Nationalities College* (Natural Science Edition), 4: 325-331.

Chen Zhihua *et al.* (2000). A research on relation between body size of Chinese yak and ecological factors of habitation. *Journal of Southwest Nationalities College* (Natural Science Edition), 4: 403-406.

Dong Shikui *et al.* (2002). Availability and utilisation of shrubs as protein sources for yak grazing on alpine meadow on the Qinghai-Tibetan Plateau, China. *Proceedings of the third international congress on yak, in Lhasa, China, 4-9 September 2000*. International Livestock Research Institute (ILRI), Nairobi. pp. 273-279.

Duan Zhongxuan & Huang Fengying (1982). Investigation report of yak resources in Zhongdian. *Journal of China Yak*, 1: 75-82.

Han Zhengkang & Lu Tianshui (1980). Study on physiological lactation features in yak. *Journal of Nanjing Agricultural College*, 1: 137-146.

He S.Y. *et al.* (1997). Zhongdian Yak. *Journal of China Yak*, 1: 1-5.

Ji Qiumei *et al.* (2000a). Analysis on milk output and milk quality of three good types of yak in Tibet. *Journal of Gansu Agricultural University*, 3: 269-276.

Ji Qiumei *et al.* (2000b). Analysis of producing flesh and flesh quality in three fine kinds groups yaks of Tibet. *China Herbivore*, 5: 3-6.

Ji Qiumei *et al.* (2000c). Research of yak produce performance in the Pali. *China Herbivore*, 6: 3-6.

Jia H.G. (1966). An investigation and study on yak in Tibet. *Collection of Theses of Comprehensive Survey* in Tibet, China, Scientific Publishing House, Beijing, China. pp. 1-19.

Jialin, B. *et al.* (1998a). The milking performance of dual-purpose crossbred yaks. *Animal Science,* 66: 471-473.

Jialin, B. *et al.* (1998b). Meat production from crossbred and domestic yaks in China. *Animal Science,* 66: 465-469.

Joshi, D.D. (1982). *Yak and Chauri Husbandry in Nepal*. H.M. Kathmandu, Government Press, Singha Durbar. XVII, 145 pp.

Katzina, E.V. (1993). [Lactation and biological properties of yak milk associated with nutritive value.] *Sel'skokhozyaistvennaya – Biologii*, No. 2: 108-114. [*CAB Animal Breeding Abstracts*, 63, No. 680.]

Lang Jie, Zhou Daorong & Wu Xianzhi (1999). Report on the breeding by milk ability of Maiwa yak. *Journal of Sichuan Grassland*, 4: 50-53.

Lei Huanzhang *et al.* (1983). Report on the investigation of yak in Qinghai. Investigative report on the resource of livestock and poultry breeds in Qinghai province. pp. 50-101.

Lei Huanzhang *et al.* (1985). Studies on the ecological reaction of criss-cross grazing of yak and its hybrid in the cold and warm seasons. *Journal of China Yak*, 2: 13-23.

Li Quan *et al.* (2000a). Measurement of growth and development in domestic yak in Guoluo Prefecture. *China Herbivores*, 2: 24-26.

Li Quan *et al.* (2000b). Measurement of milk performance in domestic yak in Guoluo Prefecture. *Chinese Journal of Animal and Veterinary Sciences*, 3: 10-11.

Li Shihong *et al.* (1985). The observation on yak's heat resistance. *Journal of China Yak*, 1: 10-13.

Liu Haibo (1989). *China Yakology*. Sichuan Science and Technology Publishing House, Chengdu, China. pp. 119-123.

Long Ruijun (1995). *Seasonal dynamics of nutrient metabolites in serum of grazing yak on alpine grassland*. PhD thesis, Gansu Agricultural University, Lanzhou, China.

Long R.J. *et al.* (1999*a*). Effect of strategic feed supplementation on productive and reproductive performance in yak cows. *Preventive Veterinary Medicine*, 38: 195-206.

Long R.J. *et al.* (1999*b*). Nutritive values of native forage of the Tibetan Plateau of China. *Animal Feed Science and Technology*, 80: 101-113.

Lu Guanghui (1980). The regulation of change of yak's body weight and relationship between its slaughtered age and different seasons under the condition of natural grazing. *Abstract Collection of Theses of Animal Husbandry and Veterinary Medicine of China*, pp. 26.

Lu Zhonglin *et al.* (1982). The hair quantity of Luqu yak. *Journal of Southwest Nationalities College* (Animal Husbandry and Veterinary Sciences Edition), 1: 17-20.

Ma Zongxiang & Dou Yaozong (1981). Investigation on Pengbo yak. *Journal of China Yak*, 3: 63-68.

Ma Zongxiang & Dou Yaozong (1982). Study on the growth pattern in terms of seasonal body weight change. *Journal of China Yak*, (1): 21-28.

Mkrtchyan Sh.A., Umansky, M.S. & Kmet, A.M. (1993). Meat amino acid composition of yak different ecotypes. *J. the Report of Russian Academy Agricultural Science*, part 4: 57-63.

Ouyang Xi *et al.* (1985). Studies on the cold resistance of yak. *Journal of Southwest Nationalities College* (Animal Husbandry and Veterinary Sciences Edition), 4: 28-34.

Pu Ruitang *et al.* (1987). Determination on the meat composition and meat performance of Tianzhu White yak. *Journal of China Yak*, 4: 22-25.

Ryder, M.L. & Stephenson, S.K. (1968). *Wool Growth*. Academic Press (London & New York). XVIII+ 805 pp.

Sarbagishev, B.S., Rabochev, V.K. & Terebaev, A.I. (1989). 9. Yaks. In: *Animal Genetic Resources of the USSR*. FAO Animal Production and Health Paper No. 65, Rome. pp. 357-364.

Smirnov, D.A. *et al.* (1990). Meat yield and meat quality of yaks. *Sel'skokhozyaistvennykh Nauk Im. V.I. Lenina (Soviet Agricultural Sciences)*, No. 1: 46-49.

Song Jianxin *et al.* (1982). Yak's productivity in plateau grassland. *Journal of Veterinary Science and Technology*, 2: 24-28.

Wang Jie (1984). Observation on the ultramicroscopic structure of the hair fibre of yak. *Journal of Southwest Nationalities College* (Animal Husbandry and Veterinary Sciences Edition), 4: 9-14.

Wang Jie & Quyang Xi, (1984). Physical features of yak hair. *Journal of Southwest Nationalities College* (Animal Husbandry and Veterinary Sciences Edition), 1: 25-29.

Wei Ronglu *et al.* (1981). Analyses of effect on meat of F1 hybrid of inter-specific cross between female yak and common bull. *Journal of China Yak*, 2: 5-15.

Wen Yongli *et al.* (1993). [Influences of two simple methods of supplement during the winter on the performances of female yaks.] *Journal of Southwest Nationalities College* (Natural Science Edition), 19: 236-241.

Wen Yongli & Chen Zhihua (1994). [The linear relation between 184-day milk yield of Maiwa female yaks and its correlative traits.] *Journal of Southwest Nationalities College* (Natural Science Edition), 20: 166-170.

Wen Yongli *et al.* (1994). Study on the milkability of Jiulong yak cows. *Journal of Gansu Agricultural University* (Special issue, June 1994): 161-163.

Wu G.Y. *et al.* (1983). Study on the physical and chemical characters of hair fibre of special animal. The Proceedings of the Conference on Physical and Chemical Characters of Hair in China.

Xue Bai *et al.* (1999). Effect of Melatonin on down growth and production of Menyuan yak in Spring. *China Herbivore*, 6: 12-13.

Xu Guilin (1985). Effects of different methods of milking, suckling and feeding on the gains of calf yak and young yak. *Journal of China Yak*, 2: 39-43.

Xu Guilin *et al.* (1983). Analysis of factors concerned with the milking performance and milk quality of yak. *Journal of China Yak*, 1: 21-29.

Xue Jiyin *et al.* (1981). The property and utilization of yak's down hair. *Journal of China Yak*, 1: 1-5.

Yang Rongzhen *et al.* (1997). Report on growth and development of domestic yak progenies rejuvenated by wild yak. *Proceedings of the second international congress on yak, in Xining, China, 1-6 September 1997*. Xining, China, Qinghai People's Publishing House. pp. 21-23.

Yuan Youqing *et al.* (1994). Feed additive experiment to improve milk yield of yak. *Journal of China Yak*, 2: 11-13.

Zeng Wenqun & Chen Yishi (1980). Yak in ancient China. *Journal of China Yak*, 1: 71-74.

Zhao Bingyao *et al.* (1984). An experiment on the cross combination of inter-specific hybridization between female yak and common bull. *Journal of China Yak*, 1: 47-70.

Zhang Degang (1998). Supplementary feeding on urea molasses multi-nutrients blocks and effects on productive performance of yak cows. *Acta Pratacultural Sinica*, 1: 65-69.

Zhao Longquan *et al.* (1994). Hair and down hair analysis of yak of Plateau type in Qinghai Province. *Journal of Qinghai Animal Husbandry and Veterinary Medicine*, 2: 29-31.

Zhang Rongchang (1975). Evaluation on the performance of yak's hair production in Nannigou Production Group on the Zhuaxixiulong grassland of Tianzhu county. *Journal of Gansu Agriculture University*, 3: 49-52.

Zhang Rongchang (1977). The hair quality of white yak on Zhuaxixiulong grassland of Tianzhu county. *Journal of Gansu Agriculture University*, 2: 42-47.

Zhang Rongchang (1989). *China: the yak*. Gansu Scientific and Technology Press, Lanzhou, China. 386 pp.

Zhang Rongchang, Kong Linglu & Jin Yong (1983). The milking characters of yak and Pian Niu. *Journal of China Yak*, 1: 14-18.

Zhang Rongchang *et al.* (1986). Determination on the main composition in milk of Tianzhu White yak. *Journal of China Yak*, 2: 23-26.

Zang Yinsong (1985). Observation and analysis on milk production of yak in Qilian area. *Journal of China Yak*, 1: 51-56.

Zhong Guanghui *et al.* (1993). Study on meat performance of Jiulong yak. *Journal of China Yak*, 4: 12-15.

Zhong Guanghui *et al.* (1996a). Correlation analysis between body formation traits and heart girth in Jiulong yak. *Journal of Southwest Nationalities College* (Natural Science Edition), 4: 409-413.

Zhong Guanghui *et al.* (1996b). Measurement of Jiulong yak milk compositions. *Journal of Sichuan Grassland,* 4: 45-47.

Zhong Guanghui *et al.* (1996c). The fibre production of Jiulong yak. *Journal of Southwest Nationalities College* (Natural Science Edition), 2: 165-168.

Zhou Shourong (1984). Study on the forage and feeding habits of yak. *The research on the utilization and exploitation of grassland in the northwestern part of Sichuan province.* Sichuan National Publishing House, Chengdu, China. pp. 134-137.

Sichuan Grassland Institute (1982). Experiment on fattening of yak and F1 hybrids from Holstein-Friesian and yak under the grazing condition. *Journal of China Yak,* 1: 29-33.

Bat-Erdene, T. (1993). *Yield, composition and technological quality of yak milk.* Uliastai Hot, Mongolia.

Longri Breeding Farm (1993). Report of growth and development of the Maiwa yak. *Journal of China Yak,* 3: 14-15.

Research Co-operative Group on yak (1980-1987). The 30 investigation reports on China yak resources. *Journal of China Yak,* Issues 1-26.

NW China Animal Science Institute (1960). Crossbreeding of wild yak with the domestic yak. *Proceedings of NW China Animal Institute,* 3: 420-425.

7   PERFORMANCE OF HYBRIDS OF YAK WITH *BOS TAURUS* AND *BOS INDICUS* CATTLE

OVERVIEW

Hybridizing of yak with *Bos taurus* cattle, and in some countries also with *Bos indicus*, is done by using the local cattle in natural service or by using semen of "improved" breeds like the Holstein-Friesian (and many other breeds) in artificial insemination (to produce "local" or "improved" hybrids, respectively). The hybrids are less well adapted to the harsh conditions and high altitudes typical for yak and are kept at intermediate elevations. The "improved" hybrids especially need better management and feeding than yak.

The first hybrid (F1) females, especially those with "improved" breeds of sire, reach sexual maturity sooner and are first mated a year earlier than the average yak. F1 females can return to heat several times in the same season, if not pregnant, and will generally calve every year. Calf survival is similar to that in the yak. Consequently, overall reproductive rate of the hybrids, especially the "improved" ones, is higher than in the yak. F1 males are sterile. Although their sexual functions are intact, their semen does not contain sperm. The reasons for this have been under investigation for a long time, and although there are a number of possible causes known, there is, as yet, no resolution. Sperm production does not resume until the third backcross at the earliest (15/16 yak or cattle), and often not until the fourth backcross is reached. In practice, there are few backcrosses after the first, since they have no role in the livestock economy.

F1 hybrids generally grow faster and become larger than the yak – and also larger than some of the local cattle. Backcrosses to the yak, or to breeds of local cattle, are smaller than the F1. "Improved" hybrids are larger than the "local" hybrids.A larger size of hybrid animal also leads to greater meat production, although dressing percentages and other attributes of the carcass are usually fairly similar to those of the yak. The hybrid animals, from crossing yak females with "improved" breeds of cattle, however, are capable of slaughter at much younger ages than the traditional yak steer, or the "local" hybrid steer.

Milk yield is higher in hybrids than in the pure yak and often higher than in the local types of cattle (for example, the small hill cattle of some countries). Milk yield of the hybrids is especially increased if their sires are from "improved" breeds. Backcrosses give less milk than the F1. The fat percentage of the milk of hybrids is usually lower than that of yak.

Strict interpretation of this and similar results in terms of heterosis is, however, difficult, since the different types of hybrid, the pure yak and cattle breeds are not usually kept and managed together under identical conditions. This applies with even greater force when "improved" breeds of cattle are involved. Holstein-Friesian or Simmental cattle, for example, are not kept at high altitudes alongside the yak and certainly not managed in the same way as the yak. Nor are the reciprocal hybrids produced by mating females of the "improved" cattle breeds, say, the Holstein-Friesian, to yak bulls. The presence of both the reciprocal hybrids alongside both the parental types is required for any strict interpretation of the role of heterosis. The circumstantial evidence for heterosis from hybridization of yak and other species of cattle, both local and "improved" breeds, is considerable. The strongest part of that evidence is the poorer performance of the first backcross (from F1 females mated to bulls of yak or of other cattle) relative to the F1. This is as expected if heterosis plays a part in enhancing the productivity of the hybrids.

Introduction

As indicated in Chapter 3, the hybridization of yak with cattle of other species has been practised since earliest times. Originally such hybridization occurred with cattle of the local breeds, generally referred to as "yellow cattle" (*Bos taurus*) in China and with cattle of both *Bos taurus* and *Bos indicus* cattle (zebu) species elsewhere. This practice is still extant. Nevertheless, in recent decades, encouragement has been given by scientists and officials to expand the use of "improved" breeds of cattle for such hybridization. This has been facilitated by the introduction of artificial insemination and the use of frozen semen. As referred to earlier (Chapter 3), the use of A.I. is, inevitably, restricted to more accessible areas. Moreover, the expense of acquiring and maintaining bulls of the "improved" breeds of cattle for semen production in the yak-rearing territories (as well as the poor survival of such bulls) means that, except in a few localities, most hybridization of yak continues to be done with the locally available cattle.

Interpreting the results of hybridization
(the question of heterosis from yak-cattle hybrids)

The purpose of any crossbreeding or hybridization is to combine some of the good qualities of the breeds or species being crossed or hybridised (from additive genetic effects). Further, there is a possibility that the performance of the hybrids will exceed the average of the two parental types (from the action of non-additive genetic effects). Any such superiority of the crossbred or hybrid above the parental means is described, in performance terms, as heterosis – or hybrid vigour. In the case of hybrids of yak with *Bos taurus* or *Bos indicus* cattle, there is a difficulty in apportioning credit between additive effects and heterosis. This arises firstly because the pure-bred animals of *both* species are rarely, if ever, kept together under *identical* conditions of environment and management. Secondly, the reciprocal hybrids between the species (i.e. progeny of yak female with cattle male *and* of cattle female with yak male) are either not both produced (and in the case of exotic "improved" cattle *never* produced) or, if produced, then not kept alongside the parental species under the same conditions. Yet, the presence together of all these four types (both parental species and the reciprocal hybrids) is a requirement for any strict assessment of the magnitude of heterosis.

In general, the hybrids occupy a different niche from that of the pure yak in the economy of the pastoral mountain regions, mostly at the lower elevations. Part of the explanation for this may arise from a less well developed physiological adaptation of the hybrids to high altitude, for example in terms of their pulmonary haemo-dynamics (see Chapter 4). As shown in Chapter 3, hybrids are more prevalent in environmentally more favoured areas and at the somewhat lower elevations in the range of yak territory. Local types of cattle, in turn, are most prevalent in still less demanding and agriculturally mixed areas of these regions. As for females of the "improved" breeds of cattle (e.g. Holstein-Friesians), they are not kept in typical yak territory as they do not survive in these harsh conditions, nor are such females mated to yak bulls to provide the reciprocal hybrids. Moreover, as noted in Chapter 5, hybridization is often done early in the breeding season with yak cows at their first oestrus (between June and September), so that, on average, hybrid animals are born earlier in the year than are the pure yak. The purpose of doing this, generally, is to reduce the chances of being left with cows that have not conceived to cattle bulls or to A.I. and still provide an opportunity to expose these cows to yak bulls from October to the end of the breeding season. This procedure increases the overall reproductive efficiency of the herd (Zhou Minhai, 1998). But in terms of comparing the performance of hybrids with that of yak or cattle it introduces a further complication. Date of birth affects the subsequent performance of the animals because they have a better start before the following winter. Such an advantage can be seen over the first two years of life, and possibly longer.

Nevertheless, the comparisons of the performance of hybrids with that of yak and, where possible, cattle are highly suggestive of a part played by heterosis. This arises because the performance is not only better than that of the yak when kept alongside them (although without certainty that they are treated alike or strictly contemporary) but also, in some cases, better than that of the local cattle (again with reservations about the similarity of treatment of each). A few comparisons of the different types (pure yak, pure cattle and both types of hybrid) have been claimed from Mongolia and some early studies in Russia (see Chapter 11, part 2) where a heterosis effect is strongly asserted.

In relation of hybridization with "improved" breeds of cattle, the argument for the occurrence of heterosis is stronger, if rather academic. It arises from the assumption that females of the improved breeds would not survive for long under the conditions tolerated by the yak at high altitudes (any more than did the bulls of these types – see Chapter 3). Further it must be assumed that females of such breeds of cattle (e.g. Holstein-Friesian or Simmental) would not lactate satisfactorily without much additional feeding, even if they were to survive for a time. Therefore, the presumption is that purebred females of the improved breeds would yield effectively nothing if kept like typical yak. On these assumptions, the performance of their hybrids with yak is clearly above the average of the parental types (in fact, providing a good example of what geneticists call "over-dominance"). This result, however, has its roots in genotype-environment interaction – and the argument is based on assumptions and not on direct experiment.

Less controversial evidence for heterosis arises from the poorer performance of backcrosses (B1) relative to the F1. It is again rare to find results, as the theory requires, on adequately large numbers of animals involving both the reciprocal F1 hybrids and both types of backcrosses (derived from both types of F1 mated back to both yak bulls and to bulls of the other cattle species). Nevertheless, the reported results from backcrosses are as would be expected if heterosis is a feature of this interspecies hybridization.

Some results from inter-species hybridization will now be presented. Although they show, without exception, that the hybrids between the species out-perform the yak, any interpretation of the results in terms of heterosis should bear in mind the considerations discussed above. Figures 7.1 - 7.3 illustrate different hybrids.

Figure 7.1 "Local" and "improved" F1 hybrids (Both F1 animals have yak dams. That on the left has a yellow cattle sire; the one on the right has a Holstein-Friesian sire. The animals are castrates, saddled as pack animals.)

Figure 7.2 "Improved" hybrid (*Pian Niu*) being milked

Figure 7.3 "Black" *Pian Niu* (F1 from yak dam and Holstein sire)

Reproduction and fertility

The female hybrids – F1 and backcross generations – have normal fertility. The males, by contrast, are sterile until there have been several generations of backcrossing to either the yak or to cattle.

Female

Oestrous

Oestrous in the F1 females is seasonal, as in the yak, and is affected by climate and nutrition. Sexual maturity in the F1, however, occurs at least a year earlier than is typical for yak. Thus the F1 females are usually mated at the age of 25 - 28 months (in the third warm season of their life), and they calve for the first time around the age of three years. Breeding a year earlier does occur under more favourable conditions, and has been regarded for many years as a potential advantage enjoyed by such hybrids in Kazakhstan (Denisov, 1938).

Importantly in terms of overall reproductive rate, oestrous can occur several times in a season if the F1 female has not previously been mated or is not pregnant. This differs from the majority of pure yak cows in China – although repeated display of oestrous in yak is more commonly reported from some other countries, e.g. Mongolia (see Chapters 5 and 11). Also, signs of oestrous in the F1 females are more obvious than in the pure yak.

Conception rate

Among 211 F1 females in heat, Cai Li *et al.* (YRO and XF, 1983) found, by rectal palpation, that 185 had normally developed follicles – a proportion slightly higher than in contemporary yak (see Chapter 5). Nonetheless, in ordinary mass mating with yak bulls, the conception rate (75 percent) of F1 hybrid cows (F1 from yak dams and yellow cattle sires) was somewhat lower than that of yak at the same location (shown in Table 5.5). But in a specific trial conducted by Cai Li *et al.* (YRO and XF, 1983) on the Xiangdong Yak Farm using yak bulls, 155 F1 females had a conception rate of 70 percent at their first oestrous of the breeding season, but a further 25 percent conceived at a second oestrous. When using frozen semen from Holstein-Friesian bulls by A.I., the overall reproductive rate of the F1 hybrid was found to be substantially better than that of pure yak. Zhang Rongchang (1989) reported a similar observation using Hereford semen (Table 7.1).

Gestation length

Cai Li *et al.* (in YRO and XF, 1983) recorded gestation length in hybrids of yak with local cattle as being 278 days (SD 9.7) for 110 F1 cows with male calves and 271.3 days (SD 11.1) in 98 such cows with female calves. Denisov (1938) measured an average gestation length of 282 days for F1 females mated back to Schwyz cattle bulls and 265 days for those mated back to yak bulls. Corresponding results from the Datong Yak Farm

(Zhang Rongchang, 1989) showed a gestation length of F1 cows backcrossed to Hereford bulls (by A.I.) of 282.7 $\pm$ 7.8 days when carrying male calves (n19) and 277.4 $\pm$ 9.6 days with female calves (n6).

Table 7.1 Reproductive parameters of F1 and pure yak cows served by frozen semen from Hereford bulls through A.I. on Datong Yak Farm (1975 - 1978)
[Source: Zhang Rongchang, 1989]

Type	No. of females mated	Conceived of those mated (%)	Calving of those pregnant (%)	Cow with surviving calf of those pregnant (%)
F1 hybrid	211	76.3	90.7	89.7
Yak	117	39.3	67.4	96.8

Reproductive and survival rate

Survival of calves to the age of six months is very similar in F1 hybrids and first backcrosses to that in pure yak. Thus, relative to the yak, the F1 hybrid has a better overall reproductive rate over a lifetime. This arises from a combination of factors: the likelihood that the hybrid will be mated for the first time a year earlier, the greater probability that the F1 hybrid will re-mate in the same season following failure to conceive at an earlier heat period and its greater capacity to calve every year.

The equally good survival of the first backcross (B1) in observations by Cai Li (1989) requires comment since it contrasts with the views expressed by herdsmen who regard this backcross as having poor survival. This viewpoint, however, has to be seen in the context that herdsmen generally wish to keep as much milk as possible from the F1 dams for their own use or for sale. Accordingly, the B1 calves are neglected by their owners and often allowed to die. This neglect is further encouraged by the poor performance of backcrosses relative to the F1 and by the complications inherent in systematic backcrossing programmes, which would be needed to produce successive generations.

Male

The external sex organs of the hybrid male are normal and so is its sex drive. Mounting and serving of females on heat is normal, but there are no sperm in the seminal fluid. The hybrid is, therefore, a "natural" teaser bull.

First and second backcross generations are also sterile. By the third generation of backcrossing (15/16 yak or cattle blood) some spermatocytes are usually present (or even in the second backcross generation, according to a report by Zhang Rongchang *et al.*, 1991) and the occasional such male is found to be fertile. Fertility is not assured until the fourth or fifth generation of backcrossing (for a number of references on this aspect, see Zhong Jingcheng, 1994, 1996). In practice, entire males of the backcross generations are rarely seen because there is no good reason to keep them. Therefore, precise proportions of bulls showing normal spermatogenesis in successive generations of backcrossing are not available.

The precise causes of this sterility have been, and are still, the object of much investigation and speculation. Tan Chunfu et al. (1990), Zhao Shanting et al. (1990) Xu Zukang et al. (1991), Qing Fufang et al. (1990, 1993) and Liu Hui et al. (1994) found that the development of genital glands and organs in F1 males showed large differences from that in yak and cattle and also great variation among individuals.

What is certain is that no spermatogonia are found in the seminiferous tubules of the first hybrids and of the early generations of backcrosses (Zhang Rongchang et al., 1991). Possible causes for this have been considered in the structures of the X- and Y-chromosomes – these structures differ in certain respects in the hybrids from those found both in the pure yak and in pure cattle (Guo Aipu, 1983). In particular, the arm ratios differ, most notably for the Y-chromosome. It has been pointed out in a review of the subject (Li Jiyou et al., 1994) that the chromosomal arm lengths and the relative lengths of the chromosomes also vary among breeds of cattle. This has led the authors to suggest that fertility of the male yak hybrids might be restored by selecting a *Bos taurus* cattle breed with similar Y-chromosomal arm length as that of the yak. This is clearly open to investigation.

A tentative hypothesis is advanced by Zhong Jingcheng (1994, 1998) suggesting that male sterility may be due to an imbalance at many chromosomal loci, including autosomal loci. Tumennasan et al. (1997) found that reduced numbers of spermatogonia appear to characterise the testicular tubules of the F1 hybrid, and despite the identical cytological appearance of the two parental karyotypes, synaptic anomalies are seen at meiotic prophase in primary spermatocytes. The impression is gained of better meiotic pairing in the backcross B1 and B2 animals than in the F1; therefore the "Haldane Rule" is followed perfectly by the cattle-yak hybrid, namely, that sterility is confined to the male.

It has also been found that the proportions of different types of cells in the anterior pituitary gland differ in the hybrids from those in yak or cattle. A consequence is a reduced production of FSH – an essential hormone for the satisfactory function of the tubular epithelium of the testes. Yet, simple, frequent injection of FSH into the blood stream of four well-fed B2 hybrid calves did not result in the production of sperm – just a high libido in the calves at the age of 18 months (Xu Zukang et al., 1991).

Production characteristics

Body size

Birth weights of hybrids of yak with yellow cattle can be as much as 50 percent heavier than pure yak calves (shown in Table 6.1). Reports from other countries (outside China) also suggest substantial increases in birth weight in hybrids of yak females with males of local breeds – for example an increase of around 15 percent for Buryatia (Katzina *et al.*, 1994) and 30 - 40 percent for Mongolia (Zagdsuren, 1994a). The actual results will depend greatly on the types of yak and the breeds of *Bos taurus* or *Bos indicus* used and, of course, on the local husbandry conditions. But the substantial increase in birth weight, generally found to occur, is responsible in large measure for the increase in calving difficulties in yak cows with hybrid calves compared to those with pure yak calves (cf. Chapter 4). These difficulties are further accentuated by the even bigger size of calves from sires of the "improved" breeds of cattle (Table 7.2). Further investigations might show whether sire breeds differ in the incidence of dystokia caused in the cows to which they are mated – as the experience from crossbreeding among cattle breeds elsewhere would suggest.

Within locations (Table 7.2) there is a marked difference between the birth weights of the pure yak calves and the F1 hybrids from "improved" breeds. There is relatively much less variation among the breeds of sire in the average birth weights of their hybrid calves. There appears to be a clear trend of increasing average birth weight of calf with increasing average body weight of the yak dam. However, caution is required in drawing that conclusion because the different body weights of yak dams are confounded with the different locations – although, taken at face value, the trend shows, for yak, a relationship between size of dam and birth weight of calf which would be generally accepted for cattle.

Table 7.2 Birth weights of calves of yak and different hybrids of yak at various locations (differing in elevation and environment) and body weight of local yak dams (average of male and female calves)

Sire of calf	Xinjiang[1]		Longri, Sichuan[2]		Gannan, Gansu[3]		Shiqu, Sichuan[4]		Ganzi, Sichuan[5]	
	No.	(kg)	No.	(kg)	No.	(kg)	No.	(kg)	No.	(kg)
Local yak	25	14.8	25	12.4	91	14.0	71	11.5	40	9.4
Local cattle									19	12.2
Holstein-Friesian			32	23.4	40	22.0	59	19.1		
Simmental	10	26.9	9	19.5						
Charolais	18	27.2	6	24.7			20	19.1		
Hereford	16	24.1	7	20.3	17	22.5	18	16.4		
Aberdeen Angus					22	23.1	17	17.9		
Shorthorn			9	18.2						
Body weight of yak dam (kg)	257		222		210		200		179	

Sources of data: [1] AEA, 1984; [2] YRO and GISP, 1984; [3] Zhao Bingyao *et al.*, 1984; [4] Zhang Jiachuan, 1984; [5] Hu Angang *et al.*, 1960.

Body weights and linear body dimensions of adult females and steers are shown in Table 7.3 for yak and different types of hybrids, derived from observations in small herds in several parts of Sichuan province.

It is apparent from the results in Table 7.3 that the F1 hybrids from Holstein-Friesian bulls (or grade HF bulls) were the heaviest and largest, followed by the hybrids from yak mated to bulls of yellow cattle. The backcrosses were smaller than the F1. The backcrosses to yellow cattle bulls were actually smaller than the local yak, which suggests that the cattle involved in the hybridization may have been very small indeed ñ but in the absence of this information, this is speculation (but see also Table 7.4). The larger size and weight of steers relative to females corresponds to what was reported in Chapter 6. Similar results are shown in Table 7.4 but with data from all three types of animal, yellow cattle, Maiwa yak and their F1 hybrids (yak female mated to yellow cattle male), cohabiting in another area of Sichuan.

Table 7.3 Body weights and linear body dimensions of adult Maiwa yak F1 hybrids from Maiwa yak females mated to bulls of yellow cattle or Holstein-Friesian (or 75 percent HF + 25 percent yellow cattle) and backcrosses involving these types – in Hongyuan, Ruoergai and Ganzi counties of Sichuan [Pooled data from several farms; Source: Cail Li, 1989]

Type of animal	Sex	No.	Adult weight (kg)	Height at withers (cm)	Body length (cm)	Heart girth (cm)	Cannon bone circumference (cm)
Local yak	F	73	249	118.3	138.1	160.3	16.9
	S	12	443	128.7	161.5	198.0	20.6
Yak (f) x HF* (m) ("improved" F1)	F	42	357	121.8	125.3	182.7	18.5
	S	7	580	144.0	178.3	215.6	21.3
Yak (f) x yellow cattle (m) (local F1)	F	47	292	118.3	148.0	167.9	17.0
	S	14	477	128.7	173.0	197.3	20.3
F1 (f) x HF*cattle (m) ("improved"B1)	F	19	262	116.4	136.6	165.6	18.1
	S	6	521	150.0	174.5	206.5	22.5
F1 (f) x yellow cattle or yak (m) (local B1)	F	10	177	100.5	118.9	146.1	14.1

Note: f = female; s = steer (castrated male); m=male ; HF* = Holstein-Friesian or (75 percent HF + 25 percent yellow cattle).

As seen from Table 7.4, the yak in the Ganzi area were somewhat larger and heavier than the local yellow cattle and the F1 hybrids between them were bigger than either of these. This certainly suggests a substantial effect of heterosis, greater among the males than among the females. Unfortunately, the results again preclude a strict estimate of the magnitude of heterosis because of the absence of the reciprocal hybridization (the "counter-hybridization" – female cattle mated to male yak) from these trials, and the lack of certainty that treatment of all the classes was identical. Again, if speculation is in order, one might assume, on the evidence of the adult size of the local yak and the local cattle, that hybrid offspring borne by local cattle females might, if anything, be smaller than the hybrids borne by the yak females. If so, estimates of heterosis (expressed as a percentage deviation from the mid-parent levels) would be *lower* than the values that might be inferred directly from Table 7.4 (these range for females from 2.3 percent for height at withers to 12.3 percent for body weight and for males from 10.7 percent to 53.3 percent, respectively).

Table 7.4 Body measurements and body weight of contemporary adult animals of Maiwa yak, local yellow cattle and F1 hybrids in Ganzi county of Sichuan
[Source: Hu Angang *et al.*, 1960]

Type	Sex	No.	Body weight (kg)	Height at withers (cm)	Body length (cm)	Heart girth (cm)	Cannon bone circumference (cm)
Local yellow cattle	M	10	189	102.8	113.2	134.4	14.2
	F	22	170	97.7	108.7	130.0	13.5
Local yak	M	11	209	104.7	125.3	154.4	17.3
	F	127	179	102.1	121.6	145.0	14.9
F1 individuals (with yak dam)	M	6	305	114.8	134.7	179.7	18.5
	F	98	196	102.2	121.0	152.1	15.7

Evidence from other studies shows that hybrids vary in size and body weight from district to district, as might be expected from differences between districts in their environment and in the types and breeds of yak and local cattle kept (Qiu Huai, 1957; Zhao Zhengrong, 1957; Zagdsuren, 1994b). (As an example of this, it may have been be noted that the "local" F1 hybrids, as adults, were much heavier in the data used for Table 7.3 than in the data available for Table 7.4)

In the case of hybrids of yak with "improved" cattle, the breed also has an effect – as illustrated in Table 7.5.

The animals included in Table 7.5 are the same as those from the Longri location described in Table 7.2, which gave the birth weights. In relation to these birth weights, the pure yak calves had increased their weights ten-fold by 17 months old, while none of the hybrids did as well as that. However, in absolute terms, the hybrids all gained much more in weight than the yak. The differences among hybrids from different breeds of exotic sire were small by comparison, although such differences can be seen – with the Holstein-Friesian hybrids the heaviest of those tested. Intermediate weights, at three-month intervals, were also available (not shown here). From them it is of interest to note that weight losses over winter were of the same order of magnitude (11 - 12 percent), relative to weight at the beginning of winter, in the hybrids as in the pure yak.

Table 7.5 Body weights and linear body dimensions, at 6 and 17 months of age of yak and hybrids with different "improved" breeds of cattle at Longri, Sichuan (means and [SD]) [Source: Cai Li, 1989]

Yak female mated to male of:	Sex	No.	6-month weight (kg)		17-month weight (kg)		17-month linear body dimensions (cm)		
			Mean	[SD]	Mean	[SD]	Height at withers mean	Body length mean	Heart girth mean
Yak	m	14	68.9	7.4	129.8	11.0	95.3	107.8	135.4
	f	11	68.5	11.9	121.0	16.7	89.6	104.8	132.9
Holstein-Friesian	m	11	123.0	11.0	234.6	18.6	114.6	128.8	158.4
	f	21	111.6	13.6	202.4	17.3	110.8	123.7	154.3
Simmental	m	3	115.2	13.0	210.0	24.1	105.8	118.0	143.7
	f	6	77.5	15.6	162.8	24.6	102.3	114.0	133.8
Charolais	m	3	93.0	7.0	184.5	18.8	98.8	112.3	133.0
	f	3	81.3	5.7					
Hereford	m	3	81.3	10.7	181.3	12.8	100.7	109.0	139.3
	f	4	88.6	6.6	182.8	11.5	101.4	109.3	143.8
Shorthorn	m	2	86.0		162.0		102.5	112.5	139.0
	f	7	86.1	5.0	169.2	15.3	102.9	113.4	138.1

184

Like the yak, hybrids of yak with cattle show similar responses to the seasonal cycles of grass growth, with rapid growth during the warm season followed by severe loss over the winter and recovery the following year (Xiao Zhiqing, 1984). Also, the hybrids are subject to the same seasonal effects on birth weight. For example, the birth weights of F1 hybrids from yak mated to Holstein-Friesian on the Xiangdong Livestock Farm in Sichuan increased as the season progressed. Thus, 25 calves (sexes pooled) born in April weighed 21.3 kg [SD 2.6] on average at birth, 28 calves born in May 23.5 kg [SD 4.0] and 31 born in June 24.3 kg [SD 3.6].

Meat production

A number of studies have also examined the meat output, at slaughter, of hybrids of yak derived from mating of yak with both local cattle and the different exotic breeds shown earlier (Tables 7.4 and 7.5). Numbers in the breed groups examined tend to be small and there are no consistent differences between the breeds of sire in dressing percentage or the yield of meat. Nor do these differ from pure yak. There are differences in carcass weight, but only in so far as this is related to slaughter weight.

In spite of the small numbers involved in some of these studies, it seems that, potentially, there is a large difference in growth rate during the first and second summer of life between yak on the one hand and its hybrids from the "improved" breeds of sire on the other (Table 7.5) and that this difference will be reflected at the time of slaughter. Of the animals described in Table 7.5 that were slaughtered at 17 months old, it was found that the hybrids had reached slaughter weights around 50 percent greater than the yak at the same age. The hybrids had already attained an adequate degree of finish at this age relative to the yak – at the end of their second summer. Thus the hybrids provided a proportionately much greater yield of meat from the carcass than the less mature yak at that age. The loin-eye area was also two thirds larger in the hybrids than in the yak. Zhang Rongchang (1989), quoting evidence for Altai in the former Soviet Union, noted that hybrids (Simmental or Shorthorn sires) had reached up to twice the slaughter weight of the yak at 21 months of age (though only three animals per group) and were also much fatter but had very similar dressing percentages (see also Chapter 11, part 2 – CIS countries).

Katzina et al. (1994) also reported slaughter weights of hybrid animals at 18 - 20 months old that were 25 - 30 percent heavier than for yak at that age in the Buryatia region of Russia. They reported further big increases in the growth of the hybrid if slaughter was delayed for another year. The Schwyz breed (cf. Brown Swiss) has been used in this hybridization with the yak in addition to the use of local breeds of cattle – and subsequently also the Jersey and Galloway breeds (but see Chapter 11, part 2 – section on Buryatia for more recent changes in practice).

When slaughter occurred at the age more normal for yak steers, above the age of 8 years – in a study conducted in Sichuan – it appears that there was little or no difference in meat production between yak and F1 hybrids (with local cattle as the sires). Zagdsuren (1994a), however, has shown that F1 steers from yak cows mated to local Mongolian (cattle) bulls slaughtered at six and a half years old had higher carcass weights and dressing percentages than either of the parent breeds. Carcass weights of these F1 steers were 49 kg heavier than those of pure yak and 19 kg heavier than those of pure Mongolian cattle.

Supplementary feeding of corn meal, urea and bone meal during summer, in addition to grazing, and supplementary feeding of concentrates during the winter, have both been shown to give a marked response in weight gain (Langjie Zeren et al., 1987) and in the proportion of meat in the carcass of hybrids of yak with, for example, the Holstein-Friesian (Li Xuewen et al., 1983). Under similar circumstances, pure yak showed very little such response. It is questionable whether such supplementary feeding is economically worthwhile in terms of meat output alone – the answer must depend on market circumstances. It is generally considered that supplementary feeding over winter is not cost-effective (but see the following section for the effect of supplementary feeding on milk yield and see Chapter 14 for a more detailed discussion of supplementary feeding).

Milk production

As noted in Chapter 3, one of the main purposes of hybridizing the yak with cattle of other species is to provide the herdsmen with additional milk for their own use or for sale. The larger quantity of milk made available is a consequence of the higher yield from such hybrids relative to the yak but also because all or most of the milk from the F1 is taken by the herdsmen. (As noted earlier, the progeny from the F1 females (the backcrosses) are reared for meat production and not for further breeding; in some cases, these calves are (or used to be) taken from their mothers at or soon after birth.)

Table 7.6 shows the daily milk yield and its fat percentage for different types of F1 hybrids (yak females with local cattle and yak with Holstein-Friesian or part Holstein-Friesian). (The source of the information is the same as for Table 7.3.).

Table 7.6 Daily milk yield and fat percentage of yak cows and F1 and backcross cows involving the yak and its hybrids with bulls of local cattle and with Holstein-Friesian (or 75 percent HF and 25 percent local cattle) bulls – in Hongyuan and Ruoergai counties of Sichuan province ten females per group [Pooled data from several farms; Source: Cai Li, 1989]

Type of animal	Daily milk yield (kg) (at peak period)	Fat (%)
Local yak	2.0	6.3
Yak (f) x Holstein-Friesian (m) ("improved" F1)	8.0	5.4
Yak (f) x local (yellow) cattle (m) (local F1)	3.0	6.0
F1 (f) x Holstein-Friesian cattle (m) ("improved" B)	5.5	
F1 (f) x local (yellow) cattle (m) (local B1)	0.5-1.0	6.2

B = backcross, f = female, m = male

The F1 hybrids from the predominantly Holstein-Friesian bulls are seen (Table 7.6) to have yielded a much higher daily amount of milk than the yak. But the backcrosses in this case have regressed in yield, as would be expected if the initial F1 advantage is partly attributable to hybrid vigour. In the case of the ordinary F1 hybrid (F1 involving local cattle), the yield is higher than that of the pure yak, but the backcrosses, perhaps surprisingly, gave less milk per day than the yak cows. However, no milk yields are reported for the local cattle, which, as in comparable results of Joshi (1982) from Nepal, may have had lower milk yields than the yak.

Zhou Minhai (1998) reported that F1 cows with Holstein-Friesian sires gave 714 kg milk in a first lactation and those with sires that were themselves crossbred (Holstein-Friesian crossed with local cattle) gave 659 kg milk. These yields were significantly higher (P <0.01) than the reported first lactation yield of 388 kg for F1 cows from yak mated to "local" cattle sires and 244 kg for pure Maiwa yak cows (the number of cows in these studies involved is not known).

Other results from Hongyuan county in Sichuan also show that F1 hybrids from yak dams mated to Holstein-Friesian bulls (by A.I.) can produce milk in significant quantities – and much more than contemporary yak. Moreover, they start to do so a year earlier than is typical for yak – at the age of three instead of four years. If calving of the F1 females is delayed by a year to the age of four years, the first lactation yield is higher. Results for Holstein-Friesian and a mixture of other hybrids are shown in Table 7.7.

Table 7.7 Milk yield in 149 days of different types of F1 hybrid by age at calving (and parity) [Sources: YRO and GISP, 1984; Xu Guiling *et al.*, 1983]

Yak female mated to:	Age (year)	Parity	No.	Milk yield mean (kg)	SD	Fat (%) mean
HF	3	1	26	689	93	5.3
HF	4	1	15	809	130	5.2
HF	4	2	3	919	207	5.2
HF (half lactation)*	4	1	4	494	28	6.5
Various**	3	1	7	576	(194)	4.9
Yak	4	1	6	226	54	7.3

HF = Holstein-Friesian or crosses of HF with local cattle breeds
* half-lactation" – a second lactation in the year following first calving without a further pregnancy
** various breeds of exotic cattle sire used

It is also of interest from the results of Table 7.7 that the hybrids, like the yak, have the capacity to give milk in a second year without another intervening pregnancy – although, again as in the yak – the yield in the second year is reduced relative to that in the first.

How much heterosis is shown in respect of milk yield by hybrids of yak with *Bos taurus* or *Bos indicus* cattle cannot be clearly deduced from the literature – quite apart from the over-riding problems referred to at the start of this chapter. While the reduced yield of backcrosses relative to the F1, as in the results shown earlier, is consistent with heterosis in the F1, Zagdsuren (1994a), for example, presented results from Mongolia of F1 cows (yak mated to Mongolian cattle) that gave substantially more milk than those of either of their parent species (heterosis indeed, if the different groups were treated alike) – though with a fat percentage almost average between the two (see also Chapter 11, part 2). In contrast, Jain and Yadava (1985) present results from F1 hybrids of yak with hill zebu bulls in Himachal Pradesh which suggest that the daily milk yield of the hybrids was only half-way between that of the parent species (no heterosis) – but again no information is given on whether the three types of animals (ten animals in each group) were treated alike. It is quite possible that they were not, as all the animals were not from the same place. Surprisingly, the milk from this F1 hybrid is reported as having had a significantly higher fat content (7.32 percent) than that of the yak (6.45 percent) (in spite of a higher daily milk yield in the hybrid) and much higher fat percentage than that of the hill zebu cows (4.17 percent). This result is difficult to explain and at variance with other investigations.

Supplementary feeding of hybrids of yak and the Holstein-Friesian with urea, minerals and some ground corn during the warm grazing season led to an increase in milk yield of 10 percent in full-lactating animals (those that had calved that year) and 20 percent in "half-lactating" cows (those that had last calved in the previous year). This was considered to provide an economic return on the feed (Wen Yongli *et al.*, 1987). Experiments with winter feeding, with silage, hay, roots, concentrates and minerals also raised the milk yield of hybrids of Holstein-Friesian with yak, but the costs of this winter feeding were too high in relation to the extra milk obtained (GISP and WLF, 1985). Moreover, the availability of supplementary feed in winter would be severely restricted in practice to localities where pastures have been improved and where agricultural products are also available.

Some exceptional F1 cows (from Holstein-Friesian sires) when housed and well managed on Institutional farms have been recorded as giving up to 1 800 kg milk (5.7 percent fat), which suggests that a potential for higher yield from yak hybrids exists, given the right circumstances.

Milk let-down

This is more easily and quickly achieved in the hybrids than in the pure yak. About 70 percent of hybrids, and especially those with sires of the "improved" breeds like the Holstein-Friesian, do not need the presence of the calf for milk let-down – the remainder do. Milk from the hybrid females reported on by Zhang Rongchang *et al.* (1983) came out of the udder about 50 percent more quickly than from the yak cows and the pressure required to extract the milk was lower. As in the yak (see Chapter 6) and in most cattle, the rear quarters of the udder of the hybrid develop better than the forequarters and provide, according to one study (Han Zhengkang and Lu Tianshui, 1980a, b), about 54 percent of the total milk.

Concluding comment on milk yield

Milk yield of hybrids of yak with local *Bos taurus* or *Bos indicus* cattle and also those with "improved" *Bos taurus* breeds is very dependent on the breeds used to create the specific hybrid and on the location and conditions of production. It is not known, for example, if the hybrids, and the "improved" hybrids in particular (with Holstein or other exotic sires) are given preferential treatment relative to yak cows. The results presented here are intended as examples only. The common factor in nearly all the results is that the "local" F1 hybrid (using the local cattle breed for hybridizing with the yak) yield more milk than the pure yak under what are presumed to be similar conditions and that the "improved" F1 hybrid (when, for example, the Holstein- Friesian is used as the hybridizing sire) gives more milk than the local F1 hybrid.

The magnitude of the differences in yield between the groups indicates why herders like "improved" hybrid cows and why such hybrids are "officially" encouraged under appropriate conditions. However, a true evaluation of their worth must also consider the costs and not only the returns (see also Chapter 3 for discussion of limits on the potential for hybridization).

Draught

F1 hybrids of yak females mated to bulls of local cattle, and the reciprocal hybrids, are widely used for draught – both for ploughing and as pack animals. The hybrids are easily tamed and appear to have better heat tolerance than pure yak, which make them very suitable for work. The hybrids produced from mating yak bulls to female (local) cattle ("false" F1 hybrid) are used mainly for ploughing.

Liu Qigui (1981) showed that with a traditional-style plough, two ordinary F1 hybrid steers making a furrow 15 cm wide can till around 0.13 ha per day. With a more modern plough (producing a 24.8 cm-wide furrow), two mature hybrid steers in medium fat condition ploughed 605 sq m in one hour on moderately moist, flat ground. Per unit body weight, the maximum draught power of mature hybrid steers in reasonably good condition has been measured as exceeding that of the pure yak. After ploughing was finished, respiration and pulse rates of the animals returned to normal in less than half an hour.

The F1 hybrid has an excellent memory, which makes it good as a pack animal and for riding. It can find its own way home to the campsite, like an old horse, without anyone in attendance. Herdsmen will ride a F1 hybrid without a saddle, for example when herding sheep, but if the animal is needed for riding over long distances, a saddle is used.

In tests of the F1 hybrid as a pack animal on grassland, the F1 hybrid has been found to carry 75 kg, equal to 16.3 percent of its body weight, and to cover 30 km in six hours – not unlike the performance of the pure yak (see Chapter 6). The respiration and pulse rates had returned to normal in 53 minutes after reaching its destination.

References

AEA (Agricultural Exploitation Academy of Xinjiang) (1984). Report of the result of yak's interspecific hybridization. *Journal of China Yak*, 1: 71-75.

Anand, I.S. *et al*. (1986). Pulmonary haemodynamics of the yak, cattle, and cross breeds at high altitude. *Thorax*, 41: 696-700.

Cai Li (1989). Sichuan yak. Chengdu, China, Sichuan Nationality Press. 223 pp.

Denisov, V.F. (1938). Hybridization of the yak with Kirghiz cattle and the Schwyz. *Izv. Acad. Nauk. USSR (Otd. mat. est., Ser. boil)*, 863-878. (Cited in *CAB Animal Breeding Abstracts*, 7: 116-117).

GISP (Grassland Institute of Sichuan Province) and WLF (Waqie Livestock Farm) of Hongyuan County (1985). Study on increasing the milk yield of F1 hybrid by supplementary feeding in cold season. *Journal of China Yak*, 2: 30-38.

Guo Aipu (1983). A comparative study on chromosomes of Oxen (*Bos taurus*), yak (*Bos grunniens*) and their hybrids. *Acta Genetica Sinica*, 2: 137-143.

Han Zhengkang & Lu Tianshui (1980a). Study on characteristics of physiology of lactation of yak. *Journal of Nanjing Agricultural College*, 1: 139-146.

Han Zhengkang & Lu Tianshui (1980b). Features of lactation physiology of F1 hybrid of Holstein Friesian male x yak female. *Animal Science and Veterinary Medicine*, 5: 4-8.

Hu Angang, Cai Li & Du Shaodeng (1960). An investigation on yak in Ganzi County. *Journal of Southwest Nationalities College* (Animal Husbandry and Veterinary Sciences Edition), 4: 46-50.

Jain, Y.C. & Yadava, R.S. (1985). Yield and composition of milk of Himachali yak, yak hybrid and hill come. *Indian Journal of Animal Sciences*, 55: 223-224.

Joshi, D.D. (1982). *Yak and chauri husbandry in Nepal*. H.M. Kathmandu, Government Press, Singha Durbar. 145 pp.

Katzina, E.V., Davydov, V.N. & Baldanov, N.D. (1994). Elaboration of the scheme of production and usage of industrial hybrids of yak and meat cattle. Proceedings of the first international congress on yak. *Journal of Gansu Agricultural University* (Special issue June 1994) pp. 44-48.

Langjie Zeren *et al.* (1987). Supplementary feeding trial for fattening hybrids of Holstein Friesian x yak in warm season. *Journal of China Yak*, 4: 51-55.

Li Jiyou, *et al.* (1994). Advance on the research of chromosomes in yak (*Bos grunniens*). Proceedings of the first international congress on yak. *Journal of Gansu Agricultural University* (Special issue, June 1994). pp. 73-76.

Li Xuewen, *et al.* (1983). The preliminary test of hybrid's fattening and slaughtering. *Journal of China Yak*, 1: 35-37.

Liu Hui, Wang Liqing & Zheng Peizhi (1994). Quantitative histological study on the distant cells in pituitaries of yak, cattle and F1 hybrid. *Journal of China Yak*, 1: 34-36.

Liu Qigui (1981). Report of investigation of Hongyuan yak in Sichuan. *Journal of China Yak*, 3: 69.

Qiu Huai (1957). Cattle feeding, Vol. 1. Beijing, Publishing House of Animal Husbandry.

Qing Fufangm *et al.* (1990). Histological and histochemical studies on the thyroid of yak, cattle and their F1 hybrid. *Journal of China Yak*, 3: 46-48,45.

Qing Fufang *et al.* (1993). Electron microscopic observation of and stereoscopy study on the testes of yak and F1 hybrid. *Journal of China Yak*, 4: 9-11.

Tan Chunfu *et al.* (1990). Comparative anatomical observation on male genital organs of yak and their hybrids with cattle. *Journal of China Yak*, 3: 39-45.

Tumennasan, K. *et al.* (1997). Fertility investigations in the F1 hybrid and backcross progeny of cattle (*Bos taurus*) and yak (*B. grunniens*) in Mongolia. *Cytogenet. Cell Genet.*, 78: 69-73.

Wen Yongli, Wu Kang & Zhang Zhongming (1987). The study on improving milk production of female F1 hybrid with supplementary feeding in warm season in the frigid pastoral area. *Journal of Southwest Nationalities College* (Animal Husbandry and Veterinary Sciences Edition), 2: 44-47.

Xiao Zhiqing (1984). Preliminary evaluation of growth and development of F1 hybrid from different sires. *Journal of Southwest Nationalities College* (Animal Husbandry and Veterinary Sciences Edition), 2: 17-22.

Xu Guiling, Wang Gensheng, & Shi Aijuan (1983). Analysis of factors related with the milking performance and milk quality of yak. *Journal of China Yak*, 1: 21-29.

Xu Zukang, *et al.* (1991). Study on the histology, anatomy and reproductive function of genital organs in yak and their F1 hybrids. *Journal of China Yak*, 3: 18-21.

YRO (Yak Research Office) of Southwest Nationalities College and XF (Xiangdong Farm of Sichuan Province) (1983). Experiment and its result analysis on improving productive performance of yak by using frozen semen of ordinary cattle for AI. *Journal of Southwest Nationalities College* (Animal Husbandry and Veterinary Sciences Edition), 2: 17.

YRO (Yak Research Office) of Southwest Nationalities College and GISP (Grassland Institute of Sichuan Province) (1984). The research on the interspecific cross combination between female yak and cattle bull. *The research on the utilization and exploitation of grassland in the northwestern part of Sichuan province*. Chengdu, China, Sichuan Nationalities Press. pp. 107-103.

Zagdsuren, Yo. (1994a). Heterosis in yak hybrids. Proceedings of the first international congress on yak. *Journal of Gansu Agricultural University* (Special issue, June 1994) pp. 59-62.

Zagdsuren, Yo. (1994b). Some possibilities to increase meat and milk production of yak husbandry. Proceedings of the first international congress on yak. *Journal of Gansu Agricultural University* (Special issue June 1994) pp. 113-118.

Zhang Jiachuan (1984). The test of cross combination of yak and cattle. *Journal of South-west Nationalities College* (Animal Husbandry and Veterinary Sciences Edition), 1: 30-35.

Zhang Rongchang (1989). *China: the yak*. Lanzhou, China, Gansu Scientific and Technology Press. 386 pp.

Zhang Rongchang, *et al.* (1991). Study on the sperm productivity of species hybrid bulls between yak and cattle. *Acta Veterianaria et Zootechnica Sinica*, 22: 231-234.

Zhang Rongchang, Kong Linglu & Jin Yong (1983). The milking characteristics of yak and chauri. *Journal of China Yak*. 1: 14.

Zhao Bingyao *et al.* (1984). An experiment on the cross combination of interspecific hybridization between female yak and cattle bull. *Journal of Chin Yak*, 1: 47-70.

Zhao Shanting *et al.* (1990). Quantitative histological studies on the tests of F1 and its parents (yak and cattle). *Journal of China Yak*, 3: 30-33.

Zhao Zhengrong (1957). *Animal husbandry in the meddle part of Gansu Province*. Beijing, Scientific Publishing House.

Zhong Jingcheng (1994). Polygenic inheritance unbalance hypothesis about sterility of the male yak-cattle (hybrid). Proceedings of the first international congress on yak. *Journal of Gansu Agricultural University* (Special issue June 1994) pp. 284-287.

Zhong Jingcheng (1996). *Yak genetics and breeding*. Chengdu, China, Sichuan Scientific and Technology Press. 271 pp.

Zhong Jingcheng (1998). Study on mechanism of sterility of yak-cattle hybrid. *Forage and Livestock*, Supplement: 31-32.

Zhou Minhai (1998). Research report of new approach to explore hybrid vigour by interspecific hybridization of yak with crossbred cattle bulls. *Forage and Livestock*, Supplement: 33-35.

8   MANAGEMENT OF YAK

OVERVIEW

Management systems for yak predominantly follow a traditional pattern dictated by the climate and seasons, by the topography of the land and by social and cultural influences. Methods of keeping the yak vary from the primitive, where herds are allowed to roam virtually at will, to the technologically advanced. In general, a transhumance form of management predominates. During the warm season of summer and autumn, yak are on pastures at high elevations and the herdsmen live in campsites, which they move quite frequently. This gives way in winter and early spring to the grazing of winter pastures at lower elevations that are nearer to the more permanent winter abodes and villages of the herders and their families. The summer grazings are much the more extensive of the two.

Until fairly recent years, the predominant practice in China was for all yak from several families in one or more than one village to be pooled for purposes of management but subdivided into four groups: lactating cows, dry cows, replacement stock and steers (pack yak). Since the implementation in China of the "Household Responsibility" system, which includes leasing parcels of land to the herders and private ownership of the animals, the herd of each family is rarely subdivided, although the adult females are likely to be managed separately from the rest of the animals. Some pooling of resources among small family groups may still occur.

The proportions of each type of yak in the herd, the herd structure, can profoundly affect the output of milk and meat from the herd.

Grazing traditions rely on accumulated experience including knowledge of the particular properties of different types of pasture vegetation. Over-grazing has become a recognized problem, especially on the winter pastures, because an increase in the yak population has occurred, at least in several of the provinces with yak in China. This increase is due, in part, to official encouragement of extra food production and in part to the fact that many herders, perhaps most, still equate numbers of animals with wealth and status, irrespective of the intrinsic merit of the animals or their productivity.

To assist in the management of yak, there is a small range of fixtures, mainly at the winter quarters, in the form of pens and enclosures usually made of mud, turf or faeces. Wood, because of its scarcity, is used sparingly in the plateau areas. But in the alpine areas, wooden enclosures are found more often. Pens are usually associated with a tunnel-like passage for restraining animals during vaccinations or other treatments; a pit for dipping both yak and sheep is normally available; and a crush to restrain cows for mating is used in places where hand mating is practised.

Herdsmen train yak to obey commands both by voice and by use of small stones that are either thrown or projected with a sling. The purpose is to allow one person to control a large herd. The herder normally stays with the herd to protect it from attack by wolves, especially at times of calving, and to prevent the herd from straying onto another's territory. At night, the animals are tethered near the campsite to protect them from predators and for purposes of milking the cows.

During the warm season, yak are sent out to graze the summer pastures early in the morning and brought back to the campsite as late in the day as possible. In winter, the reverse happens with late out and early back. Milking, practised only during the warm season, is done once a day or, in some herds, twice. The method of calf rearing revolves around the frequency of milking of the cows. Milking three times a day is also practised for cows that do not have a calf at foot.

Apart from the important task of controlling the grazing and protecting the herd, the other main tasks of the herders involve: calf rearing, milking, supervising mating, assisting with calving (but usually only for cows giving birth to hybrid calves from "improved" breeds of cattle that tend to be too large for unassisted delivery) and harvesting the fleece (most often a combination of combing out the fine down followed by shearing or shearing alone). Other routine tasks include dipping animals against external parasites, vaccinations, castrating males and training of pack animals.

Yak and hybrids of yak and cattle are also used for ploughing for eight to ten hours a day during the planting season in areas where grazing land is combined with land suitable for cultivation. Such animals are given supplementary feeding of straw and grain. Animals used for ploughing may also be used later in the year for carrying loads on long journeys over often-difficult terrain. When working, such animals may walk continuously for seven to ten days before a rest of one or two days.

Introduction

There is no single management system that applies to all yak over the large area of its distribution. Methods differ according to country and region, influenced by altitude, climate and topography. There are differences in management related to culture and religion. Proximity to centres of population, which provide a market for yak products, also has an effect on management, since it determines whether products are used primarily by the families herding the yak or whether certain products, like milk, are exploited more for the sale of, for example, butter or cheese. (Figure 8.1 shows milk collection in progress) In some countries, for example Nepal, tourism provides outlets for products from the yak, including handicrafts usually made from the "wool".

In other countries, such as Mongolia, meat from yak is an important commercial product with slaughtering at centralized but often distant abattoirs, again affecting management practices. Generalizations about the management of yak and the uses to which yak are put are bound to be an oversimplification in respect of any specific case.

Figure 8.1 Milk collection (transported in churns)
(Photo courtesy of Gerald Wiener)

Management of yak ranges from the most primitive, seemingly unchanged by the passage of time, to the technologically quite advanced practice. There are three main types of yak farming systems on the Qinghai-Tibetan Plateau of China, namely nomadic, semi-settled and the so-called "small-holder". All of them involve a transhumance type of herding with different pastures used in the warm and the cold seasons.

The nomadic system is a traditional one dating back to ancient times. Under it, entire herds are kept together and largely left to roam the ranges to which herdsmen will go, in autumn, to hunt and shoot well-grown steers or bulls for meat. The semi-settled system was the most common system from the early 1950s to the late 1970s. With the settlement of herders, some pastures started to be fenced and supplementary feeds for winter use, such as oats, started to be planted where possible, and herd size began to be adjusted according to the availability of grazing land. Small-holder farming has been developed in China since 1980 and is expected to become the dominant system under the policy of "Household Responsibility" (Dong *et al.* 1999). This system requires yak farmers to rent grazing lands from the government – the area depending on family size. The rent is tiny and the contract is valid for 50 years.

It is hoped that the small-holder system, with its potentially greater control over grazing land and the additional responsibilities placed on herders, will encourage the adoption of newer practices in yak management. These would include supplementary feeding, more controlled rotational grazing, greater disease control, management aids to mating (e.g. A.I., where herds are accessible for this technique) and perhaps a greater use of hybridization with "improved" breeds of cattle (but see Chapter 3 for possible constraints). The expectation is that such measures would lead to a further increase in output and off-take from yak – especially when compared to the nomadic system which nowadays may account for no more than ten percent of the total yak population in China (Dong *et al*, 1999).

According to Dong, improvements expected, relative to the semi-settled system, would be in the size of the animals, in aspects of reproduction, in survival and in milk yield. Even if such improvements were not large at the individual herd level, they could lead to a significant cumulative increase in production over the yak population as a whole.

At experimental stations concerned with yak, most techniques familiar to modern cattle husbandry are under consideration, though they are not always appropriate to traditional yak husbandry or the associated environment – and not therefore necessarily practised outside the experimental situations. Multiple ovulation and embryo transfer are appearing on the scene, but only as an experimental tool in restricted circumstances. Similarly, at the scientific level, the concepts and development of new pasture management techniques are clearly recognized (e.g. Ren and Chu, 1993; see also Chapter 13). Miller (1990) has taken the view that for the vast grasslands of the Qinghai-Tibetan Plateau, a great potential exists for improving the herbage productivity of the rangeland and its livestock output, provided improved rangeland management policies are developed and implemented.

With so wide a spectrum of local environments and management practices, what will be attempted here is to provide merely an overview of what must still be regarded as standard practice for most yak, at least in the areas of China where the majority of the yak live. Where countries outside China or specific provinces within China, differ in major ways in their yak husbandry practice, or in specific aspects of yak production, this is referred to in Chapter 11. In all areas, the climate and the seasons dictate to a large extent what happens to yak.

Herdsmen's activities according to seasonal cycle

- *Early summer:* Supervising births and protecting calves; adjusting and subdividing the herd; castrating.
- *Middle of summer:* Combing out the down fibres and shearing; prophylactic vaccinations and dipping against external parasites.
- *Late summer and autumn:* Milking and processing milk; arranging mating; harvesting and storing grass for winter supplements (usually, mostly for sick and weak animals).
- *Early winter:* Culling surplus or unwanted stock; slaughtering animals for meat; counting the herd; repairing pens and enclosures for yak.
- *Middle of winter:* Allowing the pregnant cows to give priority to the developing foetus in the use of nutrients and body reserves (by stopping the milking); taking measures to protect the body condition of the yak; sheltering the animals in pens.
- *Spring:* Providing small amounts of supplementary grass as available (hay or possibly silage) and taking other measures to prevent death, particularly among the females.

Yak pastures and grazing habits

A full description of the rangeland and the plant species and their distribution will be found in Chapter 13. Only those aspects that reflect directly on the management of the yak are discussed here.

In the plateau areas, the grassland used by the herdsmen of a village can be broadly divided into two categories: what is used in the warm season (summer-autumn) and what is used in the cold season (winter-spring). The local climate and character of the land determines precisely where the areas of grassland for different seasons are located and for how long in the year each is grazed. In general, the warm-season grazing is at the higher altitudes, often on the northern slopes of the terrain and furthest from the settled homes of the herdsmen and their families. In late May or early June just after calving, the yak start to feed on the high quality and quantity of forage of the summer-autumn pastures where the cows suckle their calves, restore their weight loss and then fatten under good nutritional conditions. In late October or early November, as the production and nutritive values of natural forage decreases, the yak return to the winter-spring pasture. The cold-season grazing is then closer to "home" and in more sheltered, south-facing parts at lower elevations. The winter-spring pasture is grazed from early November to the following late April. Due to the low quantity and poor quality of the natural forage, the yak lose body weight, and in harsh, cold seasons deaths are not uncommon – quite apart from the extensive losses in periodic "snow disasters" (Wiener, 1996; Long and Ma, 1996). Supplementary feeding, when available, together with shelter, can ameliorate these problems.

The alpine areas are more varied because of the topography. The area of grassland occupied by the yak of a village can be quite large and is likely to be distributed across several mountain ridges separated by valleys. The ridges may well be above 4 000 m in altitude and the valleys much lower. Consequently, the grazing areas are more subdivided than in the plateau regions. In the alpine regions there is a separate grazing area for each of the four seasons of the year. The summer pastures are the extensive alpine meadows at the top of the mountain ranges. The spring and the autumn pastures are occupied for relatively short periods only by the animals in transit between summer and winter grazing areas. For that reason, the spring and autumn grazing areas tend to be small and are mostly on the hilly ground. The winter pastures, or "winter house" as it is called by the herdsmen, is situated in the gullies and, when possible, at the side of a forest for additional shelter. In most areas, the spring and autumn pastures or the spring and winter pastures are combined to form a three-seasonal system (see Chapter 13).

When yak are kept in areas with swamps, there is another variant in the use of grassland. The actual swamps or semi-swamps turn green relatively early in the year because they are generally at the lower altitudes.

The yak have an opportunity to graze fresh tender plants (with a high proportion of *Kobresia* and other *Cyperaceae spp.*) in the areas reserved for grazing in the spring. Summer-autumn pastures are then again at higher elevations and the winter pastures on lower ground nearer the settled areas of the herdsmen's families.

Traditionally, the nomadic way of herding yak was to keep the entire herd together, irrespective of age and sex, and to allow the yak to graze together with sheep and horses. The herdsmen lived with their animals and during the growing season moved with them as necessitated by the availability of grazing and water. In a vivid account of the grasslands of the Tibetan Plateau, Miller (1990) described the pastoral grouping and management of yak as well-adapted responses to different range and environmental conditions and ecologically sound and sustainable – while, at the same time, noting room for improvements.

The traditional use of different pastures at different seasons and the periodic movement of the animals to new grazing sites (see section, Utilization of grazing) represent some of the elements of "modern" rotational grazing systems. Official encouragement and financial subsidies are now provided for fencing of land with the intention that this should optimize pasture utilization and reduce parasite infections. In the past, such fencing to control grazing was rare largely because of the high cost. Fencing of land has further accelerated the move towards a more settled existence, starting around the 1950s, and has brought with it the division of herds for purposes of grazing and management described earlier (see also Chapter 12 for other possible consequences of fencing).

Herd ownership in relation to management

In China, the land is owned by the State, but the animals are usually owned by the herdsmen. The predominant practice until recent years was for several families or even all the families of a village to share the same pastures. If stocking rate in a particular area of the country was low, the number of yak that could be owned by a family was not restricted. However, in most parts of the country this was not so. The number of yak allowed to each family depended on family size, and the rights to grassland were fixed by agreement. There were penalties for transgressing the rules. Notwithstanding, there has been an increase in yak numbers in many parts of the yak territory. This will have arisen because of the encouragement to increase food production in China and because of a traditional view of yak herdsmen that equates the number of animals owned with status and wealth. This increase in numbers has, in turn, accentuated fears of overgrazing of the grasslands (see the following section). The most recent moves to fencing of land and its allocation to individual herders (see previous section) in turn creates both new opportunities and new problems in yak management (cf. Chapter12) and it is no longer certain that the yak of several families or of a whole village can be managed together.

Yak herd management

Before the Household Responsibility system was implemented in yak territories of China, both the animals and the grassland belonged to the State. In those circumstances, the total yak herd, as merged from the animals of several families and one or more villages, was usually divided into component herds. There was 1) the lactating-cow herd (the dairy herd, the largest of the component herds usually numbered between 100 and 150 head in the plateau areas and between 50 and 100 in the alpine areas. The dairy herd was normally allocated to the best-quality pastures available to the village). There was 2) the dry-cow herd (the "Ganba" herd) and 3) the group representing the younger replacement animals – those that had been weaned and separated from their dams (the "Yaer" herd). The herd of replacement animals was further divided to separate the males from the females. And there was 4) the steer herd (pack yak). There was no special herd for the bulls, which live with the breeding females during the breeding season and mostly alone at other times. Also, there was not usually a separate group for animals intended for slaughter for meat. Usually, the "meat" animals are merely the cull females and any chosen as suitable from among the steers and the bulls. (This would differ in countries where large-scale commercial fattening and slaughtering of yak is practised; see Chapter 11.) The hybrid F1 and backcross steers are distributed, as appropriate, among the groups used for riding, as pack animals or for draught.

Following implementation of the small-holder system, under which herders own the animals and lease the land, the family herd is rarely divided into several subgroups because of labour and herd-size restrictions. However, subdivision of the total yak herd into two groups – adult females together and the rest of the animals in another group – is still practised in some yak-raising areas by small groups of families and their relatives (Young calves remain with their dams up to weaning, which is most often in their second warm season of life when they are between 12 and 18 months old; but it can, of course, be sooner). After weaning, whenever it is, the young animals are incorporated into the mixed herd.

Other management practices such as time of weaning, provision for supplementary feed, culling strategy and so on, vary depending on herders' experience and knowledge.

The herd divisions described earlier applied primarily to daytime grazing in the warm season. At night, the yak tended to be divided again by family ownership and the different types of yak mixed and kept near the family tent. During the cold season, the families collect back their own yak to keep them on winter-spring pastures, which nowadays are increasingly fenced. As ideas, based on newer concepts of feeding and management, are accepted by herdsmen, it is likely that new systems of management will develop. This process is already apparent in some cases where specialization of production is emerging.

Yak herds vary in size depending on families. Some families have doubled the size of their herds since the time when the animals first came into their private ownership, while others have reduced the number of yak or even given up herding altogether. The herders who are now without animals have generally either leased their rangelands to others or chosen to work for others. Some of them have gone to townships or cities to find work.

Utilization of grazing

Formerly, during the warm season, a yak herd was typically moved every 40 - 60 days depending on the state of the grass and the size of the herd. Nowadays, this procedure is common only in some of the vast plain areas. The direction of movement of the herd and the route chosen is usually the same every year and the distance between campsites is generally less than 20 km. There are two ways in which the move can be made: One procedure is to move the livestock and the people, with their tents and belongings, all together in one move, until the new campsite is reached. Under those circumstances, the animals get virtually no chance to graze on route. The other way is to move the people and belongings to the new campsite first, establish the site and then move the yak gently in the course of a day's grazing toward the new campsite, which they reach at night. The former procedure is prevalent when the distance between the sites is long; the second method is more common when the distance is relatively short.

During the cold season, movements from one site to the other are few – not more than two to five over the whole period. But if the yak herd is small, or if yak are kept in pens with supplementary feeding, there may be no move at all over the whole of the winter and early spring.

Yak are versatile grazers. As already noted (see Chapter 4) they will take a variety of different herbage and are equipped to do so by their different feeding habits. This ability of the yak contributes to a better utilization of the total grazing. As pointed out by Cincotta *et al.* (1991), from a study of diet selection on the Tibetan Changtang, yak consumed a variety of forages avoided by sheep and goats, but these other ruminants consumed large quantities of some types of browse largely ignored by yak. As reported from many other situations, complementary grazing by a mixture of animal species generally leads to a better overall utilization of the total grazing resource.

Grazing traditions

Much of the grazing management of yak is part of the ingrained tradition of the herdsmen, developed through a long history of experience going back over the centuries. Much of this tradition has a sound scientific basis and is an effective means of utilizing the resources of a hostile environment to best advantage. Thus, herdsmen know well how to exploit changes in grass growth. For example, there is the use of swamp areas for early grazing in spring followed by a period on grassland with *Ophiopogon japonica*, said to cause de-worming and stimulate oestrus. Bog-meadows in June with yellow-flowered herbs of *Kobresia, Trollius* and *Caltha spp.* increase milk yield and turn the raw butter a desired orange colour. In the autumn, grazing on seeded grass is used to build up body condition to withstand the winter and early spring. In the cold season, yak are pastured in the most sheltered and warm (a relative term!), south-facing areas with as much wilted grass as possible to allow the animals some sustenance, which they obtain by scraping through the snow and ice. Many of these practices are enshrined in local proverbs and sayings that tell succinctly what to do and when.

Problems of overgrazing

Notwithstanding the great local experience of the herdsmen in exploiting their grazing territory to best advantage, serious problems from overgrazing are developing in the utilization of the yak pastures in some regions (but see also Chapters 12 and 13).

As referred to earlier, yak numbers increased over the years, at least in China. The resulting increase in stock numbers has put increasing pressure on the pastures, particularly the winter grazing lands. The winter pastures cover a smaller area than the summer pastures, but also have to sustain a larger number of animals, because numbers are always at their highest after the calf crop of that year. The winter pastures in particular, therefore, tend to be increasingly often overgrazed.

The consequences of overgrazing in terms of grassland degradation are discussed in Chapter 13.

Overgrazing of grassland has been accentuated by the fact that the income from sheep meat and wool has declined and that from yak milk and meat has increased – with a consequent decline in sheep numbers relative to yak. This in turn has created a further imbalance in the utilization of the land. In Ruoergai county of Sichuan, to take this area surveyed by Cai Li as an example, yak numbers increased between 1979 and 1984 (from 230 000 to 325 000), while during the same period, sheep numbers fell (from 619 000 to 532 000). An optimal ratio of cattle to sheep for that particular area was calculated to be 1:2.9 (more commonly 1:3.2) (Lei et al., 1986) but had been reduced to 1:2.2 by 1984. Thus, not only had stocking density (per adult animal unit) increased, but the stocking had become imbalanced in terms of the different contributions to grazing selection made by yak and sheep.   A partial alleviation of the problems of overgrazing may come from changes in herd structure and from the use of supplementary feeds.

Adjustment of herd structure

The structure of yak herds is all too often a matter of chance with the milk herd, steer herd, replacement herd, etc. not in best proportions for optimizing output. The opportunities for making changes depend largely on reproductive and survival rates and decisions on the ages at which to sell or slaughter surplus animals (or animals destined for meat). If procedures were adopted to optimise the population structure, as recommended by Cai Li et al. (1986) and many times since by others (e.g. Ji et al., 2002), it should be possible to increase overall productivity from the land while decreasing the total number of animals required. Measures would include the earlier slaughter of steers and culls and changing management procedures so as to increase the proportion of the productive animals (the lactating cows and the hybrid dairy herd) and reducing the proportion of the unproductive animals. For example, Zhen (1994) used linear programming to obtain an economically optimum structure for yak herds. Zhang, T. (1994) has pointed out that readjustments, which he describes in his study, can lead to substantial increases in output from the herd. For example, increasing the proportion of cows in the herd from a commonly found 35 percent to an attainable 50 percent would increase the milk output by 43 percent and other off-take of surplus stock by 10 percent – though with a concomitant reduction in off-take from the beef herd.

Not all localities have the same opportunities for increasing the proportion of productive cows at the expense of less productive animals. Availability of feed, climate and length of growing season, nature of the grasslands, etc. all play a part. But even small changes in the herd structure were shown, in these studies, to lead to useful improvements in off-take from the herd. This was demonstrated at the Datong Yak Farm where a 5 percent increase in the proportion of cows in the herd between 1985 and 1989 was accompanied by an increase of 14 percent in milk output. The changes that are desirable in herd structure will also depend on whether milk or beef is the primary consideration. However, attaining an optimum herd structure among yak herds in general is an ideal not yet in sight in spite of the continuing references to the need. But the related concerns about overgrazing must be addressed before permanent damage is done to the grasslands.

Apart from the wider degradation issues discussed in Chapter 13, Winter *et al.* (1992, 1994) provided a particular example, attributed to overgrazing, that highlights the wider problem.   The report relates to widespread deaths among yak in Bhutan, found to be due to pyrrolizidine alkaloid poisoning. The plants causing this (most especially some species of *Senecio*) are not very palatable and are, normally, avoided by yak or taken in only small amount. However, the plants had become prevalent through overgrazing and the yak, through hunger it was thought, consumed the plants in lethal quantity.

Supplementary feeding

There are a few opportunities for supplementary feeding of yak, except perhaps in the agricultural areas (see Chapter 14). Surplus herbage for hay or silage is not widely available, nor the equipment to make it – at least in the major yak-producing areas. A little hay is usually made but it is normally given only to sick or very weak animals towards the end of winter. Additional feeding when given can elicit a response in terms of reduced weight loss (over winter) or increased growth or milk yield, as noted from a number of trials (described in Chapter 6) and also in a study that involved winter feeding under shelter with the provision of hay and mineral licks (Liu and Cheng, 1994).

The use of urea molasses blocks, a kind of protein supplement, has been widely recommended in recent years for yak production in alpine regions (Xie *et al.,* 1997; Wang, *et al.*, 1997; Zhang, D. G, 1998). In these alpine regions, protein deficiency in forage is a serious problem due to a shortage of legumes in the swards of the natural grassland (Dong, 2001; Pu, *et al.*, 2001). The cost-effectiveness of such feeding still requires investigation both in respect of home-grown and purchased feed. In Buryatia, for example, as reported by Katzina (see Chapter 11, part 2) it is customary to give supplementary feeding to yak calves during their first winter of life. Consequently, these animals do not lose weight over that period. This could account for the fact that the yak females subsequently breed for the first time a year earlier than in most other situations and that the steers are slaughtered at an earlier age (yak in North America provide a similar example; see also Chapter 11, part 3). It is important, therefore, to judge the effectiveness of feeding not only by immediate responses but also in terms of any long-term effects.

Equipment and penning

Generally, there is little equipment to assist the herdsmen in the management of yak on range. The most usual provisions are a dipping pit used for both cattle and sheep; perhaps a silo or silage trench for use mainly by sheep; a corral with a tunnel-like passage to restrain animals for vaccinations or other treatments; and there may be a simple crush to hold cows that are intended to mate to particular bulls or to inseminate artificially. Pens are also created to provide shelter. Such pens and enclosures are used only at night and usually only during the winter and spring. They are always at the campsite or close to the habitation of the herdsmen and their families. The pens can be of various types of construction with differing degrees of permanence.

Mud pen
This is a relatively permanent construction built near the habitation of the herdsmen or at the winter campsite. It is used primarily for the cow herd, including hybrid females, and it is also used for the replacement females. The area is usually 15 x 15 m with a wall 1 - 1.2 m high, but the size can be as large as 30 x 20 m. Most of the mud pens have an additional shelter area constructed at one side of the pen facing the sun and providing extra protection from the wind. This extra shelter is constructed from a layer of clay on wooden boards knitted together with wicker. Such a pen is illustrated schematically and in a photograph in Figure 8.2.

The mud pens can stand alone, though more usually there are two or more built together and often joined by a passage with mud walls or wooden fence. A gate or gates keep the stock apart in the different pens. If several pens are connected to each other, the last pen will end in a long tunnel-like passage used for restraining the animals for vaccinations or other purposes. The passage can be roofed or open.

Faeces pen
This is a temporary structure, built and used only during the cold season. Fresh yak faeces are piled up near the campsite in a layer of about 15 - 20 cm deep every day. The first layer freezes solid overnight before the second layer is added.

Such a pen can be completed in a few days. There are two types of faeces pen: One has four walls to keep out wind and snow and provides a relatively large area used for adult yak.

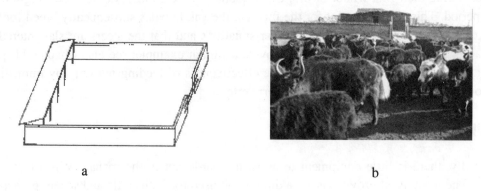

Figure 8.2 Mud (wall) pen with wooden shelter a) schematic b) photograph

The other is smaller, built on a horseshoe-shaped foundation with a diameter of about 1 m and looking, from the outside, something like an upside-down earthenware jar. It is built up gradually to its final 1 m height and is used to hold calves. The open end has its back to the prevailing wind. A wooden stake is used to tether the calf. Hay is put inside the pen to make it warmer for the calf. When the temperature starts to rise in the spring, the faeces thaws and pens made from it fall apart, to be rebuilt in the following winter.

Turf pen
To build pens with turf, herdsmen select a position on the winter pastures that faces the sun and is relatively sheltered from the wind. The height of the turf walls is at least 60 cm, though usually higher. This type of pen is used to give some shelter to pack yak and some bulls. The structure is semi-permanent but needs to be repaired each year.

Wooden compound (or corral)
Wood is in short supply on the plateau where most yak live. Therefore, wooden enclosures are often only an adjunct to a mud pen and within its perimeter. The wooden enclosure may be roofed or not. In the alpine areas, wood is more abundant and the compound may be built independently. The structure is of small wooden bars and provision is made for holding hay. During the warm season, these wooden enclosures are used to keep the calves isolated from their dams at night, while the adults graze in preparation for milking the following morning.

Other shelters
Tents made of yak hair are also used for calves in the pastoral areas. In the alpine parts, for example in Jiulong county of Sichuan, there are small shelters, called cattle shelters, found as part of the permanent buildings of the campsites. They are used by herdsmen and milkers and for processing milk and storing milk products. Such shelters can vary in area

from 10 - 20 sq m and are surrounded by a stone wall that is 1.5 m. high. Boards or bark are used for the roof. These shelters are in use whenever the herd comes to the campsite.

Management of yak herds on the range

Controlling the herd

Temperamentally, yak are at varying times wild or timid, cowardly and yet aggressive. Another part of the yak's character is its strong herding instinct. All these aspects have to be taken into account in training yak to obey commands so that a single person can control and manage a large herd. Because of the yak's timidity, the herder cannot follow too closely behind the herd for fear of it scattering. The practice of the herder is to select a high spot of ground, overlooking the herd while it is grazing. In this way, he can protect the yak from wolves and prevent the herd from straying onto grazing land set aside for other herds.

The herdsmen use special summonses to call the yak and they throw small stones to make straying animals return to the herd. A stone thrown by hand may travel 10 m, but using a sling – as is a common practice in many parts – can project a stone more than 100 m in the hands of a skilled user. Both the sound of the stone flying through the air at great speed and the sound of the sling, like the crack of a whip, provide a warning signal to the yak. The direction from which the stone comes allows the yak to know which way to go and whether to advance, muster or disperse. The sling (illustrated in Figure 8.3) used for projecting the stone is woven from yak hair and down, or sheep's wool. It is 100 - 120 cm long and has an elliptical net at its centre (7 x 15 cm) to hold the stone.

Figure 8.3 Sling of hair and yak down (or sheep wool) used to
project stones used in herding yak

However, the management of yak herds on the range varies from region to region. Landforms (mountain and plain) also lead to different approaches to managing yak herds, even in the same region. Nowadays, labour availability has a profound influence on patterns of yak herd management on the range. In general, there are two systems, which, for simplicity can be categorized as a) yak tethered at night and b) adult animals graze freely at night. Figure 8.4 illustrates a typical, or traditional, system in which yak are tethered at night near the campsite, after returning from the grazing lands, to protect them from attack by predators or from thieves and to have the cows ready for milking in the morning.

Normally, the tethering site is square and enclosed by several layers (circles) of the rope of yak hair or skin with the wooden bars at the corners. The yak is tethered to the ropes with a

40 - 50 cm (for cows and calves) or 50 - 60 cm rein (for pack yak and hybrids). There is a gap of approximately 2 m wide between any yak and 5 m between two stretches of rope. As shown in Figure 8.4, strong, aggressive pack steer and timid young cows are generally tethered to the outside, furthest from the tents, and the milking cows are tethered close to their calves (the calves in this system, cannot suckle). Once the position of each yak on the tethering sites is fixed, the yak will find their own way to their allotted place after returning from grazing.

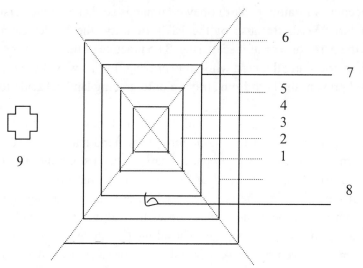

Figure 8.4 Sketch map of the tethering sites of yak herd

1 – Tethering horned dairy cows   2 – Tethering dehorned dairy cows
3 – Tethering two years old calves   4 – Tethering one year old calves
5 – Tethering package yak and first-calving cows
6 – Wooden bars   7 – Ropes for tethering
 8 – Reins   9 – Campsite (tent)

Daily schedules

The grazing schedule for yak differs with the type of herd (if subdivided) and with the season. For herds of dairy yak there will also be a variety of different schedules depending on the frequency of milking and on the particular calf-rearing practice. In sending yak out to graze, the guiding principle for the herdsmen is: "Early out and late back in summer and autumn, late out and early back in winter and spring."

The mixed herd (including pack yak and the replacement animals) is left out at pasture both day and night during the warm season. It does not return to the campsite during that period – but the herder needs to visit such a herd two or three times a week. Also during the warm season, the lactating females need to recover their body condition after the rigours of the previous winter and spring, if they are to give milk, rear calves and mate again. For that reason, the cows are allowed to graze both during the day and night, while, as a rule, the calves are penned overnight (but cf. Table 6.7 for the effects on growth of calves grazing alongside their dams overnight). This pattern of management is a typical system of free grazing at night (see also the ensuing section on management).

The following are some examples of the daily (summer) schedules for yak milked once, twice or three times a day in different localities.

- **Once-a-day milking** (practised in Ninai township of Jiulong county, Sichuan). The calves graze with their dams and suckle them (except at night).

Hours:

0500 - 0700	Yak cows recalled from their night grazing to the campsite where they are mustered without tethering.
0700 - 0900	Milking; release calves from their overnight wooden enclosure.
0900 - 1800	Animals graze the alpine grassland. Calves graze with their dams and suckle. Yak graze freely, drink water, rest and ruminate.
1800 - 2000	End grazing on alpine pasture; herd returns to campsite, calves enclosed in the wooden corral.
2000 - 0500	Yak cows allowed to graze freely on pasture near the campsite.

- **Twice-a-day milking** (practised for lactating cow herd in Muye township of Mashu district, Ganzi county, Sichuan). Calves are reared artificially in some such herds.

Hours:

0500 - 0700	Animals grazing near campsite on grass with dew.
0700 - 0900	Yak called in for the first milking. Calves released from their overnight wooden enclosure then allowed to graze with their dams and to suckle until second milking.
0900 - 1300	Yak driven to far-away pastures at higher elevations and allowed to walk slowly and gradually back downward while grazing.
1300 - 1500	Herd driven to a watering place, allowed to rest and ruminate.
1500 - 1900	Herd driven back to a point about halfway up the hill and allowed to graze at will.
1900 - 2000	End of grazing; return to campsite with drinking water on the way.

| 2000 - 2100 | Yak tethered at the campsite, second milking. |

2100 - 0500   Yak cows released to graze near campsite.

- **Three times-a-day milking** (practised at Xiangdong Livestock Farm in Ruoergai county, Sichuan).   Calves suckle their dams.

Hours:

0500 - 0800   First milking of cows.

0800 - 1300   Yak cows allowed to graze freely and have access to water at a distance from the campsite. Calves remain tethered at campsite or are tied together in pairs and allowed to graze near camp.

1300 - 1500   Yak cows driven back to campsite; second milking (without tethering).

1500 - 1900   Calves allowed to graze with their dams, away from the campsite in good weather and near the camp if weather is poor. Calves are given the opportunity to suckle and also to drink water.

1900 - 2100   Grazing period ends; calves are separated from their dams after another opportunity for suckling. The calves are then tethered to a long rope at the campsite (see Figure 8.5). The cows that have no calves – the "half-lactating" females and those that have lost their calf and are not fostering – are milked for a third time.

2100 - 0500   Calves remain tethered overnight. The cows may either be tethered or not, depending on the topography of the land and the ease with which they can be driven back to the campsite in the morning.

Management of the individual animal

The management practice and extent of technical input varies greatly among areas. A few of the most common practices are as follows:

Calf rearing

Normally, yak calves are suckled by their dams. Artificial rearing occurs only if the dam of the calf has died and no foster dam has been found or in some cases also where twice-a-day milking is practised.

Fostering is attempted when a calf has lost its dam and another cow has lost its calf.

Because of her strong maternal instinct, a yak cow that has lost her calf can be persuaded to accept another by smearing the calf to be fostered with her milk or to place the hide of her dead calf on the intended fosterling. Smearing salt on the calf will also stimulate the foster dam to smell and lick the new calf and adopt it as her own.

Figure 8.5 Tethering of yak calves to a rope

Artificial rearing is accomplished with a feeding bottle made of a yak horn without its tip and with a teat, the size of a thumb, made of yak hide attached to the end of the horn. The "bottle" is filled with milk and the calf sucks normally. The timing and the length of time of such feeding has to take account of the normal suckling behaviour and also the need of the calf for young grass so that it can establish grazing behaviour and rumination. Care is taken by the herdsmen to prevent calves sucking each other, as blockages of the *abomasum pyloris* can result from careless practice.

With normal rearing, the dam (or foster dam) is not milked for ten days, or even a month, after calving, during which time the calf obtains first the colostrum and then all the milk from the dam. When the dam starts to be milked, the calf continues to suck, to the extent permitted by the regime and graze alongside its dam. Yak calves start to nibble grass at seven to ten days old, but they have not been observed to ruminate before the age of 12 days. At night, as already noted, the calves are separated from their dams, except from dams that are not milked because they produce too little or because they are ill.

During the cold season, the cows are not milked and their calves stay with them all day and usually obtain a small amount of milk by suckling.

Calves of cows that have become pregnant again are weaned at six months old. However, calves whose dams have not conceived again that year, or do not produce a new calf in the following year, stay with their dams through a second summer; generally that is the majority of calves.

To achieve weaning, the cows and the calves are separated into different herds. In cases where the calf persists in trying to suckle, a piece of wood about 20 cm long, sharpened at both ends, is pushed through the nasal septum between the nostrils. This is removed only when the calf has stopped its attempts at suckling.

Milking

The teats of yak females are small and have to be squeezed quite hard between the fingers to extract milk (cf. Chapter 6). Milking takes place at the campsite. If the calf is tethered, the cow will be tied up, too, unless the calf is kept in a corral. The cows that are not tethered usually graze all day and yield more milk than those that are tied up for part of the day.

Tethering is done by hitching a neck rope by a wooden peg to a long rope with many rings. The rope is fixed to the ground at the campsite. (Cows are trained to become accustomed to neck ropes and to being tethered from the time they are calves). Milking the cow takes place where she is tethered. After a short time, the yak cows remember the position along the rope where they are to be tied, and they will quickly learn a new position, if given one, after a move to another campsite.

In some areas, milking also takes place in stalls. The milkers call the yak by using charming, eloquent names given to them at their first milking. A little barley powder mixed with salt may be used as an added incentive to tempt the cows into the stalls. Once there, the cow is hitched by her neck rope to a wooden pole and milked.

The milking stall is usually constructed with a left wall and a front wall of stone (100 - 120 cm long, 60 - 80 cm wide and 60 - 80 cm high) and the other sides open. The floor has stone slabs, and there is a wooden pole for securing the animal (see Figure 8.6).

Figure 8.6 A milking stall with stone slab floor, stone wall and pole for tying animal

Yet another variation of milking practice occurs when yak cows are not tethered at all. The milker goes to the cow, anywhere on the campsite, with bucket in hand and calf in tow. The forelimbs of the cow are tied with a short rope prior to milking.

The milking reflex is stimulated, in the first instance, by the calf poking the udder and being allowed to suck a little until milk let-down occurs. The calf is then removed a short distance but still within sight of the cow, and hand milking starts. The reflex has to be restimulated a second time, after a little more than half the milk has been extracted, by using the same procedure with the calf.

The milker normally squats on the right side of the cow with the pail hung from a hook on a girdle, as illustrated in Figure 8.7. The milker uses a little butter, which has been spread on the side of the pail, to lubricate the teats and milks at about 80 squeezes per minute. As milking speed can affect the milk production and grazing time of yak, the aim is to finish milking as quickly as possible (on average, not more than six minutes per yak). As yak are very sensitive to smells and voices, it is best if the milkers are not changed often and that they remain silent during milking.

Figure 8.7 Milking in progress

A small number of cows cannot be milked because they are too ferocious and protective of their calf.

Mating of female yak

In pastoral areas, mass mating of the female herd is the normal practice with between 5 and 6 yak bulls to every 100 females – though more bulls may be used in some areas; for example, Dubrovin (1992) reports the use of 8 yak bulls per 100 females in the Caucasus. This system allows competition among the bulls for mates and is part of the selection process. In some areas, artificial assistance is given to the mating process. In such cases, as when a yak cow is found to show oestrus (often by using a teaser bull), she will be caught and her forelegs tied and a rope placed around her neck. The cow is then restrained in a breeding crate or held by two men, one on each side of the cow. Three or more bulls are then driven towards the cow and allowed to compete for the mating. After the cow has been served twice (by the same bull or once each by two different bulls), the bulls are driven away and the cow is released after smearing her rump with fresh faeces to deter further mounting and mating. An advantage of such artificial restraint of the cow is that it allows selected mating to be made; but a disadvantage is that accidents and damage occasionally occur to the cow in these circumstances.

In agricultural areas, only one yak bull is normally allocated to a cow, which is restrained for the actual mating. This is safer than the competitive mating procedure of the pastoral areas and helps the herdsmen to achieve their selection objectives.

Artificial insemination is practised mainly for interspecies hybridization, as referred to in Chapters 5 and 7, and has been refined since the 1970s. Frozen semen is used from bulls of other cattle species but is also now available from yak bulls, chosen for use in improvement programmes (including the wild yak bulls referred to in Chapter 3). By experiment and experience, techniques for collection and use of semen have had to be adapted to the yak situation and the climate. In particular, great attention has to be paid to the safety of the person undertaking insemination of yak. The yak cow has to be restrained in an insemination crate (see Figure 8.8). The temperature of the thawed semen has to be maintained to prevent cold shock since the ambient temperature in the early parts of the morning can be as low as 0°C even in the warm season. For the same reason, particular attention has to be paid to the temperature of the inseminating tube and syringe. Deep insemination with the help of rectal palpation can improve the pregnancy rate. Inseminated yak cows have to be kept away from the yak bulls. If a yak bull mounts a yak cow that has just been artificially inseminated with the semen from a cattle bull, she will usually produce a yak calf, because the yak sperm seem to win in the competition to reach the egg.

Figure 8.8 Artificial insemination of yak

Pregnancy detection

Abortions and disease during pregnancy are rare. Herdsmen do not normally attempt pregnancy diagnosis. Yak cows are judged to be pregnant if they do not return on heat at the next expected oestrus period after mating. However, because a proportion of yak cows come on heat only once in a season, this negative way of assessing pregnancy has been found to lead to problems of unnecessary culling of cows that were thought to be barren but were, in fact, pregnant. There are no early visual indications of pregnancy, as there is no obvious outer swelling of the body in the early part of winter. An example of the mistaken culling of cows, because of lack of positive pregnancy diagnosis, was provided by an investigation by Cai Li, at Xiangdong Livestock Farm in Sichuan. Out of 38 yak cows that were culled in one year, 17 were found to be pregnant, and only 5 of them would have been culled anyway for other reasons. This mistaken culling, because of presumed barrenness reduces calf numbers and production from the herd. Cai Li found that rectal palpation would be an easy and quite accurate means of pregnancy diagnosis in yak under current methods of yak management (see also Chapter 5).

Calving

A yak female leaves the herd shortly before she is due to calve and seeks out a sheltered, low-lying place in which to deliver the calf. By the time the calf is born and she has licked it and it has started to suck, the herd has usually moved on. The calf is then in special danger from wolves and other predators, which are prevalent around the time of calving. The herdsman, therefore, has to pay extra attention from a distance to guard against such attacks, even when other assistance with calving is not required.

Assistance at calving

Yak cows graze all the year round but their nutrition is particularly poor in mid- and late pregnancy. They also have a somewhat shorter gestation length than *Bos taurus* cattle (see Chapter 5). As a consequence of both these factors, birth weights of pure yak calves are generally low and difficult labour is rare. Assistance at calving, therefore, is not normally required and would, in any case, be difficult to give, as yak cows are hard to approach during delivery because of their highly protective maternal instinct. However, assistance at birth is frequently necessary when a yak cow gives birth to an F1 (interspecies hybrid) calf. This is often too large for the cow to deliver unaided, especially when sires of large exotic breeds were used to produce the hybrid. Occasionally, a delivery by Caesarean section may be needed for a hybrid calf. Anaesthesia is provided by a method of electric acupuncture and local veterinary workers are readily trained in this technique. Such Caesarean delivery takes between one and two hours. The cow is conscious throughout, appears to suffer no pain and returns to normal activity immediately afterwards.

When calving is assisted, the navel cord is cut by knife. In all other cases the cord is broken during the act of the cow standing up after delivery or by the yak calf falling down. Although the broken cord is not sterilized, infections are rare.

Training of bulls for semen collection

When yak semen is required, most of the semen collection is from older bulls which are regarded as superior and because of a lack of information on the merits of young yak bulls. The training of adult bulls is therefore an important aspect of the process. The first step is for a herdsman, who knows the temperament of the particular bull to try by various means to overcome the bull's hostility. Training starts by holding the bull in a pen until it is used to being tied up and to being fed in a fixed place and, importantly, until the bull allows the herdsman to approach it. To become accepted by the bull in the pen, the herdsman will initially tempt the bull with grass and later stroke and scratch it from the front to the rear of the body and from the back to the abdomen.

The yak is most afraid of being touched on the head and, consequently, the herdsman avoids coming close to the head in the daily act of grooming. After some time, the herdsman will start to stroke the scrotum and testes of the bull and pull on its sheath and walk the haltered yak bull to its feed.

Training for semen collection follows by first getting the bull accustomed to a female in heat, while she is restrained in a crate and allowing him to mate her there. After that comes the process of guiding the sheath into an artificial vagina and allowing the bull to ejaculate into it. The temperature of the inner layer of the artificial vagina is kept between 39°C and 42°C. Eventually, a dummy cow can be used for the yak bull to mount, as happens with other types of cattle. However, a yak bull appears to be more sensitive to its surroundings, which therefore have to be kept quiet and familiar to the bull. Also, the bull has to be treated gently.

Castration of males

Males not selected for breeding are castrated. Most of this is done between the ages of one year and two and a half years. It is usual to do the castrations on a clear morning in early summer or late autumn, when the risk of infection to an open wound is reduced. First the young bull has to be caught in a pen and then put on his side for restraint. The lower part of the scrotum is sterilized with iodine and the bottom, held between thumb and index finger, cut off with a knife. The testicles are pushed out of the scrotum, the cords crushed and the wound sterilized with iodine solution and dusted with a powder to prevent infection. The scrotum is squeezed to close the cut end. The bull is then set free and walks away. The wound generally heals without complications within a week. The operation can take as little as ten seconds. With older bulls more care is required, particularly in handling the cord and sterilizing the wound.

In some areas a different technique is used. For example in the Ganzi area of Sichuan, the scrotum is slit vertically on the rear side, the testes are pushed out and totally removed. The other parts of the process are similar to those described.

Recently, a form of castration has come into use in which the testicles are pushed into the body cavity close to the belly. The upper part of the scrotum is then closed off with a rubber band to prevent the testicles slipping down again. The spermatozoa in the semen do not survive at the higher temperature inside the body. "Castration" is therefore achieved by physiological means and avoids the need for an operation. Moreover, the male will still secrete androgen after this treatment and, as a consequence, the growth rate will be greater than for the traditional steer and similar to that of an entire bull.

F1 hybrid bulls, although sterile are usually castrated at the age of one year to one and a half years.

A report by Feng and Su (1994) indicates that problems occasionally arise from the conventional form of castration. They record cases of strangulation of the small intestine by the free *vas deferens*, which is thought to have been excessively stretched during castration. The *vas deferens* was found to have wrapped itself around the small intestine as a result of strenuous movement on the part of the animal during work or other activity, when high abdominal pressure had forced a section of the intestine into the uro-genital fold that had previously been ripped open during castration. Once diagnosed, a simple operation rectified this problem in most cases.

Harvesting fibre

In China, shearing takes place usually once a year in May and June. In herds, shearing is done first on the pack yak (steers), then on the adult bulls and the replacement cows and finally on the adult cows. Animals with any skin disease have to be shorn separately from the rest. Parturient cows are shorn two weeks after calving and sick animals are shorn after they have recovered.

Cutting and plucking are alternatives to shearing. The down hair can be combed out prior to shearing. Prior to harvesting the fleece, the yak is taken into a pen and the legs tied. When shearing, which is the predominant method of harvesting the fleece, the long hair and the down are taken off together and are separated afterwards. The whole body is shorn but only a little is taken off the tail, as long tail hair may be used later.

The fleece can also be cut with a Tibetan knife, but the fibre remaining on the yak is longer than after shearing, and the total fleece yield and its down content are lower.

The plucking procedure involves grasping little groups of hair at a time, twining these around a wooden, mallet-shaped stick and pulling sharply. The yak jumps with pain at every pluck, but local people believe this promotes hair growth. The plucked hair contains little down and what is left behind may be gathered later or allowed to be shed.

With once-a-year harvesting (though tail hair is harvested once every two years), the content of down is low, irrespective of the method of harvesting used. The down hair felts readily and the quality is poor. With the increasing value of the down hairs for textiles, better methods of harvesting it are being popularized. Combing out the down with a wire comb, with teeth 1 cm distant and 10 cm long (Figure 8.9), provides a greater yield and better quality. Shearing then follows some time after the combing.

If down fibre is not to be lost, combing needs to start before the down begins to shed – which is about 20 days before the normal time for a single shearing.

Although such separate combing and shearing involves the yak being caught and restrained twice, and uses more labour, it can be economically efficient if the price for the fine down fibre is high enough. Machinery for combing is being developed to increase both the speed of harvesting and the yield of down.

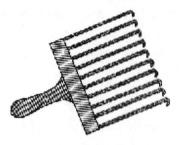

Figure 8.9 Comb used for harvesting yak down

Management of yak in agricultural areas

In some yak areas of China, there is a relatively good microclimate and some parts of the land are suitable for cultivation. This occurs mostly in valleys at lower altitudes and near some streams in subalpine or agricultural-pastoral regions. The number of animals kept by a family is normally small and includes pure yak and F1 hybrids, with the latter often predominating in a mixed herd.

In northwest China such a herd will be kept in a backyard or a pen near the family abode. But in southwest China, such farmers have a permanent house, usually two or three storeys high. The upper floors are for the family and the ground floor serves as a pen for the animals – horses, cattle (including the yak), sheep, goats and pigs, all together. Usually there is no window to the pen, and a single gate provides access for both people and animals. A small courtyard often supplies the light and ventilation for the pen. The pen does not normally have a separate bedding area or feed trough, nor is there a special channel for collecting the dung. The animals move around freely and lie down where they wish. Farmers or herders frequently spread straw or leave straw chaff or weeds on the ground to keep the animals comfortable. The straw or waste is removed with the faeces in the spring and used as manure prior to cultivating the land. Sanitation in the pen is poor, but the animals keep warm, particularly in the enclosures used in northwest China.

During the warm season, the female yak and F1 hybrids are driven to the pastures, far from the farming area and are milked there. A few cows are retained in the pen at the homestead for milking and allowed to graze nearby during the day. During the cold season, all the animals are housed at night when they are given supplementary feed of straw and other crop by-products; during the day they graze stubble.

The use of yak and yak hybrids as draught and pack animals is of particular importance, although they are also used for milk and meat. The males – both pure yak and hybrids – kept for work are castrated and have nose rings inserted when a year old. They start to be trained for work from the age of two years and start working around the age of three or four years.

During the busy period of spring cultivation, the animals used for ploughing are given supplementary feed, including barley grain or peas. The animals plough for about eight to ten hours daily and receive their supplementary feed at every rest stop and at night (see Figure 8.10).

Figure 8.10 Yak bullocks ploughing in Yushu, Qinghai (Photo courtesy of Peter Horber)

A typical ploughing schedule
(for example, at the Tuobo township of Ganzi county in Sichuan) is as follows:

Hours:

0600 - 07.00	Give grass and access to water.
0700 - 0800	Allow rest in preparation for work.
0800 - 1000	Ploughing.
1000 - 1100	Rest (at ploughing site), give barley straw.
1100 - 1300	Ploughing.
1300 - 1500	Resting; supplementary feeding of grass and other feed, provide water.
1500 - 1700	Ploughing.
1700 - 1730	Short rest; give supplementary feed and grass
1730 - 1930	Ploughing.
1930 - 2000	Stop work and return to pen (or graze); provide water.
2000 - 0100	Provide grass and grain, and comb the animal.
0100 - 0600	Animals housed or allowed to graze outside.

During the busiest part of the season, ploughing may continue for ten hours a day and the return for feeding and rest in the evening may be delayed by a couple of hours. After the period of cultivation is over, the draught animals are driven to natural grazing and stay there until the winter, when they are housed. Some of the draught steers are used as pack animals, after a period of rest following the ploughing.

Both yak and F1 steers are used as pack animals. The animals work all the year round with little rest, apart from the autumn, when the grass is forming seed and the animals are allowed to graze and get fat. When working, the pack animals will walk continuously for seven to ten days and then rest for one or two days. The animals walk during daylight hours and graze and feed at night. A typical schedule is as follows:

0400 - 0600	Muster the pack animals from their grazing, saddle up and tie on loads. The drivers have their breakfast.
0600 - 0900	On journey (the loads may be re-arranged on the way).
0900 - 1030	Rest with loads; grazing allowed on adjacent pastures.
1030 - 1300	On journey.
1300 - 1400	Rest period without grazing.
1400 - 1700	On journey.
1700 - 1800	Stop for night, unload animals, let animals on to pastures for grazing, drinking water and resting until 04.00 the following morning, when the procedure is repeated.

Yak and the hybrid animals used for carrying loads are also used for riding (Figures 8.11 and 8.12), for which they may be saddled or not. They are not harnessed like horses; a nose rope is all that is required by the rider to control speed and direction. Yak are also used for work (Figure 8.13).

Figure 8.11 Pack yak
(Both yak and hybrid steers are used)
(Photo courtesy of D. Steane)

Figure 8.12 Riding (Both yak and hybrid animals are used)

Figure 8.13 Yak at work in Mongolia (Photo courtesy of Horst and Barbara Geilhausen)

References

Cai Li *et al.* (1986). Optimization of the age-sex distribution of yak's population and the correlated slaughter program in Ruoergai county. *Journal of Southwest Nationalities College,* (Animal Husbandry and Veterinary Sciences Edition), 1986 (4), 22-30.

Cincotta, R.P. *et al.* (1991). Foraging ecology of livestock on the Tibetan Changtang; a comparison of three adjacent grazing areas. *Arctic and Alpine Research,* 23, 149-161. [Herbage Abstracts, 62, 116.]

Dong S. K (2001). The stability of mixture grassland of cultivated perennial grass and its regulation in alpine region of Qinghai-Tibetan Plateau of China. PhD Dissertation. Gansu Agricultural University, Lanzhou, China.

Dong S. K., Long R. J. & Gera den D. (1999). Yak farming on the Qinghai-Tibetan Plateau of China. *NCTR Livestock Newsletter,* (1&2): 10-14.

Dubrovin, A.X. (1992). Yak breeding in the northern Caucasus. *Zootekhniya*, No. 3-4, 18-20.

Feng D.G. & Su L. (1994). Small intestinal strangulation with deferent duct in 40 castrated Pianius. Proceedings of the first international congress on yak. *Journal of Gansu Agricultural University* (Special issue June 1994), pp. 327-330.

Ji Qiumei *et al.* (2002). *Resources of yak production in Tibet and reasons for the degeneration of productive performances.* Proceedings of the third international congress on yak, in Lhasa, China, 4-9 September 2000. International Livestock Research Institute (ILRI), Nairobi, pp 300-307.

Lei H. Z. *et al.* (1986). Study on selecting and breeding the superior type of yak. *Journal of China Yak*, 1986 (2), 10-22.

Liu Q. & Cheng W. D. (1994). Studies on fattening yak. Proceedings of the first international congress on yak. *Journal of Gansu Agricultural University* (Special issue June 1994), pp. 224-227.

Long, R. J. & Ma, Y. G. (1996). *Qinghai's yak production systems*. In: Miller, D.G., Craig S.R., & Rana, G.M. (eds). Proceedings of a workshop on Conservation and Management of Yak Genetic Diversity, at ICIMOD, Kathmandu, Nepal 29-31 October 1996. ICIMOD (International Centre for Integrated Mountain Development), Kathmandu, pp. 105-175.

Miller, D.J. (1990). Grasslands of the Tibetan Plateau. *Rangelands,* 12, 159-163.

Pu X. P. *et al.* (2001). Introducing Legume forages to alpine region of Tibetan Plateau. *Grasslands of China,* 2001(3): 17-21.

Ren J. Z. & Chu C. P. (eds) (1993). Proceedings: Conference on Grazing Industry in Southern China. Gansu Grassland Ecological Institute, Gansu Science and Technology Press.

Wiener G. (1996). Disasters waiting to happen – yak. *Asian Livestock,* XIX (8) 93-95

Winter, H. *et al.* (1992). Pyrrolizidine alkaloid poisoning of yaks *(Bos grunniens)* and confirmation by recovery of pylloric metabolites from formalin-fixed liver tissue. *Research in Veterinary Science,* 52, 187-194.

Winter, H. *et al.* (1994). Pyrrolizidine alkaloid poisoning of yaks: identification of the plants involved. The Veterinary Record, 134, 135-139.

Wang W.B. *et al.* (1997). Effect of concentrate supplement on yak body weight gain during grazing summer season. *Proceedings of the second international congress on yak, in Xining, China, 1-6 September 1997*. Xining, China, Qinghai People's Publishing House, pp. 135-136.

Xie, A. Y. *et al.* (1997). Determination on degradability of several kinds of protein feeds in yak rumen. *Journal of Qinghai Animal Husbandry & Veterinary*, 12 (4): p 34-37

Zhang T. H. (1994). Making excellent scheme of yak herd construction turnover. Proceedings of the first international congress on yak. *Journal of Gansu Agricultural University* (Special issue June 1994), pp. 168-172.

Zhang D. G. (1998). Supplementary feeding of urea molasses multi-nutrient blocks and effect on productive of yak cows. *Acta Pratacultural Sinicak,* 7 (1): 65-69.

Zhen Z. C. (1994). Population structure of yak herd in Naqu prefecture of Tibetan autonomy. Proceedings of the first international congress on yak. *Journal of Gansu Agricultural University* (Special issue June 1994), pp. 172-175.

9   DISEASE IN THE YAK

(Chapter revisions by Tashi Dorji[1] in collaboration with Walter Roder[2] and by Yu Sijiu[3])

OVERVIEW

Yak and cattle often share the same habitat, especially during the winter season. It is not surprising, then, that many of the diseases observed in cattle are also reported in yak. From specific studies and surveys it appears that the incidences of some diseases may be high and this is attributed to lack of economic incentive for prevention and treatment in many cases. Incidences of some major diseases have, however, been reduced through strategic anthelmintic therapy and other treatments.

Introduction

Most of the general literature on yak highlights the remarkable ability of the animals to reproduce and survive in an exceptionally harsh environment and at the same time provide useful products for their owners. The inference might be that the hardiness of the yak also reflects healthiness, in the sense of absence of or resistance to disease. It is important, therefore, to note that yak are prone to most or all the diseases found in cattle elsewhere and that losses associated with such diseases are often quite high.

Information on the insidious losses of production resulting from disease is not readily available, though the economic consequences of such loss could be high. Vaccines and other prophylactic measures, as well as curative treatments, are not widely used even when they are indicated and are known to be effective.

The general paucity of treatment of disease is a consequence of several factors, including the remoteness of much of the yak territory, low cost-effectiveness of treatment (especially as treatment costs may often be relatively high), the traditional nature of much yak keeping and, possibly, a lack of knowledge or recognition of disease by herdsmen. It may also be attributed to the relatively low productivity of yak, which results in limited economic return from any treatment. However, the extent to which these factors apply differs from region to region and among countries with yak.

---

[1] Tashi Dorji Livestock Programme Officer at the Renewable Natural Resources Research Centre, Ministry of Agriculture, Jakar, Bumthang, Bhutan;
[2] Walter Roder is advisor Agronomist at the foregoing;
[3] Professor Yu Sijiu is Dean of the Faculty of Veterinary Medicine Science, Gansu Agriculture University, China

There are regional and national differences in the inputs of technical and veterinary advice to herdsmen and in the size of yak herds, which has a bearing on whether the products from the herd are primarily for home consumption or are marketed. In some countries and in relation to some diseases, vaccination is provided free by the State.

Many of the disease problems observed in yak may be caused or magnified by stress from the feed deficit in winter and early spring and from weather conditions, including the periodic disasters caused by these conditions. The overall incidence of most diseases is not accurately known for the yak population at large, although authors providing results from specific studies sometimes infer a wide prevalence. Information on some of the disease conditions affecting yak, as reported in a selection of the literature, is summarized in this chapter.

Bacterial diseases

Anthrax

This disease has a long history in China. Herdsmen recognize the clinical symptoms of the disease and its danger to themselves and do not eat the meat of affected yak. Vaccination of yak is used to control it in many areas. Lu and Ling (1985 a, b) recorded in 1958 and 1960 incidences of around 4 percent and mortality of 19 percent in a part of Sichuan and incidences ranging from low to high for areas of Tibet, all with high mortality rates. In Nepal, Joshi et al. (1997) reported an anthrax outbreak that had occurred in the Karnali yak rearing areas during 1990. The outbreak was effectively controlled through vaccination.

Botulism

This condition is caused by a toxin produced by *Clostridium botulinum* (type C has been identified in Tibet). Botulism was common among yak in China prior to 1955, but the incidence has since declined. However, Lu and Ling (1985a) recorded 9 193 cases in some counties of Tibet between 1971 and 1979, of which 4 048 were fatal. Vaccination is used as a control in some areas. The bacterium multiplies rapidly in dead carcasses, and it seems likely that the access that yak have to these is accentuated by the custom of disposing of carcass remnants and bones of slaughtered animals on pastures near the campsites of the herdsmen. Carcasses of animals that have died on the range are another source of infection. The yak may become infected either through direct chewing of bones of such carcasses, something they are known to do in cases of mineral deficiency (phosphorus in particular), or the infection may be picked up from polluted water.

Pal (1993) quotes the occurrence of botulism (strains B and C) from several countries with yak.

Brucellosis

This infectious disease, which has importance throughout the world, is common among yak and its hybrids. Concern with Brucellosis is made the greater by the fact that it is readily transmitted to humans. In Sichuan, Qinghai and Tibet, sample groups of yak were tested over the period 1952 - 1981, and an average of 17.4 percent (1.8 - 56.3 percent) tested positive (Local Disease Control Office, 1983). Wang and Yao (1984) reported that between 13 percent and 17 percent of yak in various groups on Haiyan pastures in Qinghai province had positive tests and that there was a significant reservoir of *Brucella* infection among wild animals as well as among sheep and dogs. Yuan (1979) examined 49 Maiwa yak in Honyuan county (Sichuan) by serum agglutination test and obtained six positive reactions. Joshi (1982) also referred to a substantial incidence of positive tests and clinical disease in Nepal and in countries of the former USSR and in Mongolia, but information on the more recent situation in these countries has not been obtained.

In China, S2 vaccine (swine strain vaccine) has been widely advocated for *Brucella* control measures since 1982. In a study conducted to monitor the effects of the vaccine against Brucellosis in growing yak, Chen and Zhang (1997) tested a total of 9 944 serum samples and 452 samples from aborted foetuses from Guoluo prefecture. The results indicated that the number of Brucellosis-positive samples fell from 21 percent prior to vaccination to 0.4 percent. *Brucella* species were not isolated from foetal material. Abortion rate in pregnant yak cows also decreased from 18.1 percent before conducting the program in the Guoluo prefecture to 2.8 percent. In a similar study in yak herds in west Sichuan, Pen *et al.* (1997) reported that the rate of *Brucella* infection fell from 56.5 to 6.3 percent within four years of S2 vaccination. At the same time, the abortion rate was reduced from 7.4 to 5.4 percent.

Both *B. melintensis* and *B. abortus* have been identified as agents with the former the more prevalent in China and the latter more commonly isolated in the former USSR (Joshi, 1982). The strain of *B. melintensis* found most commonly was Biovar 3, followed by Biovar 2 (Chen, 1983; Peng, 1987). Diagnosis and testing, which depend on laboratory methods, is undertaken mostly for investigation purposes and not for practical yak production.

Vaccination is sometimes used to reduce the spread and prevalence of the disease (noted by Joshi [1982] for countries of the former USSR and for Mongolia) but this practice is not widespread. Testing and slaughter are not considered to be viable options for control – at least not in the present circumstances of yak husbandry. The implications of Brucellosis in yak for human health may require consideration.

Calf scours

In some herds, 30 - 40 percent of calves, particularly the spring-born, develop profuse diarrhoea though this does not necessarily impair the general condition of the animals. The stools are of a thin, pasty to watery consistency, sometimes containing blood.

Traditionally, affected animals are given a drink made from medicinal herbs. However, scours in young calves, mostly from birth to four days of age, have also been reported as a major cause of death in two studies with yak. Both studies implicate *E. coli*. Yan and Ran (1981) reported an incidence of almost 80 percent within the first month of life falling to around 20 percent after that. A report by Lensch (1996) indicates that a mortality rate due to *E.coli* infection in yak calves was 20 - 30 percent.

In general, recovery rates are high if anti-bacterial treatment is given, but such treatment is not widespread. Tian *et. al.* (2002) studied the antibiotic sensitivity of 12 antibiotics on 68 strains of *E. coli* from healthy yak. Results showed that acquired drug resistance of *E. coli* was not a problem in yak in Qinghai as antibiotic use is not common (see section, Viral diarrhoea / mucosal disease).

Contagious bovine pleuropneumonia

This disease is caused by *Mycoplasma mycoides* and occurs among yak, between two and ten years old, principally in winter and spring when the animals are more closely confined than in the summer. In one such period, Hu *et al.* (1960) recorded an exceptionally high incidence of 54 percent in Ganzi county of Sichuan province. Lu and Ling (1985a) reported an incidence of 1.9 percent for herds in Tibet and a mortality of around 17 percent among those affected. Though vaccination is an effective option for control, it is not widely practised.

Chlamydia infection

Relatively recently, *Chlamydia* infection has attracted attention because of the apparent susceptibility of yak. Wang (1990) examined 102 yak and found the incidence to be 10.8 percent. In another report, Yuan (1991) showed an incidence of 42.7 percent among 553 yak. Shuai Yongyu *et al.* (1988) reported that abortions in yak in a part of Qinghai province were diagnosed as caused by *Chlamydia psittaci* infection. Tests on serum samples collected from yak that had aborted showed positive tests in 45 of 155 samples. Ma (2002) conducted a study to monitor the prevalence of *Brucella* and *Chlamydia* in Qinghai province. Out of 526 samples screened, only one sample was positive for *Brucella* and 15 samples were positive for *Chlamydia*, indicating that the incidence of abortion in yak due to *Chlamydia* may be of significance.

These studies show in respect of this form of abortion, as for many diseases, that yak are susceptible and that the infection exists in yak-producing areas. They do not indicate the overall incidence of the disease in that area of the country, or whether it is prevalent elsewhere.

Leptospirosis

This disease, which causes a generalized but serious illness in yak, was reported to have occurred in parts of Sichuan in the period 1980 - 1982, according to a report by Cheng *et al.* (1985). These authors recorded an incidence of 10 - 20 percent and a mortality of 30 - 50 percent. Agglutination and complement fixation tests on 187 serum samples were positive in 53 cases. Vaccines have been tried against the disease in the former USSR, but results were not satisfactory (Nivsarkar *et al.* 1997).

Lymphadenitis

Lymphadenitis can cause severe economic loss among yak. Multiple, hazelnut- to walnut-size abscesses appear on the skin of the neck and lower jaw and eventually rupture. They interfere with the animal's ability to feed with resultant loss in weight. Treatment in the primary phase with penicillin and streptomycin has yielded good results (Kosykh, 1964). Joshi (1982) reported serious economic loss from the disease in Nepal but quotes a report from southern Buryatia in the 1960s where the incidence appeared even more serious. Sporadic outbreaks of this disease have also been reported to occur among yak in Russia (Lensch, 1996).

Mastitis

Mastitis occurs in yak, but it is believed that the incidence is less than among dairy cattle, perhaps on account of the relatively low milk yield of yak and the suckling of calves. An outbreak in Hongyuan county of Sichuan was reported by Weggi (1983) to be due to streptococcal infection and similar in epidemiology, clinical symptoms and in response to medication to that found in cattle. The outbreak affected some 10 percent of the yak recorded by Weggi and coincided with a period of hot, dry weather and overcrowding on pastures at that time.

Joshi *et al.* (1997) reported that in a study of mastitis in yak herds in Nepal, the bacteria isolated from the milk were mainly *Staphylococcus aureus, Streptococcus agalactiae* and other *Streptococcus spp.* and *Coliform spp.*

Pasteurellosis

This disease is reported to occur every year in yak-producing areas and takes the form of a haemorrhagic septicaemia. Lu and Ling (1985a) noted in parts of Tibet between 1976 and 1979, a 0.34 percent incidence of haemorrhagic septicaemia among yak, with a mortality rate among affected animals of nearly 36 percent. A higher incidence of 2.3 percent with 89 percent mortality among animals in Baiyu county (Sichuan) was reported by Yang (1987). Joshi (1982) noted the occurrence of haemorrhagic septicaemia among hybrids of yak with local cattle in many districts of Nepal but made the point that these were in the lower and middle hill regions where the disease can be virulent and result in high mortality and that the incidence was much more limited in the higher alpine areas. Pal (1993) also quoted the occurrence of the disease among yak in India. Nivsarkar *et al.* (1997) reported that mass vaccination has effectively controlled the disease in other livestock species but has been little used in yak.

Salmonellosis

The disease is common among yak in China, mostly among calves between 15 and 60 days of age (*S. typhimurium, S. dublin* and *S. newport* have been isolated). Between 1960 and 1980 an incidence of 40 percent, with a mortality rate of 35 percent, was recorded for five counties of Gansu province (Lu, 1986). Similar studies from 25 counties in Tibet (1976 - 1979) recorded 5.2 percent incidence and 26 percent mortality (Lu and Ling, 1985a) and 10.5 percent incidence with 56 percent mortality in Qinghai (Deng, 1983). Effective vaccines have been produced in several of the Chinese provinces but are not widely used by the herdsmen.

Tetanus

Tetanus occurs occasionally in yak breeding areas. Ma and Kang (1993) reported that during 1959 - 1989, 32 yak suffered from tetanus and 31 of them died. The disease has been under control recently because of improvements in yak management.

Tuberculosis

Yak are susceptible to the bovine strain of *Mycobacterium tuberculosis*. Although the disease is known to occur in yak, there is little quantified information available and no control schemes are in place. Lu and Ling (1985a) tested 1 749 yak in Tibet with a single intradermal test and found that 12.7 percent of animals reacted positively, but some of these showed no other visible lesions. In Nepal, out of 23 tuberculin tests conducted in yak, three were found positive (Joshi *et al.*, 1997).

Other bacterial diseases

Other bacterial diseases reported for yak include Blackquarter (Joshi *et al.* 1997), *Coxiella burneti* infection (Geilhausen, 2002), Kerotoconjunctivitis and Camphylobacterosis.

Viral diseases

Foot and Mouth disease

This disease was well known in yak in the past. In 1960 an outbreak was recorded in Ganzi county of Sichuan with an infection rate of 72 percent and a mortality rate of about 4 percent. Strain O caused the highest mortality. Joshi (1982) and Joshi *et al.* (1997) reported a number of outbreaks in different parts of Nepal among yak and hybrids of yak with local cattle. They state that quarantine of affected animals is used in alpine regions of Nepal with the intention of allowing the lesions to heal and that vaccination, though effective, is not widely used. Pal (1993) referred to an outbreak in Sikkim in 1973 caused by the virus of strain A. Prasad *et al.* (1978) reported an outbreak among yak in the state of

Himachal Pradesh. A virus of strain O, previously reported from Nepal, was isolated in that outbreak.

Infectious Bovine Rhinotracheitis

The Infectious Bovine Rhinotracheitis is caused by a herpes virus and can cause abortion in severe cases. Qu and Li (1988) tested 126 yak serum samples with 45 samples positive to ELISA and 44 positive to the neutralization test.

Rinderpest

Yak are highly susceptible to Rinderpest with reported mortality rates of 90 - 100 percent. In China, the disease has been eradicated through vaccination since 1955. Prior to then, the disease was widespread (Liang Daxin, 1948); around one million yak are said to have died of it between 1928 and 1941 in the provinces of Qinghai, Gansu and Sichuan alone. A further outbreak in Qinghai in 1944, also reported by Liang Daxin, claimed 20 000 yak within seven months. Joshi (1982) refers to outbreaks with mortality rates up to 90 percent in parts of Nepal prior to 1966. Vaccination programmes, such as those in Mongolia and in the former USSR, as in China and elsewhere, may well have brought the disease under control.

Viral diarrhoea/mucosal disease

Gao *et al.* (1999) collected serum samples from yak herds in the pastoral regions of the northwestern and southwestern provinces of Shaanxi, Gansu, Ningxia, Qinghai and Sichuan for the detection of antibodies against bovine viral diarrhoea/mucosal disease (BVD/MD). The authors found that the detectable rate of BVD/MD in yak herds reached 30.08 percent, with the infection rate of Sichuan yak herds the highest (38.46 percent), followed by Gansu (29.41 percent) and Qinghai (28 percent).

Other viral diseases include pox and rabies (Joshi, 1982); Vesicular stomatitis (Lensch, 1996); calf diphtheria and *arthritis* (also listed, unusually, under viral diseases) (Joshi *et al.*, 1997); parainfluenza 3, bovine Herpes virus 1 and bovine diarrhoea-mucosal disease are also reported to occur in yak (Geilhausen, 2002).

Parasitic diseases

Ectoparasites

Ticks, fleas, lice and mites

These have all been found in yak, though herdsmen do not, in general, recognize their importance or the irritant effect on the animals.

Ticks: A report by Biswas *et al.* (1994) documents infestations with ticks of five genera, among yak is tracts of Arunachal Pradesh of India and lists the types found and the sites os infection on the animal. According to Lensch (1996), ticks cause moderate to severe infestation in cattle and yak on grassland in all regions of Mongolia. Clinical symptoms in severe infestations include restlessness and anaemia. Referring to yak in Mongolia, Lensch and Geilhausen (1997) wrote: "Ticks are found on the animals' eyelids, in the outer ear, on the cranial side of the neck and on the anterior and posterior thighs. Tick infestation is at its height in the rainy season from May to September. Ecological planning is recommended for tick control and should take into account seasonal variations, range of hosts, and known infected areas. The traditional method used by Mongolians of moving the cattle and yak to more or less tick-free grazing land during the summer months, largely protects the animals from (heavy) tick infestation." Joshi (1982) also referred to ticks among yak in Nepal and draws attention to the possible disease transmission caused by them there.

Fleas: when they occur, are found on any part of the yak's coat. As recorded by Lensch and Geilhausen (1997), the fleas "sometimes occur in conjunction with ticks on grazing land. The clinical symptoms are pruritus, anaemia and localized skin damage."

Lice: The report of Biswas *et al.* (1994) also provides evidence of infestation by lice of one genus in Arunashal Pradesh. There are apparently on report of this parasite in yak from elsewhere.

Mites: of a number of different families have been recorded in yak and yak hybrids in Nepal (Joshi, 1982). The main families are *Psoroptidae* and *Sarcoptidae* and cause the disease commonly called "mange". The clinical symptoms are persistent itching and chronic inflammation of large areas of the skin, especially of the back. Like in Nepal, Yu also observed mite infestations of yak in China (mainly yak calves of one to two years old).

Babesiasis (tick-borne)

This disease is caused by *Babesia bigemina* a protozoan parasite. In Aba prefecture of Sichuan province in 1981, 549 cases of yak infected with the disease were found and 273 of them died. In 1985, the disease broke out elsewhere in Sichuan province where around 500 yak died from it (Yu *et al.*, 1989). The organism is transmitted by ticks, and the symptoms are fever and haemoglobinuria.

Yak hypodermiasis (warble or gad fly)

On the basis of a study by Wang Yanhong (1994), yak hypodermiasis is a significant problem in yak. Jiang *et al.* (1997) reported that out of 1 149 yak examined in Sichuan province, the parasite rate of hypoderma larvae was 84.2 percent. Young yak between one and three years old were reported to be the more susceptible. Three varieties of

Hypoderma, namely *H. bovis*, *H. lineatum* and *H. sinese,* have been identified, with *H. lineatum* the most prevalent, accounting for 70 - 80 percent of all cases (Jiang *et al.,* 1997).

Larvae from warble fly (gad fly), cause damage to the skin as they burrow into and emerge from the hide, particularly on the back and loin of the yak. Apart from physical damage to the hide and loss to its value, there is irritation to tissues and secretion of toxins that retard growth and development in young yak and reduce milk yield and meat yield of adults. Death results in severe cases. Intramuscular injection of a vermicide (Ivomec) was fully effective in killing the larvae. In one trial, 110 out of 2 393 untreated yak died, but out of 500 that had been injected with Ivomec, only 2 died; the treated yak were also in better condition (Jiang *et al.*, 1997).

Lensch (1996) (basing his information on the personal communication of a study attributed to Minarz and Dorz, dated 1970) wrote that, in that study, 96 percent of adult yak and all juvenile yak examined were infested with *H. bovis* with infestation rates of 11 larvae per day in adults and 40 per day in young animals and that up to 280 larvae were found to be present in yak calves.

Also according to Lensch (1996), at the much higher elevations in Tibet (relative to Mongolia) fly strike usually remains untreated. Lensch (1996) also wrote that there appear to be no scientific reports of warble fly infestations from Bhutan, India or Kyrgyzstan; he noted, however, that in Mongolia, as in some parts of China, economic loss from warble fly attack in yak could be very serious if an intensive control program were not in place.

Endoparasites

Gid disease (Coenurosis)
Samdrup (1992) provides evidence that gid (Coenurosis) is a parasitic disease of economic importance for yak herdsmen in Bhutan. The cause of death is the intermediate stage of *Coenurus cerebralis* of the tapeworm Multiceps. The adult form parasitizes canines, including dogs, wolf, fox and jackals. Watchdogs, which are kept by herders to control and protect their yak from wild carnivores, are the main intermediate hosts in Bhutan. Yak become infected by grazing on pastures contaminated by dog faeces containing Multiceps (Tenzin, 1979). About 70 percent of the gid cases were reported in young animals of one to two years old (Tenzin, 1979). An eradication programme for gid was introduced consisting of deworming yak calves with Albendazloe and Fenbendazole and dogs with Niclosamide. As reported by Wangdi (1996), the programme was successful in reducing yak mortality due to gid in yak herds in one of the worst-affected areas of Bhutan from 40.3 percent in 1992 to 1.5 percent in 1994.

In a survey conducted to investigate the presence of hydatid cysts among 50 yak in Sikkim, 80 percent were found positive for the cyst (Ansari and Rai, 1991). In China, the incidence of hydatid cysts in the 535 Gannan yak examined was reported to be 41.8 percent (Li *et al.,* 1985). Joshi *et al.* (1997) reported on a similar disease condition due to tapeworm of *Echinococcus spp.* in Nepal yak.

Liver fluke

This is a common occurrence in yak in China and elsewhere where wet conditions exist. It is caused by *Fasciola hepatica* and, from an economic point of view, is one of the most important diseases in yak, as it considerably impairs the animal's performance. Infestation rates of 20 - 50 percent are common, though a study by Shuqiu Cheng *et al.* (1994) refers to infestation rates up to 80 percent of yak in some grassland areas.   Lensch (1996) noted that risks of liver fluke infestation are greatest at altitudes below 3 000 m and that in northwestern Tibet, at elevations between 4 500 m and 6 000 m, fascioliasis seemed to be of no importance. Zhu and Jiang. (1986) collected more than 7 000 snails in three areas of Sichuan and found the principal host snail to be *Galba pervia*. Herdsmen try to control infestation by restricting grazing of yak on marshland in the spring to only half a day at a time and to prevent access to marshland after rain. Marshlands are also burnt in winter. Dosing with triclabenzadole is effective in yak (Zhu and Jiang, 1986), but the extent to which it is used is not recorded.

Joshi (1982) noted significant infestation by liver fluke of both yak and their hybrids with cattle in many villages in Nepal. Out of 100 yak faecal samples tested in Nepal, 58 were reported positive for the presence of liver fluke eggs (Joshi *et al.,* 1997).

Roundworms

A report by Liu (1994), from studies in Tibet, suggested that roundworm infestations and the associated larvae may be a common problem in yak, though not as extensive as among the sheep on the same pastures. Many genera of roundworm were isolated (and listed by Liu, 1994), but the prevalence of different genera varied with the time of year. Liu (1994) noted that routine antiparasitic treatments were restricted to government yak farms and a few selected private farms but that the majority of yak were not involved in any treatment programme because worm infestation does not cause visible symptoms that might alert yak herders to a problem.

Wangdi (1996) examined faecal samples collected at random from 26 adult yak and 81 yak calves from western Bhutan. The results showed that in the adult yak, 19 percent were positive for *Strongyle spp.*, while among the calves 37 percent were positive for *Strongyle spp.,* 2 percent for *Coccidia spp.* and also 2 percent for *Trichuris spp.*

Pal (1993) quoted one study on yak in Sikkim showing 62 percent of yak infected with helminths. Another report based on a study conducted by the National Research Centre on yak in India in 1995 indicated that of the 63 yak faecal samples examined in Arunachal Pradesh, 32 were positive for various helminth eggs (Trichuris, Strongyles, hookworms, Dicrocoelium and Ascaris).

Miscellaneous conditions

Contagious skin diseases

Various contagious skin diseases, including ringworm (attributed to the fungi *Trichophyton* and *Microsporum*) and a chronic dermatitis, caused by the bacterium *Dermatophilus congolensis*, are also reported to occur in yak.

Pyrrolizidine alkaloid poisoning

Large numbers of deaths among yak in one part of Bhutan were found by Winter *et al.* (1992, 1994) to be due to Pyrrolizidine alkaloid poisoning. Several toxic plants were found to be involved, with species of *Senecio* predominating. It was concluded that the yak had been induced to eat these plants, which they would normally avoid, due to hunger arising from overgrazing of the pastures concerned. This matter is also referred to in Chapters 8 and 13).

Contaminated water

Yak can die suddenly or after protracted illness after drinking water from stagnant ponds, marshy areas and potholes (Dahl, 2000). The cause of the problem is not fully explained. This is a common condition in yak in Bhutan. The stagnant water appears red and oily and covered with greenish surface scum. A surprisingly high mortality rate of 39 percent was reported from a yak herd in central Bhutan (Sharma, 1996). In a separate study conducted in central Bhutan, Dorji (2000) reported that 37 out of 130 yak deaths were due to "poisoning" from contaminated water. Death occurs, especially during the onset of the winter season, when the yak return to their winter pastures. Although conclusive evidence could not be established, analyses of water samples collected from the affected areas have revealed the presence of blue green *Cynobacteria* algae (Dahl, 2000). Provision of an antidote, comprising activated charcoal and magnesium oxide (which can adsorb a variety of toxic chemicals) and broad-spectrum antibiotics, if administered in the early phase of the disease, was reported to be beneficial.

Mineral and trace element deficiency

Problems of mineral or trace element deficiency or imbalance are not specifically reported in the literature from yak-producing countries. An observation from Whipsnade Wild Animal Park in England (where a small herd of yak have lived since the 1940s) indicated that the yak there showed several of the symptoms of copper deficiency on the same diet that other *Bovidae*, and local domestic cattle in particular, find adequate, or nearly so, in respect of copper content (Nick Lindsay, Curator, and Edmund Flack, veterinarian at

Whipsnade, personal communication, 1994). Copper supplementation of the yak diet and occasional copper injection has brought improvement in the health, vigour and performance of the yak (Edmund Flack, personal communication, 1994). This suggests at least the possibility that yak may have an inadequate copper uptake due to an inherently low capacity of yak to absorb dietary copper – because a genetic component to the uptake of copper is well documented in other species (Wiener, 1987). More recently, Claus and Dierenfeld (1999) have reviewed and discussed the topic and provided more evidence of copper deficiency in captive yak.

Copper deficiency can result in poor growth and poor fertility, among other symptoms – but poor growth and poor fertility, by themselves, do not necessarily indicate copper or any other mineral or trace element deficiency, as overall poor nutrition may be the cause of the problem. In actual mineral and trace element deficiencies, appropriate supplementation will generally improve the conditions caused.

Traditional veterinary practices

Inherent remoteness and inaccessibility of the yak-rearing areas makes the delivery of conventional health services difficult. Because of this, herdsmen have acquired special local knowledge to deal with various livestock diseases by themselves.

Jest (1975) reported that yak are often bled from the jugular vein or the underside of the tail to provide blood for human consumption (originally for the benefit of the local people but now [Corneille Jest, personal communication, 2002] developed into a lucrative "industry" to cure gastric ills (such as among the Thakali in northern Nepal). However, the herders also claimed that this practice had benefits for the animal by "fortifying" it and renewing its old blood (see also Chapter 10). Craig (1997) provides information on traditional healing techniques, said to include principally moxa treatment (moxibustion) and bloodletting, practised by the local healers in Mustang and by Dolpo yak herders of Nepal and claimed as a cure for lameness and to "fortify" the yak.

Dorji and Tshering (1999) reported on diverse uses in Bhutan of herbal preparations and traditional healing methods for ailments such as Foot and Mouth disease, Blackquarter, plant and water poisoning, fractures and parasitic diseases. Hu Songhua (2002) describes four herbal prescriptions (*Powder of Dandelion*, *Decoction of Snakegourd and Burdock Achene*, *Ease Powder* and *Decoction of Eight Precious Ingredients*) and acupuncture methods for the treatment of bovine mastitis.

References

Ansari, M. Z & Rai, M.K (1991). Studies on occurrence and incidence of hydatid disease in yak in Sikkim. *Indian Veterinary Journal* 68, 112-114

Biswas, D., Barari, S.K. & Pal, R.N. (1994). Ticks and lice infestations in yak. Proceedings of the first International Congress on Yak. *Journal of Gansu agricultural University* (Special issue, June, 1994), pp. 322-324.

Chen, P & Zhang, N. (1997). A surveillance on effects of S2 vaccine against brucellosis in growing yak. *Proceedings of the second international congress on yak, in Xining, China, 1-6 September 1997.* Xining, China, Qinghai People's Publishing House, pp. 234-235

Chen, Z.X. (1983). The distribution and characteristic of Brucellosis in Qinghai Province. *Journal of Animal Science and Veterinary Medicine of Qinghai Province.* 6, 4-6.

Cheng, Z.D. *et al.* (1985). Leptospirosis in yak in some area of Sichuan Province: a retrospective study. *Chinese Journal of Veterinary Science and Technology,* 1, 17-19.

Claus, M. & Dierenfeld, E.S. (1999). Susceptibility of yak (*Bos grunniens*) to copper deficiency. *The Veterinary Record,* 145, 436-437

Craig, S. (1997). Traditional Tibetan veterinary practices in pastoral areas of northern Nepal. *Proceedings of the second international congress on yak, in Xining, China, 1-6 September 1997.* Xining, China, Qinghai People's Publishing House, pp. 255-260

Dahl, N. (2000). An investigation report on algae poisoning in yak. *Journal of Renewable Natural Resources Bhutan,* 1 (2), 65-73

Deng, C.H. (1983). Salmonellosis in yak. *Veterinary medicine of China,* supplement, 1983. pp 28-29.

Dorji, T and Tshering, G. (1999). Ethnoveterinary practices in Bumthang dzongkhag. *Journal of Renewable Natural Resources Bhutan,* Vol 1. Issue 1, pp 104-115.

Dorji, T. (2000). *Genotypic and phenotypic characterisation of the yak and yak farming systems in Bhutan.* MSc. Thesis, 2000. The University of Melbourne, Australia.

Durbar, Khatmandu, XVII, 145 pp.

Gao Sh. D. *et al.* (1999). Serologic monitoring of bovine viral diarrhoea/mucosal disease in yellow cattle and yaks in partial regions of the southwestern and northwestern five provinces. Chinese J. of Vet. Sci. & Tech., 29(7) 17-18.

Geilhausen, H E. (2002). Serological survey on infectious disease of a white yak herd in the Gansu province. *Proceedings of the 3rd international congress on yak held in Lhasa, P.R. China, 4-9 September 2000.* International Livestock Research Institute (ILRI), Nairobi, Kenya. pp 445-449.

Hu Angang, Cai Li & Du Shaodeng (1960). An investigation on yak in Ganzi County. *Journal of Southwest Nationalities College,* (Animal Husbandry and Veterinary Sciences Edition), 1960 (4), 46-50.

Hu Songhua (2002). Treatment of bovine mastitis with medicinal herbs and acupuncture. *Proceedings of the third international congress on yak, in Lhasa, China, 4-9 September 2000.* International Livestock Research Institute (ILRI), Nairobi, pp 450-453.

Jest, C. (1975). Dolpo – Communautés de langue Tibétaine du Népal. *Cahiers Népalais. Editions du Centre national de la Recherche Scientifique.* Paris (1975) chapt.7 (part on yak: pp.135-142)

Jiang, X., Huang, X. & Yang, X. (1997). Study on bovine hypodermiasis on the northeastern grassland in Sichuan. *Proceedings of the second international congress on yak, in Xining, China, 1-6 September 1997*. Xining, China, Qinghai People's Publishing House, pp. 243-247.

Joshi, D.D. (1982). *Yak and chauri Husbandry in Nepal*. H.M. Government Press, Singha.

Joshi, D.D. *et al.* (1997). Epidemiological aspects of yak diseases in Nepal. *Proceedings of the second international congress on yak, in Xining, China, 1-6 September 1997*. Xining, China, Qinghai People's Publishing House, pp. 229-233.

Kosykh, A.P. 1964. Treatment of purulent lymphadenitis in yak. *Trudy Buryat, Selkhoz Inst.*, 18, 24-32.

Lensch, J (1996). Krankheiten: In *Der Yak (Bos grunniens) in Zentralasien* (eds. Jurgen Lensch, Peter Schley and Rong-Chang Zhang). Duncker & Humblot. Berlin 1996, pp 237-246.

Lensch, J.H & Geilhausen, H.E. (1997). Infectious and parasitic diseases in the yak. *Proceedings of the second international congress on yak, in Xining, China, 1-6 September 1997*. Xining, China, Qinghai People's Publishing House, pp. 223-228.

Li, *et al.* (1985). An investigation on echinococcosis in yak at Lugu county, Gansu province. *Chinese Journal of Veterinary Science and Technology* No. 1. pp 25-26.

Liang, Daxin (1948). Yaks in Xikong. *Journal of Chinese Agricultural Association,* No.186.

Liu, W.D. (1994). Observations on growth-decline rule of roundworm and its larva in yak's stomach and intestine. Proceedings of the first international congress on yak. *Journal of Gansu Agricultural University.* (Special issue, June 1994), pp. 339-342.

Local Disease Control Office of Central Government (1983). Brucellosis and its control in China. *Government document*, 1983, 12 pp.

Lu, G.Z. & Ling, C.W. (1985a). Animal infectious disease in Tibet. (Publisher?), pp. 175-206.

Lu, G.Z. & Ling, C.W. (1985b). Animal infectious disease in Sichuan province. (Publisher?) pp. 84-85, pp. 219-221.

Lu, W.F. (1986). Current research of yak salmonellosis in China. *Animal Science and Veterinary Medicine of Gansu Province.* 3, 23-25.

Ma, J. and Kang Sh. R. (1993) Outlining of general survey of contagious disease of yak in Gannan. *Journal of China Yak,* 1993 (2), 31-33.

Ma Lizhong (2002). A diagnosis study of Brucellosis and Chlamydia in yak. *Proceedings of the third international congress on yak, in Lhasa, China, 4-9 September 2000*. International Livestock Research Institute (ILRI), Nairobi, pp. 463-464.

Mohanty *et al.* (2002). Use of herbal medicine for anoestrus management in yak. *Proceedings of the third international congress on yak, in Lhasa, China, 4-9 September 2000*. ILRI (International Livestock Research Institute), Nairobi, pp 368-370.

Nivsarkar, A. E., Gupta, S.C & Gupta N. (1997). *Yak Production*. National Bureau of Animal Genetic Resources, ICAR, New Delhi.

Pal, R.N. (1993). Domestic yak *(Poephagus grunniens* L.): a research review. *Indian Journal of Animal Sciences,* 63, 743-753.

Pen, X. *et al.* (1997). The immune effects of S2 vaccine against yak brucellosis in epidemic area. *Proceedings of the second international congress on yak, in Xining, China, 1-6 September 1997*. Xining, China, Qinghai People's Publishing House, pp. 234-235.

Peng, X.K. (1987). Brucellosis and its characteristics in Sichuan Province. *Journal of Southwest Nationalities College,* (Animal Husbandry and Veterinary Sciences Edition), 1987 (2), 32-35.

Prasad, S. *et al.* (1978). Isolation of foot-and-mouth disease virus from yak. Veterinary Record. 102, 363-364.

Qu, X. Y & Li, C. H. (1988). Studies on diagnosing infectious bovine rhinotracheitis in yak by ELISA. *Chinese Journal of Veterinary Science and Technology.* 3, 5-8.

Samdrup, T. (1992). *Gid surveillance in yak under Lingshe dungkhag-tour report,* Parasitology Unit, RVEC, Thimphu, Bhutan, pp 1-30.

Sharma, B (1996). *Report on water poisoning in yaks (Dur yak herds).* Bumthang, Ref. No. RVL/14/95/1642-8 dated, Jan 1996. Department of Crop and Livestock Support Services, Ministry of Agriculture, Bhutan.

Shuai Yongyu *et al.* (1988). Diagnosis of enzootic abortion in yak. *Scientia Agricultura Sinica,* 21, 76-81.

Shuqiu Cheng, *et al.* (1994). Study on Fascioliasis. Proceedings of the first international congress on yak. *Journal of Gansu Agricultural University* (Special issue, June 1994), pp. 324-327.

Tenzin, D. (1979). Studies of gid disease in yak with special reference to control measures. *Journal of Animal Husbandry of Bhutan,* pp. 1-4.

Tian Yun., Lu Chengping & Xiao Luzhong. (2002). Drug susceptibility test of *E. coli* isolates from healthy yak of Qinghai. *Proceedings of the third international congress on yak, in Lhasa, China, 4-9 September 2000.* International Livestock Research Institute (ILRI), Nairobi, pp. 439-444.

Wang J.L. (1990) Investigation on chlamydiosis of yak. *Journal of China Yak,* 1990, (3), 51-52.

Wang, J.L. & Yao, R.Q. (1984). Brucellosis infection in hare, mouse and wild birds. *Wild Animal,* 2, 42-43.

Wang, Yanhong (1994.) Experiment of prevention from yak hypodermiasis larva in Tianzhu. Proceedings of the 1st International Congress on Yak, *Journal of Gansu Agricultural University.* (Special issue, June 1994), pp. 343-345.

Wangdi, P. (1996). Survey of gid eradication program: incidence of coenurosis in yak population at Lingshe dungkahg. *Yak Newsletter* (Volume no. 2, November, 1996), pp. 12-24.

Weggi, S. (1983). Observation on streptococcal mastitis I yaks. *Chinese Journal of Veterinary Medicine,* 9, 12-14.

Wiener, G. (1987). The genetics of copper metabolism in animals and man. In: *Copper in Animals and Man* (eds, J.McC. Howell & J.M. Gawthorne), Vol. 1. Bocca Raton, Florida, CRC Press Inc., pp. 45-61.

Winter, H., *et al.* (1992).Pyrrolizidine alkaloid poisoning of yaks *(Bos grunniens)* and confirmation by recovery of pylloric metabolites from formalin-fixed liver tissue. *Research in Veterinary Science,* 52, 187-194.

Winter, H., *et al.* (1994). Pyrrolizidine alkaloid poisoning of yaks: identification of the plants involved. *The Veterinary Record,* 134, 135-139.

Yan, Z.S. & Ran, G.C. (1981). An investigation report on yak calf scours in Yajiang County. *Infectious Diseases in Livestock,* 1981 (2), 30-33.

Yang, C.Y. (1987). An investigation report of Pasteurellosis in Baiyu County *Animal Science and Veterinary Medicine of Sichuan,* 1987 (1), 34-35.

Yu J.F. *et al.,* (1989). Investigation on bovine *babesiasis* of yak. *Journal of China Yak,* 1, 40-42.

Yuan W.H. (1991) Investigation on the infection of yak chlamydiosis. Journal of China Yak, 1991, (2), 49-51.

Yuan, S.Y. (1979). *An investigation report on animal husbandry and veterinary medicine techniques of Ganzi Tibetan Autonomous Prefecture.* Scientific and Technology Committee of Sichuan Province, Scientific and Technology Association of Sichuan Province.

Yuan, S.Y. (1979). An investigation report on Maiwa Yak Brucellosis. *Journal of Southwest Nationalities College* (Animal Science and Veterinary Sciences Edition), 1979 (6), 30-32.

Zhu, H.Q. & Jiang, X.S. (1986). A study on liver fluke host of yak and sheep in Northwest of Sichuan. *Journal of Southwest Nationalities College,* (Animal Husbandry and Veterinary Sciences Edition), 1986 (1), 25-26.

OVERVIEW

Almost everything from the yak is used to sustain the life of the herdsmen and their families and is used either directly or sold to provide an income.

Milk in its raw state is used principally as a component of "milk tea", which is drunk liberally. Butter, made in traditional fashion, is the main product from the milk in most places and has many uses apart from its use as food. Skimmed milk is used in a variety of ways, including a form of cottage cheese ("milk residue"). A Swiss-type manufactured cheese is made especially in Nepal.

Meat is obtained mostly from animals slaughtered before the onset of winter when they are in good condition, but animals that die accidentally are also used. Meat is eaten fresh around the time of slaughter, but over a more prolonged period after being naturally frozen. Meat is also preserved by drying. Dried meat keeps longer than frozen. Sausage is made both from meat and from blood or from a mixture of the two. Some parts of the viscera are eaten; others are used as casings for sausage or as storage containers for other products. Much of the viscera is left unused on the pastures where this material can become a pollutant. Hooves, after canning, have become a popular and nutritious food in pastoral areas and other places. Blood, apart from use in sausage, is also used to make into a meal as a protein feed for animals. Bone is usually made into handicrafts but is also widely sold for the manufacture of bone meal and glue.

The hides are processed simply and dried before tanning locally or in factories. The leather has many different uses. Pelts of calves that have died are also processed and made into coats for children. The coarse hair and the fine down find many uses from making ropes to garments to tents. The hair from the yak's tail is used ceremonially and as a fly-whisk. Yak heads and tails are also made into ornaments and given as gifts. Yak faeces is used principally as fuel, after drying or, in some localities, used by the herdsmen in building walls, for example.

Introduction

The herdsmen and their families obtain nearly all their needs from the yak. The products from yak during their lifetime are milk, hair and down, draught power, and dung for fuel, and after slaughter there is the meat and various products from the organs and non-consumable parts of the body and the hide. The majority of these products are used by the herdsmen and their families, but some of them are sold. Income can be derived from most of the products and also from the sale of pack animals and animals for breeding. Where yak herds are in the proximity of hill towns and villages, there is a ready market for the products, which then provide cash value to yak production. (Some of the economic and marketing considerations are discussed in Chapter 12).

At present, most of what is sold from the yak are primary products, or close to primary, and so the economy, based on the yak, benefits little from the added value that accrues from processing, or from the manufacture of more sophisticated products. Butter and various forms of soft cheese, made by the herdsmen, are sold or used in barter for other necessities – and sometimes, as in parts of India (Chapter 11, part 3), used as a means of paying rent for grazing land. Factories built in Nepal for the manufacture of a Swiss-style hard cheese and in China for the manufacture of yak leather goods and textiles are the beginnings of developments designed to provide new markets for the pastoral people. These developments arise from national concerns to raise the living standards of the people in these remote mountain areas and to improve the economy of these regions.

The rest of this chapter considers the products and describes briefly how they are traditionally and, for the most part, currently used. In general, what follows applies to yak-producing parts of China. It is likely, however, that the traditional methods of making and using yak products are essentially similar among yak herders in most areas.

Milk and milk products

Though the milk yield of individual yak females is low, there are many of them and so the total quantity of milk produced is substantial. Milk is used primarily in the areas of the country where yak are most widely distributed and in the regions of the mountain pastures. In areas where yak have only relatively recently been introduced, on the periphery of the main territory, there is no tradition of using milk from the yak or from the hybrid offspring of yak males with the females of local cattle. These "local" hybrids give relatively little milk and are used mainly for draught purposes (as distinct from the hybrids of "improved" dairy breeds of cattle and yak cows). In recent years, the price of yak milk has become high in China and, as a result, is an important part of the herders' income.

Raw milk
Whole milk is usually drunk only by people who are ill or weak, but it is also given to children and old people. Some of this milk is drunk raw, being considered more nutritious that way, but mostly the milk is boiled first, as encouraged for health and hygiene.

Yak milk yield, as evident from the results given in Chapter 6, has a high content of solids around 18 percent, including about 7 percent of fat. The milk has a fragrant, sweetish smell and whole milk also tastes somewhat sweet, even without adding sugar – so when drunk by herdsmen sugar is never added.

Raw milk is used mainly for the beverage called "milk tea" – a mixture of tea and milk – drunk at all times of the year. This is a staple part of the diet of the herders and their families. In the warm season, when there is plenty of milk available, or when given to guests, the brew will contain 20 percent milk, or even more, and the colour of the drink is yellow. Herdsmen and their families more usually drink a light tea with only 5 percent milk added and the colour is then milky white with a tinge of yellow. The milk tea is brewed from tea leaves (cut from a tea brick), which is added to water and boiled for a few minutes; raw milk is added in the proportion required and boiling continues for a further few minutes. Some people may add a little salt. Sugar is never added, but the milk itself has a sweetish taste already. Tibetan people may add some *zanba* to the brew, making it both a food and a drink for themselves and their guests. *zanba* (also *tsampa*) is the staple food of Tibet. It consists of roasted oat or barley flour, or a mixture of the two, made into a paste with yak butter and is usually rolled into balls for eating.

Normally, whole milk is used in the tea, but skimmed milk is also used in order to increase the amount of butter that can be produced from the available milk supply.

Milk boiled with mushrooms is regarded as a delicacy by herdsmen. Salt is usually added to the milk-mushrooms stew – and the boiling is thought to give protection from poisoning in case the wrong mushrooms have been used.

In pastoral areas, raw milk is customarily used to rear young yak calves and lambs or kids that have lost their mothers or that cannot suckle enough milk from weakened mothers. Pets, such as cats and dogs, are sometimes allowed yak milk in addition to meat.

Raw milk is also sold to milk-powder plants that have been built in recent years to produce milk powder as well as butter and other milk products. Some milk is sold for direct consumption in towns and villages, or in the upland areas it may be bartered for food grain.

Butter
Butter is the principal product from yak milk and it represents one of the staple foods of the local people. It is also the principal milk product traded by herdsmen. The raw butter contains 12 - 15 percent water, 1 percent protein and the rest fat. (Old butter contains about 3 percent water.) Butter production is regarded as the yardstick of the quality of yak milk, and herdsmen pay great attention to it.

There are two main ways in which the herdsmen make yak butter in China. The traditional and still most prevalent method is to churn the butter in a wooden bucket or it can be squeezed while in a bag made of hide. Milk separators are in use in some areas and reduce the amount of work needed to make the butter. Cream separated in this way prior to churning produces the best butter with a lower water content and a longer storage life than by older methods.

Churning

Making butter by churning involves allowing the milk to stand for a day to ferment. The milk is then heated to about 20°C. The warm milk is poured into a churn varying in size of up to 80 cm high and 60 cm in diameter. A stick for stirring is held in the centre of the churn by the lid. Figure 10.1 shows a medium-sized churn in use. The herdsmen (more often the womenfolk) rotate the stick until the fat solidifies and it is difficult to churn further. The churning takes between one and four hours depending on the size of the churn used and the quantity of milk. The herdsmen then remove, by hand, the lumps of milk fat floating on the surface and wash it in water. Next, water is squeezed out and the butter is formed into cylindrical or cube-shaped blocks by using a plank of wood. Lastly, the butter is wrapped for storage in a bag of calf hide, or yak rumen (or, in some places, wrapped in broad, hard leaves) and may be placed in a wooden container. Each bag weighs approximately 50 kg. The butter will keep usable in this way for one or two years without going mouldy.

Figure 10.1 Butter making in a churn

Squeezing

To make butter in a hide bag, the milk is first heated, as before, and poured into the bag made of calf or goat hide. The herdsman blows into the bag to expand it and closes the opening. The bag is shaken until the fat solidifies into globules, then the contents of the bag are poured into another container. The rest of the procedure is similar to that already described.

Machining

Before using a milk separator, the milk is first heated to 30° - 35°C and then filtered. The separator operates by turning a handle at a standard speed until the fat has separated from the other components. The fat is called raw butter and is put in a separate container. Some herdsmen add a little sour milk to the raw milk as a starter in order to increase the amount of butter made.

End products

The raw butter can be made into fresh butter, sour butter and pure butter depending on the different processes. Fresh butter is made by washing raw butter in water and squeezing out the water, as before, and salt can be added to make it more tasty. Sour butter is made by adding some sour milk to raw butter and fermenting for half day, following the same process as for fresh butter. Pure butter is made by heating the raw butter to remove protein and water. Edible pigment and additives can be used to make butter more colourful and to make it keep longer. Some additives, with the recommended amounts (as a percentage) in butter, are shown in Table 10.1

Table 10.1 Recommended content of additives in butter
[Source: Editing Committee of Science of China Yak, 1989]

Additives	Vitamin C (%)	Vitamin E (%)	Lecithin (%)	Citric acid (%)	NDGA (%)	Dehydro-genation acetic (%)	Vitamin K_3 (%)
Contents	0.02	0.03	trace	0.01	0.01	0.02 - 0.05	0.01 - 0.001

Utilization

Butter is used for a number of foods, including *zanba*, pancakes and dishes fried in it. It is also added to milk tea and consumed salted or unsalted according to the area. When milk is not available, butter is used in tea in some areas in place of raw milk. Some people prefer butter, particularly, it is said, herdsmen in Northwest Sichuan and in the Tibetan pastoral areas.

Another use is to mix melted butter with roasted flour, in equal quantities. The mixture is then kneaded and stored until used. When required, this dough is melted into salted or sugared water and eaten that way, or it is mixed with seeds, such as peanut, sesame, walnut, soybean or Chinese dates. These ingredients add flavour and make the food a favourite among Tibetan people for welcoming their guests.

Butter is used also for many purposes other than food, including its use for tanning and for polishing fur coats. It is used as a fuel in domestic lamps and by lamas in sacred lamps. Butter is used by women on their skin and hair, and it is also used as a lubricant to assist in hand milking. Butter is a component of some Tibetan medicine. When mixed with different colouring materials, butter is also used to make moulded sculptures. Larrick and Burck (1986) describe some of these sculptures as huge – sometimes two or three storeys high – and fashioned by monks for religious ceremonies and New Year celebrations.

"Hard" cheeses

Nepal was one of the first countries in Asia to establish a cheese industry and was the only country in the world producing yak cheese until the 1980s. More than four decades have passed since the founding of Nepal's yak cheese industry (Joshi *et al*, 1999). Hard Swiss-style *Gruyére* cheese is now produced from the milk of *nak* (female yak) and *chauri* (female hybrid) (Thapa, 1996). Bhutan (Tshering *et al.*, 1996), Mongolia (Davva, 1996), India (Pal and Madan, 1996) and Pakistan (Khan, 1996) are also now trying to produce yak cheese.

Production methods

Thapa (1996) described cheese production in the following way: "Before making cheese, raw milk (7 - 8 percent fat and 9.5 - 10 percent SNF) is standardized to a 3.5 percent fat content through cream separation. The excess cream is churned into butter. The milk for the cheese is then pasteurized at 65°C for five minutes by immersing the milk in a can in a bath of boiling water. The milk is then cooled to 30°C by immersing the can in a cooling water trough. This cheese milk is transferred to a 200 - 300 litre copper kettle and put on a traditional fire. Then a 0.5 percent culture (*Str. Thermophilus* and *Lactobacillus helveticus* 1:1) is added. After five minutes, a rennet solution (2.5 g dissolved in 500 ml boiled and cooled water per 100 litres of milk) is added and stirred for one minute before it is allowed to set at 33°C. The kettle is covered.

"The top curd is turned after 30 minutes and allowed to set for another five minutes. The curd is then cut and stirred for 25 minutes at 32°C. It is allowed to settle for five minutes before the high temperature scalding treatment is begun. The curd is heated to 53°C for 30 minutes over an open flame, at which time the curd is separated out with a cheesecloth once the producer thinks the curd is sufficiently firm. The curd is then placed in moulds and pressed with stone slabs. The block is turned at 15 minutes, 30 minutes, 1 hour, 1.5 hours, 2 hours, 5 hours and after overnight pressing.

"Cheese blocks are brined (22 percent) for 48 hours. They are then stored for curing at 10° - 15°C under ambient temperatures. The cheese is given a daily salt washing for three weeks; after five months it develops a good flavour. The green, or raw, cheese yield is 11 percent. Six to eight percent of the cheese weight is lost after five months of curing.

"The chemical composition of three-month-old yak cheese is around 68.2 percent of total solid (TS), 49.4 percent of butterfat on a dry matter basis (BFDMB) and 1.37 percent of salt and the pH is 5.75. By comparison, three-year-old yak cheese contains 76.9 percent of TS, 46.8 percent of BFDMB and 3.12 percent of salt (Schulthess, 1986)."

In Nepal, cheese production is being viewed as a commercial enterprise (Joshi *et al.,* 1999). The yak cheese industry is of significant importance for rural income and employment. Though the industry is not large, it represents a positive and successful example of agro-industry – although, according to the assessment of the industry in Nepal by Joshi *et al.* (1999), not all individual factories are profitable, and there are problems, including some with quality control and others with environmental effects (for example, deforestation as a result of providing wood for fuelling factories), which need to be considered. More than 4 000 people are said to earn their living, directly or indirectly, from yak cheese production in Nepal. Yak cheese is ideal for the promotion of an agro-industry based on livestock products. Due to its high value and market demand, yak cheese can be exported to other countries (Colavito, 1994). According to Sherchand and Karki (1996), income from the production of yak cheese was estimated to be the equivalent of nearly

US$300 000 in 1994 (at the then exchange rate of approximately US$1 = 50 Nepal rupees), excluding wholesale and retail profits. If yak cheese had not been produced in these areas, the milk would have been used to produce *churpi* (dried cheese) and *ghee*, thereby incurring, according to the same authors, a financial loss equivalent to around US$100 000. Such amounts may seem small when compared to the turnover in some other industries, especially in more developed regions, but the extra income from a yak cheese industry can be significant for the relatively small and remote rural communities of yak producers in these Highland regions.

Milk residue (other types of cheese)

In China, some "milk residue" (as it is called by the herdsmen) is normally made from skimmed milk but occasionally from whole milk. Whichever milk is used, it is heated to 50° - 60°C and sour milk is added to make the liquid curd. The mixture is poured into a wicker basket or gauze bag to allow the whey to run off. The curds are fresh milk residues. Then they are spread on a cloth to be dried. Figure 10.2 shows milk curds drying outside a tent in Sichuan province and Figure 10.3 shows cheese at a more formed stage laid on the roof of a tent in Mongolia.

Figure 10.2 Milk curds drying outside a tent

Figure 10.3 Yak cheese drying on the roof of a tent

Half-dried residue contains about 20 - 30 percent, sometimes 40 percent of water. Dried residue contains little water. The dried milk residue from skimmed milk is white and hard, that from whole milk is yellow and brittle. The protein content is around 55 percent and the lactose 21 percent. Fresh milk residue is taken as a snack with milk tea and also used in other ways, such as fried or eaten with added salt and sugar. Half-dried residue is usually kept as a ration by herdsmen who are out with their animals at pasture and is also taken as a snack with milk tea. Dried residue is often mixed with butter to make *zanba*.

In Bhutan, skimmed milk is poured into a large pan where it is slowly heated and stirred continuously until cheese is formed. The cheese is either used fresh or processed further into hard cheese for marketing. Two types of dried cheese, *chuto* and *hapiruto*, are made, depending on the market for which they are intended. *Chuto* is made by slicing a circular cheese into small pieces and hanging the pieces in strings of 20.

After boiling them in milk, the strings are hung on a pole in the tent and allowed to dry until they become hard. *Hapiruto* is made in larger pieces and dried on 20-piece strings until it is rock hard.

In India, milk products from yak are primarily *churpi* (hard, dried cheese) and butter. Skimmed milk is processed into *churpi,* which is kept in un-tanned bags. These products have no market value outside herding communities.

Milk cake

This is a product mainly of whole milk, though sometimes skimmed milk is used. It is similar in production to "milk residue" but is harder and looks like "cake". It is usually eaten with butter and sugar and is then considered more delicious by the herdsmen; and it is one of the dishes offered to guests.

Whey

After butter, milk residue and cheese have been made, the whey is rarely used in the pastoral regions. But in the agricultural-pastoral areas it can be used to feed pigs. The whey is also used in making leather by a traditional process.

Sour milk

Sour milk is a favourite among herdsmen and their families all year round, but especially in the warm season when milk is being produced in substantial amounts. Freshly boiled milk is poured into a pail and when the temperature has fallen to 50°C, a little sour milk is added and mixed until the temperature has dropped to 40°C. The pail is then covered and wrapped in wool to keep it warm. Five or six hours later in the warm season, and longer in winter, the milk will have soured. This product can be made from either whole or skimmed milk – the former having more colour and taste. The sour milk is drunk alone or sometimes mixed with *zanba*. A technology to produce yak sour milk is now being developed for wider application, as there is a demand for the product (Huang Y. K. *et al.*, 1999).

Milk skin

Milk skin (as it is called by the herdsmen) is a milk product in yak-raising areas of China, made especially in Muslim communities. Raw milk is poured into a pail and heated to near boiling (around 85°C); then, on slower heat, the milk is stirred with a ladle. When dense foam appears, the pail is removed from the heat and allowed to cool. After 12 hours, a thick layer of milk skin (around 1cm) forms on the surface of the milk. The skin is then removed and dried for two to three days. Sometimes water in which rice or millet has been boiled is added to the raw milk for dilution (making up approximately a quarter to a third of the total quantity) to produce a low-fat milk skin. Milk skin made from either whole or skimmed milk is usually served as a snack with milk tea but can also be cooked in dishes or eaten as a "sandwich" (as a filling between two slices of home-made bread or in a bun).

"Toffee"

Larrick and Burck (1986) refer to a product the consistency of toffee (*korani,* in Sherpa) made by boiling milk very slowly to dehydrate it.

Milk wine

In Mongolia, milk is also fermented into an alcoholic drink as noted by Magash in Chapter 11, part 2.

Meat and meat products

Yak are an important source of meat for the herdsmen and their families, but the meat is also sold. Even in areas and countries where religious taboos inhibit the slaughter of the animals, the meat is eaten, but professional butchers, rather than the owners of the animals, do the slaughtering. In Nepal, for example, as Joshi (1982) explained, for the situation in Nepal, ordinary cattle are protected by law, but the legal code is unclear in relation to yak.

Larrick and Burck (1986) made a similar point when writing about specific places in Tibet. Animals that die accidentally are quite commonly eaten, even where killing is not the norm.

Many yak are slaughtered every year and this is normally done when the animals are in their best condition, before the onset of winter. Some of the meat is consumed fresh and much else is frozen in nature's own "deep freeze" and stored that way. Meat is also dried and keeps longer than when frozen.

The herders and their families eat meat mostly for the four to five months following slaughter. Yak are not slaughtered deliberately in spring or early summer because they are in poor condition and very lean at that time – though a few yak may die or be killed as casualties. Meat is therefore rarely eaten by herdsmen from April to July, although dried yak meat is still available.

Over recent years, the Chinese Government has built a number of small meatpacking and storage plants in the cold pastoral regions. This has allowed more slaughtering of yak at the best time and has also extended the storage season for frozen yak meat and meat products, including some retail cuts of meat. Most of this is supplied to cities.

Commercial slaughterhouses taking in yak also exist in Mongolia and some other countries, including North America where it serves the relatively new and still small yak-meat industry.

Fresh yak meat

The quality of yak "beef" is at its best in the autumn because of the good condition of the animals at that time. The method of butchering and eating by the herdsmen is quite simple. The carcass is cut into large cubes then boiled in fresh water for a few minutes. The meat is eaten with salt and with the help of a Tibetan knife. Milk tea is taken at the same time. When guests are present, the meal is more elaborate: Boiled rib-meat from the yak as well as from sheep is served and will be put on a plate and the meat eaten with the hand. There may be a steamed bun stuffed with chopped yak meat to which salt, condiments and fat have been added. The casing of the bun is thin, as the flour mixture has not been fermented. Thawed, frozen yak meat has the same flavour as fresh.

Air-dried meat

Prior to winter, the herdsmen living in the uplands cut yak meat into long narrow strips (approximately 4 - 5 cm wide and 30 cm long) and dry these suspended from woven-hair ropes. Drying takes only a few days. The air-dried meat will keep for one or two years either hung in a tent or stored in hide bags – this is a longer storage period than for the naturally frozen meat.

The air-dried meat is very dry indeed and has a distinctive flavour. Some of this dried meat is eaten as it is, only cutting or tearing the strips into smaller pieces; and milk-tea is drunk as an accompaniment. When cooking the dried meat, there are two main methods. One is to roast it by burying the meat in the stove, fuelled by yak dung, until the meat smells fragrant. It is then taken out, cleaned and cut into pieces. The other method is to soak the dried meat for several hours and then boil it in water. Salt and condiments are not usually added.

Smoked meat

There is also smoked "bacon-beef" which is similar to air-dried beef, but the fresh meat strips are first salted in a container for one or two days and then hung over the stove in the herdsman's tent to smoke. This again can be eaten either raw or cooked. The smoked meat is a product of the warm and rainy season and is made from the meat cut by the herdsmen from yak that have died of old age or from disease or have been killed by wolves.

Corned beef

Corned beef is salted "bacon-beef", which is very popular in the yak raising areas of Yunnan province, China. Frozen meat strips are rubbed for one or two minutes. When the meat becomes soft, salt and condiments are added. The meat is rubbed until it becomes wet and it is then transferred to a jar, which is sealed with paper or cloth. After 18 - 21 days, the salted meat is taken from the jar and dried in the air for about seven days. The best corned beef is reddish in colour, savoury and tasty, and after boiling, steaming or frying, it can be eaten with *zanba* and accompanied by milk tea.

Beef jerky

In Qinghai and Sichuan provinces of China, beef jerky is mainly produced in the meat-processing plants. There are two kinds of beef jerky – spiced and curry. The fresh meat is boiled in water for one to four hours, depending on its tenderness. When cooled, it is cut into thick slices 1.5 cm long, 1 cm wide and 0.5 cm, which are put into a pot and sautéed for three hours to remove some water from the tissue. Spices (Table 10.2) are placed between the meat slices, which are then covered with water and left to simmer for about three hours. The slices are taken out and hung to drip-dry for four hours, then dried at 65°C for six to eight hours. This product is known as "spiced jerky". "Curry jerky" is made by mixing the spiced jerky with curry powder. These products can be eaten directly or after additional cooking, frying or boiling.

Beef jelly

Beef jelly is a relatively new product in pastoral areas and welcomed by yak herders, particularly children and old people. It is made from the liquid that remains after boiling the meat to produce jerky. The liquid is mixed with a yeast infusion and heated to 35° - 40°C in a pot. The fat is separated from the mixture by a milk separator to leave about 1 percent fat and 3 - 4 percent total solids. The mixture is then reduced by boiling to a jelly containing about 25 - 30 percent of total solids. One percent salt, 0.05 percent monosodium glutamate, 0.025 percent beef essence and 0.001 percent preservative are added. After further mixing, the jelly is sealed in a bottle. If the colloid of Chinese caterpillar fungus is added to the jelly, it becomes more nutritious and valuable.

Table 10.2 Spices and other additions to the contents in 50 kg of "spiced jerky"
[Source: Editing Committee of Science of China Yak, 1989]

Spices	Contents (kg)	Spices	Contents (kg)
Sugar	1.05	Benzoic acid	0.05
Salt	1.90	Chilly powder	0.20
Monosodium glutamate	0.25	Soy sauce cake	0.625
Five spices (prickly ash, star aniseed, cinnamon, clove and fennel)	0.35	Yellow rice or millet wine	0.50
Sichuan pepper powder	0.15	White wine	0.25

Sausage

There are two main types of sausage filling – blood and meat. The casing for the sausages comes from the cleaned large or small intestine of the yak. Sausage, and in particular the blood sausage, is made at the time the yak are slaughtered.

Blood sausage

The blood used for sausage is from the thoracic cavity of the yak. To maximize the amount of blood in the thoracic cavity, herdsmen do not use what would be regarded as the normal method of slaughter but resort to a way of asphyxiating the yak.

When dead, the yak is skinned and the heart and lungs are removed; the large quantity of blood in the thoracic cavity is then drained off and used for making the sausage.

zanba and salt are added to the blood to make a paste before filling the clean, small intestine. This is then tied into segments (20 - 30 cm long) with sinew from yak or with hemp rope. In some areas, a little yak meat is added to the sausage mixture, and this is considered more delicious. The blood sausage is boiled in water and eaten either at the time it is made or after it has hung in a house or tent. The sausage may also be roasted on top of the stove fuelled by yak dung.

Larrick and Burck (1986) referred to an area in Tibet where occasionally blood is taken from the live yak, ostensibly for the sake of its health. Joshi (1982) referred to a similar practice in Nepal. About a litre of blood is taken from the jugular vein and when solidified, is eaten fried, boiled or mixed with *zanba* and baked into a form of bread (see also Chapter 9 under traditional veterinary practices).

Meat sausage

Meat sausage is usually encased in the large intestine. It is composed of 50 percent yak meat, 25 percent visceral fat and 25 percent blood. The meat and fat are chopped into pieces and salt, condiment and the blood added before the mixture is put into its casing. The filled large intestine is tied into segments as for blood sausage – though the segments are usually larger (about 50 cm long).

In Tibet, the herdsmen normally consume the sausage fresh. It is boiled in water for about two hours, and the casing is pierced with a needle to prevent it bursting. Meat sausage can be stored for about one month. In more recent years, herdsmen living on the cold grasslands have taken to filling the intestine of pigs with a mixture of diced yak meat, diced pork fat, salt and condiment. The sausage is tied into short segments (15 cm long), small holes are pierced into the casing, and then it is hung up in the house to be dried prior to eating.

Viscera and offal

There are large quantities of viscera and offal from the animals that are slaughtered, but they are not all used. Much is lost and is left on the pastures, which is a waste of a resource and can become a pollutant.

There is potential for better utilization – the drawback arises from the likely additional costs involved in such utilization relative to the rather low value of the product.

Viscera

Herdsmen divide viscera into edible and inedible parts. The parts regarded as edible are heart, stomach including rumen, small and large intestine, liver and kidney. The other parts of the viscera are classed as inedible by the herdsmen and, interestingly, include the lungs and the pancreas, which are eaten in some of the other parts of the world.

When yak have been slaughtered in meat processing plants, more of the viscera are eaten. Viscera from the yak are also used for making medicine that is sold locally and in the cities. The exceptions are the spleen and the pancreas, which, if kept at all, are used only as dog food.

Offal

By tradition, all inedible parts (apart from hair and hide) are regarded as offal and much of it is discarded on the grasslands. Some of it is cooked as dog food. The discards include, in addition to parts of the viscera, the horns and hoof (but see the following section), the contents of the alimentary tract and blood, other than that in the thoracic cavity (used in sausage making). (The bones might also be discarded in this way if there is no market for them.). If not eaten by birds of prey, the discarded offal can become a source of pollution when it decomposes.

As previously referred to, the thick horn of the yak bull is used as a feeding bottle for rearing calves. The empty gallbladder can be used as a casing for sausage or as a container for butter or milk. The bladder and the male reproductive organs find uses in Chinese medicine. In particular, the penis of the male yak is regarded as a strong aphrodisiac.

Hooves

Yak hooves are rich in protein, especially the colloid protein. Cartilage in hooves is higher than other tissues of yak. At present, canned yak hooves are very popular, especially in pastoral areas (Xue B. *et al.*, 2000).

Blood (other uses)

In addition to making sausage and medicine, blood is also made into meal as protein feeds for animals, especially poultry (He X. Q. *et al.*, 1988) due to its high protein content (around 18.5 percent). There are several kinds of blood meal derived from different processing methods, including ordinary meal, fermented meal and enzyme meal. Among these, enzyme meal has the highest protein content, and ordinary meal is the most easily produced.

The process of making ordinary meal involves solidifying the blood, cutting the blood block into pieces, boiling, adding salt, drying and grinding into meal (Tao L. *et al.*, 1993). A report by Huang X. S. (2000) describes that yak blood can be made into a fire-extinguishing agent for use in industry.

Bone

In local areas, yak bone is often made into exquisite handicrafts, such as combs, buttons and ornaments. Bone is also increasingly being sold for the manufacture of bone meal and glue. The bone marrow is used as a calcium supplement in medicine; bone meal, as animal feed, is rich in phosphorus and calcium and also as an ingredient of compound fertilizers. Yak bone is also used to extract bone fat. Bone paste is a new kind of food, which can be added into sausage, meat pie, meatball and dumpling (Huang X. S., 2000).

Hair and down fibre

Yak differ from other domestic cattle in that the hair is of economic use and importance. Use of the hair dates back to the time that yak were first domesticated. The hair from the yak is a valuable item and has become essential to the life of herder households. Generally, in traditional use of the hair, the down and the coarse fibres are left mixed together. Uses of mixed fibres depend on the fibre length, on the position of the body from which the hair is derived and on the down content.

The long hair that grows on the fore and rear ends of the body (the "skirt" hair – see yak in Figure 10.4) and on the legs are used to make rope for tying up the tent. The method of making the rope is as follows: The longer hairs are removed from the coat and hand rolled into a log of hair about 15 cm in diameter. A single spindle fixed into the ground is then used to spin the hair into yarn of a thickness and length depending on different requirements. To make the strands, one person turns the spindle using a hide rope while another holds the ball of hair. A rope will then be made from either three or four strands of yarn, the latter being the stronger. Rope made of yak hair is durable and withstands rain, wind and sun. Rope made from black and white yarn is admired for its appearance and is used to enhance the appearance of saddles and reins. In addition to ropes, the yarn spun from long hair is also used for weaving tents, bags, rugs and slings in Bhutan (Tshering *et al.*, 1996); clothing, tents and bags in Mongolia (Davaa, 1996); and clothing, tents, bags, sacks and caps in China (Huang W. X., 1996; He S. Y. *et al.*, 1997). Yak wool products are waterproof and durable and may be dyed if required.

In local use, down hair is most often processed mixed with coarse hair. What passes as down is shorn hair from which long fibres have been removed – this comes mostly from the "skirt" hair. Down hair from the neck, shoulder and rump of the animal is used less often and is allowed to be cast and left lying on the grazing land.

Figure 10.4 A yak at the Government Breeding Centre, Arunachal Pradesh, India showing the "skirt" hair (which can sometimes reach the ground) (Photo courtesy of D. Steane)

The way that the down mixture is used varies among the nationalities keeping the yak. For example, Tibetan people use the hair mostly to make tents while Yi people use it to make cloaks and short jackets. The procedure is first to weave the yak hair and down mixture into a blanket and then use the blankets to make tents or clothes. The processing procedure depends on what is being made. Blankets of 50 cm width, for example, are woven from two-ply yarn made into a thread. The material for the blanket is loose, clean hair shorn from the belly of the yak, with the long and coarse fibres removed. A tent (Figure 10.5) may be made from two large hair blankets interspersed with several smaller ones. Each year it may be necessary to replace one or two of the smaller blankets. Blankets are also made into a rectangular bag with an opening in the middle.

In Jiulong county of Sichuan, the herdsmen like to wear cloaks and short jackets made of a yak down-hair mixture. It is waterproof and keeps the people warm in summer or winter. With the advent of better knitting and processing methods, the clothes have been made more ornately and turned into handicrafts. One way to make clothes is similar to that for making tents – from a blanket though one with a higher content of down in the material. Another procedure is to felt the yak down first. The felt of yak down and hair is also widely used in the pastoral areas to make pads for saddles, cushions, bedding and insoles for boots. The felt pad made from the down-hair mixture is damp proof and helps people to keep warm in what is often a damp tent.

More recent developments, especially since the middle of the twentieth century, have increased the use of the down from yak for quality textiles, following trials of the materials in China. The down is used in clothes and suiting, knitted garments and blankets in China, garments and blankets in Bhutan and famous Sharma carpets in Pakistan. The textiles made from down are considered to have better lustre and feel than those made of wool. Knitwear made from yak "cashmere" (the down) fetch high prices in international markets.

Hairs from the tail of the yak were historically used as a tribute. White tail hairs are considered the best for this – and nowadays are sold to tourists. The major uses of tail hair are for clothing and fake beards used in Chinese opera and for wigs. The yak tail is also used as decoration and more practically as a fly-whisk – well-known in India but valued as such even in ancient Rome to which it was taken by merchants from the East (Zeuner, 1963).

Figure 10.5 A typical large tent in Tibet
(Photo courtesy of Horst and Barbara Geihausen)

Hide and pelt

Yak hide is generally inferior to that from ordinary cattle. It is loose and uneven in texture and often has holes from gadfly (warble fly) in it. There are large quantities of yak hide and pelt in the pastoral areas, and they have great importance in the local economy.

The method of processing the hide is very simple. The herdsmen peel the skin off the yak after slaughter or other form of death and spread it on the grassland to dry. After drying, the skin is sold to a tannery or used by the herdsmen. Some fresh hides are also sold without being dried.

Rawhide that has not been tanned and with the hair still uncut is used mainly to pack raw butter. It is also used as a wrapping for the wooden box used by herdsmen to transport their belongings. For this purpose, the fresh hide is cut into long pieces, tied on the wooden box and allowed to dry. Sometimes the whole hide is used for this purpose. The hide makes the box easy to carry and less easy to break in the frequent moves made by the herdsmen. Because of the cold climate, the raw hide does not quickly go bad and can be used over and over again, even if the box inside gets broken. Rawhide can also be cut into ropes. These traditional uses of rawhide are becoming less frequent. More often now it is the leather, made from the hide, which is used. This has improved the utilization of yak hides.

Leather from yak is usually tanned by a traditional method. For this purpose, the herdsmen soak the hide, remove from it the connective tissue under the skin and then spread old, rancid butter on the skin (fresh butter is not useful in tanning). The skin is then rolled up to allow the butter to soak in. Sometimes the skin may be pounded with feet or hands to help the butter soak in completely. When the hide is fully soaked and soft it is trimmed with a knife. As for most procedures, a number of local variants exist in methods of tanning.

The leather is used to make bags for storing food, including milk residue, and to make felt boots and soles. It can also be cut into strips of differing width, depending on use, as an alternative to rope for carrying water or firewood and to tie up animals. These leather ropes can also be used with the saddle in pastoral areas and as a form of carriage for people in agricultural parts of the country.

The leather from yak has other uses too. The sliding ropes across rivers and streams in the mountains and valleys are often made from yak hide. Boats (coracles) used to carry goods on, for example, the Brahmaputra River (Yaluzangbu River in Chinese) or the Yalong River use yak hide – as illustrated in Figure 10.6. To construct a coracle herdsmen make bags from yak hide that are blown up and a link of ten or more such bags is fixed to a wooden plank to make the boat. This will be 4 m long and 2 m wide.

a   b

Figure 10.6 a) A coracle of yak hide b) A coracle in use
(Photos courtesy of Horst and Barbara Geilhausen)

Most pelts are made from the hides of yak calves that have died. Herdsmen skin the dead calf, remove connective tissue, and soak the skin in milk whey. After the skins have soaked for a few days they are taken out and tanned with butter to make them soft. To complete the process, the hair is then combed. These yak pelts are used traditionally to make children's coats.

According to Siegfried Scheller (personal communication, 1994), yak is one of the species that has attracted particular attention from industrial manufacturers of leather in the immediate vicinity of yak herds. Such factories have been set up in parts of China, especially for processing yak hides and sheepskins. Quoting Scheller (1993), "The leather made from yak hides for shoes, leather goods and clothing is characterized by a unique handle, an interesting grain pattern and good wear and performance properties."

Head and tail

In most yak-raising areas, the head of the yak is thought to be a symbol of strength and safety, and the yak tail a symbol of wealth and luck. Therefore, yak heads and tails, with or without hair and hide on them, are made into ornaments by herdsmen or given to guests as gifts.

Faeces

Yak faeces is used primarily as fuel by the herdsmen. But as described earlier, it is also used to make pens and winter enclosures for stock and is painted onto wood fencing in the cold season to fill cracks. In agricultural areas it is sometimes used as fertilizer.

When used as fuel, the faeces are first dried. Faeces for this purpose is collected daily at the campsite at the end of the day's grazing or brought in from the range in the warm season. A stick wrapped in yak hair is used to cut the faeces into thin (1 cm) slices that are exposed to the sun for a day or longer on each side until dry. When fully dry, the faeces slices are stacked in heaps up to 2 m high and "painted" with fresh faeces to keep out rain. A drainage channel is often dug at the bottom of the heap to take away run-off water. If the heap is to be used up before the rainy season, it may not be painted. Completely dry faeces are also stored in the tent, ready for use (see Figure 10.7).

Bezoar

One unusual product from yak, as also from other cattle, is naturally cultivated bezoar stones. They have a high cash value when sold and therefore help the herdsmen to add value to their yak production. The bezoar stones are produced in parts of Sichuan, Xingjiang and other provinces by inoculating the gallbladder of the yak with an oval, hollow, plastic ball (its size like a ping-pong ball), there are many holes on its shell to allow bezoar to aggregate from inside and around the outside of the ball. To achieve the insertion of the ball requires a small operation that is performed by the herdsmen.

Thereafter, the cultivated bezoar is normally harvested (by an operation again) two years after the inoculation of the gallbladder. However, quality of cultivated bezoar, with a cholebilirubin content of about 20 percent is not as good as naturally occurring bezoar stones (with cholebilirubin content of more than 35 percent) (Yang Zhilin, personal communication, 2002,). The bezoar is sold for use in Chinese medicine.

a   b

c

Figure 10.7 Aspects of drying, collection and storage of yak dung for fuel

a) Yak dung drying
b) Dried yak dung collected for storage (Photos a and b courtesy of Han Jianlin)
c) Dried yak dung with implements for handling in Mongolia (Photo courtesy of Horst and Barbara Geihausen)

References

Colavito, L.A. (1994). The yak cheese industry of Nepal: An industry analysis and strategies for future development. Kathmandu: Dairy Enterprise Support Component of ATS Project/ Chemonics/USAID.

Davaa M. (1996). Conservation and management of domestic yak genetic diversity in Mongolia. *In*: In: Miller, D.G., Craig S.R., & Rana, G.M. (eds). *Proceedings of a Workshop on Conservation and Management of Yak Genetic Diversity* at ICIMOD, Kathmandu, 29-31 October 1996. ICIMOD (International Centre for Integrated Mountain Development), Kathmandu, pp 41-46.

Editing Committee of Science of China Yak (1989). Sciences of Yak. Chengdu: Sichuan Science and Technology Publishing House, pp 301-330.

He, S. Y. *et al.* (1997). Zhongdian Yak. *Journal of China Yak.* 1997(1): 1-5.

He X. Q. *et al.* (1988). Experiment on feeding chicken with yak blood meal. *Journal of China Yak.* 1988 (3): 48-49.

Huang X. S. (2000). The delicacy and treasure from the plateau yak (*Bos grunniens*) with its broad prospect. *China Dairy Industry.* 2000 (6): 14-16.

Huang W. X., (1996). Conservation and Management of Yak Genetic Diversity in the Tibetan Autonomous Region. In: Miller, D.G., Craig S.R., & Rana, G.M. (eds). *Proceedings of a workshop on Conservation and Management of Yak Genetic Diversity* at ICIMOD, Kathmandu, 29-31 October 1996. ICIMOD (International Centre for Integrated Mountain Development), Kathmandu, pp 93-104.

Huang Y. K. *et al.* (1999). Technology in producing yak sour milk. *Journal of Southwest Nationalities, Natural Sciences Edition.* 1999 (1): 58-60.

Joshi, D.D. (1982). Yak and Chauri Husbandry in Nepal. H.M. Government press, Singha Durbar, Kathmandu, Nepal, XVII, 145 pp.

Joshi, D.D., Awasthi, B.D. & Sharma, Minu. 1999. *An assessment of the yak cheese factories in Nepal.* National Zoonoses and Food Hygiene Research Center, Kathmandu, 75 pp.

Khan Rash (1996). Yak production and genetic diversity in Pakistan. In: Miller, D.G., Craig S.R., & Rana, G.M. (eds). *Proceedings of a workshop on Conservation and Management of Yak Genetic Diversity* at ICIMOD, Kathmandu, 29-31 October 1996. ICIMOD (International Centre for Integrated Mountain Development), Kathmandu, pp 57-60.

Larrick, J.W. & Burck, K.B. (1986). Tibet's all-purpose beast of burden. *Natural History*,95,56-65

Pal R. N. & Madan Moti Lal (1996). Yak production in India. *In*: Miller, D.G., Craig S.R., & Rana, G.M. (eds). *Proceedings of a workshop on Conservation and Management of Yak Genetic Diversity* at ICIMOD, Kathmandu, 29-31 October 1996. ICIMOD (International Centre for Integrated Mountain Development), Kathmandu, pp 29-39.

Scheller, S. (1993). Leder vom Dach der Welt. Leder-und Häutemarkt, 45, 43-64.

Schulthess, W. (1986). Nepal: Dairy Development 196-86. Kathmandu: SATA.

Sherchand L. & S. Karki (1996). Conservation and management of yak genetic diversity in Nepal. *In*: Miller, D.G., Craig S.R., & Rana, G.M. (eds). *Proceedings of a workshop on Conservation and Management of Yak Genetic Diversity* at ICIMOD, Kathmandu, 29-31 October 1996. ICIMOD (International Centre for Integrated Mountain Development), Kathmandu, pp 47-56.

Tao L. *et al.* (1993). Possibility of making plasma meal, haemoglobin meal, SOD, thrombin and fibrin meal with blood of yak and other animals. *Journal of China Yak.* 1993(4):31-33.

Thapa Tek. B. (1996). Yak cheese production in Nepal. In: Miller, D.G., Craig S.R. & Rana, G.M. (eds). *Proceedings of a Workshop on Conservation and Management of Yak Genetic Diversity* at ICIMOD, Kathmandu, 29-31 October 1996. ICIMOD (International Centre for Integrated Mountain Development), Kathmandu, pp 165-171.

Tshering L., Gyamtsho Pema & Gyeltshen (1996). Yaks in Bhutan. In: Miller, D.G., Craig S.R., & Rana, G.M. (eds). *Proceedings of aWorkshop on Conservation and Management of Yak Genetic Diversity* held at ICIMOD, Kathmandu, Nepal 29-31 October 1996. ICIMOD (International Centre for Integrated Mountain Development), Kathmandu, Nepal. pp 13-24.

Xue B. *et al.* (2000). The determination of nutrient contents of canned yak and Tibetan sheep hooves and the design of nutrient label. *Chinese Qinghai Journal of Animal and Veterinary Sciences.* 2000 (6): 9-10.

Zeuner, F.E.(1963). *A History of Domesticated Animals.* London, Hutchinson, pp.352-353.

11   YAK IN DIFFERENT AREAS AND COUNTRIES OF THE WORLD

OVERVIEW

A large proportion of the descriptions and examples pertaining to yak and yak husbandry in preceding chapters were taken from published investigations and experience with yak in China, and much of that information is relevant to yak anywhere. But even within China there are some differences among the principal provinces with yak in the environment and in the relative importance of yak in the life of the people and the economies of the provinces. The first part of this chapter will draw attention to these aspects through separate accounts for Tibet, Qinghai, Sichuan, Gansu, Xinjiang and Yunnan.

The second part deals with yak in the other countries, mostly in Asia and adjacent to China, with their own traditions of yak keeping. Numbers of yak in these other countries may seem small relative to those in China, but, nonetheless, the yak in these other mountainous regions have significant local importance. Much of the detailed information on yak in earlier chapters would be instantly recognizable as also relating to yak in these other countries. Certainly, there are features of yak and yak production special to several of these areas, many of which also support significant investigational and development work with yak. Where appropriate, additional information is provided on the performance of yak and on different aspects of yak production in such countries.

The third part of this chapter deals with yak in "new" environments, principally a relatively small population in parts of North America and fewer in Europe, with some of the animals kept for commercial purposes and others in zoos and wild animal parks. The one common element for these yak is that a significant number of the generally small herds are found in conditions that are atypical of those for yak in the traditional territories. Few of these animals in the "new" environments suffer the nutritional deprivations over winter and early spring that are so common for yak in their native habitats, and many are kept at relatively low elevations and in temperate climates.

YAK PRODUCTION IN SIX PROVINCES (REGIONS) IN CHINA
By Han Jianlin[1]

The purpose of this part is to provide more detailed information on the environment and yak husbandry of the six principal provinces with yak in China as a supplement to the general information from China given elsewhere in this book and in particular to the brief mention of these provinces in Chapter 1. (A map of the Qinghai-Tibetan plateau in the Appendix shows the provinces and some of the locations – not the prefectures – referred to here).

Tibetan Autonomous Region

General information
Tibetan Autonomous Region (Tibet) (known as Xizang in China), on the Qinghai-Tibetan plateau (26°52' - 36°32'N, 78°24' - 99°05'E) has an average altitude above 4 000 m a.s.l. The total area is 1 128 400 sq km - 1 000 km from south to north and 2 000 km from east to west and making up one eighth of the total Chinese territory. It borders Xinjiang, Qinghai, Sichuan and Yunnan provinces in China, and the countries of India, Nepal, Myanmar and Bhutan. The northwest of Tibet is dry and cold and the southeast is relatively warm and humid (rainfall decreases 100-fold from east to west – from 5 000 down to 50 mm/year). The main climatic features are prolonged sunlight, strong radiation, low overall temperature (annual average well below zero) but with large variations, as daytime temperatures in summer can be quite high. There are two distinct seasons: clear and dry, and humid.

For purposes of administration there is one municipality and six prefectures in Tibet (Table 11.1.1). Statistics collected for November 2000 showed 2.62 million residents in Tibet, of which 2.41 million were native Tibetans (National Bureau of Statistics, China, 2001).

Yak population
Animal husbandry is the basic industry of Tibet. In recent years, animal husbandry and the rural economy have developed rapidly. Tibet is one of the five largest pastoral areas in China. Animal husbandry is essential to the livelihood of the local people. Tibet has a total area of 64.8 million ha of rangelands, of which 59.5 million ha are usable pastures. The total livestock population is about 23 million. The policy for livestock development is guided by the principle of "controlling the number of animals, increasing off-take,

---

[1] Han Jianlin is a molecular geneticist at the International Livestock Research Institute, Kenya. He is also Professor of Animal Genetics and Breeding, Gansu Agricultural University, China and Executive Secretary of the International Yak Information Center and China Yak Breed Association in Lanzhou, China

guided by the principle of "controlling the number of animals, increasing off-take, bettering the structure of production, and improving the profitability of livestock development" (Wang Wenpei, 2002).

Tibetans describe yak as *Nuo*, meaning treasure and refer to it as "the treasure of the plateau" or "the boat of the plateau" due to its ability to use the highland pastures more efficiently than other livestock and by providing the most to the livelihood of the people living in the area (Yang Xuqing, 2002). The yak is the most important of domestic animals for Tibetan herders and therefore plays a key role in animal husbandry in Tibet (Wang Wenpei, 2002). Northern Tibet is the area generally accepted as that in which yak were originally domesticated some 4 500 years ago (cf. Chapter 1). Cai Li (1989) reported that in 1983 there were 3.2 yak per sq km in Tibet and one yak for every three persons, but since then there has been a slight increase in yak numbers (see Table 11.1.1).

Among the various prefectures of Tibet, yak numbers and the populations of other livestock differ substantially and are shown in Table 11.1.1. Over the past 20 years there has been a slight decline in yak numbers in Nakchu, which has the largest yak population among the prefectures, and a slight increase in Chamdo where yak-cattle hybrids have a significant role, with more than half the total number of hybrids found in the main agro-pastoral areas of eastern Tibet (see Table 11.1.1) where cultivation of land is also an important feature.

The highest density of yak are found in the eastern part of Tibet in the counties of Lhasa and Chamdo and surrounding areas (between 5 and 23 yak per sq km) while the lowest densities (less than 1 yak per sq km) are found in vast tracts of the north of Tibet and in a smaller area in the very Southeast.

In Nakchu, the prefecture with the largest number of yak, income from animal husbandry accounts for 80 percent of the GDP. The prefecture is vast, has a low animal and human population density and is diverse in terms of agro-ecozones, pasture types, livestock production systems and economic activities varying from east to west. In general, the yak husbandry in Nakchu is considered to be poor (Yang Xuqing, 2002). From Table 11.1.2, it can be seen that percentages of yak in the total livestock population decline with an increasing altitude and a decreasing annual rainfall from east to west in the prefecture. Huang Wenxiu (1996) suggested that the climatic variation was the reason for the varying livestock pattern across the prefecture with the west being cold and dry and with a semi-desert type of pasture where sheep and goats predominate (see Chapter 13). Yak in the eastern part also have the higher productivity as seen in Table 11.1.3 (Yang Xuqing, 2002).

The three recognized breeds in Tibet - the Pali, Sibu and Jiali (Alpine) – are found in the Shigatse, Lhasa and Nakchu prefectures, respectively (cf. Chapter 2). The Sibu are being associated with an agro-pastoral area and the Jiali and Pali are almost exclusively pastoral.

Table 11.1.1 Number (thousands) of yak and yak hybrids and
other livestock in the prefectures of Tibet in 1999
[Source: Tibetan Bureau of Agriculture and Animal Husbandry, 1999]

	Yak	Hybrids	Cattle	Sheep	Goat	Horse*	Pig
Lhoka	249.8	21.0	207.4	1 172.9	411.9	54.8	24.4
Shigatse	531.5	53.8	309.0	3 016.7	1 518.9	74.4	4.4
Nyingtri	148.2	56.3	313.6	80.9	88.4	41.7	106.6
Lhasa	436.1	13.9	161.9	572.2	433.3	49.0	28.1
Nakchu	1 444.5	1.1	10.0	4 028.1	1 253.6	91.4	2.6
Ngari	133.7	2.0	6.9	1 253.5	1 042.9	19.1	0
Chamdo	971.9	187.3	197.7	941.1	976.2	145.8	32.7
Total	**3 915.7**	**335.4**	**1 206.5**	**11 065.4**	**5 725.2**	**476.2**	**198.8**

* Donkey and mule are included.

Table 11.1.2 Climate and yak distribution in Nakchu prefecture in 1999
[Source: adapted from Yang Xuqing, 2002]

Location	Average altitude (metres)	Average annual temperature (°C)	Average annual rainfall (mm)	Total livestock ('000)	Yak ('000)	Percentage of yak in total livestock
East	4 300	1.5	600	1 250	541.5	43.3
Central	4 600	-2.0	410	2 482	608.6	24.5
West	4 700	-3.0	250	3 179	305.7	9.6

Table 11.1.3 Performance attributes of yak in Nakchu in 1999
[Source: adapted from Yang Xuqing, 2002]

Location	Reproductive rate (%)	Marketing rate (%)*	Average individual meat yield (kg)	Average individual milk yield (kg)	Average individual undercoat yield (kg)
East	69.0	12.7	101.9	136.5	0.41
Central	50.8	12.4	102.0	74.5	0.54
West	44.9	9.8	99.1	41.8	0.73

*Surplus stock available for sale.

Yak herd structure

Wei Xuecheng (1994) estimated herd structure of Tibetan yak to be 1.8 percent breeding bulls, 35.3 percent reproductive females, 28.6 percent castrated males and 34.3 percent calves.

More recent data show that herd structure varies somewhat among the three breeds as shown in Table 11.1.4. The Pali breed has the highest proportion of females, particularly in the productively important older age groups (four years old and older). The relatively large proportion of mature males retained in the Sibu breed is because a significant number, which are castrated, are used for draft purposes in that part of Tibet.

Table 11.1.4 Herd structure of the three yak breeds in Tibet in 1997-1998
[Source: adapted from Ji Qiumei *et al*., 2002a]

Breed	No.	Percentage of total yak		1 year		2 years		3 years		4 years		>5 years	
		M	F	M	F	M	F	M	F	M	F	M	F
Pali	2,059	35.8	65.2	8.1	8.9	6.2	5.6	4.4	5.0	3.2	6.1	13.9	39.6
Sibu	1,081	46.0	54.0	7.5	9.4	4.8	5.3	4.3	3.9	4.6	4.4	24.8	31.0
Jiali	20,952	37.2	62.8	6.1	8.2	6.0	9.0	4.8	6.1	4.4	7.5	15.9	32.0

Because of the importance of cultivation in the territory of the Sibu yak breed, it is also associated there with a larger variety of other livestock species than is the case for the other two Tibetan yak breeds. These other species also compete for resources. Ji Qiumei *et al.* (2002a) argued that to improve productivity not only of the yak but from animal husbandry in general, a key issue is to optimize both species and herd structures. They point out, in particular, the competition for grazing resources from horses that are no longer used for transport but remain as an indulgence, and the presence of too many goats with poor cashmere production, especially in the Sibu and Pali yak producing areas. Thus, yak production cannot be considered in isolation from other factors.

Hybrids of yak with local Tibetan cattle are produced in the Jiali and Sibu yak areas but not in the more remote areas of the Pali yak.

Productivity

Milk production
Peak milk production in the Tibetan yak is in August (Dou Yaozun, 1990). On this basis, five-day milk yield of the three breeds, herded on natural pastures, were recorded in August and used to estimate the milk yield from May to October by Ji Qiumei *et al.* (2000), as shown in Table 11.1.5. The estimates suggest that the three breeds differ in milk

261

yield; but although all were at pasture, they are kept in different parts of Tibet. Breed and environment are therefore confounded. For the same reason, it is uncertain what conclusions to draw from the fact that these yields are lower than those normally quoted for the Tianzhu White and the Jiulong breeds in other parts of China. The milk composition figures for these breeds are shown in Table 6.2 (where it may also be noted that the estimates of milk yield given for the Jiali breed based on older data [Zhang 1989] are lower than those shown in Table 11.1.5 – unfortunately, reasons for the difference cannot be adduced from the publications).

Table 11.1.5 Estimated total and monthly milk yield of the three yak breeds* in Tibet in 1997-1998 [Source: adapted from Ji Qiumei *et al.*, 2000 and 2002a]

Breeds	Milking method	No.	Total (kg)	May	June	July	Aug.	Sept.	Oct.
Pali	Full milking	15	214.8	25.8	34.4	47.3	53.7	36.5	17.2
	Half milking	10	184.8	22.2	29.6	40.7	46.2	31.4	14.8
	Average		199.8	24.0	32.0	44.0	50.0	34.0	16.0
Jiali	Full milking	23	192.0	23.0	30.7	42.2	48.0	32.6	15.4
	Half milking	25	103.2	12.4	16.5	22.7	25.8	17.5	8.3
	Average		147.0	17.7	23.6	32.5	36.9	25.1	11.8
Sibu	Full milking	11	216.0	25.9	34.6	47.5	54.0	36.7	17.3
	Half milking	25	143.4	17.2	22.9	31.6	35.9	24.4	11.5
	Average		179.7	21.6	28.8	39.5	44.9	30.6	14.4

* Three breeds are kept in different areas of Tibet.

Meat production

Ji Qiumei *et al.* (2002a) provided some recent results on body dimension of yak in Tibet that they believe show a decline in the performance relative to earlier years, particularly of the Sibu yak (although, because of relatively small numbers involved, the possibility of sampling errors affecting the comparison cannot be ignored). As possible causes for a decline, the authors point to additional pressure put on grazing by "unconfined" yak derived from a Tibetan cultural practice of releasing a small proportion of animals (up to 5 percent in some areas), quite apart from generally suboptimal grazing practices. To improve matters they suggest the need for supplementary feeding, especially in winter, a reduction in the proportion of unproductive animals in the herd, males especially, and attention to selection of breeding stock, as well some "social" measures. However, if a decline in productive performance of yak in Tibet over the past 20 years is real, it could well point to a systematic deterioration in the pastures and their use – in line with the view elaborated in Chapter 13. (Yang Xuqing, 2002) also reported a lower production of meat, milk and down hair from the yak in Nakchu prefecture in 1999 compared to 1991 (discreet years not being ideal for showing time trends), but the reproductive rate increased between these two years (see the following section, Reproductive performance.) Without further information, it is not possible to conclude whether the decrease in individual yak performance might have been due to increased stocking on the same grazing resources or whether that in turn led to deterioration of the pastures, as argued in Chapter 13.

Ji Qiumei *et al*. (2002b) examined five animals of the Jiali and six of each of the other two breeds for carcass characteristics. The results suggest that Jiali yak may have a higher dressing percentage – and hence meat yield – than the Sibu, but more studies will be needed to indicate whether the differences found are significant. The study does, however, provide some useful information on several carcass characteristics of yak and some other compositional data.

Hair and undercoat yield
Ji Qiumei *et al*. (2001) reported the results of hair and undercoat production from a survey of Tibetan yak in 1997-1998. Jiali yak had the best yield among the three breeds of the most valuable component of the fibre – the undercoat – with an average of 0.6 kg per adult animal.

Reproductive performance
The reproductive patterns of the yak in Tibet are as described in general terms in Chapter 5. According to Ji Qiumei *et al*. (2002a), there were no substantial differences among the three breeds of yak in Tibet in either female or male reproductive performance. As might be expected of a breed in an agro-pastoral area, the females of Sibu breed tended to show first oestrus and be mated perhaps a year earlier than the others. In general, females calve once in every two years, and the twinning rate is only 1 - 2 percent. The calving rates by natural service are shown as 30.8 percent, 48.4 percent and 45.7 percent of the cows mated every year for the Jiali, Pali and Sibu yak, respectively. There is a tendency to keep bulls to an old age beyond their reproductively best performance. But because these bulls keep their dominant ranks in the herds, this custom both lowers calving rates and unnecessarily increases pressure on the grazing by keeping unproductive males.

In contrast to the decline in meat, milk and fibre yield from yak in Nakchu, Yang Xuqing (2002) also reported that reproductive rate in 1999 was greater than in 1991. The proportion of breeding females in the population increased from 32 percent in 1991 to 45 percent in 1999 and the percentage of cows with a live calf at six months, among those mated, rose from 47 to 57 percent.

Wei Xuecheng (1994), Bhu Chong (1998) and Wang Wenpei (2002) reviewed the progress on the research on yak in Tibet. Recent research has centred firstly on basic studies of the ecology of the region and the biology and physiology of yak. Secondly, surveys have been conducted to better understand the available resources of land and livestock. Thirdly, breeding programmes have been further developed and fourthly, the commercialization of livestock production has been promoted so as to increase the economic profitability.

Attention can be drawn to two specific programmes that are of particular relevance to Tibet and yak production. One concerns a project at Dangxiong Yak Research Centre involved with the taming of semi-wild yak for semen collection and the concomitant freezing and use of this semen in A.I. (Zhang Yun, 1994, 1997 and 2002), particularly at the high elevations of the Nakchu prefecture (Tashi Dorji, 2002). The second is involves a selection and breeding programme for the establishment of two nucleus herds – one for the Pali breed and the other for the Sibu breed – on the Linzhou Farm (Yan Yonghong, 1994; Yun Den, 2002). The farm now has 605 breeding animals in the two herds. By 1999 the farm had supplied 580 top yak bulls for use in various parts of Tibet. In Linzhou county itself there were 32 260 improved yak – approaching half the yak population of the county. Records show that these improved yak were more than 50 percent heavier than local yak at equivalent ages. Milk yield was about a third better than that of the local (unimproved) yak, which accounted for 42.8 percent of the total yak population in the county. These results are taken as pointers to the improvements possible if such breeding programmes were developed more widely. The research activities on yak in Tibet are led by scientists of the Tibetan Livestock Research Institute of Tibetan Academy of Agricultural and Animal Sciences (TAAAS).

Tibet is one of the few remaining areas in China where wild yak are still extant – in particular in the Changtang region in the north of the country. Information about the wild yak can be found in Chapter 3.

Qinghai province

Qinghai, located between 31°39' and 39°19'N and between 89°35' and 103°04'E, covers an area of 722 000 sq km and is 1 200 km from east to west and 800 km from north to south. Like Tibet, it is one of the large pastoral areas in China. The province is situated on the northeastern part of the Qinghai-Tibetan plateau in northwestern China and bordering other yak territories in Tibet, Sichuan and Gansu. The average elevation of Qinghai province is 4 000 m a.s.l. but 80 percent of the land area lies between 3 000 m and 6 800 m. The annual average temperature is 3.7° - 6°C and rainfall 300 mm. There are seven administrative prefectures (Haidong, Hainan, Haibei, Huangnan, Yushu and Guoluo Tibetan autonomous prefectures and Haixi Mongolian and Tibetan autonomous prefecture) and the Xining city municipality. The human population was 5.1 million in 1999.

The main rangelands are located in the vicinity of Qinghai Lake. They cover an area of approximately 36.5 million ha – China's fourth most extensive rangeland area. About 87 percent of this rangeland is usable. The rangelands are of the alpine meadow vegetation type but can be classified into many rangeland types, groups, and subtypes (Liu Yingchun and Zhou Qingping, 2002; see also Chapter 13). Among the 16 rangeland types, alpine meadow at an altitude of 2 800 m - 4 200 m is the most extensive formation (29.6 million ha) and about 84 percent is usable by livestock.

Yak are found in nearly all counties of Qinghai province. Some hybridizing with local cattle is also practised, but not widely. For a long time Qinghai had the largest yak population among the provinces of China. For example, in 1981, there were an estimated 4 787 000 yak representing more than 95 percent of all the bovines in the province (6.65 heads per sq km). The proportion of yak in the total bovine population had remained roughly constant over many the years (Zhang Rongchang, 1989). However, as noted in Table 11.1.6, numbers started to fall after 1996 but more so in some prefectures than in others.

Liu Zubo *et al.* (1989) divided the distribution of yak in Qinghai into three ecological areas. The first of these with more than three quarters of all the yak in Qinghai consists of cold and highland pastures along the Qilian mountains, Kunlun mountains and with the Tanggula mountains at its southwestern end at altitudes above 3 500 m, average annual temperatures below 0°C and a seven-month long cold season with relatively low air pressure and high humidity. This area extends across Yushu and Guoluo and parts of Huangnan, Haixi and Haibei. The Plateau yak is found in this region. A second area is of a transitional agricultural type in the vicinity of Qinghai Lake with altitudes between 2 600 m and 3 500 m, and a mean annual temperature between 0.1° and 5.1°C.

Table 11.1.6 Yak numbers (thousands) in seven main yak-raising prefectures of Qinghai province Source: adapted from Long Ruijun and Ma Yushou, 1996; Qinghai Animal Husbandry Bureau, 1999, 2000]

Prefecture	1991	1992	1993	1994	1995	1996	1999	2000
Yushu	1 502.0	1 544.4	1 585.7	1 494.7	1 461.3	1 396.5	893.6	870.6
Guoluo	1 183.5	1 224.3	1 243.6	1 200.3	1 238.3	1 224.5	1 092.2	1 078.5
Hainan	699.5	720.9	707.5	641.9	666.1	609.6	448.0	435.2
Huangnan	536.9	653.3	665.5	623.9	686.7	600.9	564.3	561.8
Haibei	499.0	498.1	490.3	451.8	451.1	446.6	420.2	412.4
Haixi	207.7	205.5	205.5	200.4	198.9	181.6	179.4	181.5
Haidong	153.7	154.7	166.0	154.4	348.3	358.2	138.1	95.2
Total*	**4 782.3**	**5 001.2**	**5 064.1**	**4 767.4**	**5 050.7**	**4 817.9**	**3 773.6**	**3 635.2**

*The totals are for the seven main prefectures only, in addition there are small numbers in other prefectures (the overall total for the year 2000 is 3.716 million; see Chapter 1).

It includes a small part of southern Haibei and most of Hainan and southern Haixi with 12.7 percent of the yak in Qinghai. The breed of yak here includes the Huanhu yak.

The third area in this classification is the agricultural area with altitudes between 1 600 m and 2 800 m and mean annual temperatures between 2.7° and 8.7°C. It comprises the vicinity of Xining, most of Haidong and a small part of southern Haibei, eastern Hainan and northern Huangnan where another 11.6 percent of the yak in Qinghai are raised (cf. Table 11.1.6).

A question of concern is why yak numbers in Qinghai should have declined in recent years in a territory where yak are the predominant bovine and its importance to the economy is paramount. Long Ruijun and Ma Yushou (1996) have shown that there were some changes in aspects of performance and output between 1991 and 1995, suggesting a decline over the years. These authors attributed this to earlier overstocking and a deterioration of the grazings. They use as an example Maduo county of Guoluo prefecture, which is near the source of the Yellow River (average altitude of 4 200 m). The 2.3 million ha of alpine meadow pastures account for 88 percent of the total area in that county, and animal husbandry is the basic industry.

Encouragement during the 1970s and 1980s to improve standards of living by "converting" more of the grasslands into animal products led to an explosive increase in stock numbers. This then led to marked overgrazing and subsequent deterioration and even desertification of many of the pastures (cf. Chapter 13). This, in turn, forced a large reduction in stock numbers and almost half of the local herders lost their traditional pastures and livelihoods. The capacity of both livestock and people to withstand the periodic natural disasters of heavy snow or sand storms was thus also compromised. Unusually low winter and high summer temperatures, leading to severe drought in the latter part of the 1990s, and blamed by some on global warming, and the stresses placed on scarce water resources further exacerbated a difficult situation (Tao Baoxiang et al., 2000). Yet another factor that may have contributed to these problems is uncontrolled mining in this county (employing at one time 50 000 people).

A similar picture of increasing yak populations and a subsequent marked decline, forced by rangeland deterioration, can be demonstrated for the whole of Yushu prefecture and in turn suggests a reason for the recent decline of the yak production in Qinghai from its former foremost position in China.

There has been significant research effort related to yak in Qinghai since 1990. It is led by staff of the Qinghai Academy of Animal and Veterinary Sciences and the Lanzhou Institute of Animal and Veterinary Pharmaceutical Sciences of the Chinese Academy of Agriculture Sciences, as well as by staff of the Qinghai General Animal Husbandry and Veterinary Station and the Datong Yak Farm. Effort has gone into crossing domestic yak cows with wild and semi-wild yak bulls by both A.I. and natural mating, with claims of significant genetic improvement (cf. Chapter 5) (Yang Rongzhen, 1997, 1998; Yang Rongzhen et al., 1997; Li Jiye et al., 1998; Yan Shoudong, 1998, 2002).

There are many studies on yak nutrition at the Qinghai Academy (e.g. Hu Linghao, 1994; Hu Linghao et al., 1997, 2002; Han Xingtai et al., 1994a, b, 1997a, b, 2002) and significant work on animal physiology, management, health and disease, particularly in relation to parasite control (as shown in the proceedings of successive international yak congresses).

Sichuan province

There are more than four million yak and yak hybrids in the western and northern parts of Sichuan located between 26°03' and 34°19'N and between 97°21' and 110°12'E, currently the largest yak-raising province in China (cf. Chapter 1). The province borders on Tibet and Qinghai to the west, to Yunnan in the south and Gansu in the north. Unlike the other major yak-raising provinces, Tibet and Qinghai in particular, the eastern side of Sichuan province, especially in the Chengdu basin, boasts vast areas of agricultural and horticultural production, including fruit growing, and was regarded, in the past, as the granary of China. Some of the oldest and largest irrigation schemes in the world (dating back to the third century B.C.) capturing the flow of the Min River and extensive terracing ("the land of a million steps") ensure this production. Extensive timber production on the borders with Yunnan province and industrial production also help to make this a rich province.

Yak, in western parts of Sichuan, are found in all counties in Ganzi Tibetan autonomous prefecture (approximately 28° - 34°N, 98° - 102°E) and in Aba Tibetan and Qiang autonomous prefecture (30°35' - 34°19'N, 103°30' - 104°37'E) in the northeastern end of western Sichuan and most of counties in Liangshan Yi autonomous prefecture in the southern part of western Sichuan. As one of the five largest pastoral areas in China, there are about 20 million ha of highland pastures. Yak contribute 50 percent of the total beef production (52 000 tonnes of meat annually) and 70 percent of the total milk production (180 000 tonnes annually) in Sichuan (Lin Xiaowei and Zhong Guanghui, 1998), much of it from Ganzi and Aba (Zhong Jingcheng and Chen Zhihua, 1998). The Jiulong breed of yak is found in Ganzi and the Maiwa breed in Aba (cf. Chapter 2). The largest concentration of yak is in the most western and northern parts of the yak territory of Sichuan.

Liu Zubo et al. (1989) categorized the yak in Sichuan into three areas: the main pastoral area on north-western plateau where 80 percent of all the yak are found among 12 counties (with between 100 000 and 400 000 yak each); a transitional agricultural area in central western Sichuan where 18 percent of yak are kept spread among 16 counties; and the mountainous agro-area in southwestern Sichuan where yak are found isolated in 18 counties, with about 2 percent of the total yak in the province.

The two most important prefectures for yak in Sichuan are Ganzi, with about 56 percent of the total yak of the province and Aba with about 42 percent. About 20 years or so ago, the yak population of Ganzi accounted for 61 percent of the total; since then, numbers have increased more in Aba than in Ganzi, most likely because of a better access to markets for yak products in Aba (Cai Li, 1989; Zhong Jingcheng and Cheng Zhihua, 1998). Some more detail is warranted for these two prefectures.

The numbers in Ganzi are shown in Table 11.1.7 and indicate both the large increase over the years of the yak population in particular.

Ganzi lies in western Sichuan on the eastern edge of the Qinghai-Tibetan plateau. The topography is diverse with an average elevation of 3 500 m but higher in the northwest than the southeast. The plateau region is interspersed with several huge mountains and rivers. Annual rainfall ranges from 500 to 800 mm (falling mostly in the warm season between May and October) but declines from southeast to northwest with increasing altitude. The diverse nature of the land across its 153 000 sq km leads to a diversity of climates, from cold high mountain zones to subtropical valleys. The Jiulong breed of yak (see Chapter 2) finds its home in the core area of Ganzi, the cold mountainous counties of Jiulong and Kangding where it was known as a Yak country as long ago as the Han Dynasty (206 B.C. to 220 A.D.).

Table 11.1.7 Number of yak and other livestock in the Ganzi prefecture (thousands)
[Source: adapted from Zhao Yonghua, 2000]

Year	Total livestock	Yak and hybrids	Cattle	Sheep	Goat	Pig
1950	2 577.8	1 326.0	108.4	608.9	445.1	89.5
1970	3 380.5	1 442.7	207.2	853.0	703.0	174.6
1980	4 559.1	1 970.7	250.8	1 242.5	846.9	248.2
1985	4 576.6	2 111.1	311.6	1 070.0	820.6	263.3
1990	4 542.3	2 212.3	343.1	962.7	762.5	261.7
1995	4 605.1	2 284.8	380.0	967.2	688.5	284.6
1998	4 632.1	2 286.8	398.0	939.2	702.4	305.7

The human population of Ganzi was about 852 000 people of 25 nationalities in 1995, with Tibetans comprising around 78 percent of them. Livestock is the principal means of livelihood of the people, but there is an area of cultivated land with crops – 7 000 ha relatively small compared to the 140 000 ha of grazing land, some of the grazing land being fenced. Ganzi has its own Animal Husbandry and Veterinary Institute where selection and breeding of the Jiulong yak has been a key programme for the past 40 years (Ding Xiaotao, 2000).

Aba prefecture covers little more than half the area of Ganzi but has nearly the same human population, 60 percent of whom are Tibetan or Qiang. In general, the northwest of Aba consists of mountains and a high plateau with an average altitude of 3 500 - 4 000m and a cold climate. The southeast of Aba has high mountains interspersed with deep valleys – a difference from top to bottom of 5 430 m – leading to a diversity of climatic conditions.

In 1997 there were 1.376 million pure yak and 329 000 hybrids in Aba with reproductive females accounting for just under 38 percent – better than in some areas but still short of an optimum herd structure (see Chapter 8). With an increase in the yak population and a larger number of yak marketed, there has been an increase in output over recent years (milk, meat, fibre, skin) but also noted has been a reduction in individual carcass weights of animals slaughtered. This was attributed largely to uncontrolled use of unselected and poor breeding bulls, none of which met standards that had been officially laid down (Zuo Xuemin and Jian Shanglin, 1998).

To address the perceived inadequacies of the breeding, 20 breeding herds with 1 200 breeding females of the Maiwa breed of yak were established in four counties in Aba in 1988. Subsequently, 120 selected breeding bulls were produced annually, for a time, for use in local herds.

However, the breeding herds were not maintained so the scheme represents a false start. Yet, because of the great importance attached to improvement of the yak in Aba, and of the Maiwa breed in particular, new plans are being developed (Zuo Xuemin and Jian Shanglin, 1998) and are said to be in the process of being enacted.

One of the problems encountered in Aba is that a number of natural winter disasters affected sheep and goats more than they did the yak. The increase in the yak population was thus partly at the expense of sheep and goats. Consequently the utilization of the pastures is now considered to be suboptimal (Zhong Jingcheng and Chen Zhihau, 1998).

Hybridizing of Maiwa yak by A.I. with the semen of the Holstein Friesian, Simmental, Shorthorn, Hereford and Charolais breeds has been extensively practiced in Aba since 1978, aided by a subsidy payment for the insemination service up to 1992 and much promoted by Cai Li and his colleagues. However, there is a continuing, market-driven demand for milk, and this is leading to a continuing use of hybridization in spite of the fact that herders now need to pay for the insemination services.

Pu Jiabi *et al*. (1997) reviewed research and development activities on yak with particular emphasis on work at the Sichuan Yak Development Institute. Zhong Guanghui (1998), in turn, reviewed the extensive research activities on yak undertaken by the scientists of the Animal Science Department of the Southwest University for Nationalities, which has its campus in Chengdu. The department has a history of yak research (it was the base for the work of the late Professor Cai Li, originator of this book) and along with other departments of the university is charged with the training of students of minority nationalities, which include those involved in work in the yak territories.

Gansu province

Gansu, located between 32°31'and 42°49'N and between 92°45' and 108°46'E, is the fifth largest of the pastoral areas of China with about 9 million ha of usable pastures and about 900 000 yak (in 1997). The province is situated at the northern end of the Qinghai-Tibetan plateau and borders on Qinghai province to the south and Inner Mongolia Autonomous Region to the north – Gansu is flanked in the north by the western stretches of the Great Wall of China. Agriculture sustains 19.3 percent of the GDP in Gansu, and livestock production is its major component by contributing about 28.8 percent to the GDP from the agricultural sector in 2001. However, mining for ten main-coloured metals, including lead and zinc, and other heavy industry are of significance in the province.

Yak in Gansu, totalling around 900 000, are concentrated in two regions: Gannan Tibetan autonomous prefecture in southwest Gansu, home to the Gannan yak, and the Qilian mountain area in west-central Gansu where the Tianzhu White yak are raised – more detail is given in Chapter 2. The altitude of these regions varies from 1 400 to 4 700 m and the average annual temperature is just above freezing (1.2°C). But the lowest recorded temperature was -29.6°C. At the present time only a relatively small amount of hybridizing occurs of yak with local cattle.

Nearly half the population of 530 000 people of Gannan is Tibetan, and about half of these are pastoralists. Based on records of 1999, animal husbandry accounted for more than 60 percent of the GDP from the agricultural sector. Gannan, with 2.7 million ha of highland pastures, has more than 80 percent of all yak in Gansu province. Yak numbers have remained relatively stable over the period from 1981to 1995 (the last available) in each of the seven counties of Gannan (Han Jianlin and Zhang Rongchang, 1996).

The remaining yak in the Qilian mountains are in the Tianzhu Tibetan autonomous county (numerically the most important with about 80 000 yak) and some neighbouring districts. The Qilian mountains average between 4 000 m and 5 000 in altitude and have an average annual temperature of 0°C. The ancient Silk Route passed through from the east and a national nature reserve was established in the late 1980s to protect forestry, a water catchment area and wildlife.

Particular aspects of breeding and research on the Tianzhu White breed have been referred to in Chapter 2 and the special properties of this breed have attracted both interest and funding for conservation projects for the past ten years from provincial and national governments in China.

Gansu Agricultural University, located near Lanzhou, the capital of the province, is an active centre of research in matters related to yak, including studies of anatomy, reproductive physiology, genetics, breeding and nutrition. A department of grassland sciences is concerned with aspects of range management. The university also houses the International Yak Information Centre (IYIC) for the documentation and dissemination of published literature on the yak. In addition, the Lanzhou Institute of Animal and Veterinary Pharmaceutical Sciences of Chinese, Academy of Agriculture Sciences has been involved for 20 years in initiatives to tame and use wild yak. It has played a key role in developing the improved yak breed from crossing domestic with wild yak, the Datong yak, on the Datong Yak Farm in Qinghai, described in some detail in Chapter 2. Another centre of importance for pastoral livestock production, because of its contribution to the understanding of grasslands and grassland ecology, is the Gansu Grassland Ecology Research Institute based in Lanzhou.

Xinjiang Uigur Autonomous Region

Xinjiang (also Sinkiang) is situated at the northwestern corner of China with a total population of around 17 million of many different ethnic groups. It is a vast and remote area with no less than 48 million ha of grasslands (14.5 percent of all the usable pastures in China) and 45 million livestock in the year 2000. The autonomous region is bordered by Mongolia to the northeast, Russia to the north, and Kazakhstan, Kyrgyzstan, Tajikistan, Afghanistan and parts of Jammu and Kashmir on western sides, Tibet to the southeast and Qinghai and Gansu provinces to the east. It is China's single largest political unit. Massive mountain ranges almost enclose it on three sides – the Tianshan mountains to the north and the Kunlun mountains to the south being the highest. The main crops are cotton in southern and eastern Xinjiang, particularly in the southern Turpan Basin. Wheat is grown in northern and southwestern Xinjiang, sugar beet in northern Xinjiang and rice in northwestern and some central parts of Xinjiang. In addition, soybean, grape, hop, sunflower, peanut, apple and pear are also very important cash crops produced in various parts of Xinjiang. In recent years the cotton, oil and natural gas industries are becoming the most important economic resources in Xinjiang.

About 7 million ha of the total grasslands, at average elevations of 2 500 - 5 500 m, are said to be suitable for yak husbandry but even here the density of yak is low with only about 230 000 yak in total. Numbers have increased slowly over the years (e.g. 172 000 in 1987) but have not reached the claimed potential of a million yak (Fang Guangxin and Liu Wujun, 1998). The yak, named "tank on the plateau" by the local herders in Xinjiang, are found in some numbers all over the province but chiefly in the Bayingolin Mongolian autonomous prefecture – home to the Bazhou yak – and in the Kyrgyz prefecture, both in the southern parts of Xinjiang alongside the Kunlun range and Altay mountains. Other, smaller concentrations of yak are found in the southern Tianshan mountains.

Wild yak are still claimed to live in the Altay and Kunlun mountains, and there is some concern in Xinjiang for their conservation in the face of the wild yak being hunted, here as elsewhere, for food by both miners working in Xinjiang and by local herders (Luo Ning *et al.*, 1996).

An initial introduction of yak from Tibet to the Bayingolin region of Xinjiang took place early in nineteenth century, which formed the foundation herd of the Bazhou yak. Frozen semen of the wild yak and breeding animals of semi-wild yak from the Datong Yak Farm were brought to the area in 1981 - 1983 for purposes of improving the local yak. The Tianzhu White yak were also imported in 1989 to counteract perceived negative effects of inbreeding and for further genetic improvement (Turshen Abudula *et al.*, 2002). According to Turshen Abudula *et al.* (2002), the F1 crosses between Bazhou and Tianzhou White yak achieved better growth than the local yak.

Concern for continuing development of all aspects of yak husbandry and marketing in the province and the training of workers arose from a consultative meeting in 1995 and is the in process of implementation (Fang Guangxin and Liu Wujun, 1998).

Yunnan province

Yunnan is one of the largest provinces of China bounded by Tibet and Sichuan to the north and Lao PDR, Vietnam and Burma to the south and southeast. There were some 50 000 yak in northern Yunnan, mainly in counties of the Diqing Tibetan autonomous prefecture. This is the home of the Zhongdian yak, one of the most ancient and respected of the yak races. Even yak herders from Tibet and Sichuan were said to seek out these yak (Liu Zubo *et al.*, 1989). Possibly because of the relative remoteness of yak in Yunnan and the small contribution of yak to the overall economy of the province there is little recent published information on yak from the area, or on the Zhongdian yak – even the estimate of numbers dates back to 1980 – as noted by Xu Guifang and Wang Zhigang (1998).

The major part of the economy of Yunnan relies on the mining and export of a wide range of minerals including tin (the province has one of the world's largest deposits) and copper as well as a host of more precious minerals and other materials including coal, iron and marble.

References

Bhu Chong (1998). Present situation of research and production of yak industry in Tibet. *Forage and Livestock*, Supplement: 38-40.

Cai Li (1989). *Sichuan yak*. Chengdu, China, Sichuan Nationality Press, 223 pp.

Ding Xiaotao (2000). Research on animal husbandry in Ganzu Prefecture – challenge in the twenty-first Century. *Journal of Gazi Science and Technology*, No. 1.

Dou Yaozun (1990). Tibetan yak. *Collection of papers on the Tibetan Animal Husbandry and Veterinary*, 1980-1990. Lhasa, China.

Fang Guangxin & Liu Wujun (1998). Present situation, constraints and future actions of yak husbandry in Xinjiang. *Forage and Livestock*, Supplement: 50-51.

Han Jianlin & Zhang Rongchang (1996). Present conditions and future prospects of yak husbandry in Gansu Province, China. *In*: Miller, D.G., Craig S.R., & Rana, G.M. (eds). *Proceedings of a workshop on Conservation and Management of Yak Genetic Diversity* at ICIMOD, Kathmandu, 29-31 October 1996. ICIMOD (International Centre for Integrated Mountain Development), Kathmandu, pp. 123-129.

Han Xingtai *et al*. (1997a). Cannulation of major splanchnic blood vessels and portal blood flow in yaks. *Proceedings of the second international congress on yak, in Xining, China, 1-6 September 1997*. Xining, China, Qinghai People's Publishing House, pp. 94-99.

Han Xingtai *et al*. (2002). Peptide and amino acid metabolism in the gastro-intestinal tract of yaks. *Proceedings of the third international congress on yak, in Lhasa, China, 4-9 September 2000*. International Livestock Research Institute (ILRI), Nairobi, pp. 259-264.

Han Xingtai, Hu Linghao & Xie Aoyun (1997b). The RNA content and the RNA-N: bacterial nitrogen ratio in the bacterial mixture separated from yak rumen. *Proceedings of the second international congress on yak, in Xining, China, 1-6 September 1997*. Xining, China, Qinghai People's Publishing House, pp. 105-107.

Han, Xingtai *et al*. (1994a). The nitrogen metabolism of growing yaks fed diets containing different level of crude protein. Proceedings of the first international congress on yak. *Journal of Gansu Agricultural University* (Special issue June 1994), pp. 204-206.

Han, Xingtai, Xie Aoyun & Hu Linghao (1994b). Microbial protein synthesis of the rumen of yaks receiving diets containing straw and concentrate in various proportions. Proceedings of the first international congress on yak. *Journal of Gansu Agricultural University* (Special issue June 1994) pp. 218-221.

Hu Linghao (1994). Study on energy metabolism and runimal metabolism in growing yaks. Proceedings of the first international congress on yak. *Journal of Gansu Agricultural University* (Special issue June 1994) pp. 188-195.

Hu Linghao *et al*. (1997). Studies on metabolism and supplement methods of nitrogen in growing yaks. *Proceedings of the second international congress on yak, in Xining, China, 1-6 September 1997*. Xining, China, Qinghai People's Publishing House, pp. 85-93.

Hu Linghao, Liu Shujie & Chai Shatuo (2002). Advances in yak nutrition research. *Proceedings of the third international congress on yak, in Lhasa, China, 4-9 September 2000*. International Livestock Research Institute (ILRI), Nairobi, Kenya. pp. 237-250.

Huang Wenxiu (1996). Conservation and management of yak genetic diversity in the Tibetan Autonomous Region. In: Miller, D.G., Craig, S.R., & Rana, G.M. (eds). *Proceedings of a workshop on Conservation and Management of Yak Genetic Diversity* held at ICIMOD, Kathmandu, 29-31 October 1996. ICIMOD (International Centre for Integrated Mountain Development), Kathmandu, pp. 93-104.

Ji Qiumei *et al.* (2000). Milk production performance and quality of milk in three ecotypes of yak in Tibet. *Journal of Gansu Agricultural University*, 35: 269-276.

Ji Qiumei *et al.* (2001). Fiber production and physical characters of three ecotypes of yak in Tibet. *Chinese Journal of Animal Science*, 4: 29-30.

Ji Qiumei, *et al.* (2002a). Resources of yak production in Tibet and reasons for the degeneration of productive performances. *Proceedings of the third international congress on yak, in Lhasa, China, 4-9 September 2000.* International Livestock Research Institute (ILRI), Nairobi, pp. 300-307.

Ji Qiumei, J. *et al.* (2002b). Beef production of three yak breeds in Tibet. *Proceedings of the third international congress on yak held in Lhasa, China, 4-9 September 2000.* International Livestock Research Institute (ILRI), Nairobi, pp. 479-483.

Li Jiye *et al.* (1998). Urgent issues to the development of yak industry. *Forage and Livestock*, Supplement: 45-46.

Lin Xiaowei & Zhong Guanghui (1998). Present situation and development strategy of yak husbandry in Sichuan. *Forage and Livestock*, Supplement: 26-28.

Liu Yingchun & Zhou Qingping (2002). Sustainable development of rangeland resources on the Qinghai-Tibetan plateau, China. *Proceedings of the third international congress on yak, in Lhasa, China, 4-9 September 2000.* International Livestock Research Institute (ILRI), Nairobi, pp. 165-171.

Liu Zubo, Wang Chengzhi & Chen Yongning (1989). Yak resources and qualified populations in China. In: Chinese Yakology. Sichuan Scientific and Technology Press, Chengdu, China. pp. 36-77.

Long Ruijun & Ma Yushou (1996). Qinghai's yak production systems. In: Miller, D.G., Craig S.R. & Rana, G.M. (eds). *Proceedings of a workshop on Conservation and Management of Yak Genetic Diversity* at ICIMOD, Kathmandu, 29-31 October 1996. ICIMOD (International Centre for Integrated Mountain Development), Kathmandu, pp. 105-114.

Luo Ning, Gu Jinhe & Aireti (1996). Yaks in Xinjiang. In: Miller, D.G., Craig S.R., & Rana, G.M. (eds). *Proceedings of a workshop on Conservation and Management of Yak Genetic Diversity* held at ICIMOD, Kathmandu, 29-31 October 1996. ICIMOD (International Centre for Integrated Mountain Development), Kathmandu, pp. 115-122.

National Bureau of Statistics, China (2001). *Communique on major figures of the 2000 population census*. Published on 2 April 2001, Beijing.

Pu Jiabi, Shi Yongjie & Ben Zhengkun (1997). Yak subject in development. *Proceedings of the second international congress on yak held in Xining, China, 1-6 September 1997.* Xining, Qinghai People's Publishing House, pp. 17-20.

Qinghai Animal Husbandry Bureau (1999). *1999 animal husbandry economic annals of Tibetan Autonomous Region.* Lhasa, China.

Qinghai Animal Husbandry Bureau (2000). *2000 animal husbandry economic annals of Tibetan Autonomous Region.* Lhasa, China.

Tao Baoxiang, Dong Shuochen & Zheng Jie (2000). Urgent call for action of protection of the water resource from the start point of the Yellow River. *Morning Beijing*, 17 August 2000; *Science and Technology Daily, China*. 7 August 2000.

Tashi Dorji (2002). Report on experiment of artificial insemination by frozen yak semen in an area with altitude of 4 500 m a.s.l. *Proceedings of the third international congress on yak, in Lhasa, China, 4-9 September 2000.* International Livestock Research Institute (ILRI), Nairobi, p. 345.

Tibetan Bureau of Agriculture and Animal Husbandry (1999). *1999 animal husbandry economic annals of Tibetan Autonomous Region*. Lhasa, China.

Turshen Abudula *et al*. (2002). Review of the research and development of Bayingolin yaks in Xinjiang, China. *Proceedings of the third international congress on yak, in Lhasa, China, 4-9 September 2000*. International Livestock Research Institute (ILRI), Nairobi, pp. 320-323.

Wang Wenpei (2002). Brief introduction to agricultural and animal husbandry development in Tibet Autonomous Region. *Proceedings of the third international congress on yak, in Lhasa, China, 4-9 September 2000*. International Livestock Research Institute (ILRI), Nairobi, pp. 559-561.

Wei Xuecheng (1994). Yak production and research in Tibet. Proceedings of the first international congress on yak. *Journal of Gansu Agricultural University* (Special issue June 1994) pp. 134-137.

Xu Guifang & Wang Zhigang (1998). Present situation and proposal for future development of yak industry in China. *Forage and Livestock*, Supplement: 6-8.

Yan Shoudong (1998). Observation on the growth and development of crossbred wild yak. *Forage and Livestock*, Supplement: 46-47.

Yan Shoudong (2002). A study on the improvement of yak reproductive performance by introducing wild yak blood. *Proceedings of the 3rd international congress on yak held in Lhasa, P.R. China, 4-9 September 2000*. International Livestock Research Institute (ILRI), Nairobi, Kenya. pp. 324-327.

Yan Yonghong (1994). Report on the selection breeding of Linzhou yak. Proceedings of the first international congress on yak. *Journal of Gansu Agricultural University* (Special issue June 1994), pp. 159-160.

Yang Rongzhen (1997). Review of yak research in Qinghai Academy of Animal and Veterinary Sciences. *Proceedings of the second international congress on yak, in Xining, China, 1-6 September 1997*. Xining, China, Qinghai People's Publishing House, pp. 285-287.

Yang Rongzhen (1998). Present situation and suggestion of development of yak production and research in Qinghai. *Forage and Livestock*, Supplement: 48-49.

Yang Rongzhen *et al*. (1997). Report on growth and development of domestic yak progenies rejuvenated by wild yak. *Proceedings of the second international congress on yak, in Xining, China, 1-6 September 1997*. Xining, China, Qinghai People's Publishing House, pp. 21-25.

Yang Xuqing (2002). Yak production and strategy for its further development in Naqu Prefecture of Tibet, P.R. China. *Proceedings of the third international congress on yak, in Lhasa, China, 4-9 September 2000*. International Livestock Research Institute (ILRI), Nairobi, pp. 335-337.

Yun Den (2002). Preliminary results of selection and breeding for improved yak production in Linzhou County, Tibetan Autonomous Region, China. *Proceedings of the third international congress on yak, in Lhasa, China, 4-9 September 2000*. International Livestock Research Institute (ILRI), Nairobi, pp. 316-317.

Zhang Rongchang (1989). *China: the yak*. Gansu Scientific and Technology Press, Lanzhou, China. 386 pp.

Zhang Yun (1994). The relationship between season and age of stud yak bull in Damxung. Proceedings of the first international congress on yak. *Journal of Gansu Agricultural University* (Special issue June 1994) pp. 303-307.

Zhang Yun (1997). Tame of the stud yak bulls for producing frozen semen. *Proceedings of the second international congress on yak, in Xining, China, 1-6 September 1997*. Xining, China, Qinghai People's Publishing House, pp. 163-164.

Zhang Yun (2002). Experiment on oestrous synchronisation for artificial insemination with frozen semen in yaks. *Proceedings of the third international congress on yak, in Lhasa, China, 4-9 September 2000.* International Livestock Research Institute (ILRI), Nairobi, pp. 349-352.

Zhao Yonghua (2000). Promote the economic development of animal husbandry in Gazi Prefecture with advantage of development of the western China – Suggestions to the improvement and development of the breeding animals in the Gazi Prefecture. *Journal of Gazi Science and Technology*, No. 2.

Zhong Guanghui (1998). Brief introduction of research activities on yak by the Department of Animal Science of Southwest Nationalities College. *Forage and Livestock*, Supplement: 60-61.

Zhong Jingcheng & Chen Zhihua (1998). Present situation, problem and strategy of the development of yak industry in Sichuan. *Forage and Livestock*, Supplement: 28-30.

Zuo Xuemin & Jian Shanglin (1998). Present situation and development strategy of yak husbandry in Aba Prefecture, Sichuan. *Forage and Livestock*, Supplement: 36-38

PART 2

YAK IN OTHER COUNTRIES WITH A LONG TRADITION OF YAK KEEPING

Bhutan

By Tashi Dorji, Walter Roder and Lham Tshering[2]

The kingdom of Bhutan is located in the eastern Himalayas. It borders the Indian states of Sikkim in the west and Arunachal Pradesh in the east, both of which are home to small populations of yak (see section on India). West Bengal and Assam border on the south of Bhutan and on the northern and northwestern border lies the Tibetan Autonomous Region of China.

Bhutan is a small country – the maximum north-south distance being 170 km and the longest east-west distance 300 km. Its topography is completely mountainous with elevations ranging from a few hundred meters in the south to peaks over 7 000 m along the northern boundary. The climate is dominated by the monsoon with dry periods in the winter and wet summers. Permanent snow cover is found at elevations above 5 000 m. Precipitation varies widely; while south-facing slopes may receive up to 4 000 mm, high-altitude valleys, sheltered behind ridges, may receive less than 700 mm.

Importance of yak at the national and regional level

Yak rearing is the main source of livelihood for the Bhutanese population living at high altitudes. According to the 1997 livestock census, there were 37 700 yak in nine districts of Bhutan and about 10 percent of the country's population depended on yak production (Gyamthso, 1996). Consequently, the yak production system has considerable national importance, unlike in many other yak-rearing countries. Milk and meat are the most important products, but yak are also used as riding and pack animals and they provide fibre, fuel and fertilizer (use of manure or ash after burning manure).

Yak play an important role in the religious and cultural life, especially for the pastoralists but also for the Bhutanese population in general. Some of the yak-herding communities have their own distinct culture and dress habits. Geographical and social isolation is a major problem faced by yak herders. It is not uncommon for winter camps to be reached only by walking for one to three days from the nearest road point. Summer camps are even more remote and access to school and medical services present great difficulties for the yak-erding communities.

---

[2] Tashi Dorji is Livestock Programme Officer at the Renewable Natural Resources Research Centre, Ministry of Agriculture, Jakar, Bumthang, Bhutan; Walter Roder is Advisor Agronomist at the foregoing Centre; Lham Tshering is Deputy Chief Veterinary Officer with the National Artificial Insemination Programme, Wangchutaba, Thimphu, Bhutan.

Genetic and physical characterization of yak populations

The genetic diversity within Bhutanese yak populations has been assessed using genetic distance, which is used as a measure of genetic similarity. Genetic distance was estimated from allele frequencies using eight microsatellite markers. From these distances, representations of the relationships were obtained between three yak populations, one yak hybrid (yak crossed with cattle) and four cattle populations (which are involved in hybridizing with yak) (Figure 11.2.1). The branch length of the tree is an indication of the genetic distance and populations that are closely related would be placed in the same clade. Higher "bootstrap" values, which are the figures at the nodes (and represent the percentage occurrence in 1 000 replications of the resampled loci), indicate strong support of the relationships among populations. From this study, substantial differences between yak populations from eastern Bhutan and those from other parts (central and west) of the country were apparent. Dorji *et al.,* (2002), therefore proposed that Bhutanese yak populations could be categorized into two breeds, namely *Merakpa* yak of eastern Bhutan and *Haapa* yak of western and central Bhutan. Yak from the eastern region of the country are distinctly smaller in size and body weight compared to those of western Bhutan (Table 11.2.1)

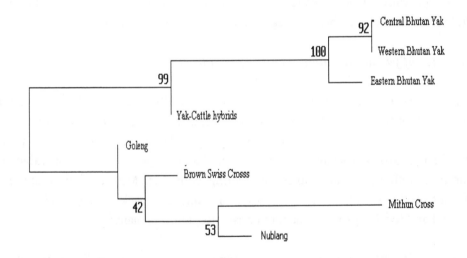

Figure 11.2.1. Unrooted neighbour-joining phylogenetic tree representing the genetic relationships among the yak and cattle populations
(Goleng = local *Bos taurus*, Brown Swiss cross = Brown Swiss crossed with local cattle, Mithun cross = *Bos frontalis* crossed with local cattle, Nublang = local *Bos indicus*). The numbers at the nodes are the percentage of support for each cluster in a bootstrap re-sampling of 1 000 trees with replacement.

About 73 percent of yak in eastern Bhutan, 65 percent in central and 60 percent in western Bhutan are black in colour. Other common colours include a mixture of black and white and brown. Absolute white or albino animals constitute less than 5 percent. The proportion of polled animals were 17 percent in east Bhutan yak while it was less than 10 percent in central and western Bhutan population. Long, hairy forehead type yak are also common among eastern Bhutan yak.

Table 11.2.1 Body measurements (mean ± s.e.) of adult yak in three regions of Bhutan

Trait	Western Region		Central Region		Eastern Region	
	M (n=31)	F (n=32)	M (n=9)	F (n=19)	M (n=6)	F (n=12)
Height at withers (cm)	136.0 ± 1.2	117.0 ± 0.8	129.0 ± 1.9	110.0 ± 5.8	128.0 ± 2.0	113.0 ± 1.6
Body length (cm)	159.0 ± 1.7	137.0 ± 1.2	152.0 ± 4	133.0 ± 1.2	148.0 ± 1.7	133.0 ± 2.3
Chest girth (cm)	194.0 ± 1.7	165.0 ± 0.9	185.0 ± 3.5	165.0 ± 1.3	177.0 ± 2.8	160.0 ± 1.6
Body weight (kg)*	419.0 ± 11.0	264.0 ± 4.0	369.0 ± 22.0	252.0 ± 4.5	323.0 ± 12.0	239.0 ± 8
Height at hips (cm)	107.0 ± 0.9	97.0 ± 2.2	101.0 ± 1.8	91.0 ± 0.9	101.0 ± 1.2	93.0 ± 1.7
Cannon circumference (cm)	21.0 ± 0.2	17.0 ± 0.2	20.0 ± 0.3	16.0 ± 0.2	19.0 ± 0.2	16.0 ± 0.2

M = male; F = female; n = Number of animals;
*Body weight (kg) estimated from (Chest girth, m)^2 x (Body length, m) x 70;

Hybridization

Mating of yak with cattle for better milk or draft production is practised on a modest scale, especially in central and eastern Bhutan. The most common approach involves mating yak cows with bulls of a small Tibetan breed (Goleng, *Bos taurus*). Occasionally *Bos indicus* bulls on yak cows or yak bulls on *B. taurus* or *B. indicus* cows are also used to produce hybrids. Female offspring are backcrossed to yak or cattle for more than five generations. A modest number of yak hybrids from Brown Swiss crossbred bulls (Brown Swiss crossed with local cattle) with yak cows and their reciprocal crosses are also available, but due to difficulties in implementing a recording scheme, it was not possible to generate reliable performance data. Recent genetic studies indicated limited gene flow from cattle to yak (Dorji *et al.*, 2002, Figure 11.2.1). Most herders retain only the F1 generation in the herd due to reduced productivity and quality of subsequent backcrosses. It is mostly the herders with few animals that practise repeated backcrossing beyond the F1 stage.

This restricted practice of backcrossing may in turn have limited introgression of cattle genes in the yak population. Another reason could be positive selection against cattle alleles in later backcrossed generations.

Production parameters

The normal breeding season is from June to September. Most Bhutanese yak have their first calf when they are around four to five years of age. Two calves in every three years is the norm and less than 20 percent of cows calve annually (Dorji, 2000; Gyamtsho, 1996). Bulls are first put into service when they are three or four years old.

Gyamtsho (1996) recorded a daily milk production of 1.2 kg in July and 0.90 kg in October from yak in western Bhutan. Highest yields were obtained from animals of seven to ten years age and in their third and fourth lactation. During a survey carried out in November 1999, Dorji (2000) measured morning milk yields of 0.74, 0.58, and 1.4 l for yak in Western Bhutan, yak in Central Bhutan and *Zom* (F1 of yak crossed with cattle) in central Bhutan, respectively.

When a yak cow conceives again she may refuse access to the calf and it is usually at this time that the calves are weaned.

Harvesting of yak hair takes place in May and June. The outer hair is cut using scissors or a knife. Only castrates and females are sheared while the breeding bull is never sheared to retain its superior appearance in front of the other bulls. An average hair yield of 1 kg and 0.3 kg were measured from shearing 8 males and 22 females, respectively (Gyamtsho, 1996). Dorji (2000) reported hair yields of 0.8 - 1.0 kg per animal. The staple length of the hair varies from 20 to 40 cm (Gyamtsho, 1996). The inner soft wool tends to loosen during early summer and is plucked by hand. The average wool yield from castrated yak varies from 0.2 to 0.4 kg per year (Dorji, 2000; Gyamtsho, 1996).

Production systems

The animals are herded in a transhumance pattern, depending on the state of the grazing. The alpine summer pastures, at around 5 000 m, are grazed until late September or early October. Thereafter the herds begin to descend to winter pastures on lower ground at an altitude of around 2 500 m - 3500 m.

All yak-herding families have permanent homes near their winter pastures. Wooden fences or stone walls to provide some protection may surround winter and summer camps. Temporary shelters are provided for the calves.

Winter pastures at elevations ranging from 3 000 m to 3 800 m are generally used from November to April. During the summer, the herders move with their animals to pastures ranging from 3 500 m to 5 000 m. Usually herders also carry out some cultivation near their permanent settlements. Species commonly cultivated include barley, wheat, mustard, potato, buckwheat, radish and turnip.

The average herd size per household was 85 animals in western and 42 animals in central Bhutan (Dorji, 2000). Yak herding families may also own cattle, sheep and horses. A few monasteries and wealthy families have large herds of yak and sheep, tended by herders under well-defined tenure agreements (Dorji, 2000). The proportion of yak owned by absentee owners ranges from 34 percent in western Bhutan to less than 10 percent in the eastern area.

In general, yak cows are not milked for the first three to four weeks after calving. After that, milking is done in the morning only by keeping the calf separate during the night. Calves are allowed to suckle for a brief moment to initiate milk flow. When milking, one to two teats are left for the calf without being milked. Milk is processed into butter and cheese by individual herders using traditional methods.

Meat and milk products are sold and/or used to barter for rice, chillies, salt, tea, etc. Yak meat receives a premium price, about 60 - 100 percent higher than the beef of other cattle.

There is no special group of animals raised for meat. Unproductive females and male castrates are generally slaughtered during October and November when they are in prime condition. Yak herders in central Bhutan do not slaughter animals because of religious sentiments. Meat from animals that die of natural causes or accidents is, however, consumed or sold.

To reduce inbreeding and improve the population, yak semen was imported from China and used from 1990 to 1997. A total of 82 inseminations were made and 45 progeny recorded (Tshering *et al.,* 2002). Detailed information on the productivity of the A.I. progeny is not yet available. The trial demonstrated difficulties in using artificial insemination because of logistical (accessibility) and management problems (heat detection, exclusion of breeding bulls).

Yak health

The Government provides free veterinary health care. But because of the remoteness and the migratory system of husbandry, access to the services provided is limited, especially during the summer months. Gid disease *(Multiceps multiceps)* remains the single most important disease causing high mortality rates in some regions (Table 11.2.2).

Systematic gild control programmes initiated in the 1960s resulted in a dramatic reduction of mortality rates. In the past decade the problem has, however, come back with a vengeance.

Poisoning by plants or stagnant water (locally termed as *baduk* and *chuduk*) is another major cause of mortality, especially in the central region where no culling is practised (see Chapter 9).

Table 11.2.2 Causes of mortality in yak during 1997-1998. Results from a survey of 22 herds (1 353 animals) in western and 32 herds (1 879 animals) in central Bhutan [Source: Dorji, 2000]

Cause of mortality	Animals lost (%)	
	West Bhutan	Central Bhutan
Gid	5	0.9
Diarrhoea & weakness	2	1.6
Plant and water poisoning	0	2
Liver fluke	0.7	0
Predators	0.3	1.2
Fallen from cliff	1	0
Others	2	1.3
Total	**11**	**7**

Grassland resources and their management

Yak production depends largely on grassland resources at elevations ranging from 3 000 m to 5 000 m. The dominant species in alpine grazing lands belong to the genus: *Carex, Juncus, Agrostis, Festuca, Kobresia, Poa, Rododendron, Potentilla, Primula and Danthonia* (Roder, 2002). The major components of the vegetation consist of broadleaf species (Table 11.2.3). With an increase in altitude, grass species are gradually replaced by sedges.

The dry matter production varies widely, influenced by soil conditions, rainfall, elevation, exposure, and management. Dry matter yield estimates have been published in the range from 0.7 to 3.0 t ha^{-1} for temperate grasslands at elevations below 3 000 m and from 0.3 to 3.5 t ha^{-1} for alpine grasslands at an elevation above 3 000 m.

Herders generally use sound management systems with rotational grazing. Households with small herds often pool their animals together. The grazing land belongs to the Government, and most herders have grazing rights for one or more pastures either individually or on a community basis. In some regions absentee landlords own large areas of grazing land. Grazing areas in the vicinity of permanent settlements at mid-elevations

(2 000 - 3 000 m) are often used by cattle for summer grazing and by yak for winter grazing. Overgrazing is frequently mentioned as the main cause of low and/or deteriorating grassland yields.

Table 11.2. 3 Vegetation cover and composition for selected regions[1]

Region	Altitude	Sites	Broad leaf	Grasses	Sedges	Bare ground[2]
Laya	3 800 - 4 000 m	3	44 (41-47)[3]	16 (12-23)	15 (9-22)	26 (17-35)
Laya	4 100 - 4 200 m	5	46 (20-70)	8 (1-19)	25 (15-35)	21 (6-38)
Lunana	4 100 - 4 800 m	4	41 (4-83)	15 (1-46)	30 (0-91)	15 (1-30)
Lhingshi	4 400 - 4 600 m	3	42 (12-72)	9 (7-12)	16 (6-30)	33 (5-75)
Domchen	4 110 - 4 300 m	4	61 (49-67)	8 (3-15)	29 (21-35)	1 (0-3)
Gorsum	3 210 - 3 360 m	3	45 (36-53)	25 (11-41)	14 (8-17)	4 (3.3-5.4)

[1] Methods used were: Region 1-4, visual estimates from plots of 0.1 m^2; Region 5 and 6, point method along line transects (Roder, 2002).

[2] Including moss

[3] Values in bracket indicate range observed across sites for a particular region.

The grassland resources are shared with a wide variety of wild animals of which the takin *(Budorcus taxicolor),* the blue sheep (*Pseudovis nayaur*), the sambar (*Cervus unicolor*) and the musk deer *(Moschus chrysogaster)* are the most important. In recent years, some of these species, especially the blue sheep, have increased in number, supposedly due to a decline in the population of its predators.

The traditional use of fire to control unwanted shrubby species is illegal currently, but possible changes in the law allowing for controlled burning are under discussion. Increasing production appears feasible as combined effects of white clover introduction and P-application have been shown to result in 8.2-, 3.2- and 0.6-fold increases in dry-matter yield at elevations of 2 700 m, 3 300 m and 4 020 m, respectively (Roder, 2002).

Fodder production is distinctly seasonal. Growth in the winter pasture area starts in May only, with the onset of the rainy season. Again, plant growth ceases towards the end of October when moisture and temperature become limiting. The gradual decline in fodder quality and quantity over the winter months leads to substantial live weight losses. The scarcity of fodder during the winter months can become quite serious in parts of Western Bhutan, with relative high concentrations of animals around the winter camps.

Hay, straw from barley and buckwheat and turnip are the most common winter fodder preserved in small quantities (generally less than 100 kg per animal) to supplement grazing and to provide emergency fodder during periods when the pastures are snow covered. Most authors agree that increasing winter fodder availability and quality should be given priority. For this, lucerne, white clover, tall fescue, cocksfoot and oat are the most promising species.

Future of yak

The resources used in the yak production system are very marginal, and thus, the opportunities for increasing the production are limited. Problems associated with geographical and social isolation are likely to further constrain future developments. In spite of this, yak will continue to be an important component of the Bhutanese landscape and society and will become an important attraction for tourism.

Although the permanent grasslands may have only limited potential for generating higher production, their management will become more important, not least because of the issue of watershed management (hydropower, other needs) and concerns with biodiversity in fauna and flora and with the development of tourism.

Management of the fodder resources will be the main leverage to achieve higher production levels. The finalization of rules and regulations, now drafted, governing the use and maintenance of natural grasslands (relating to ownership and taxation and the management/ownership of tree cover) will contribute substantially towards maintaining the biophysical resources and towards optimizing production from these resources.

References

Dorji, T. (2000). Genotypic and phenotypic characterization of the yak (*Bos grunniens*) and yak farming systems in Bhutan. MSc. Thesis. Institute of Land and Food Resources, University of Melbourne, Australia.

Dorji, T. *et al*, (2002). Genetic diversity of Bhutanese yak (*Bos grunniens*) using microsatellite markers. *Proceedings of the third international congress on yak, in Lhasa, China, 4-9 September 2000.* International Livestock Research Institute (ILRI), Nairobi, pp. 197-201.

Gyamthso P. (1996) Assessment of the condition and potential for improvement of high altitude rangeland of Bhutan. Diss. ETH No 11726, Zurich.

Roder, W. (2002). Grazing resources for yak production systems in Bhutan *Proceedings of the third international congress on yak, in Lhasa, China, 4-9 September 2000.* International Livestock Research Institute (ILRI), Nairobi, pp. 100-103.

Tshering, L. *et al.* (2002). Artificial insemination trial in yak in Bhutan. *Proceedings of the third international congress on yak, in Lhasa, China, 4-9 September 2000.* International Livestock Research Institute (ILRI), Nairobi, pp. 363-365.

Countries of the Commonwealth of Independent States
(Including the Russian Federation and a special contribution on Buryatia)

Section 1 – *CIS countires in general*
by Gerald Wiener[3]

Yak are bred in many parts of the territories of the former USSR, now known as the Commonwealth of Independent States (CIS), but in what can best be described as isolated, generally mountainous, areas within this vast region. In particular, yak have been kept for a long time in Kyrgyzstan, with perhaps the largest population of yak among the republics, Tadjikistan, Mountain Altai (adjacent to the yak population of Mongolia), West Sayan (Tuva) and East Sayan (Buryatia).

In addition, yak have been established since the 1970s in the northern Caucasus and re-established in central and south Yakutia. Yak keeping in Tajikistan is included in an article by H. Kreutzmann on yak in Western High Asia and a separate account of yak in Buryatia and Yakutia is provided by E.V. Katzina later in the next section.

Unfortunately, it was not possible to obtain a comprehensive update on numbers of yak and advances in the practices of yak keeping for the Russian Federation as such, possibly because no one was willing to speak for the whole territory since the establishment of the independent republics. Undoubtedly, the interest in yak in various parts of the former Soviet Union was second only to that in China, and the research publications from these areas represent a major contribution to academic knowledge on yak. For this reason the section on the Russian Federation from the first edition of this book still provides a valid introduction to these important contributions to knowledge.

Sarbagishev *et al.* (1989), writing about yak as one of the animal genetic resources (of the former USSR) refers to a total yak population in 1984 of 136 000. The consensus of opinion is that these numbers are now significantly lower. Among the more recent estimates of numbers of yak, the largest yak population is in Kyrgyzstan at around 20 000 animals (D. Miller personal communication), Tajikistan was said to have between 14 000 and 15 000 (see article on Western High Asia by H. Kreutzmann) and 2 900 in Buryatia (see next section). All of these represent reduced numbers relative to those previously published. Estimates given in the first edition of this book, based on a 1984 census, provided the following numbers for other areas or countries within the Federation: Tuva – 32 000, Altai – 16 000 and the northern Caucasus – 3 700.

---

[3] Gerald Wiener is an Honorary Professor, Gansu Agricultural University, China and is attached to the Centre for Tropical Veterinary Medicine, University of Edinburgh and the Roslin Institute, Edinburgh, UK. He was also Deputy director of the former AFRC Animal Breeding Research Organization in the UK.

Judging by the decline in numbers in areas where relatively recent estimates are available and from the views of visiting researchers, it seems likely that there has been a general decline in the yak population in all these countries over the past 20 - 30 years, but especially since the political and social re-organization in these countries.

Nonetheless, areas such as the northern Caucasus and Yakutia, where yak were introduced (or re-introduced) in relatively recent times, appear to have maintained yak production.

In general terms, the yak in these northern regions are kept at somewhat lower altitudes than the yak on the summer pastures of Tibet and Qinghai. Altitudes at which yak are kept vary between the various areas of the CIS countries. The most commonly quoted elevations are between 2 500 m and 3 500 m, but both lower and higher altitudes are also involved. As in other yak territories, different pastures are used in summer and in winter, but the use of the same pastures year round is also reported. The ability of yak to survive even in deep snow, avoiding the need to move them to more sheltered areas is referred to as a particular advantage of yak keeping, right from the time when yak first attracted considerable scientific attention (e.g. Denisov, 1935). Mochalovskii and Abdusalamov (1973) referred to this point again in relation to the introduction of yak from Pamir to the northern Caucasus (altitude 2 500 - 3 700 m). They reported that even in two exceptionally hard winters following the importation, the yak did not have to be brought to the lower slopes in the winter as they had no difficulty in pawing through the snow to find feed – and in so doing created a pathway for sheep.

Yak in the various countries of the CIS differ to some extent in size and performance. Sarbagishev *et al.* (1989) stated that the yak of Kyrgyzstan were substantially larger than those of Tajikistan. But this is on account of the fact that those of Kyrgyzstan were not milked and bred only for meat. Average dimensions were given as follows for adult males and females respectively: height at withers 123 cm and 109 cm; body length 137 cm and 125 cm; and heart girth 178 cm and 165 cm. Denisov (1935) stated that the yak of Kyrgyzstan were identical to those of China, but since there is also much variability among the yak in China itself, this statement is not as informative as it appears at first sight. Denisov also referred to the yak of the Altai region as being inferior, at that time, and similar to those then prevalent in Mongolia. Kozlovskii (1960) offered the view that yak in the Gorno-Altai region were becoming closely inbred, which could explain Denisov's poor opinion of its yak population (see Chapter 3, section on inbreeding). Koslovskii advocated the introduction of unrelated males or crossbreeding with other cattle.

Sarbagishev *et al.* (1989) referred only to the use of yak for meat and milk. There is little doubt that on the former state and cooperative farms, then predominant, this was the prime purpose. It is apparent from other sources that in some of the more remote areas of the Russian Federation yak are also used as pack animals and for riding.

In their article on yak in the former USSR, Sarbagishev *et al.* (1989) gave the mating season for yak in Kyrgyzstan as varying with altitude. In the Tyan Shan, at elevations of 2 400 - 2 500 m, mating started in late June (sometimes earlier) and continued to late October (but occasionally into January). In the Altai valley with more severe conditions, and an altitude of 3 000 - 4 000 m, mating did not begin until mid-July and ended in mid-October. The yak were said to be poly-oestrous and oestrous periods were reported to last for one to two days (with a range of 10 - 118 hours). Cows that calved later than August did not generally breed again in that year. Conception rates were reported to improve at higher altitudes – from 83 percent in Tyan Shan (2 600 - 3 400 m) to 98 percent in the Pamir mountains (3 900 - 4 200 m). As also noted in Chapter 4, Sarbagishev *et al.* quoted other investigators of yak in the then USSR to show that the rearing of the yak calf and its subsequent condition are major factors in determining the age at which the females reach puberty and are mated for the first time. In areas where the yak cows were not milked, this age was usually 16 - 18 months. In general, the heifers calved for the first time at the age of three years, which is a year earlier than typical for many of the yak-producing areas in China (see Chapter 4) or in other countries to the south, adjacent to the Himalayas.

With the extension of yak to other areas within these territories, attention was being given to work on the adaptation of young yak males to lowland environments and to the problems associated with synchronization of oestrus in the females, so that A.I. could be the more successfully used. This was applied particularly in the move of yak to parts of the Caucasus and Yakutia. It seems that the yak was, and still is, judged to be a more economical producer of meat than other species. This point was made by Smirnov *et al.* (1990) in relation to the yak from the Tuva region that were introduced to a part of the northern Caucasus. From figures given by the authors, the cost of keeping a yak was marginally less than that of keeping a sheep; a unit gain in live weight from a yak cost only one sixth of a similar gain by beef cattle on the same farm. (Data on meat production from the yak given by these authors are referred to in Chapter 6.) A similar point is made in the section on Buryatia based on a report from V. N. Davydov and E. V. Katzina (personal communication, 1994)

There is a wealth of publications from experiments and investigations on yak and yak hybrids, emanating from the former Soviet Union and now continuing in several of the independent republics of this region. The book by Denisov (1958), *Domestic yak and their hybrids*, is an important reference and widely quoted. Another important source of information on yak in the former Soviet Union is a book by Schley (1967). A significant proportion of the early literature on yak from the then Soviet Union is concerned with a detailed characterization of the yak, including some of its physiological and biochemical attributes.

The production-orientated studies are, however, dominated by the role of hybridization of the yak with *Bos taurus* cattle – both local breeds and breeds that had originated elsewhere, but some of which had been in those parts of the world for a long time.

The concern with hybridization continues to the present. A paper by Katzina *et al.* (1994) dealt with a scheme designed specifically for meat production from hybrids with the yak. This was investigated in two parts of Buryatia at elevations of 1 200 m and 2 500 m, respectively, but as noted later, in the section on Buryatia, less than 10 percent of the yak population there is represented by hybrids. The essence of the scheme was to exploit the fact that successful meat production from relatively young animals is a two-stage process: to combine good maternal qualities with good intrinsic growth and meat qualities of the calf itself. To produce the maternal line, hybrids were made using yak females with a dual-purpose (milk-meat) type of the Schwyz breed (referred to in earlier years as Brown Swiss) and a second variety of hybrid was produced by using a milk-type Jersey from Denmark on the yak. The former of these breeds recurs frequently in the earlier literature on hybridization with the yak, while the Jersey was chosen to exploit, it was said, its relatively small size (hence small feed requirements), high-milk yield and fat percentage, ease of calving and early maturity. The hybrid (F1) females (of each variety) were, in turn, mated to bulls of "local" breeds of cattle – the Kalmyk and the Kazakh Whitehead, both regarded predominantly as meat breeds; or they were inseminated (by A.I.) with frozen semen from the Galloway, a British beef breed, also accustomed in Scotland to relatively harsh winter conditions. Katzina *et al.* (1994) pointed out that though the level of heterosis expected in the backcrosses is lower than that in the F1 (half or less), the backcross calves benefit from having F1 mothers. These F1 dams combine the characteristics of the breeds chosen but also express heterosis in their maternal qualities. The early results of these trials showed that the success rate of obtaining hybrid calves from the yak was only of the order of 25 percent (cf. Chapter 5). However, weaning weights were achieved of 120 kg for hybrids with the Galloway and 111 kg for those with the local cattle, as against 92 kg for yak. The Galloway hybrids also over-wintered more successfully, having the better coat insulation.

As already referred to, the interest in hybridization with yak goes back many years in what was then the Soviet Union. Denisov (1935) referred to the use of the Swiss Brown (later named Schwyz) as well as local Kyrgyzstan (Kazakh) cattle in hybrids with yak on a number of state farms, and gave some early results on body weights and body dimensions. He noted that in some respects the hybrids were closer to the yak and in other respects closer to the cattle breed. Denisov (1938) provided data from Kazakhstan on lactation milk yield as follows: yak 608 kg milk (6.8 percent fat), hybrids with the Kyrgyzstan cattle 1 124 kg (5.7 percent), the Kyrgyzstan cattle 1 155 kg (4.4 percent) and hybrids of yak with Schwyz 2 022 kg (5.3 percent). Denisov stated specifically that the local cattle, the yak and the hybrids were all herded together.

These results, therefore, meet most of the criteria for estimating heterosis (only the reciprocal hybrids appear to be missing), unlike many of the other results referred to in this book where this point is in doubt. Denisov's results suggest strongly the importance of heterosis in the milk yield of the hybrids.

An even earlier report of hybridization occurs in a paper by Vlasov *et al.* (1932) that is based on observations in the Oirat district (Altai) where much of the subsequent work continued. At that time, the authors reported a yak stock of 6 800 and 570 hybrids, again with the cattle, the yak and the hybrids grazing together. Ivanova and Ljubimov (1951) recorded work at the Gorno-Altai agricultural experimental station, giving milk yields of local Siberian cattle as 700 - 800 kg (4.3 percent fat), yak as 300 - 350 kg (5.5 - 6.7 percent), and hybrids of these two as 900 - 1 100 kg (4.9 - 5.1 percent). They also reported on the use of the Simmental in such hybridization and significantly noted that cows of this breed, as well as Siberian cows, had also been mated to yak bulls since 1929.

Backcrossing of the hybrids to Simmental produced, in the second and third generation cows giving 2 362 kg milk (4.9 percent fat) in a single lactation. By 1950, there were 300 progeny of *inter-se* matings, because an aim of the breeding work was to produce a more productive (synthetic) breed suited to the conditions. (More recent publications do not refer to this "synthetic" breed, suggesting that it might not have been successful in the long run. It may be also, although this is speculation, that the males of the backcross generation had not yet achieved full fertility – which is usually expected only after four or five generations of backcrossing). Later work in Gorno-Altai also involved the use of the Shorthorn breed of cattle (Gaidyseva, 1963).

Other areas of the Russian Federation from which investigations on yak and yak hybrids are reported include the Tuva region where Katzina and Maturova (1989) reported on the reproductive function in the yak, living there at an altitude of 1 500 - 2 500 m. Because of the northerly latitude of this region it is very cold with less than seven frost-free days per year. The yak were outdoors throughout the year but received some supplementary feeding when the ground was frozen. Nevertheless, the yak were breeding, on average, a year sooner than typical for most parts of China. Some results on the reproduction of these yak are given in Chapter 4. Trials involving meat production from yak and local breeds of cattle were also reported from Tajikistan (Norov and Dorotyuk, 1988) and other parts of the Pamir mountain range, bordering on Afghanistan.

Only a very small proportion of the many possible references to work with yak and their hybrids have been included here, selected in part to provide a historical perspective on the status and development of yak production in these countries. The impression that comes across is that the general approach to yak keeping has been to encourage the use of the yak, for meat production especially, as a genotype with particular merits in particular situations. Thus, the yak is acknowledged for its ability to exploit pastures and environments where cattle or sheep are also kept but where the use of the yak helps to extend the use of the natural resources. It does so by virtue of its great resistance to cold and to hardship and its adaptability to a low-quality diet. In addition it is also claimed that the yak produces meat more economically from a given resource than do other cattle. Yak are therefore useful both in their own right and as a component of the genotype in hybrids with *Bos taurus*. This is an unsentimental and business-like approach to the role of the yak in animal production in countries where state farms and cooperatives were the norm for many years. This approach to the utilization of the yak also provided the incentive for the later introduction of the yak to some countries that were formerly without them. This makes use of the animals for their special qualities in harsh environments. Yak are thus kept in these areas on their own merits, uninhibited by the traditions that surround yak in their native territories.

References

Denisov, V.F. (1935). [Some data on the yak and its hybrids in Kyrgyzstan.] Trud. Kirghiz. Kompl. Eksp., 4, 115-171. [CAB Animal Breeding Abstracts, 4, 298-300.]

Denisov, VF. (1958). Domestic yak and their hybrids. Selkhozgiz: Moscow. 116 pp.

Ivanova, V.V. & Ljubimov, I.M. (1951). [The introduction of a breed with high butterfat yield into farms in Gomo Altai.] *Sovetsk. Zootch.* 1951, (3), 26-37. *[CAB Animal Breeding Abstracts, 20,* 456-4.57.]

Katzina, EX, Davydov, V.N. & Baldanov, N.D. (1994). Elaboration of the scheme of production and usage of industrial hybrids of yak and meat cattle. Proceedings of first International Congress on Yak. *Journal of Gansu agricultural University* (Special issue, June 1994). pp. 44-48. (Reprinted in *Asian Livestock (FAO Bangkok)* 1994, XIX(10), 137-139.)

Katzina, E.X. & Maturova, E.T. (1989). [The reproductive function of yak cows.] *Doklady Vsesoyuznoi Ordena Lenina Akademii Sel'skokhozyaistvennykh Naukim VI. Lenina,* 1989, No. 4, 26-29. *[CAB Animal Breeding Abstracts,* 58, No. 352.]

Kozlovskii, B. (1960). [The greater use of commercial crossing in yak breeding.] *Molochnoe i Myasnoe Skotovodstvo, 5(11),* 32-36. *[CAB Animal Breeding Abstracts, 29,* 270.]

Mochalovskii, A. & Abdusalamov, Sh. (1973). [The Pamir yak in the Caucasus.] *Molochnoe i Myasnoe Skotovodstvo,* 1973, No. 8, 21. *[CAB Animal Breeding Abstracts, 42,* No. 163.]

Norov, A. & Dorotyuk, E. (1988). [Meat production of bulls of different genotypes in Tadzhikistan.] *Molochnoe i Myasnoe Skotovodstvo,* 1988, No. 1, 43-44. *[CAB Animal Breeding Abstracts,* 57, No. 1472.]

Sarbagishev, B.S., Rabochev, V.K. & Terebaev, A.I. (1989). 9. Yaks. *In: Animal Genetic Resources of the USSR. FAO Animal Production and Health Paper* No. 65, Rome, pp. 357-364.

Schley, P. (1967). Der Yak and seine Kreuzung mit dem Rind in der Sowjetunion. *Giessener Abhandlungen zur Agrar and Wirtschaftsforschung des Europaischen Ostins,* 44. 131 pp. Wiesbaden.

Smirnov, D.A. *et al.* (1990). Meat yield and meat quality of yaks. *Sel'skokhozyaistvennykh Nauk Im. V I. Lenina. (Soviet Agricultural Sciences)* No. 1, 46-49.

Vlasov, P, Gershenzon, S. & Poliakov, A. (1932). [Hybrids of yak and cattle.] *Probl. Zhivotn. no.* I , 48-57. *[CAB Animal Breeding Abstracts, 1,* 95-96.]

Section 2 – *Buryatia – with some notes on Yakutia*
account based on information from E.V. Katzina[4]

Buryatia

The Republic of Buryatia lies in the southern part of eastern Siberia between Mongolia and Lake Baikal. (Lake Baikal is the world's largest fresh-water lake – 636 km long and between 25 km and 79 km wide). Yakutia lies to the north of Buryatia, in the central part of eastern Siberia. Yak in Buryatia are kept on farms on the Okinsky plateau of the East Sayan mountains at altitudes of 1 400 m - 2 500 m and at 1 200 m - 1 800 m in the Zakamensky district of the Lake Baikal watershed (50° - 54°N and 100° - 104°E). The yak in these two districts were formerly isolated from each other and thought of as sub-populations of the Buryat type. However, exchange of males takes place nowadays between the two areas, and they are regarded as genetically close and similar in other respects. Breeding females constitute 40 - 45 percent of the total number of yak. Yak formerly in the Tunkinskyi district are no longer present. Overall, the number of yak in Buryatia have declined dramatically from 169 000 in 1924 to a total of less than 3 000 in the year 2000. Figures for the main districts are shown in Table 11.2.4.

Table 11.2.4 Yak numbers in Buryatia in different years

Districts	1947	1981	1992	1998	2000
Okinskyi	3 954	4 215	9 090	2 560	2 720
Zakamenskyi	1 032	850	1 500	120	180
Tunkinskyi	222	96	0	0	0
Total	**5 208**	**5 161**	**10 590**	**2 680**	**2 900**

Reasons for the decline in numbers are partly organizational and partly due to displacement by other cattle. Former collective farms (*kolchoz*) and former State farms (*sowchos*) have undergone organizational change following the break up of the former Soviet Union into independent republics. Alongside these changes, there has been a displacement of the yak by meat and milk cattle breeds such as the Kalmyk, Kazakh white-headed, Simmental-Buryat hybrids, Galloway and Simmental. These have found favour at the relatively low altitudes of the mountain-taiga belt (1 000 - 2 000 m) to which yak in Buryatia had become acclimatized.

Now only small peasant farms keep yak; however, the Okinsky yak gene pool is preserved in a herd at the "Tuyaya" pedigree farm.

---

[4] E.V. Katzina is a senior scientist of the Institute of General and Experimental Biology, Siberian Branch, Russian Academy of Sciences, Ulan-Ude, 670047, Russia.

According to E.V. Katzina, the Buryat population of yak was regarded historically as the same as the yak of the adjacent territories of Mongolia and Tuva. However, the Buryat yak have been isolated from these populations for a considerable time and analyses of antigenic factors in blood now suggest a relatively low degree of relationship between Buryatia and Mongolian yak (Mashurov and Davydov, 1998) (cf. Chapter 15).

In the mid-1980s, 32 yak of the Zakamenskaya population were taken to the Kizhinginsky district of Buryatia where they acclimatized and where they are breeding on the plain territory of the taiga zone with year-round grazing. Losses from predation have been negligible, and among diseases only foot rot is relatively widespread.

Figure 11.2.2 Yak female of the East Sayan (the Okinskaya subpopulation), six years old, 289 kg (2 300 m a.s.l. altitude) (Photo courtesy of E.V. Katzina)

Figure 11.2.3 Yak female and male of the East Sayan (the Sanaginskaya subpopulation), female is seven years old, 262 kg; male is five years old, 420 kg (1 200 m a.s.l. altitude) (Photo courtesy of E.V. Katzina)

The climate of Buryatia is one of extremes, with large variations in temperature across the seasons. Temperature in winter can fall to -50°C. In the summer, temperatures can occasionally reach +60°C (at ground level), but even in July it is not uncommon for the temperature at night to drop to -2°C from the heat of the day. Day length is seven to eight hours in winter and 17 - 18 hours in summer. Frost-free days number only between 41 and 79 per year. Precipitation varies between 275 mm and 410 mm per year, with two thirds of the annual rainfall in the three months from June to August – with July generally being the wettest month. Snow can fall in August, and snow cover in winter is to a depth of 6 - 15 cm. In general, the winter in Buryatia is severe, windy and very cold and the summer short and, on average, cold. The average annual temperature is 5° - 6°C.

Yak are not normally milked in Buryatia – all production being geared to meat. The yield of milk from yak is estimated to vary between 360 kg and 450 kg per lactation for yak calving in April (lactation length six to seven months) and 150 - 160 kg for those calving in June (four to five months of lactation).

The following results are given by E.V. Katzina in relation to the yak reproduction:

Age at first mating:	4 - 28 months (depending on development of the calf before the onset of winter in the year of birth)
Calving interval:	one year for between 40 percent and 87 percent of the females (two years for the remainder)
Gestation length:	mean 258.8 days (SD 30.9 days)
No. of calves (annually): *per 100 females*	variable from 40 to 87
Breeding season	late July to mid-September
Calving season	April to May (rarely March to early July)
Survival of adult yak	100 percent in a favourable winter, 60 - 70 percent in a winter with deep snow.
Calf survival	80 - 100 percent

Table 11.2.5 Daily milk yield, protein content and fat content of Buryat yak cows calving in March to May – according to month of lactation [Source: Maturova and Katzina, 1990]

	Calving March-May						Calving June-August					
	Milk (kg)		Protein (%)		Fat (%)		Milk (kg)		Protein (%)		Fat (%)	
	M.	s.e.	M.	s.e.	M.	s.e.	M.	s.e.	M.	s.e.	M.	s.e.
1st	1.5	1.8	5.0	0.84	7.0	0.59	2.5	3.0	5.6	0.87	6.8	0.48
2nd	3.4	4.3	7.1	0.44	7.6	0.51	1.5	1.0	6.2	0.72	7.2	0.50
3rd	4.5	3.8	6.8	1.05	8.0	0.56	1.3	0.8	6.3	0.65	7.3	0.67

M. = Mean

The results on daily milk yield reinforce the findings of several other studies in different countries, that peak yield coincides with the month of highest herbage production – in or around July – when herbage quality is also still good.

A report by V.N. Davydov and E.V. Katzina (personal communication, 1994) shows that F1 hybrids of yak with other cattle yielded about 100 kg more milk than the yak in the 1940s but that the yields from hybrids in the 1990s were much higher. It has to be assumed that this may be due to the use of different breeds of cattle to produce the hybrid.

Table 11.2.6 provides some information on the milk composition of yak, local cattle, Simmental cattle and hybrid cows from yak dams mated to Simmental bulls.

Table 11.2.6 Composition (mean ± s.e.) of the milk of yak, cattle and hybrids

	Yak	Buryat**	Simmental	Khainyik***
Number of animals	15	14	15	15
Content of:				
Dry matter, g (%)	18.5 ± 0.75	13.9 ± 0.54*	13.6 ± 0.62*	15.3 ± 0.61*
Fat, g (%)	7.7 ± 0.44	4.7 ± 0.23*	4.4 ± 0.35*	5.5 ± 0.28*
Protein, g (%)	5.5 ± 0.41	3.9 ± 0.18*	3.7 ± 0.17*	4.9 ± 0.27

*Significance (P<0.001) of difference relative to yak milk.
** Local cattle
*** (Simmental male mated with yak female)

Interestingly, the percentages of dry matter and of fat in the milk of the hybrids were slightly below the average of those in the yak and the Simmental. In situations where butter or cheese production was the aim (as in several of the other yak-keeping countries) this effect on milk composition – if universal – would tend to counterbalance any advantage of the hybrid in terms of milk yield alone. (It is not clear from the information received whether the yak, the cattle and the hybrids shown in Table 11.2.6 were kept together and managed and fed alike).

The protein of the yak milk contains proportionately more casein than present in the protein of milk from cattle and the albumin fraction is also proportionately higher in yak milk.

The results in Table 11.2.7 show that the management of young animals (see section, Management) prevents weight losses over winter, although slowing the rate of gain. This is contrast to a number of studies reported in Chapter 6 showing large weight losses, even in calves, over the winter period. Results on growth reported by Maturova and Katzina (1990) show that weights at birth and up to two months of age were greater for calves born in July and August of the year than those born earlier. However, by six months old, the early-born calves were almost 40 kg heavier than those born late in the season.

This reflects clearly the effect of milk and feed availability on calf growth over the season. It also shows that being born late in the year is a disadvantage for a calf because its condition is poorer at the onset of the first winter of its life, and this, in turn, retards its subsequent development to puberty.

As referred to above, the main purpose of yak keeping in Buryatia is meat production. Table 11.2.8 provides some slaughter data.

Table 11.2.7 Body weight (kg) of male and female yak at different ages in Buryatia – calves born in March-May [Source: Maturova and Katzina, 1990]

Age (month)	Male			Female		
	No.	Mean	SE	No.	Mean	SE
Birth	50	13.1	0.4	50	14.1	0.3
1	50	23.2	0.7	50	20.6	0.5
2	50	37.5	1.2	50	34.8	0.9
3	46	54.6	1.7	48	51.0	1.4
4	46	73.4	1.2	47	68.0	1.8
5	43	87.6	1.6	45	79.6	1.7
6	40	96.7	1.6	43	89.7	2.7
7	35	107.3	2.9	40	101.3	3.3
8	35	110.2	3.3	39	104.8	2.4
9	34	112.0	2.8	37	107.3	4.0
10	34	112.8	2.2	37	103.5	2.6
11	34	129.4	3.0	37	115.1	1.7
12	34	129.4	3.0	37	115.1	1.7
18	32	192.3	5.9	34	175.9	4.2
20	32	205.3	6.7	34	185.2	4.7
Adult	11	386.4	10.8	32	261.1	3.7

The weights of hybrids at 30 months of age averaged 345 ± 1.6 kg for males and 308 ± 1.3 kg for females; weights of three- to four-year-old males were 459 (417 - 512) kg and 387 (310 - 425) kg for females at the fifth calving. The hybrids represent only between 8 percent and 10 percent of the animals in commercial yak herds. All hybrids are produced by natural mating. The hair and down fibre is not collected from yak in Buryatia.

Management

According to E.V. Katzina, the yak in Buryatia are managed extensively to simulate as closely as possible the natural conditions dictated by the availability of suitable pastures. During the summer, the yak graze freely on alpine and subalpine pastures.

From October to May, yak are allowed on winter pastures on lower slopes. Supplementary feed in the form of hay is provided only in extremely harsh winters – except for young animals, which receive daily supplements. Most of the calving takes place on the winter pastures. The calves have access to all the milk of their dams. Although yak are not given veterinary treatments, they appear to have fewer illnesses than other types of cattle.

The summer pastures contain 45 - 50 percent Carex *sp.*, 32 - 37 percent grasses, 10 - 13 percent legumes and 5 - 8 percent cereals. The herbage grows densely to a height of about 18 - 25 cm. Leaves and branches of trees and shrubs are quite insignificant in the diet of Sayan yak.

Table 11.2.8 Carcass data for three yak slaughtered at each of two different ages
[Source: Maturova and Katzina, 1990]

	18 - 19 months		30-31 months	
	Mean	SD	Mean	SD
Live weight (kg)	201	6.2	241	10.5
Carcass weight (kg)	98	4.3	120	6.5
Dressing (%) Weight (kg) of:				
Meat	73	22	86.5	18.6
Bone	19.6	0.2	22.9	2.9
Subcutaneous fat	2	0.7	4.1	0.9

Investigational work

Research with yak has been active in Buryatia and neighbouring regions since the 1930s (several of the studies are referred to in this book). Earlier studies were largely descriptive of the economics and productivity of the yak and of its characteristics – particularly in relation to meat production. E.V. Katzina reported already in 1995 (first edition of this book) that the scale of research had then declined and become more fragmentary than formerly. Emphasis was given in the Buryat Institute of Biology of the Siberian Branch of the Russian Academy of Sciences to research on conservation and the rational use of yak – including the hybridization scheme already referred to. The introduction of yak to parts of the northern Caucasus and central Yakutia was part of that rationalization. Attention was also given to grazing technology and management. As part of the conservation strategy, consideration was given to re-introducing yak into the wild. Many studies were being undertaken into more fundamental aspects of the biology of the yak and its hybrids. E.V. Katzina provided a list of the 50 most important studies published over recent years, which was lodged for ready access with the FAO Regional Office in Bangkok and with the International Yak Information Centre.

More recently, E.V. Katzina has reported on a substantial amount of research work on the amino acid composition of meat from yak of various types and with comparative data for cattle (Mkrtchyan *et al.* 1993). There is also work on yak immunology that forms the basis of the studies on genetic distancing, referred to earlier (Mashurov and Davydov, 1998). Work on the biological properties of yak milk has been extended (Katzina, 1993). Extensive anatomical investigations on the development of the yak in different periods, from the embryonic stage through to skeletal ossification in later life, have also been carried out at the Buryat State Agricultural Academy (Vasilyev, 1991). E.V. Katzina (2002) has also provided evidence, rare for the yak, of heritabilities of body weight at various ages from birth to two years old in the range 0.25 - 0.38, remarkably similar to the plentiful estimates in cattle.

Yakutia

Yak were first introduced to this sparsely populated region of eastern Siberia in 1842, before the establishment of the area as an independent republic. Several further importations followed. The yak acclimatized well (Solomonov *et al.* 1980) and became a profitable enterprise. The second successful importation of yak occurred in the early 1920s, following the eradication during the Russian civil war of the yak previously there. Yak sent to the Magadan Oblast region (far northeast of Russia) in 1935 - 1936 did not do well because of helminth infection of the yak in what turned out to be an unsuitable, wet and windy seaside climate. Further yak were sent from Buryatia to central and southern Yakutia (both Buryat type and Altaic type yak) in 1971, 1973 and 1974 – a total of 167 head – and acclimatized well.

The severe climatic conditions of Yakutia required that scientists work out a new strategy for keeping yak in these conditions. During the summer, the yak graze on pastures for about 170 days (about six to seven weeks longer than cattle). For the first 10 - 30 days of the grazing period, the yak receive supplementary feed in the form of 1.5 - 2 kg hay and 1 kg mixed fodder per head per day. Subsequently, the pastures in summer provide sufficient green forage for the requirements and fattening of yak. From October to May, yak are given winter rations of hay (4 - 5 kg) and mixed fodder (1 kg) in two feeds per day (in the coldest weather the amount of hay is increased because the concentrate feed freezes to the lips and mouth cavity of the animals and cannot be given). In late autumn, the yak are still allowed out to pasture after their morning feed, provided the temperature is not below -30°C. Shelter is available to the animals in winter in the form of three-sided sheds, allowing 2 sq m per yak, and "warm" ice holes provide water.

Weaned calves, mothers with suckling calves, weakened animals and pregnant females 10 - 15 days prior to calving before calving are kept in separate groups. Newborn calves are wiped dry with hay before the dam is allowed access to her calf.

Growth rates of calves, comparing 60 yak with an equal number of cattle, were found to be higher in percentage terms in yak (probably because of their relatively low birth weight) than in cattle over the first three months of life, but not in absolute weight gains (yak weight increased by 42.5 kg [29 percent] over that period and cattle around 61 kg [25 percent]). Weight gains of yak calves during the first three months of life were found to average 487 g per day for females and 529 for males. The three-month period in the second summer (age 12 - 15 months) saw average daily gains of 443 g and 537 g for females and males, respectively. Over winter, the young stock still gained weight but at a slower rate (177 g per day for females and 194 g for males in the period from 6 to 12 months, and 152 g and 219 g per day, respectively, during a three-month period – age 15 - 18 months – during the second winter of life. The management system developed for yak in Yakutia seems to have produced somewhat different results from those in more traditional yak rearing regions.

Economics

The forage costs and the general expenses of keeping animals were found to be significantly lower for yak than for cattle, as shown in Table 11.2.9

Table 11.2.9 Forage costs and general expenses (roubles) per animal per year in Yakutia

Species	Forage costs	General expenses
Cattle	238	560
Horse	27	145
Yak	91	240

From such evidence and the report by Davydov and Katzina referred to earlier, the point is made that the cost of producing milk and meat from yak and yak hybrids is less than the cost of production from cattle. The reason given is that the yak (and hybrids) use mountain pasture almost exclusively and that they consume only very little hay and make virtually no use of forage from arable land. Thus, the cost of producing 50 kg of yak meat is approximately a third of the cost of producing such meat from cattle in Buryatia. (The cost of 50 kg of weight gain was 98 - 111 roubles for yak and 304 - 345 roubles for cattle kept under the same conditions – and a final 30-day period of fattening at the end of the grazing period was highly cost effective in yak).

References

Katzina, E.V. (1993). Lactation, biologic properties of milk of yaks. *J. Sel'skokhozyaistvennaya Biologiya*, 2: 108-115.

Katzina, E.V. (2002). Some genetic parameters of body weight in yaks of the Buryat ecotype. *Proceedings of the third international congress on yak, in Lhasa, China, 4-9 September 2000.* International Livestock Research Institute (ILRI), Nairobi, pp. 313-315.

Mashurov, A.M. and Davydov, V.N. (1998). Revealing characteristics of immunogenic resemblance and distance between Buryat yaks and other bovine populations. *Siberian Vestnic of Agriculture Science*, 3-4: 89-92.

Maturova, E.T. and. Katzina, E.V. (1990). *The yak of Sayan.* The Buryatia Scientific Centre of the Siberian Division of the USSR Academy of Sciences, Ulan Ude, 1990. 168 pp. (in Russian)

Mkrtchyan, Sh.A., Umansky, M.S. and Kmet, A.M.. 1993. Meat amino acid composition of yak different ecotypes. *J. of the Report of Russian Academy Agricultural Science*, 4: 57-63.

Solomonov, H.G., Kyselev, U.A and Slepzov, M.K. (1980). *Acclimatization of the yak in Yakutia.* Novosibirsk: Nauka, 102 pp.

Vasilyev, K.A. (1991). *Morpho-functional characteristics of the yak ontogenesis by development periods*. Ulan-Ude: Buryatskoye knizhnoye izdatel'stvo (Buryat Publishing House), 224 pp.

Yak husbandry in India
By R.N. Pal [5]

The yak-rearing states of India are Arunachal Pradesh, Sikkim, Uttar Pradesh, Himachal Pradesh and Jammu and Kashmir. The first three of these, bordering the southern slopes of the Himalayas, have a cold, humid climate, while the two northerly states are cold and arid. Numbers of yak are shown in Table 11.2.10. The total of about 51 000 yak in 1997 represents a marked decline from the 132 000 yak reported for the year 1977 (Pal, 1993a). Gupta and Gupta (2000) and Nivsarkar *et al.* (1997) published even lower numbers of around 40 000 for recent years – largely because they suggested a lower number for Jammu and Kashmir. However, changes in numbers of yak over the years seem to differ among states – some having remained static in numbers.

Reasons suggested for the decline in size of the yak population include socio-economic causes, one of which is a desire for an easier and more comfortable lifestyle on the part of the younger generations (Pal, 1993a). The closure of the border with Tibet to the former traffic in yak may also be a contributory factor and has affected the availability of new sources of breeding stock. Nivsarkar *et al.* (1997) suggested that hybridization on a large-scale of yak with local Tibetan cattle was another factor leading to this sharp decline in the pure yak population.

Yak types

There are a number of different phenotypic types among Indian yak. The "common" yak resemble medium size hill cattle in conformation; "Bisonian" yak are bigger animals; "Bare-back" yak have a long body and little hair on their backs. Yak with a particularly hairy forehead, long-haired yak and white yak represent the fourth type described in more detail by Pal *et al.* (1994). It is not suggested that these types represent different breeds as such as they occur within the same districts or even within herds.

Among the ten colour patterns noted for yak in India, the majority are black (29 percent) or black with white patches (40 percent). Some 15 percent are grey in colour and the remainder of the population is made up of small proportions of brown with white patches, pure white and various mixtures, including piebald and skewbald animals.

---

[5] R. N. Pal was formerly the Director of the National Research Centre on Yak (at Dirang, Arunachal Pradesh) of the Indian Council of Agriculture Research.

Table 11.2.10 Pure yak population in the Indian states (from 1997 census)

States	District	Number	Total	M : F*
Arunachal Pradesh	West Kamang	1 379	8 480*	1:1.54
	Tawang	6 853		
	West Subansiri	248		
Sikkim	North	4 865	5 346	1:245
	West	441		
	East	40		
Uttar Pradesh	Pithoragarh	102	318	N/A
	Uttarkashi	175		
	Others	41		
Himachal Pradesh	Chamba	2 365	5 690	1:0.82
	Kinaur	1 321		
	Lahul Spiti	1 997		
	Others	7		
Jammu & Kashmir	Kashmir Div	191	31 379	1:1.04
	Laddak Div	25 662		
	Jammu Div	5 526		

*Ratio of males to females.

Breeding and hybridization

The Indian yak population is thought to suffer from inbreeding due to the nonavailability of new yak germ-plasm from Tibet for the past five decades (as referred to earlier) and because of the practice of prolonged use of the same bull within herds. Exchange of breeding bulls among herds and selection schemes have not become established as regular practices, although the intentions appear to exist as part of the yak projects of the National Research Council.

Hybridization with local cattle is practised only randomly, although the F1 hybrid is generally more productive than either parental species. It has to be stressed, however, that yak and the F1 rarely run together on the same grazing, except in winter. During the growing season, the F1 are at mid-altitudes and the yak at the highest altitudes. Claims for higher growth and milk output from the F1 relative to the yak must therefore take account of a possible nutritional advantage enjoyed by the F1. In terms of milk output, though the quantity from the F1 is higher than from the yak, the fat content is less and total fat production may be similar for yak and F1. The F1 provides a lower income from hair and the fine undercoat than the pure yak, but both types are good pack animals. The performance of animals from successive stages of mating yak with cattle (beyond the F1 stage) was found to be inferior to the F1 (Pal, 1992) – and producing animals beyond the F1 is discouraged because the different types are also difficult to differentiate visually. Nivsarkar *et al.* (1997) also shared the concern, expressed in Chapter 3, that even when there was a case for hybridizing to increase milk output from the herd, the extent of this should be restricted so as not to threaten the replacement of the pure yak population.

As in neighbouring countries, different names are attached to each of the various types of hybrid offspring from any such matings.

Management and nutrition

Traditional yak management in the Indian states is similar to that practised in countries like Bhutan, Nepal and the Tibetan Autonomous Region of China. An open seasonal migratory system is, however, confined to particular areas due to restrictions placed on movement by the different tribal clans. A considerable part of the high hills in the alpine region is stony and difficult terrain for grazing, with only small pockets of green meadow and the availability of water (Pal, 1993b). The social structure of the clans influences yak keeping. In Arunachal Pradesh, for example, a yak herder pays a royalty for the grazing right in the alpine area if he is not a member of the clan that has the rights to the area. Any numbers of herders are permitted to graze their animals, irrespective of the carrying capacity of the area, provided this is not opposed by the other occupants. The extra animals thus brought on to the grazing lead to over grazing and this has, in turn, resulted in the deterioration of the grazing land. The concept of stocking rate appears to be irrelevant to the village heads so long as they receive their royalty. A tenant system of yak rearing was once very popular. Affluent people owning a number of yak used to give away the right to their animals to small herders in return for a pre-arranged quantity of produce, such as *churpi* (wet cheese) or butter. This tenant system is gradually declining in popularity.

In the traditional seasonal migratory system, the alpine pastures (4 500 m and above) are grazed for the four months of June to September. The middle hills (3 500 - 4 500 m) are grazed from March to May as the animals migrate up to the high pastures and again on their return during October and November. The winter (December to the end of February) is then spent on grazing below 3 000 m.

This scheme is common to most yak herders in India. During the three peak-winter months the herders and their families stay in the village, and their yak graze adjoining pastures alongside other cattle, sheep and ponies. This concentration of stock during the winter has also led to a marked deterioration of the pastures and a consequent increase in the weed population. Occasionally, these weed components have been found to be toxic to yak (as recorded by Winter *et al.*, 1994; Mondal *et al.*, 1998).

Evaluation of alpine pastures at four sites (4 000 - 4 300 m) in the summer identified about 25 plant species of which only four were grasses (*Carex* sp, *Cyperus vesiculosa* and *Festuca rubra*) and the rest were herbaceous. Plant density varied from 1 742 per sq m to 3 988 per sq m with height varying from 9 - 10 cm (Pal *et al.*, 1993).

As elsewhere, lack of winter feed leads to heavy weight loss (25 - 30 percent) of yak over that period, requiring recovery and new weight gain during the summer months. Efforts to improve the supply of winter feed by the introduction of different varieties of exotic, cold-temperate grasses has not been successful; new efforts may be directed at improving local grasses and other edible species.

The most likely cost-effective strategy for reducing winter weight loss of yak, apart from improved grazing management, may come from providing locally available roughages treated with urea, as a supplement to grazing. Preliminary trials with yak in India suggest an improvement in crude protein digestibility but, perhaps due to the small scale of the trials, have not yet shown significant effects in dry matter intake or on body weight changes (Pal *et al.*, 2002; see Chapters 8 and 14).

Yak diseases

Disease among yak is most prevalent when the animals are on the mid-range and lower-range pastures from October to May. The diseases reported are similar to those in Chapter 9 but with a particular prevalence of ticks and lice. Helminth infections are especially common in calves where these can cause heavy mortality. Among viral diseases, Foot and Mouth disease is the most serious but seasonal, with highest incidences recorded in February and March. As already noted as a consequence of overgrazing, the intake of toxic weeds – pyrrolizidone alkaloid in *Senecio* in particular – has created problems (Mondal *et al.* 1998).

Reproduction and production

Under Indian conditions, the reproductive performance of yak is similar to that recorded in other yak-rearing countries. Typically, puberty in females first appears around 36 - 40 months of age when body weight is on average 184 ± 8 kg (79 percent of mature size). Oestrus cycle length is 20.1 ± 1.3 days and oestrus length 6 - 31 hours with an average of 15 ± 6. Most yak cows calve only once in every two years.

Males appear to be sexually mature at five years old when they have attained their final body weight and a scrotal circumference of around 27 cm (26.3 ± 1.3) – an increase in that circumference from the age of three years of 9 cm (Mohanty *et al.*, 1999).

Milk yields of the yak vary but average from 1-2 kg per day while that from hybrids is fractionally higher (Jain, 1986). Total solids, solids-not-fat, fat, and ash are reported as 15.6 percent, 7.1 percent, 8.6 percent and 0.42 percent, respectively (Mondal and Pal, 1996). *Churpi*, a wet soft cheese, and butter, both made from fermented milk, are the principal milk products.

Yak meat is popular among the local hill people but has not found other outlets, possibly due to the poor conditions of slaughter and marketing. The meat is preserved by salting and drying.

As elsewhere, the hair and fine wool from yak are utilized (see Chapter 10) but provide little income. The yak in India are also valued as pack animals.

A number of studies have been conducted at the National Research Centre for Yak in India on aspects of adaptation of yak to high altitude and some of the parameters involved. References to some of this work is found in Chapter 4.

Yak in the cultural and religious life of the highland peoples

Animals in different forms and shapes are widely depicted in oriental cultures. The highland people in the Indian Himalayan states, as in neighbouring countries, profess Buddhism and consider the yak of celestial origin. The yak appears symbolically in the Buddhist scriptures in different forms and is extant in the mythology. Yak also feature in dances, festivities and pantomime.

Yak in the Indian development plans

The number of yak in India is insignificantly small compared to the number of cattle and buffalo, and the people depending on the yak for their livelihood are few, relative to the large population of the country. Still, the yak is of vital importance to a section of the people in the mountainous regions adjacent to the Himalayas. Government recognition and support for yak keeping did not appear in any of the Indian five-year plans until Plan 6, which saw the establishment of the National Research Centre for Yak in 1989. Characterization of yak genetic resources was also considered, and a pilot study was done by the National Bureau of Animal Genetic Resources (Karnal, Haryana) in the yak-raising areas.

The work of the National Research Centre is helping yak herders with investigations to improve husbandry services and to investigate some of the underlying scientific and practical problems that limit output. Many of the problems need long-term consideration, but most of the herders are more interested in short-term solutions and this divergence of view creates tensions. A second and perhaps more serious problem for the future of yak production in India is that the younger generation appear unwilling to shoulder the responsibilities and relative hardships of yak rearing. Some yak herds are disposed of or slaughtered for want of a willing family member prepared to take over from the present elderly owner. The future for yak in India is therefore uncertain, but an improved economic structure for the industry assisted by improved husbandry practices may create a more willing new generation of herders.

References

Gupta, N. & Gupta, S.C. (2000). Yak – status and conservation. *In*: Sahai, R. and Vijh, R.K (eds.), *Domestic animal diversity – conservation & sustainable development*. SI Publications, Karnal, India, pp. 179-187.

Jain, Y.C. (1986). Milk potential of yaks. *Indian Farming,* 35 (12): 25-37.

Mohanty, T.K. *et al.* (1999). Andrological evaluation of yak bull. 1. Correlation between age, body weight, scrotal and body measurements. *Indian Journal of Animal Reproduction*, 20: 130-133.

Mondal, D. & Pal, R.N. (1996). Chemical composition of yak milk. *Indian Journal of Dairy Science*, XLIX: 12.

Mondal, D. *et al.* (1998). Pyrrolizidone alkaloid poisoning in yak. *Veterinary Record*, 144: 508-509

Nivsarkar, A.N., Gupta, S.C. & Gupta, N. (1997). *Yak production*. Indian Council of Agricultural Research, New Delhi, 394 pp.

Pal, R.N. (1992). Yak hybrids. *Asian Livestock*, XVII (8): 85-88.

Pal, R.N. (1993a). Halting the decline of the yak population in India, *World Animal Review*, 76: 56-57.

Pal, R.N. (1993b). Yak (Poephagus grunniens L.) of India. Animal Genetic Resources Information, 12: 63-71.

Pal, R.N., Basu, A. & Barari, S.K. (1993). High altitude pastures for yak. VI. Animal Nutrition Research Workers' Conference in Bhubaneshwar, 13-16 September 1993.

Pal, R.N., Barari, S.K. & Basu, A. (1994). Yak (*Poephagus grunniens* L.), its type – a field study. *Indian Journal of Animal Sciences*, 64: 853-856.

Pal, R.N., Pattanayak, S. & Mohanty, T.K. (2002). Urea enriched finger millet straw (*Elensine coracana*): Effect of feeding on yak. *Proceedings of the third international congress on yak, in Lhasa, China, 4-9 September 2000*. International Livestock Research Institute (ILRI), Nairobi, pp. 251-258.

Winter, H. *et al.* (1994). Pyrrolizidine alkaloid poisoning of yaks: identification of the plants involved. *Veterinary Record,* 134: 135-139.

Yak in Mongolia
By A. Magash[6]

Mongolia, in Central Asia, extends 1.5 million sq km and a distance of 2 400 km from east to west. The lowest altitude of the country is 560 m above the sea level. The major part of the country is hilly or mountainous, reaching altitudes of 1 500 - 4 000 m in the high mountainous areas. The climate is extreme, with temperatures in winter, the longest season, at around -20°C on average, but it can be much colder. Summer temperatures are relatively warm at around 20°C. Typically, there are large temperature fluctuations across the year and even in the course of a day. The pleasantest time of year is the autumn, with light winds and clean healthy air. Blue skies occur throughout the year with an annual total of 280 - 300 days of sunshine.

Large expanses of grasslands cover around 80 percent of the total territory of the country and contain a wealth of different plants. These vast rangelands meet all the requirements of a traditional, nomadic animal production. Management of the grasslands provides an opportunity to produce large quantities of valuable livestock products with minimal inputs from five different kinds of stock. Livestock production in Mongolia is crucial for the life of the people and for the economy of the country and provides the basis for 80 percent of exports.

Figure 11.2.4 A general view in Mongolia (Photo courtesy of Horst and Barbara Geilhausen)

In this context, cattle production has particular importance with a population of 3.1 million cattle, of which 610 100 are yak. Cattle as a whole supply 40 percent of the meat and 80 percent of the milk products. Yak provide a fifth of the meat from "cattle" and a third of the butter.

Yak are an indispensable part of the animal husbandry in the high mountain regions where yak are used both for transport and for their productive capabilities. In recent years, the textile industry has greatly increased its demand for yak fibre. The production of hybrids between yak and other cattle is also of great significance because of their better meat and milk production relative to that of the parental types. Yak in Mongolia share with yak

---

[6]A. Magash is Director of the National Yak Research Centre, Agricultural University of Ulaanbaatar, Mongolia.

elsewhere the ability to withstand periods of hunger and to make up quickly in the spring the large weight losses sustained over winter.

The yak represents a high degree of adaptation to the ecosystem. No other domestic animal can utilize the vegetation available at 2 000 - 4 000 m in Mongolia with territories marked by steep, treacherous slopes, moor land, bogs and lakes. The morphological and physiological characteristics of the yak (see Chapter 4) endow the animal with an ability to resist cold, to scrape through snow for fodder (which covers the ground for 100 - 150 days of the year) and to graze very short grass – all essential in these unfavourable conditions.

Yak keeping

The natural grasslands of Mongolia can be divided into mountain and woodland pastures, mountainous steppe and desert steppe. The mountainous pastures are on the mountain plateau at 1 800 - 3 500 m above sea level. The actual yak grazing lands are typically above the tree line at 2 000 m in the north rising to 3 000 m in the Mongolian Altai. The dominant plant species range from grasses, e.g. *Festuca spp.,* and *Stipa spp*, at lower altitudes to sedges, e.g. *Kobresia spp.*, and *Carex spp.* at the higher altitudes. A precipitation of 300 mm of rain in the Chovsgol-Changai mountains and in the Altai is enough for reasonable hay production (though lower in the Altai) and perhaps quite high yields under exceptional circumstances (Lhagvajav, 2000).

The grasslands are very suitable for the yak by virtue of composition and location. They provide an adequate diet from May to September and in many areas a surplus of feed above requirements for three months. From October to April there is a deficiency in nutrient availability for the animals. There is, therefore, a significant annual imbalance in the provision of fodder between the short growing season and the longer non-growing periods - accentuated by the body heat loss during the winter period. However, the arid climate allows for the natural freeze-drying of the dead herbage and this supply of feed normally lasts until the spring (Barthel, 1971) and makes it possible to over-winter the yak without supplementary feed.

The grazing ecology and climate make many demands on the yak herder and lead to a transhumance form of husbandry. With the changing seasons, the migrations normally follow a rotation starting in the valley bottom (where the animals are in the winter) and proceeding vertically to the high summer pastures only to return, in good bodily condition, to the lower ground via the autumn pastures. These rotational migrations can be accomplished by the herders without great difficulty with whole yak herds and within a traditional allotment of land for grazing. Large herds might be divided into two groups to allow for a division of labour. The first group consists of the milking and breeding females as well as the stock males. The second group is made up of the cull cows, three-year-old heifers (first insemination), young fattening stock, castrates and old yak for fattening. The second group is taken to the high alpine pastures while the first group is kept on the summer pastures at intermediate altitudes.

For over-wintering, the animals are penned in sheds or protected in fenced enclosures. In Mongolia, these enclosures are circular and made of brushwood and reeds. The possibility of enclosures using stone walls or wooden paling is being considered.

Yak population

Numerically, Mongolia comes second to China in the size of its yak population. The yak and hybrid yak (F1) population declined in number over the years from 1940 to 1970 but thereafter increased, as shown in Table 11.2.11.

Table 11.2.11 Number of yak and yak hybrids (F1) in different years (in thousands)

Year	Yak	Hybrids (F1)
1940	725.8	73.8
1950	561.0	52.4
1960	495.0	69.2
1970	452.2	69.1
1980	554.5	50.7
1990	566.9	70.0
2000	610.0	66.3

Yak are found in 13 of the provinces of Mongolia and 9 of these have 90 percent of all the yak. There are a few small herds in districts of the central and southern Gobi province. Seventy percent of the yak herds are concentrated in the Hangai and Hovsgol mountains, 29 percent in the Mongolian Altai and only about 1 percent in the Gobi Altai and Hentii mountains. The yak population works out at just under one yak for every three of the human population in Mongolia.

Mongolian yak

Coat colour varies greatly, but black and brown are the predominant colours with black genetically dominant. Spotted and white animals also occur. Black, or mostly black, animals account for 68.5 percent and brown, or predominantly brown, for 16.9 percent of the total; a further 8.9 percent are mostly grey (Bat-Erdene, 1961). Ninety percent of yak of both sexes are polled.

Two types of yak can be distinguished in Mongolia, according to the area where they are raised – the Hangai and the Altai mountain yak.

Hangai yak
The large-framed Hangai yak stems from the traditional yak-keeping provinces of Arhangai, Ovorhangai, Bayanhongor and Hovosgol were yak are found on mountainous and woodland pastures at elevations of 1 800 - 3 000 m, with a dry and cold climate. The

type is large and fecund and is used for transport, meat and milk. Colours vary greatly and up to 90 percent of the animals are polled. They are good at compensatory growth and rapidly regain in the spring and summer the weight losses sustained over the previous winter. A breeding station for the improvement of yak production has been in existence in the Ih Tamir district of Arhangai province since 1983. Figure 11.2.5 shows a polled yak cow suckling her calf.

Altai yak

As the name implies, these yak come from the Mongolian Altai region. The climate is characterized by great temperature fluctuations, inadequate precipitation and dry air. The average temperature over the year is $0^{o}C$ and reaches a minimum of $-30^{o}C$. The Altai yak is an alpine type and less good on the plateau. These yak utilize the high mountain grazings, which do not provide a secure supply of feed and are frequently overgrazed. The yak are able to withstand long periods of nutritional deprivation. Colours are predominantly black or black and white. The majority have long, well-developed horns. The body is long and covered with thick hair. In reproductive terms, the Altai yak is similar to the Hangai. The Altai yak is thought to be capable of improvement, particularly in relation to meat production.

Figure 11.2.5 A polled yak cow and her calf in Mongolia (Photo courtesy of Horst and Barbara Geilhausen)

Reproduction

An account of reproductive characteristics of yak is given in Chapter 5, which includes many of the results from studies in Mongolia. What follows are some of the particular statistical parameters of the reproductive cycle in Mongolia.

The essential factor in yak reproduction is its seasonality. As reported by Magash (1990a), the mating season lasts from July to November. The frequency of oestrus is highest among yak females in July and August and has markedly declined by October. The altitude of the grazings and the associated vegetation has a large influence on the breeding season. Post-partum anoestrus lasts on average 90.2 days (but from 30 to 172 days) among free-ranging Mongolian yak. The most important factors influencing the duration of this rest period are the time of calving and the age of the female. There are a number of possibilities for reducing this duration. These include: supplementary feeding of yak cows that calve in March or April; not milking first- and second-calving cows with calves at foot for the first

30 - 45 days after calving (the young cows are not yet fully grown); or separating calves from their dams during the period of lactation and rearing them apart.

Yak females can be mated up to three times in a season under Mongolian conditions. Conception to first mating is on average 70.5 percent but can vary over the months from 63 to 81 percent. On average, 29.3 percent of females return for a second mating and of these nearly two thirds conceive, raising the final pregnancy rate by 19.3 percent. Among those remaining non-pregnant, 10.2 percent still develop signs of oestrus and are mated. This increases the final pregnancy rate by another 4.6 percent, giving an overall 94.4 percent of the yak females becoming pregnant, on average, over the season. The month of mating and the age of the cow affect conception rates (cf. Chapter 5).

It is important for the profitability of yak production that the cows should, as far as possible, calve annually. The calving interval of 215 cows, involved in one of our experiments, averaged 355.6 days (range from 299 to 442 days). The length of gestation and the inter-pregnancy interval strongly influence this parameter. For intensive reproduction, the calving interval should not exceed 365 days. Only about two thirds of the yak cows achieve this optimum annual calving interval.

As shown in Chapter 5 (Table 5.13) from the work of Magash (1990b), young yak bulls mount each cow more often than do the older bulls, and they have a higher fertilization rate (90.7 - 96.3 percent for young bulls, compared to 76.3 - 96.8 percent for the older bulls). The adult bulls, however, serve many more cows, partly because they drive the young bulls away. These studies suggest that yak bulls should not be allowed to run with the herd in an uncontrolled way and that the number of cows per bull should be restricted to 10 - 15.

Calving takes place in Mongolia from March to August, but the main period is in the months of April and May when, on average, 68.2 percent of the pregnant females calve. Also on average, calving occurs in 80.9 percent of the cows that had been mated and did not return to service. *Brucella abortus* and *Clamydia psittaci* were isolated by blood tests on cows that aborted and from aborted foetuses.

There has been significant research in Mongolia on the use of technical aids to assist reproduction in yak, such as oestrus synchronization, artificial insemination and pregnancy diagnosis by hormone treatment (Magash, 1991). Results from this work are also referred to in Chapter 5.

Size and meat production

According to Bat-Erdene (1961) the body weights of adult Mongolian yak range from 400 to 500 kg for males and from 270 to 280 kg for females. Body measurements of Mongolian yak are shown in Table 11.2.12.

Table 11.2.12 Body dimensions (mean ± s.e. and range) of Mongolian yak
[Source: after Bat-Erdene, 1988]

	Height (cm)	Length (cm)	Heart girth (cm)
Bulls (5)	128.2 ± 0.96	152.4 ± 0.64	204.0 ± 0.83
	(123 - 130)	(146 - 162)	(198 - 210)
Cows (160)	108.1 ± 0.41	120.9 ± 0.48	168.8 ± 0.79
	(102 - 118)	(114 - 132)	(157 - 187)
Castrates* (37)	127.4 ± 096	137.3 ± 0.12	189.1 ± 0.53
	(115 - 139)	(120 - 150)	(177 - 219)

*Three to six years old.

Slaughter of yak in Mongolia is seasonal and occurs at the end of the pasture growing season. After each winter, the animals intended for slaughter are collected into groups according to age and sex and taken to the high mountain regions where vegetation is sufficient to provide a good level of nutrition. During this grazing period, live weight gains are between 43 and 88 kg and live weights at slaughter between 190 and 440 kg. Table 11.2.13 shows some weights for animals in above-average condition.

Table 11.2.13 Average live weight and dressing percentage of Mongolian yak in above-average condition [Source: after Bat-Erdene, 1988]

Class of animals	No.	Live weight (kg)	Dressing percentage
Mature male castrates	12	440.0	53.4
Mature females	13	334.7	49.3
1.5-year-old male castrates	22	190.2	51.3

Yak meat has an average composition of 65.1 percent water, 19.5 percent protein, 14.5 percent fat and 0.9 percent ash. The fat content of the yak meat is lower than that from cattle in the same region. The energy content of yak meat is around 2 450 kcal per kg (Bat-Erdene, 1988).

The meat from the yak is red, or deep red, because of a high haemoglobin and myoglobin content. The muscle fibres in yak meat are thicker than those of other cattle, and there is no intermuscular fat. The subcutaneous and internal fat is yellow. In Mongolia, there is thought to be no difference in taste between yak meat and beef from cattle.

Several high-quality products are derived from yak meat. Because of the seasonal slaughter, yak meat is dried in thin slices, called *Borts*, which can be kept for more than a year and is carried by the herders as they move from one location to another during the grazing season.

Demand for meat is high in Mongolia and yak meat plays an important role. Nyamgerel (1999) estimated the annual production of yak meat in Mongolia at 40 000 tonnes. To achieve high meat output requires the exploitation of the far-distant summer pastures in the alpine and subalpine regions.

Meat production is highest when calves are allowed to suck their dams to the full as this maximizes calf growth. The requirements of milk production from the yak, however, demand that calves are allowed as little as possible of their dams' milk. The common practice in Mongolia is for calves to be weaned quite early and herded separately from their mothers during the milking season – apart from the presence of the calf to initiate milk let-down. The needs of meat and milk production therefore compete, but the emphasis can be varied depending on the relative value of the two products in particular circumstances. The strategy for rearing young stock so as to provide the best compromise for both meat and milk production is, as yet, unresolved.

Meat packing plants exist in the urban areas, but yak herds are normally remote from these. Opportunities for herdsmen to market their own dairy products in central markets are also limited as such markets can be as much as 1 000 km distance. The problems of marketing yak produce so as to provide herders with a better income still need resolution.

Milk production

Yak make an important contribution to the supply of milk and milk products in Mongolia. Lactation length is determined by the date of calving, as the end of milking coincides with the end of the grazing season. Early calving thus allows longer lactations, about 200 - 230 days when calving in May or June. For the sake of their calves, cows are not milked at the beginning or end of lactation, thus reducing the milk off-take to less than the potential. The main milk production period is from June to October. If an estimate of the milk taken by the calf is included, the milk yield of Mongolian yak cows varies between 560 and 740 kg (Table 11.2.14).

Table 11.2.14 Milk yield of yak (mean and range) by month of calving
[Source: after Bat-Erdene, 1993]

	March N = 34	April n = 26	May n = 12	June n = 11
Lactation length (days)	283 (232 - 331)	258 (210 - 300)	231 (180 - 285)	206 (171 - 280)
Milk yield (kg)*	737 (635- 1 018)	673 (526 - 754)	607 (488 - 711)	564 (382 - 645)

*Includes an estimate of the milk taken by the calf.

As shown in Chapter 6, yak cows have their highest daily milk yield in July because of the good grazing available then. Regardless of calving date, the milk production by the cow declines from September to November. Yak cows become dry around then.

Also as seen for other yak rearing areas (cf. Figure 6.3), lactation yield among first calvers is only around 77 percent of the yield of cows in their third lactation. Composition of yak milk in Mongolia is similar to that shown in Chapter 6.

In addition to butter and cream, cheese and yoghurt are also made. Traditionally in Mongolia, yak milk is also fermented in a leather pouch and distilled as a "milk wine" (*Archi*) into a clear alcoholic drink.

Other uses of the yak in Mongolia

Draught
As in other countries of central Asia, yak are sought after as pack animals in Mongolia to carry a variety of different goods over mountain passes. Yak are also used for the wagon transport in moving the herders from one encampment to the other. Yak have to carry wood, food, wool, milk and drinking water for long distances. Yak are also used in forest work to loosen heavy tree trunks. In distant mountainous regions, where other forms of transport are not available, a yak will carry 100 kg without a problem and can haul up to 150 kg on its back. The walking speed of a fully loaded yak is approximately 4 - 5 km per hour and 20 - 30 km can be covered in a day.

Fibre, skin and horn
In Mongolia, yak are shorn in the spring and between 1 310 and 1 750 g of fibre are obtained from adults, though this consists of the three components: coarse outer hair, wool and down and the proportions of these vary with age (see Chapter 6). The uses to which the fibre, hide, horn and dung are put in Mongolia are similar to their uses in China.

Hybridization

Yak have been mated with other cattle in Mongolia since earliest times. However, mating of pure yak cows to bulls of "improved" cattle breeds is not normally practised in Mongolia.

For the first generation of hybrids (F1), a distinction is made between yak cows mated to bulls of domestic cattle (*Saran Hainag*) and the reciprocal mating of females of domestic cattle with yak bulls (*Naran Hainag*). In both cases there is a heterosis effect on body size, meat and milk output, capacity for work, vitality and longevity, all of which are increased relative to both the parental types. The sterile, hybrid males are castrated and are larger in mass and height than yak. They have a quiet temperament, which makes them attractive for use as draught oxen.

The milk of the hybrids contains between 5 and 8 percent fat. The F1 with the yak dam withstands lower temperatures better than the F1 with the (Mongolian) cattle dam, but it is less good at withstanding the high summer temperatures. The herder has to consider these maternal effects when deciding on the type of hybrid required.

The hybrid (F1) cows distinguish themselves from both the yak and the domestic cattle in Mongolia by calving annually with similar feeding and management. They also have a higher milk yield (816 kg per lactation on average) and are heavier (on average 80 kg more than yak females and 70 kg more than Mongolian cows).

Backcrossing of the hybrids is of less interest to herders, as the heterosis effect largely disappears. In spite of the less good performance of the backcrosses, they tend to be retained in the herd because calves are not slaughtered in Mongolia, as calf meat is not liked.

In order to investigate whether a more productive backcross could be made, various breeds of cattle have been used experimentally. Ivanova (1956) used Simmental bulls and recorded an improvement in meat output and particularly in milk yield (but with reduced fat percentage) relative to backcrosses using bulls of Mongolian cattle or yak on the F1. Bat-Erdene (1988) tried bulls of the Alatau breed with the F1 cows and noted a small increase in body weight and milk yield relative to the F1 (but it is not recorded whether the differences were statistically significant). Most recently, Dagviihorol (1999) investigated the use of the Hereford breed in various combinations as shown in Table 11.2.15.

As seen from Table 11.2.15, by age 30 months, animals of the backcross to the Hereford were heavier than the other groups and especially the backcross to the yak. It is of interest, however, that the backcrosses appeared to lose more weight over winter (24-month weight minus 18-month weight) than the F1.

Table 11.2.15 Body weight (mean ± s.e. [kg]) of various hybrids
[Source: after Dagviihorol, 1999]

Age	F1 x H* n = 10	(F1xY*) x H* n = 8	F1 x Y* n = 13	F1* n = 12
At birth	26.1 ± 0.7	19.8 ± 0.5	21.1 ± 0.3	17.7 ± 0.5
6 months	106.6 ± 5.3	75.4 ± 6.2	81.0 ± 6.2	102.3 ± 7.2
12 months	115.3 ± 3.2	94.6 ± 4.4	94.2 ± 11.0	112.3 ± 5.6
18 months	226.0 ± 8.8	203.4 ± 6.8	167.7 ± 11.9	220.3 ± 7.9
24 months	197.0 ± 6.5	170.4 ± 7.0	150.5 ± 9.1	206.0 ± 3.7
30 months	306.0 ± 8.3	276.5 ± 8.5	228.5 ± 7.7	288.0 ± 4.2

* F1 = Yak cow mated to Mongolian domestic cattle bull; H = Hereford bull; Y = Yak bull.

In practise, hybrids account for between 9 and 13 percent of the yak population. Only pluriparous yak cows are used for mating to cattle in order to avoid problems at parturition

References

Barthel, H. (1971). *Land zwischen Taiga und Wuste.* Geographische Bausteine, Nene Reihe, H. otha, Leipzig (in German).

Bat-Erdene, T. (1961). *Biological peculiarities of Mongolian yak and their hybrids.* Synopsis of MS degree thesis, Moscow (in Russian).

Bat-Erdene, T. (1988). *Biological and farming peculiarities of yak.* Synopsis of doctorial thesis, Moscow (in Russian).

Bat-Erdene, T. (1993). *Yield, composition and technological quality of yak milk.* Uliastai Hot, Mongolia.

Dagviihorol, V. (2000). *Rost i miasnaia produktivnost molodniaka gerefordsirovannogo. Skota.* Synopsis of MS degree thesis (in Russian).

Ivanova, V.V. (1956). *Gibridi simmentalskogo skota s yakami.* In Simmental-sirovanii skot. Moscow (in Russian).

Lhagvajav, T. (2000). *Ondor uulin busiin beltseeriin urgamalin torol ba garts.* Synopsis of MS degree thesis. Ulaanbaatar (in Mongolian).

Magash, A. (1990a). Statische Massmalen diagnostischer Zuchthygienemerkmale bei Yak Kühen in der Mongolei. *Wiss. Zeitschift der Humboldt-Universität zu Berlin R. Agrarwiss*, 39: 359-366.

Magash, A. (1990b). *Beitrag zur Physiologie und Biotechnologie der Fortpflanzung beim weiblichen Yak.* Synopsis of doctorial thesis, Berlin (in German).

Magash, A. (1991). Anwendung biotechnischer Verfahren bei der Reproduction des Yaks. *Monatschefte für Veterinärmedicin*, 46: 257-258.

Nyangerel, E. (1999). *Sarlagiin buteegdehuun uildverlel ba tuunii sah seel.* Synopsis of MS degree thesis. Ulaanbaatar (in Mongolian).

Yak in Nepal
Based on information supplied by D.D. Joshi[7]

The kingdom of Nepal borders India to the south and the Tibetan autonomous region of China to the north. Across a south-north distance of a little more than 160 km, the land rises from 100 m altitude, with a tropical and subtropical climate, to the highest parts of the Himalayas (6 000 - 8 000 m), including Mount Everest on its border, with a mixture of temperate and arctic climate. Yak are confined to the northern districts of Nepal at the higher elevations. Many hybrids of yak with domestic cattle (Kirkho/Lulu and Nepalese hill cattle) are kept on neighbouring, somewhat lower ground and sometimes alongside the yak. Joshi (1982) considered that without yak and yak hybrids it is doubtful if people would live in much of northern Nepal. In total, according to D.D. Joshi (personal communication, 2001), there are around 20 000 yak and about 40 000 yak-cattle hybrids in the 18 alpine districts of Nepal. These numbers represent a decline from an estimated 200 000 yak and hybrids in 1961. At the least, a part of the decline in numbers is attributed to government restrictions on livestock numbers and movement in Nepal's national parks. Also, the impact of tourism and the attractions of other ways of making a living have reduced the incentive to pursue yak herding with its attendant rigours (Joshi, 2000).

From east to west across Nepal, the Himalayas have numerous valleys, glaciers, ridges, peaks and rivers that give rise, geographically, to the various alpine districts of the country and with peoples often isolated from each other and differing, in some cases, ethnically, in culture and in dialect. The villages in these districts vary in the relative importance attached to livestock in general and the different classes of stock - yak and hybrids of yak with local cattle, sheep and goats, horses and mules and poultry. Joshi (1982) provided a detailed account of this - and though the specific numbers involved have changed, the background is still largely valid.

Nepali yak, according to Joshi, are smaller than those in various parts of China (cf. Chapter 6) with the following data (Table 11.2.16) from animals in three districts in Nepal.

Table 11.2.16 Weights and linear body dimensions of yak in Nepal
[Source: after Joshi, 1982]

	Male	Female	Castrated
Number of animals	15	25	10
Live weight (kg)	245	215	337
Height at withers (cm)	105	102	116
Length – pins to shoulder (cm)	110	105	124
Heart girth.(cm)	140	130	157

---

[7] D.D. Joshi is Director of the National Zoonoses and Food Hygiene Research Center, Nepal.

(In order to clarify a possible confusion arising in the literature on the size of yak in Nepal, it should be noted that Joshi (1982) quoted in his book some larger average values than those shown in Table 11.2.16, for what are described as "well-grown yak in Nepal. These larger average values are the same as those given by Epstein (1977) in relation to Nepal, but they, in turn, are identical to values also given by Epstein (1969) for yak in China - with the male and female figures attributed to a personal communication (Chen Lin-feng, 1963) and those for castrates to another Chinese source. According to D.D. Joshi (personal communication, 2001), more recent estimates of the size of yak differ little from those shown.

Most of the yak are black or black with some white markings. Pure white yak are rare, but highly prized. Most yak are horned, but a few polled yak are found and not as greatly valued. Polled bulls are always castrated and then used for riding.

Milk is the main commercial product from yak and from the hybrids of yak with cattle. Nepal's appreciation for yak products differs from China in one important use of the milk: In Nepal, in addition to the butter and other products made by herders from milk for their own use, large quantities of milk are sold and made into a Swiss-style hard cheese and into butter in processing factories built in the yak milk-producing areas. A very full account of these factories and an assessment of their operation is given by Joshi *et al.* (1999). The most recent figures, for the year 1997 - 1998, show a production of 176 tonnes of cheese and 26 tonnes of butter. The cheese in particular fetches a high price and is sold, principally to tourists in Kathmandu. According to these authors, demand for cheese still greatly exceeds supply, but notwithstanding, not all the factories operate at a profit. Although the yak cheese commands a higher price than cheese made from cattle or buffalo milk, the costs of production are also high because production is only seasonal, and the factories do not therefore work the year round. In addition, transport costs are high. Paudyal (1993) referred to a Winrock research report on cheese production in Nepal that suggested that as a consequence of the profitable sale of milk for cheese making, yak calves are being deprived of milk to the extent that calf mortality has increased.

Figure 11.2.6 Milking yak in Nepal
(Photo courtesy of Dept. of Information, HMG, Nepal)

Yak meat is eaten in Nepal, although for religious reasons slaughter is usually undertaken by butchers and not by the herdsmen. The fibre and the hides of the yak are used in the same way as in other countries.

Hybrids with yak are made with the type of cattle similar to, or the same as, the humpless dwarf cattle of Tibet known there as *Kirko* (or *Khirko*), but also as *zo-lang* (and referred to as *Goleng* or *glang* in Bhutan, and also in some parts of Nepal). The so-called Lulu cattle, used in some districts, are almost certainly the same type (K. P. Oli, personal communication, 1994). Hybrids are also made with the Siri hill cattle, a zebu type. Hybrids arise by mating the cattle bull to yak females (*Dimjo* or *Dim-dzo*) or the other way around (*Urang*).

There is a staggeringly large breed terminology (listed by Joshi, 1982) dealing with no less than 124 different combinations of yak with different local types of cattle, both zebu and *Bos taurus*. Names really begin to multiply among the various backcrosses to different breeds in different districts.

Joshi *et al.* (1994) provided some average values for performance characteristics of yak and hybrids, which are shown in Table 11.2.17.

Table 11.2.17 Performance characteristics of yak and yak hybrids in Nepal
[Source: adapted from Joshi *et al*, 1994]

	Female yak	Hybrid (*Dimjo*)	Hybrid (*Urang*)	Hybrid Brown Swiss cross
"Average" age at first calving (month) that is to say, calving at age:	44 Some at 3 years, mostly at 4 years old	35 Mostly at 3 years old	44 Some at 3 years, mostly at 4 years old	48 4 years
"Average" calving interval (days) that is to say, a calf:	660 Generally 1 every 2 years	425 Mostly 1 each year	425 Mostly each year	NA
Gestation length (days)	258	270	270	270
Lactation milk yield (kg)	200 - 700	1 690	1 300	1 046
Main lactation length (days)	180	260	260	305
Live weights (kg)				
Birth	9	NA	NA	13
Adult male	325	365	340	NA
Adult female	240	235	220	NA
Breeding season (month of year)	9 - 11	8 - 10	8 - 10	8 - 10
Calving season (month of year)	5 - 7	4 - 6	4 - 6	4 - 6

The live weights given for both the male and the female yak in Table 11.2.17 are greater than those quoted earlier, also from Nepal, in Table 11.2.16. The weights of the hybrids on the farms surveyed were greater than those of the pure yak. This may be because such hybrid males are sterile and likely to be castrated and used for work. The female hybrids were slightly less heavy than the corresponding pure yak. Of the two types of hybrid, those born to yak dams (the *Dimjo*) were the larger and gave more milk – reflecting perhaps a maternal effect related to the small size of the cattle dams. The hybrids were also larger and more productive than the parental cattle types. Unlike the general situation where yak, cattle and the hybrids are kept in different areas, usually differing in altitude, D.D. Joshi (personal communication, 2002) stressed that the data in Table 11.2.17 are based on yak and hybrids kept in the same places.

The difference in performance between the two reciprocal crosses of the hybrid type is also reflected in the fact that farmers prefer the *Dimjo* (yak dam) to the *Urang* (cattle dam), according to Joshi (1982). Although the cows of the cattle types are smaller than the yak females, it is unusual for the maternal effects from the dam to last to such a marked extent into the adulthood of their progeny. An explanation for the large reciprocal difference is not altogether clear. Since there are also differences in size and performance among the different types of cattle used for hybridizing with yak, it may be that females of the smaller types of cattle are mated to yak bulls, and bulls of the larger types of cattle to yak females. This is speculation, but, if true, it would fit the facts – and perhaps determining this might be reason enough to gather evidence to confirm or refute these suggestions.

It is of interest that the hybrids of yak with Brown Swiss, calving, on average, for the first time even later than the pure yak, also gave less milk than hybrids with local cattle. The poorer performance of hybrids with fathers of exotic breeds relative to local types of cattle was reinforced by D.D. Joshi (personal communication, 1994) by reference to disappointing performance of hybrids of yak with Holstein-Friesian and Jersey in Nepal. But this differs from experience in some other countries and might be related to the management accorded hybrids relative to yak in various situations. A.I. was not used for hybridization with yak in Nepal. More recently, D.D. Joshi (personal communication, 2001) stated that hybridization of yak with exotic breeds of cattle is no longer practised.

Some reproductive data were given by Paudyal (1993) based on results from the breeding records of the yak-breeding farm situated in Solukhumbu, one of the most important of the yak-producing districts of Nepal. Over a 15-year period (1974 - 1989), 544 matings of female yak were made resulting in 307 conceptions (56.4 percent) and 293 calves (53.9 percent), of which 15 were stillborn. The average calving interval was 616 days – suggesting that a majority of the animals calved only once every two years. It is of interest, however, that there was a steady improvement at this farm over that 15-year period in the annual calving rate and a sharp drop in the interval between successive calves. Thus, in successive five-year periods, the proportion of calves born (per yak female mated) increased from 0.44 to 0.58 to 0.70 and the calving interval declined from an initial 851 days, to 704 in the middle period and 514 days in the last five-year period. There has therefore been a remarkable improvement in the overall reproductive rate. There was also some increase, over that period of years, in the growth rate of the calves in the first 12 weeks of life – but no change in the birth weights. Unfortunately, the changes that must have taken place at the farm to lead to such improvements were not specified.

In general, management of yak in Nepal follows a transhumance pattern, with high altitude summer pastures, where the animals are not given feed supplements and winter grazings take place on somewhat lower ground in more sheltered valleys. In many of the valleys, crops are also grown and many of the yak and hybrids spend the winter in sheds where they have to be fed.

Joshi *et al.* (1994) described the "average" yak herd as having: 32 cows (of which half are dry and half are lactating), 3 breeding bulls, nearly 12 pack yak, approximately 10 females and 10 males younger than five years, 12 yearlings and a little more than 15 younger calves – a total of around 94 animals. No update on these numbers is available.

Joshi (1982) also provided some results on the economics of keeping yak and hybrids (*chauries*). For present purposes, D.D. Joshi (personal communication, 2001) suggested that the figures communicated previously should be multiplied by a factor of ten to account for inflation. (This has been done below.) It follows from Joshi's suggested adjustment for inflation that although gross margins have increased over the years in absolute terms, the purchasing power of the extra money has also declined in proportion, due to inflation. The herders are, therefore, unlikely to be better off. Although absolute figures are likely to change further with time, it is the comparison of the pure yak with the *chauries*, which engenders the most interest. Thus:

For a yak bull

The capital investment required:	17 820 rupees
(13 500 rupees of this for procuring the animal)	
Recurrent costs per year (mostly feed)	4 730 rupees
Annual returns	11 090 rupees
Gross margin	*6 360 rupees*

For a lactating yak female

The capital investment required	18 150 rupees
(13 500 rupees of this for procuring the animal)	
Recurrent costs per year (mostly feed)	6 210 rupees
Annual returns	26 090 rupees
(10 000 rupees from sale of calf, 16 000 rupees from sale of milk)	
Gross margin	*19 880 rupees*

For a lactating chaurie (hybrid)

The capital investment required	23 100 rupees
Recurrent costs per year (mostly feed)	10 400 rupees
Annual returns	25 000 rupees
(5 000 rupees from sale of calf, 20 000 rupees from sale of milk)	
Gross margin	*14 600 rupees*

Thus, Joshi's figures suggest that the annual gross margin from the lactating yak was more than a third higher than that from the lactating hybrid female, in spite of the lower absolute milk yield of the yak. The yak female needed a smaller capital investment than the hybrid and the yak calf had a higher value than the calf from the hybrid cow. If these figures were to apply more widely they might suggest that even under these largely pastoral conditions a relatively "high-input-high-output" strategy (the hybrids) is not necessarily the most profitable. However, the hybrid, or at least the *Dimjo* kind (cattle male mated with yak female), has advantages that, over a lifetime, might more than compensate for a lower annual return and higher initial investment. Thus, the *Dimjo* hybrids calved on average almost a year sooner than the yak and were more likely to have a calf every year. Thus, over the lifetime of a cow of say 12 years, the gross margin from the hybrids should be the greater. However, the gap between the yak and the hybrids will be narrowed by the ability of yak to produce milk – perhaps half the "normal" quantity – also in a year subsequent to a calving, even if they have not calved again in that second season. Moreover, the main end-product is not fresh milk but butter and cheese, and the gap in income between the yak and the hybrid is likely to be further narrowed as payment for milk is based on fat content (Joshi *et al.* 1999) – and the fat percentage of yak milk is higher than that of milk from the hybrids.

Nepal enjoys a considerable tourist trade, which in turn provides a ready market both for the cheese and some of the other value-added products from the yak – a point emphasized by Joshi *et al.* (1994) in discussing future developments.

However, as already referred to in relation to the overall decline in yak numbers, there are changes taking place that affect the livestock husbandry of the Northern Areas of Nepal. Joshi *et al.* (1994) pointed out, for example, an increasing use of yak and yak hybrids for transport in mountaineering expeditions and for trekking. This development changes the emphasis given to the different uses of the yak by people such as the Sherpas who have a tradition of yak keeping. Other writers have suggested, however, that the overall need for yak is declining in the face of other forms of transport.

Bishop (1989), in a detailed study of one village in Nepal, reported that older people there were no longer as willing as in former times to endure the hardship of high altitude life on the lonely summer pastures. They were thus changing from being milk producers to being breeders of hybrid animals. To produce the hybrids, they were using cows at the lower altitudes nearer the villages and mating them to yak bulls. The hybrid animals were then sold as replacement stock, making for an easier life for the herdsmen and their families compared with milk production from yak. Cox (1985) studied in great detail one particular area in Nepal – the relatively isolated Langtang valley area in the northeastern border region. The study looked in detail at the role of the yak on all aspects of the life of the people there, including the cultural and ritualistic side, and noted changes in social and economic attitudes, partly as a result of the opening of a cheese factory in the area. An earlier account of the husbandry and productivity of yak and its hybrids in the same valley was given by Bonnemaire and Teissier (1976). A similarly detailed account was given for another area of Nepal (the Tarap valley in the northwest) by Jest (1976), who also commented on what was then the beginning of an impact of industrial cheese making on the economy of yak production.

Joshi *et al.* (1994) refer to a deterioration of the yak breeding stock in Nepal and quote, by way of example, the Langtang area, which has a tradition of supplying yak-breeding stock. The deterioration was said to arise from the enforced reduction of movement of breeding stock across the border with the Tibet region. As for some other countries, there is thus an increasing risk from inbreeding in the yak population, reflected in reduced performance and poorer reproductive efficiency.

References

Bishop, N.H. (1989). From zomo to yak: change in a Sherpa village. *Human Ecology, 17,* 177-204.

Bonnemaire, J. & Teissier, J.H. (1976). [Some aspects of breeding at high altitudes in the central Himalayas: yaks, cattle, hybrids and crossbreds in the Langtang Valley (Nepal).] In: Le Yak. Son role daps la vie materielle et culturelle ties eleveurs d'Asie centrale. *Ethnozootechnie* No. 15, France, 91-118.

Cox, T. (1985). Herding and socio-economic change among Langtang. Tibetans. Contributions to Nepalese Studies,. 12, 63-74.

Epstein, H. (1969). Domestic Animals of China. Commonwealth Agricultural Bureaux, Farnham Royal, England. pp. 20-25.

Epstein, H. (1977). Domestic Animals of Nepal. Holmes & Meier, New York. pp. 20-37.

Jest, C. (1976). L'6levage du yak dans 1'Himalaya du Nepal. In: Le Yak. Son r61e dans la vie materielle et culturelle des 61eveurs d'Asie centrale. *Ethnozootechnie* No. 15, France, 78-90.

Joshi, D.D. (1982). *Yak and Chauri Husbandry in Nepal.* H.M. Government Press, Singha Durbar, Kathmandu, Nepal, XVII, 145 pp.

Joshi, D.D. (2000) Impact of National Parks and tourism on yak farming system in the alpine Himalayan region of Nepal. Yak Newsletter (International Yak Information Centre [IYIC]) No. 5 (September 2000) pp. 12-13

Joshi, D.D. *et al*, (1994). Yak production in Nepal. Proceedings of the first International Congress on Yak. *Journal of Gansu agricultural University* (Special issue, June 1994). pp. 105-112. [Reprinted in *Asian Livestock (FAO Bangkok),* 1994, XIX (10), 132136.]

Joshi, D.D., Awasthi, B.D. & Sharma, Minu (1999) An assessment of the yak cheese factories in Nepal. National Zoonoses and Food Research Center, Kathmandu, Nepal. 75 pp.

Paudyal, R.M. (1993). The yak and its importance in Central Asia and particularly Nepal. MSc Thesis, Centre for Tropical Veterinary Medicine, University of Edinburgh. 67 pp.

Yak keeping in Western High Asia
Tajikistan, Afghanistan, Southern Xinjiang Pakistan,
By Hermann Kreutzmann [8]

The borderlands of Tajikistan, Afghanistan, Pakistan and Xinjiang (China) belong to a contiguous region dominated by high mountain ranges. The eastern Pamir mountains, eastern Hindukush, Karakoram, the west Kun Lun Shan mountains and the western Himalayas meet in this region and provide substantial grazing grounds at high elevations. The ecology and orography of Western High Asia are characterized by enormous levels of glaciation at high altitudes in contrast to extremely arid valley systems. Wherever groundwater is close and/or fountains/springs available extensive pasture areas are found in flat bottomed upper valleys. While artemisia steppe reaches up to levels of 3 800 m, the fertile pastures of Western High Asia are to be found at higher elevations. Already in the thirteenth century, Marco Polo mentioned the fertile pastures and the top quality meat produced there. He highlighted the special feature of "pamir", which resembles a wide valley covered by grass and valuable fodder plants (cf. Kreutzmann, 2000b). These pastures were desired by nomads and mountain farmers who competed for their seasonal use during summers. Kirghiz nomads and Wakhi mountain farmers are the prominent groups who grazed their flocks on the high pastures of Afghanistan, Tajikistan, Xinjiang. Wakhi farmers are found in the eastern Hindukush and Karakoram of Pakistan, while Balti and Astori people are herders in the eastern Karakoram and western Himalaya. In Chitral, there are Kho mountain farmers and Gujur pastoralists.

The type of yak kept in this area closely resembles the yak of neighbouring China. The colour patterns range from black to white with grey shades in between. The frugal conditions – especially during winter – result in heavy weight losses as winter feeding is a rare exception. The summer season in rich and fertile pastures enables the yak to gain substantial weight. This cycle of storing energy during summer for the harsh winter conditions applies to all animals in the herds of pastoralists and farmers and is thus similar to the situation in the main yak-rearing areas of China.

The yak provides their owners with products mainly for home consumption. Milk is used for household needs if sheep milk is not sufficiently available for the preparation of the saltish milk tea accompanying each meal. Surplus milk is converted into yoghurt from which a small quantity is consumed by the household. The top layer of cream (*merik*) is removed for direct consumption or, in cases of huge quantities the cream, is converted into butter as is traditionally done by Kirghiz nomads. The remainder of the yoghurt can be converted into fresh butter as well. Some people dehydrate the fresh butter (*maska*) through heating and create durable butter fat (*ghee, rughun*) by this process. The surplus butter milk is partly consumed by the household; the bulk is boiled down in a huge pot, and a viscous substance emerges after more than a day of boiling. It is then formed into

---

[8]Hermann Kreutzmann is Professor of the Department of Kulturgeographie und Entwicklungsforschung, Institut fuer Geographie, Universitaet Erlangen-Nuernberg, Germany.

little cakes and finally dried in the sun on a special platform out of reach of any animal. After some days, hard blocks of this protein cake (*qurut*) reach the required state of dehydration so that they can easily be stored for consumption in winter (cf. for milk-processing, Kreutzmann 2000a, p. 99). The *qurut* is known from Iran to the Tibetan Plateau as a sour substance that is used in food preparation especially for soups. Thus, nothing is wasted from the sometimes-large quantities of milk.

All the tasks – beginning from milking to processing it into a variety of consumable products – fall into the female domain. In some societies, as in the Wakhi communities, this is related to the traditional obligation of women to spend the summers in the high pastures. Men support the women during the movement of herds from the homestead to the pasture, from stage to stage, and on the way back to the winter settlement. While herding the flocks and milk processing falls to the women folk, men are responsible for cutting and processing the yak hair, as well as for slaughtering. Some family members and especially children accompany the women to the pastures. Exceptions to this general rule are manifold. Where the household configuration is unfavourable, older household members take up responsibilities, or relatives are involved in a system of share-herding or taking turns.

The utilization of yak dung is different in nomadic and farming societies. Combined mountain farming, i.e. the combination of crop raising and livestock keeping, resembles an interrelated production system in which the livestock provides animal manure for fertilizing fields. Where yak dung is accessible within a reasonable distance to cultivated land, the practice of fertilization is common. Nowadays, the transport of dung from remote high pastures to the fields in the permanent settlements is rare. In nomadic communities, yak dung is predominantly collected as fuel for fires, both for cooking and for heat, and stored near the houses or the yurt encampments.

Yak meat is consumed mainly within the households, while in recent years communities with market access have started to sell it to local butchers (e.g. in Hunza, Gorno-Badakhshan, Sarikol). At the end of the summer grazing season, when the animals are at their peak weight and cold conditions prevail, yak are traditionally slaughtered to fulfil the meat requirements for the winter. The meat is cut into thin pieces and dried.

Yak hair is utilized for different purposes. Ropes are made from it for all the needs in a pastoral environment. The majority of hair is made into threads of which coarse rugs (*sherma*) are made to cover the sleeping spaces in the *yurt*, or the house. Yak tails are used as dusters. These products rarely reach the markets. Overall it can be said that yak products are traditionally household-related and that other animals such as sheep and goats are kept for marketing and trading. In recent years, this pattern has been abridged and the yak and its products play a role in the transborder exchange of goods and for bartering.

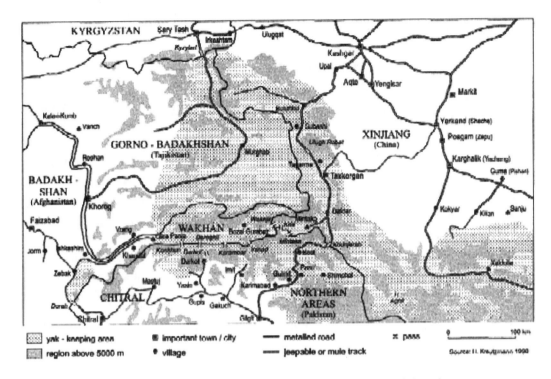

Figure 11.2.7 Distribution of yak keeping in Western High Asia

In Western High Asia, yak keeping (Figure 11.2.7) forms one prominent section of animal husbandry in addition to keeping herds of sheep and goats in a much wider area. The regions in which yak keeping is practised are briefly introduced in the sections that follow, and the socio-economic context and recent changes are discussed. Table 11.2.18 gives the numbers of yak and yak hybrids in the various regions.

Tajikistan

In the eastern Pamir, part of Tajikistanûs Gorno-Badakhshan district, Kirghiz herders, and a few Wakhi, keep yak herds nowadays around traditional supply stations like Murghab (formerly Pamirski Post) and Langar in Rajon Ishkashim. From there they undertake seasonal migrations to the summer pastures at higher elevations.

Under Soviet rule, Tajikistan's economy was completely integrated into the union system, with significant effects even on the remote mountain areas - as the case of Gorno-Badkhshan reveals. The Wakhi members of *sowchos roi kommunizm* in Rajon Ishkashim kept yak (in Tajik language: *khashgau*) in the upper parts of the Amu Darya valley and in Khargushi Pamir. The whole agricultural system was devoted to animal husbandry because all other food supplies were imported from outside. Even high-protein fodder (50 tonnes) was brought in to sustain a herd of 450 yak year round in the Pamirs. This was the sole case of extra feed in the area and strongly linked to Soviet breeding strategies developed for the Pamirs. Here, only male animal herders were employed in the high pastures.

325

Basically, nomadism became regarded as mobile animal husbandry under the conditions of collective resource management and in the context of the prevalent socio-economic set-up.

Table 11.2.18 Yak populations and their distribution in Western High Asia*

Region	Yak numbers	Yak hybrids	Area of distribution
Tajikistan: eastern Pamir	14 000		Gorno-Badakhshan: Murghab
Tajikistan: western Pamir	300		Gorno-Badakhshan: Ishkashim
Afghanistan: Hindukush	approx. 1 000		Wakhan
Afghanistan: Pamir	1 500		Little and Big Pamir
Pakistan: eastern Hindukush	1 000	1 220	Chitral
Pakistan:eastern Hindukush/Karakoram	4 000		Ghizer: Gupis, Ishkoman, Yasin
Pakistan: Karakoram	> 1 500		Hunza
Pakistan: Himalaya	4 000	< 20 000	Baltistan
Pakistan: Himalaya	200	5 500	Astor
Xinjiang: Taghdumbash Pamir	approx. 10 000		Taxkorgan county

*[Sources: Ehlers and Kreutzmann, 2000; Kreutzmann, 1986, 1996, 2000b; Longy and Gely, 2000, unpublished; Nazir Ahmad, 2000; Nüsser, 1999, 2000; Schmidt, 2000; Stöber, 2001; and personal communication with Clemens, Nüsser, Schmidt and Stöber, 2000.]

With the independence of Tajikistan and the related transformation of socio-economic structures, individual ownership of land (1996 - 1999) and cattle were re-introduced. Yak-herding is organized through the farmers' association; the herders keep 70 percent of the production while the rest belongs to the association. The Wakhi of Ishkashim are the only nonKirghiz yak herders of the western Pamir and still control a herd of 300 yak.

The Soviet state-run economy had selected the eastern Pamir as the prime yak-producing region and mainly Kirghiz pastoralists were involved. Nearly 14 000 yak now are kept in Rajon Murghab. The majority of yak herds continue to be controlled by State-run enterprises or farmers' associations that are the successor organizations of the *kolchos* and *gozchos*. The adverse economic conditions of the transformation period have impoverished the Kirghiz herdsmen because herds are small, food supplies meagre and additional food from the market is expensive. Basically, the majority of agriculturists in Gorno-Badakhshanskaya Autonomous Oblast (GBAO) are dependent on humanitarian aid at present.

The situation was aggravated by substantial losses of livestock in February - March 1999 when in Rajon Ishkashim alone, 5 000 head of livestock, including 300 yak, were lost to unexpectedly high snowfall. The socio-economic transformation has forced the majority of people to follow a subsistence strategy based on agricultural and livestock resources. The present income levels are far below previous ones, and it remains to be seen if this resource-based strategy will succeed.

Afghanistan

Yak keeping in Afghanistan is restricted to the Badakhshan province, i.e. Zebak and Wakhan (including the Little and Big Pamir). No data are available for the Zebak region at present. The Pamir region of Wakhan is better known (cf. Dor, 1976, Shahrani, 1979) and has a long record of yak keeping. Pauperized Wakhi farmers utilizing the Pamirs for summer grazing have competed with rich Kirghiz nomads controlling most of these Pamirs. Impoverished Wakhi did take up jobs as animal herders for Kirghiz herd owners and turned eventually to nomadic strategies (Kreutzmann, 1996). The proportion of yak (Kirghiz language: *kotoz*) was about one tenth of the total livestock numbers within the community's herds of about 40 000 animals. The introduction of animal herding as a service – rich herd owners gave their animals to poor community members on a contract basis – had led to an increase in the number of animals in the Pamirs. The peak number of livestock was reached prior to the exodus in the aftermath of the Afghan Saur Revolution. In 1978, a group of 1 300 Kirghiz fled to Pakistan. They accounted for all 280 *yurts*, or household units, in the Afghan Pamirs. Not all members of the Kirghiz group of Rahman Kul joined him in eastern Anatolia after four years of exile in Pakistan. Rahman Kul alone had to leave behind 16 000 sheep and goats, more than 700 yak, 15 horses and 18 Bactrian camels – while the whole community of the Afghan Pamirs had possessed more than 40 000 animals, of which only a small herd of 6 000 had been taken to exile in Pakistan. Rahman Kul migrated with his group of 1 132 Kirghiz in August 1982 to Turkey. None of the livestock went with them.

A small group of 200 Kirghiz returned to the Little Pamir from Pakistan by October 1979 (Shahrani, 1984). The community under the leadership of Abdurrashid Khan grew to 102 yurts in Pamir-e Kalan (Great Pamir) and 135 yurts in Pamir-e Khurd (Little Pamir) by 1999. The number of yak varied at around 1 400 head, compared to nearly 9 000 sheep and goats, 160 horses and 90 Bactrian camels. All forms of animal husbandry have been limited to subsistence survival strategies in recent years, as traditional exchange lines have been interrupted due to adverse political conditions. Presently, the Kirghiz are engaged in yak breeding and in limited barter trade with entrepreneurs from neighbouring Hunza in Pakistan. The itinerant traders supply basic necessities in exchange for yak and yak products. Yak are not mated with other types of cattle by the Kirghiz nor the Wakhi.

Southern Xinjiang

a) Taghdumbash Pamir
The Taxkorgan or Sarikol (name of the former principality) area contains three different ethnic groups: Sariqoli, Wakhi and Kirghiz (here less than 5 percent of the population). The former two groups (82 percent of the inhabitants) follow a combined mountain agriculture composed of crop raising and animal husbandry with seasonal utilization of

327

Pamir pastures, while the Kirghiz specialize solely in livestock. All three groups traditionally moved their flocks within the Taghdumbash Pamir and paid tribute to the Mir of Hunza who exercised control over these pastures until 1937 (Kreutzmann, 2000a). While Kirghiz lived at the higher elevations, Sariqoli approached from the northern low-lying villages. Only the Wakhi founded their settlement of Dafdar (3 400 m) in the heart of the Taghdumbash Pamir, about a century ago, with the consent of the Chinese authorities. All three groups compete for the fodder resources there.

After the Chinese Revolution in 1949 and the formation of the Tajik Taxkorgan autonomous county in 1954, collectivization took place and rural communes were established in the villages. The basic infrastructural assets, such as school, police, mail, health post, barefoot doctor, commune administration, shops, mosque, etc. have been provided to all communities in the Taghdumbash Pamir.

In post-revolutionary times, the number of livestock increased by a factor of 4.75, to 128 800 head in 1984. During the following decade, the growth slowed down, and in 1994 the number of livestock was reported in the census at 147 586. This figure covers all stocks of Bactrian camels, horses, donkeys, yak, other cattle, sheep and goats. Natural grazing provides the most important local resource utilized through animal husbandry: The area covered by grasslands extends to 6.09 million mu, of which 97.6 percent belong to natural grazing, while 0.13 million mu are irrigated meadows (1 mu equals 0.067 ha; Table 11.2.19). More than two thirds of the economic turnover of Taxkorgan county derives from animal husbandry. In 1984, for example, animal products grossed 2.75 million yuan, compared to 1.18 million yuan from crop raising (Kashgar Prefecture Chronicle, 1985). The situation has not changed much recently and underlines the economic importance of livestock husbandry in the Pamirs.

In the heart of the Taghdumbash Pamir, a veterinary station specializing in yak breeding was established in Mazar (south of Dafdar along the Pakistan-China Friendship Highway) by utilizing the local knowledge of Tajik and Kirghiz animal herders who found employment there. About 400 persons reside at Mazar breeding farm, which has about 5 000 sheep and 500 yak (Schaller *et al.,* 1987). Much larger herds of yak are kept by the Wakhi and Kirghiz of the Karachukur Valley, which drains the western-most part of the Taghdumbash Pamir. This side valley has become the only Kirghiz-dominated pasture region of the Taxkorgan county. The number of yak grew from 5 909 in 1981 to 8 147 in 1990, the highest figure since 1976. The trading and export value of yak has been limited. Only rarely were small consignments of yak exported to the neighbouring Hunza valley in Pakistan. In recent years this transborder trade has ceased to exist. The products of milk, butter, *qurut*, hair and meat, are mainly utilized for local purposes. Additionally, the transport capabilities and frugality of yak are regarded as major assets of the animals in the Chinese Pamirs. No hybridization is practised here.

Table 11.2.19 Potential fodder availability of pastures in the Pamir regions*

Region	Total area (ha)	Grazing area (ha)	Grazing area Total (%)	Available grazing potential To be utilized (tonnes)	To be utilized (%)	Not to be utilized (tonnes)	Not to be utilized (%)	Total (tonnes)
Western Pamir	2 468 700	1 113 390	45.1	40 990	22.4	141 260	77.6	181 250
Wakhan	249 200	146 030	58.6	2 630	17.8	12 120	82.2	14 750
Eastern Pamir	2 839 700	1 099 900	38.7	61 400	45.3	74 400	54.7	135 800
Pamir (total area)	5 308 400	2 213 290	41.7	102 390	31.9	215 660	68.1	317 050
Sarikol (Taxkorgan)	5 038 250	374 313	7.4					555 370

*[Source: Walter and Breckle (1986) and data provided by the county administration Taxkorgan 1991, 1998]

b) Western Kun Lun Shan: Muztagh Ata and Kongur regions

The Kirghiz of Kizil Su traditionally followed a long-distance nomadic migration cycle between the summer grazing grounds in the Pamirs and the irrigated oases of the mountain forelands. They spent the winter occupied with herding and various other businesses in the towns of Kashgar and Yarkand. This pattern has been abridged in the last 50 years. Nowadays, the Kirghiz nomads are confined with their herds to the Pamir regions year round. Only for marketing purposes do they leave their mountain abodes and travel on foot with their flocks, or on the back of trucks, down to the Sunday markets of Kashgar and/or Yarkand. Thus, the sheep and goats cover the distance of 280 km easily and without great loss of weight. Only rarely are some yak also marketed.

The pasture system has been adjusted to changed frame conditions. On average, the herds of the Kara Köl Kirghiz consist of between one and two horses and a similar number of donkeys and between two and three Bactrian camels. These animals are preferred for transportation and travelling purposes. The additional livestock amount to about 12 yak, 98 sheep and 40 goats (Kreutzmann, 1995). These numbers represent more than a tripling of the large livestock and a doubling of sheep and goats over the past 20 years. In 1976, the peoples' commune of Subashi (Karakul) owned a total number of livestock of about 10 300 animals (Myrdal, 1979). In addition to State ownership of flocks, private property rights for a limited number of animals had been assured for the nomads. The carrying capacity of accessible pastures was estimated at 40 000 animals; by 1991 the number exceeded 30 000. By comparison with the overall livestock development in Aqto division, where livestock numbers grew by a factor of 1.3 from 1976 to 1991 and cattle numbers (including yak) by 1.65, the growth in Kara Köl is out of proportion (Aqto Täzkirisi 1994). In the remote, high-altitude yak and sheep-breeding area the livestock numbers grew three times faster. In this area, relaxed attitudes of the Chinese authorities toward agricultural and livestock production have led to an increased market orientation – especially since the reforms of 1978. The quality of pastures was improved by irrigation and fencing of meadows. Grass is cut by scythe and winter fodder is stored to cover the long period of meagre natural grazing in the winter settlement (*kishlok*) of Subashi at an altitude of 3 600 m.

Administratively, the Kara Köl grazing zone forms part of the Aqto division, which is one of the four subunits of the Kizil Su Autonomous Oblast where the majority of China's 119 300 Kirghiz reside (data of 1994). The majority of the Kirghiz of Kizil Su has become sedentary agriculturists, while the inhabitants of the higher Pamirs continue to follow mobile livestock husbandry exclusively. The *kishlok* of Subashi is equipped, like other communes, with infrastructure institutions as mentioned above and with a veterinary post controlling the quality and health status of animals. The "survival" conditions of the harsh environment disguise the fact that the animals raised in these productive pastures compete very well in the profitable markets of the urban oases along the southern silk route (Tarim basin).

Pakistan

Yak breeding in Pakistan can be found in the upper valleys of mountain ranges from the Hindukush to the Himalayas (Figure 11.2.5). Only mountain farmers dwelling at the upper limit of settlements are engaged in yak breeding. They have augmented their flocks by keeping yak in addition to other livestock. One major distinction has to be made between the different yak-breeding areas in northern Pakistan: The western part is dominated by herds where hybridization is not done while in the East, and particularly in Baltistan and the Nanga Parbat region, hybridization is practised. Some exceptions occur in the eastern Hindukush as well. As long ago as 1926, a table of hybridization practices in the Gilgit district was compiled after a survey by the colonial administration. Even at that time, the bureaucracy was curious about the variety of domestic animals in the area. It suggested (as referred to by Kreutzmann, 1986, p. 103) that the F1 females (*zumo*) from mating yak bulls to cows of "other" cattle were regarded as the best milkers and the F1 males (*zoi*) the best bullocks for ploughing. (The reciprocal F1 was not known to occur). Females of the first backcrosses (in both directions) were still regarded as good milkers but inferior to *zumo* (F1). Later generations of backcrosses with cattle males were regarded as useless and those with yak bulls eventually approached the yak type. The efforts and inputs from veterinary departments into yak breeding were rather limited, a situation which has not changed much since. Development projects have concentrated on improving cattle, sheep and goats by introducing outside stock (Farman Ali and Khaleel Tetlay, 1991). Yak breeding and interbreeding remains the farmer's responsibility and changes depend on his activities. In recent years, more research on yak keeping in northern Pakistan has taken place.

a) Baltistan

The Tibetan-speaking Muslim population in Baltistan is well known for its hybridization practices. Schmidt (2000: 124-126) has collected data about the practices in the Shigar Valley. The Balti term *hyag* for yak is basically restricted to male yak while the females are termed *hyaqmo*. Hybridization with common bulls (*xlang*) and common cows (*ba*) is a regular feature of Balti animal husbandry. The female offspring of the hybrids are distinguished from the male by the suffix – mo. In Baltistan, the most common F1 hybrids are *zo* and *zomo,* which are regarded as well adapted and suited animals for the agricultural tasks: *Zo* are frequently employed for ploughing the fields and threshing purposes. The *zomo* is esteemed for its milk-producing qualities that exceed the average yield from a *hyaqmo*, the female yak.

In the villages of the Shigar Valley, the average male bovines kept by Balti households varied between 1.2 and 5.6, while the range for females was 3.0 to 10.6, which is rather high when compared with the number of goats that fluctuates between 6.1 and 15.2 and that of sheep between 2.8 and 16.1 (survey in 1997 - 1998 by Schmidt 2000, p. 128). Schmidt (personal communication, 2000) estimated about 1 200 yak and 5 500 - 6 000 hybrids for the whole of the Shigar Valley. A concentration of yak keeping in Shigar is in the upper parts of the valley, namely in Basha and Braldu, where substantial yak herds are to be found, while the low-lying villages keep many fewer yak. They replenish their herds with stock from the high-lying valleys of Basha, Braldo and Thale. The yak purchased there are intended for hybridization, as people esteem the hybrids in the low-lying areas for milk production and as work animals for ploughing and threshing. Yak here are rarely used as pack animals. Generally speaking, there is a similar pattern of yak keeping in Baltistan as in the adjacent districts. To the east, hybrids form the majority while to the west, the proportion of hybrids decreases.

The eastern part of Baltistan is characterized by a higher animal population density and smaller pastures. Thus it would be reasonable to estimate 4 000 yak and less than 20 000 hybrids for the Baltistan district. Some uncertainty remains as to the size of yak herds on the Deosai Plateau, which borders the disputed Kashmir area (M. E. Schmidt, personal communication, 2000).

b) Astor: Nanga Parbat region
Yak hybrids are distributed in the Astor region of the Northern Areas in a similar manner as in Baltistan. Yak keeping is found here, except in the northern declivity of the Nanga Parbat and in the neighbouring villages of the Indus Valley (Clemens and Nüsser, 2000: 162-163, Nüsser, 1998: 110). The Shina-speaking population values hybrids, such as *zoi* (male) and *zomo* (female). Yak bulls (in Shina language: *bépo*) are shared among a group of farmers and can be hired for hybridization for a fee (*yakluk*). The main yak-breeding area around the Nanga Parbat is the Rupal Gah. In Tarishing, 3 yak and 100 hybrids were recorded (Clemens and Nüsser, personal communication, 2000). In a recent livestock census, three out of four households were interviewed. The number of yak recorded was rather low at 189, compared 2 642 *zoi* and 2 580 *zomo* (Nazir Ahmad, 2000). Yak and hybrids represent one fifth of the bovides in the cattle category.

c) Hunza and Nager
In Hunza, a few Burusho keep yak but the majority of yak are with the Wakhi high mountain farmers of Gojal in the upper Hunza Valley. The Burushaski language uses the

terms *bépay* for both female and male yak kept at least part of the time near the homesteads and *yabá* for male yak that stay the year round in the high pastures. Although *argun bépay* is listed for a hybrid, hybridization is very uncommon, especially in the upper valley. The Wakhi use the terms *zugh* for male yak and *zughghev* for the female. A number of villages in Gojal keep yak (Kreutzmann, 1986), and they are mainly those with access to extensive and remote pastures, such as Pasu and the Batura region, the upper Chupursan valley and the Abgerchi people as well as the Shimshali.

A total of approximately 1 000 - 1 500 yak are kept in small numbers as part of the household herds. Nonlactating yak are kept in remote locations such as the Khunjerab Pass region and the Shimshal Pamir. The hub of yak breeding in Hunza is the Shimshal Valley where animal husbandry plays a bigger role than in other parts of Gojal in which agricultural activities are being replaced by nonagrarian jobs. Shimshal still is quite remote and controls extensive and fertile pastures – which is what led the former ruler to establish the settlement in the first place. The system of staging, i.e. utilization of pastures at different altitudes, is rather complex (Figure 11.2.8) because a number of fertile, but remote, high pastures are included in the system. According to the degree of a herder's control required, lactating and nonlactating animals are separated and are led to different pastures. The altitude range of yak pastures varies between 3 100 m in the lower Shimshal and 5 300m in the uppermost areas. The bulk of yak are pastured during the summer in Shuijerab and Shuwart where more than 400 yak are gathered (cf. Figure 11.2.8). About 100 yak are led on a difficult path into the Ghujerab valley, which is accessible only from Shimshal and to other side valleys. All recent surveys estimated the number of yak in Shimshal alone as between 500 and 1 000 (cf. Butz 1989, p. 5). The fluctuation relates to animal losses due to bad weather conditions. The high value reflects increases in livestock numbers from purchasing stock from outside the area.

In recent years, some farmers from Hunza have been engaged in some yak trading with their Kirghiz neighbours in Afghanistan to supply the civil and military meat market of the Northern Areas. In the same manner, yak have been imported from the Chinese Pamirs. This strategy has led to the improvement of local herds, as good breeding animals were kept by the farmers or specially purchased.

Yak meat is now available in butcher shops in the business centres of Hunza and Gilgit on a regular basis, a feature unknown a decade ago. In the Nager area, some hybrids were reported from Minapin at the foot of Rakaposhi mountain and from Hispar at the mouth of the Hispar glacier.

d) Chitral, Yasin and Ishkoman
In Chitral, Northwest Frontier province, there are three areas where yak (Khowar language: *zogh*) are kept. First, between Shandur Pass and Buni Zom about 700 yak – with hybrids only in the upper valleys, such as Laspur Gol (a valley on the western foot of Shandur Pass, 3 700m), about 50 yak in Phagram Gol (on the northern side of the Buni Zom mountain).

The second area is located on the northeastern face of Tirich Mir, where about 70 yak and hybrids in Shagrom, Tirich Gol, and about 400 in Khot, a side valley of Turkho (Nüsser, 1999 and personal communication, 2000). The third area with yak is the Wakhi region of Upper Chitral where extensive pastures are utilized and individual households keep up to 60 yak (no hybridization), with an average of 9.6 among the 116 households (Kreutzmann, 1996 – see pp. 67 and 133). These figures are derived from empirical studies in the 1990s; the agricultural census data are either not available or are not reliable as samples are not regularly taken in the remote locations where mountain farmers keep yak and census data are more often restricted to the more easily accessible regions.

A similar situation applies to the Yasin and Ishkoman valleys, Ghizer district. In Yasin, yak are kept in the Thui valley (approx. 150), in Barkulti (approx. 50) and in Darkot and the Nazbar valleys. It was reported that no hybrids are kept and that the maximum number is well below a total of 500 yak in Yasin (Stöber, 2001 and personal communication). In Ishkoman, Wakhi and Gujur (former nomads) keep yak in the Karambar Valley (<500). The Wakhi settled here as refugees in the late nineteenth century and introduced yak keeping in Ishkoman. The Gujur arrived later and first offered their services as animal herders in the region before becoming independent animal husbandry people. In suitable locations, they adopted the practice of yak keeping from their neighbours.

The major yak herds are found in the Gupis area, which resembles the upper parts of the Ghizer district close to the Shandur Pass (3 700m) region and the neighbouring Chitral district. A recent survey (Juergen Clemens, personal communication, 2000) showed 3 095 yak for Gupis alone. Overall, the proportion of yak in the Ghizer district is approximately 5 percent of all bovides; cattle, sheep and goats are kept in roughly similar proportions

In all cases, yak augment the livestock of mountain farmers in a complex system of irrigated crop farming and animal husbandry. Nonlactating yak are regularly kept outside the homesteads for almost the whole year; calves and their mothers spend some short periods in the permanent settlements prior to their migration to the high pastures.

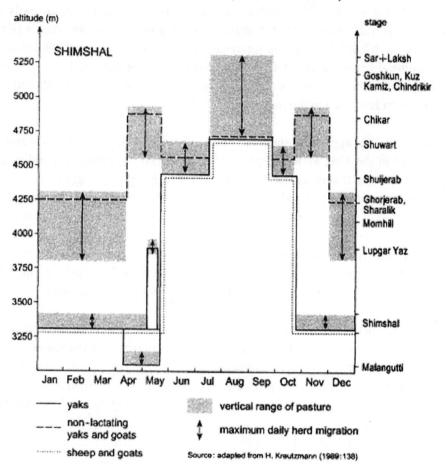

Figure 11.2.8 Staging of animal husbandry in Shimshal (Northern Pakistan)

References

Aga Khan Rural Support Programme (1991). A report on livestock in the Northern Areas. Gilgit.

Aqto Täzkirisi (1994). Statistics on livestock development [in Uighur]. Aqto, 159-160.

Butz, D. (1989). Pastures and pastoralism in Shimshal. Gilgit (Preliminary report to Aga Khan Rural Support Programme).

Chakravarty-Kaul, M. (1998). Transhumance and customary pastoral rights in Himachal Pradesh: Claiming the high pastures for Gaddis. *In:* Mountain Research and Development, 18, 5-17.

Clemens, J. & M. Nuesser, (2000). Pastoral management strategies in transition: Indicators from the Nanga Parbat region (NW-Himalaya). *In:* E. Ehlers & H. Kreutzmann (eds.) High Mountain pastoralism in Northern Pakistan. Stuttgart, Steiner-Verlag, pp. 151-187.

Dor, R. (1976). Note sur le yak au Pamir. In: Ethnozootechnie 5, 126-132.

Dor, R. & C. Naumann (1978). Die Kirghisen des afghanischen Pamir. Akademische Druck- und Verlagsanstalt, Graz. 199 pp.

Ehlers, E. & H. Kreutzmann (eds.) (2000). High Mountain pastoralism in Northern Pakistan. Steiner-Verlag, Stuttgart. 209 pp. (Erdkundliches Wissen Vol.132).

Farman Ali & Khaleel A. Tetlay (1991). Dynamics of livestock development in Northern Areas, Pakistan. Gilgit (Aga Khan Rural Support Programme, Conference and workshop papers No. 20).

Kreutzmann, H. (1986). A note on yak-keeping in Hunza (Northern Areas of Pakistan). *In*: Production Pastorale et Société, 19, 99-106.

Kreutzmann, H. (1995). Mobile Viehwirtschaft der Kirgisen am Kara Köl. Wandlungsprozesse an der Höhengrenze der Ökumene im Ostpamir und im westlichen Kun Lun Shan. In: Petermanns Geographische Mitteilungen, 139, 159-178.

Kreutzmann, H. (1996). Ethnizität im Entwicklungsprozeß. Die Wakhi in Hochasien. Dietrich Reimer-Verlag, Berlin. 488 pp.

Kreutzmann, H. (1998). Yak-keeping in High Asia. Adaptation to the utilization of high-altitude ecological zones and the socio-economic transformation of pastoral environments. *In*: Kailash (Kathmandu), 18 (1-2), 17-38.

Kreutzmann, H. (2000a). Livestock economy in Hunza. Societal transformation and pastoral practices. In: E. Ehlers & H. Kreutzmann (eds.): High Mountain pastoralism in Northern Pakistan. Steiner-Verlag, Stuttgart. 89-120.

Kreutzmann, H. (2000b). Animal Husbandry in High Asia. Yak-keeping at the Upper Pastoral Limits. In: Miehe, G. & Zhang Yili (eds.): Environmental Changes in High Asia. Proceedings of an International Symposium at the University of Marburg, Faculty of Geography 29 May to 1 June 1997 under the auspices of the Unesco. Marburg/Lahn: Selbstverlag (Marburger Geographische Schriften Vol. 135), 361-375.

Myrdal, J. (1979). The Silk Road. A journey from the High Pamirs and Ili through Sinkiang and Kansu. Random House, New York.

Nazir Ahmad (2000). Livestock census for the year 2000. Astor: Aga Khan Rural Support Programme Diamer (mimeographed).

Nüsser, M. & J. Clemens (1996). Impacts on mixed mountain agriculture in Rupal Valley, Nanga Parbat, Northern Pakistan. *In:* Mountain Research and Development 16, 117-133.

Nüsser, M. (1998). Nanga Parbat (NW-Himalaya): Naturräumliche Ressourcenaussstattung und humanökologische Gefügemuster der Landnutzung. Dümmler-Verlag, Bonn. 232 pp.

Nüsser, M. (1999). Mobile Tierhaltung in Chitral: Hochweidenutzung und Existenzsicherung im pakistanischen Hindukusch. In: Janzen, J. (ed.): Räumliche Mobilität und Existenzsicherung. Dietrich Reimer-Verlag, Berlin. 105-131.

Schaller G.B. *et al.* (1987). Status of Large Mammals in the Taxkorgan Reserve, Xinjiang, China. In: Biological Conservation 42, 53-71.

Schmidt, M. E. (2000). Pastoral systems in Shigar/Baltistan: communal herding management and pasturage rights. *In:* E. Ehlers & H. Kreutzmann (eds.): High Mountain pastoralism in Northern Pakistan. Steiner-Verlag, Stuttgart. 121-150

Shahrani, M. N. (1979). The Kirghiz and Wakhi of Afghanistan. Adaptation to Closed Frontiers. Seattle and London, University of Washington Press.

Shahrani M. N. (1984). Afghanistan's Kirghiz in Turkey. In: Cultural Survival Quarterly 8, 31-34.

Stöber, G. (2001). Zur Transformation bäuerlicher Hauswirtschaft in Yasin, Northern Areas, Pakistan. Asgard-Verlag, St. Augustin. (in press).

Walter H. & S.W. Breckle (1986). Pamir - eine ökologisch gut untersuchte Hochgebirgswüste. In: H. Walter & S.-W. Breckle (eds): Ökologie der Erde 3. Gustav Fischer-Verlag, Stuttgart and New York. 327-361.

PART 3

YAK IN NONTRADITIONAL ENVIRONMENTS
By Gerald Wiener[9]

OVERVIEW

Information is presented here on yak kept commercially in around 90 herds in the USA and Canada with a total of perhaps 2000 animals (pure and hybrid). Yak are also found in small commercial herds in parts of Europe and in New Zealand. In addition, there are a significant number of zoos and wild animal parks in several parts of the world that have, or have had, collections of yak, many of them successfully self-reproducing herds. The common factor for all of these yak is that they are in climatic and management situations which are quite atypical of those in the traditional yak-keeping territories. The successful survival and reproduction of the yak in these nontraditional environments is, therefore, of wider interest for the potential adaptation of yak to a variety of conditions worldwide.

North America

Since the early 1980s there has been a growing interest in yak by commercial breeders and ranchers in the USA and Canada hoping to exploit what they claim to be the low maintenance needs of yak and the potential for lean meat production through what is referred to as "crossbreeding" with other cattle – but should, more accurately be termed "hybridizing". At the time of writing there are an estimated 90 breeders, but perhaps fewer, with a total of not more than 2 000 yak and hybrids between them. These numbers are lower than reported earlier (Wiener, 2002) as breeders have recently found difficulty in penetrating the meat market, except on a local basis (J. Delaney, personal communication, 2002). Individual herds vary in size from less than ten animals to more than 400. The great majority of yak breeders in North America are members of a breed Association, the (American) International Yak Association (IYAK), but some of those still registered with the Association no longer have yak.

From a biological point of view, perhaps the most interesting aspect of this commercial use of domestic yak in North America is that many of the herds are located in parts of the country where the climate and general environmental conditions are very different from those traditional for yak. Around half of all the herds, including the largest, are in areas close to the Rocky mountain range at elevations up to around 2 600 m above sea level, where yak might be expected to feel perfectly "at home". Some of the remainder are in hill areas in other parts of the country, but a significant proportion of the herds are in

---

[9] Gerald Wiener is an Honorary Professor, Gansu Agricultural University, China and is attached to the Centre for Tropical Veterinary Medicine, University of Edinburgh and the Roslin Institute, Edinburgh, UK. He was also Deputy director of the former AFRC Animal Breeding Research Organization in the UK.

seasonally hot parts of the country at low altitudes and in typically temperate climates – some close to the Pacific coast. The single largest herd is in Nebraska, east of the Rocky mountain range at 1 280 m above sea level and with an annual rainfall averaging 420 mm.

Overall, the herds are located from northerly parts of Alberta in Canada to central USA and from the Pacific coast to close to the Atlantic. This clearly shows an ability of the yak to adapt to non-traditional conditions – in spite of the contrary view expressed in some of the early literature on the subject, which is also part of the "received wisdom".

A historical note on the introduction of yak to Canada and Alaska

The introduction of yak to Canada and Alaska in the early part of the last century represents the most northerly latitudes in the distribution of the yak (other than the progenitors of the modern yak). The origin of the yak in this region is not clearly documented. It is known that six head of Chinese yak were sent to Canada in 1909 (from England, according to Lensch et al., 1996), as a gift from the Duke of Bedford, but by the following year only one male and three females had survived and for the next two years the animals failed to reproduce. This, as noted by White et al. (1946), was attributed to the low altitude at which the yak were kept. Reproduction started when the animals were moved to higher altitudes (and probably, therefore, lower temperatures) in the Rocky Mountain Park near Banff in Alberta, Canada. In 1919 most of the yak were transferred to Buffalo Park, Wainwright. In 1921, some yak were included in the hybridization experiments with domestic cattle and American bison then in progress at Wainwright with the aim of producing an animal for meat production for the harsh pastoral conditions of northern Canada. Few of the interspecies hybrids survived (Deakin et al. 1935) and this series of trials was suspended in 1928.

Similar experience occurred in Alaska (White et al. 1946). Over the years 1919, 1923 and 1930, a total of three male and six female Chinese yak, born in Canada, were taken to the Fairbanks Experiment Station in Alaska, at an elevation of approximately 130 m. The yak had great difficulty in breeding, but these difficulties diminished and the general condition of the yak improved when they were moved to a plateau at an altitude between 400 m and 800 m. The intention was to produce animals suitable for the grasslands in the Alaska mountains, southern Yukon territories and plains and tundra of the Alaska-Canada border. Hybrids were produced experimentally with Galloway cows whose hybrid offspring were heavier at slaughter than either the yak or the pure Galloway. However, the hybrids did not appear to withstand the extremely low temperatures of winter as successfully as the pure yak. These trials were also suspended, in the early 1930s.

In theory, it is feasible that the entire North American yak population could be derived from the single, documented, importation to Canada, but this seems improbable. Offspring from the original importation of yak survived in national parks or zoos, but these institutions may also have imported additional yak from abroad through dealers. There are unconfirmed reports that some of the present-day yak there are derived from an importation to the Bronx Zoo in 1890. Also, as the section on yak in zoos later in this Chapter shows, some significant breeding of yak, and also a few yak hybrids with cattle, occurred in North American zoos from the 1920s onward.

Surplus animals and dispersal of zoo collections could well have provided progenitors for the present commercial population – though documented evidence of that has not been found.

Characteristics and performance

Most of the information that follows was provided by members of the (American) International Yak Association (IYAK). Animal performance results are based on figures from about 16 herd owners.

The primary aim of the yak breeders in North America is lean meat production, but fibre is also valued especially in some smaller herds. Only one of the respondents to our survey trained yak for packing and trekking but not on a commercial basis. A very small number of yak are also kept out of curiosity or as pets. During the period of expansion of this niche market, much of the interest and income of breeders came from the sale of breeding stock, but this may be changing. Milk from the yak, though referred to in the promotional literature of IYAK, does not appear, as yet, to have found a market, although one or two breeders report some trial milking for the manufacture of yoghurt.

Coat colours of the yak are: all black, black with some white markings (called trim), which predominates, black and white (described as "royal") and a "gold" colour, present in small numbers and said to be recessive to black.

Birth weights of yak calves are quoted as varying from 13 - 27 kg, weaning weights, generally at four to five months of age, as 65 - 70 kg for some farms thought to be providing above-average rearing conditions. Adult weights of yak cows were quoted in the range 240 - 360 kg and yak bulls 550 - 680 kg, though one yak bull in Canada was reported to weigh 820 kg.

Some females are mated for the first time as early as 18 months of age, but two to two and a half years is more common. Calving annually is normal, but one of the herd owners noted that half his yak cows had only two calves in three years. Bulls are not generally used for mating until three years old, although some younger ages were reported.

Few health problems were encountered but the need for routine vaccinations and deworming, especially in humid conditions, was referred to by several of the herd owners.

Feeding and management

Most of the feed is natural grazing in summer and hay in winter. Some breeders use grain as an enticement to gather the animals, but a few feed it as a supplement – especially for finishing. All the respondents to the survey provided mineral blocks and some mentioned a need for an adequate amount of copper in the block to promote health and the breeding of the yaks (as noted in Chapter 9). A greater feed efficiency was claimed for the yak and their hybrids relative to other cattle and hence a need for relatively smaller quantities of feed and pasture per kilogram live weight of animal.

Generally, the yak were kept out-of-doors all year-round. Calves remain with the dams up to weaning at, usually, four to five months old. The yak were regarded as reasonably tame and, with few exceptions, easily handled and easily confined by fencing.

Possible heat stress for yak was mentioned but did not amount to a problem. The animals sought some shade and water for cooling in periods of high heat in summer, but even this was thought to be unnecessary by some of the respondents.

Discussion

The performance information suggests that the range of birth weights of yak calves may be a little higher than those in traditional yak areas in China. Also, the inferred growth rate of calves to weaning, perhaps exceeding 400 g per day, is also higher than the gains of around 300 g quoted elsewhere in this book. However, this should not occasion surprise as the calves in North America are reared under what can be regarded as good conditions and with access to all the maternal milk, while in the traditional yak territories herders normally take some milk for domestic consumption – thus restricting the intake by the calf. Experimental results from China, quoted in Chapter 6, show similar improvements in calf growth when the calves are given access to all their dams' milk. Some of the adult weights, particularly of breeding bulls, also appear slightly higher than usually reported for domestic yak, but this is likely to be a consequence of feeding rather than a genetic difference.

The owners of the herds surveyed reported what are higher reproductive rates for their yak than are common in the more traditional circumstances. This includes both an earlier average onset of breeding and, mostly, annual calving. This is almost certainly attributable to the feeding conditions in summer and the almost universal use of supplementary feeding in winter, as well as the provision of mineral blocks and health care. Consequently there is no large loss of weight or condition of the animals over winter and during pregnancy.

Questions remain regarding the origin of the North American yak population and hence its genetic relationship to other yak populations and breeds. It is also not known how closely related the animals are within the North American yak population and whether inbreeding is or might be a problem as the genetic base of the population might well be small. Future research may resolve some of these questions.

It seems almost inevitable that over time there has been some introduction of *B. taurus* genes into the American yak gene pool. Preliminary results, from a recent analysis of some 43 blood samples from yak of three of the herds in the USA (Han Jianlin, personal communication, 2002), suggest the presence of mitochondrial DNA from cattle in many of these particular samples. However, it is unlikely that such introductions of *B. taurus* blood would be responsible for the apparent adaptation of the yak in North America to the varied and non-traditional environments. For yak, any such introduction of genes can come only through hybrid females, as the hybrid males are sterile. The process of hybridizing seems to be random and varied and without selective intent for "adaptation". Moreover, it would also be unlikely that natural selection for adaptation could have been effective over the short period of 90 years or so under consideration. These points were given more detailed consideration by Wiener (2002).

More information about the distribution and performance of the yak in North America were provided by Wiener (2002) and can also be obtained from the IYAK Web site (www.yakpage.com).

Europe

A small herd of 26 yak was established, in the 1990s, in the Zermatt region of Switzerland at an altitude of 1 600 m. The animals were acquired over a period of two or three years from a dealer, but the origin of these yak is not recorded (Agir, 1997). More recently, Michael Goe (personal communication, 2002) reported that this herd had grown to 37 yak (and one hybrid cow) with the herd in Emd (Canton Valis); in addition, he reports two other herds of 20 animals and one of 15 yak and a further number of very small herds (two to seven animals). The total number of yak for Switzerland was estimated to be 140. The yak in the herd first reported were used for trekking.

The only other herd, according to Horst Geilhausen (personal communication, 2002) that is extant in Europe, outside zoos, numbers eight to ten animals in the south Tirol of Austria. It was established in 1985. The owner is said to accompany his animals personally to the mountain pastures in the spring of the year and from this one might infer that the yak are kept in more sheltered parts over winter. (The origins were not conveyed to Professor Geilhausen). The presence of yak in parts of France, as in the last century and earlier (see Chapter 1) is no longer reported.

New Zealand

A small herd of about 15 yak is kept at the very top end of South Island of New Zealand on a farm just above sea level with an annual rainfall of 2 400 mm and a mild climate – with summer temperature often in excess of 30°C.

The yak originated in the mid-1980s from the Toronto Zoo and first went to a holding in central South Island at an elevation of about 300 m, with cold dry winter but hot summer, where the yak bred well. They were transferred to their present farm in 1990 and, according to the owner (information from the year 2000), after a period of acclimatization, the yak started to reproduce well, calving annually in November (late spring-early summer). Some of the yak have been sold to other farms in the area as a foundation for new herds. The owner reports that his yak have had no health problems and, like the ranchers with yak in North America, notes that his yak appear to eat much less than his other cattle and thrive on roughage.

Yak in zoos and wild animal parks

The basic information in the first part of this section was kindly provided by the Wildlife Conservation Society in New York in the form of a Taxon report, which lists animals, past and present, by location Other information is acknowledged in the text.

Yak have been present in zoos and wild animal parks in Europe, North America and Asia for well over a century. Some of the collections, past and present, are very small and transient, relying on purchases from elsewhere. Other zoos have more substantial and self-reproducing herds, which in turn have surplus stock available for disposal. The critical point of interest, from the point of view of yak adaptability, is that these zoos represent conditions that are quite different from those experienced by yak in their native habitats. Success or failure in captivity provides some further clues therefore to the adaptability of yak to a variety of different environments.

Most of the zoos take part in a registration system for their animals – with the information published in a Taxon report. The information here is based on such a report and it provides evidence of 110 zoos and wild animal parks with yak either past or present (up to the year 2000). Not all zoological institutions, however, participate in this information scheme, so this number is a minimum estimate.

Three of the collections have had, over a period of years, well in excess of 100 yak each (Winnepeg, Canada; Whipsnade, England, with the largest number currently extant, and Bronx, New York, USA – collection now dispersed). One of the zoo collections (Milwaukee, Wisconsin, USA) dates back to 1914 (but with a last entry in 1949). One other, (San Diego) dates back to 1928 (but the last entry is in 1980), and the remainder are from 1940 onwards, with the majority starting after 1980. Many of the collections started were dispersed within ten years or so. (In terms of dates, one animal was found in these records born at the National Zoological Park in Washington as early as July 1901, many years ahead of other yak at this zoo, and then traded to Regent's Park Zoo in London the following January). For zoos or parks that had yak in the year 2000, the average number of years that they had had their yak herds was around 20. Zoos now without yak had kept their herds or animals for only half that time. A few of the zoos have exhibited only the odd yak or two and have not bred them. Table 11.2.20 summarizes the information on a country basis showing 102 locations. Because of the dispersal of many of the collections and disposal of animals, the number of yak extant (in the year 2000) is only a fraction of the total number recorded over the years.

Nearly all the yak represented in the survey were born in captivity or can be presumed to have been. But there is no information readily available on the origin of some of the early acquisitions and no information of the source of animals acquired from dealers. There is no absolute certainty that all the captive yak are pure or whether they are hybrids with infusions of blood from other cattle. However, the zoos represented in this report keep accession and breeding records, and the great majority of the animals are listed as pure domestic yak and only a small minority is labelled as hybrids or as possible hybrids.

Only three zoos claimed some wild yak in their collections; the largest of these, Chicago zoo, in the period 1974 - 1981, with 17 animals. Unlike the domestic yak in the zoo collections, none of the wild yak survived for more than three years.

It is clear from the summary in Table 11.3.1 that captive yak have existed and are still found in a wide variety of climates and environments and from the available evidence those in small herds have bred and survived successfully in captivity. The environments, captivity apart, are for the most part atypical of the conditions in the native habitats of the yak. Most of the locations of the zoos and wild animal parks are at relatively low altitudes, some close to sea level, and thus do not present the "typical" atmosphere low in oxygen. Also, summer temperatures at many of the locations will be high, even relatively so at night. Winters will be temperate in many cases, and average annual temperatures will be at higher average levels than for yak in their native territory. (This is similar to the conditions referred to earlier in relation to a proportion of the yak kept commercially in North America.)

Some reconciliation is therefore needed between the obvious tolerance of the yak of these "unusual" conditions and the reputation of yak for poor adaptation to low altitudes and high ambient temperature (based on yak-keeping experience in their principal territories and a little evidence from small-scale studies).

Table 11.3.1 Yak collections – past and present – in zoos and wild animal parks*

Country	Total No. of collection	Total No. of yak	In the year 2000	
			No. collections	No. yak
Europe				
Austria	1	2	-	-
Belgium	3	74	3	22
CIS countries**	6	31	4	24
Denmark	2	53	2	32
England	2	122	2	35
Estonia	1	49	1	16
Finland	1	51	1	1
France	3	13	1	2
Germany	13	129	6	18
Holland	8	134	4	15
Hungary	2	66	1	2
Italy	1	26	1	5
Latvia	1	16	1	2
Poland	5	80	4	29
Portugal	1	24	1	4
Spain	2	12	1	5
Sweden	2	121	1	10
Americas				
Canada	6	328	2	7
Mexico	1	1	-	-
USA	41	662	10	39
Total	**102**	**1994**	**46**	**257**

* Not all zoos participate in the information scheme represented by the Taxon reports or appear in ISIS abstracts – these zoos (and some countries) are therefore missing from the Table.

**One of these zoos is in a CIS country. At least two zoos (Moscow and St Petersburg) in the Russian Federation, but not listed in the Taxon report, are known to have had, or currently to have, yak collections.

The apparent success of commercially kept yak in parts of North America (see earlier section) further underlines this point. Winter *et al.* (1989) also refer to this conundrum. Perhaps it is all a question of the time allowed for such acclimatization and how the animals are managed on arrival.

It can be surmised, for example, that in past times on the trade routes from Tibet southward into Nepal and India, yak would fairly rapidly descend from cold mountain regions into near-tropical conditions and that this may have produced not only heat stress in the animals but a reputation for intolerance of heat, which has become part of the received wisdom.

This is conjecture, of course, and the opportunity to record the physiological r
yak on such treks to a descent from cold to near-tropical conditions no lo⸍
itself readily. (Although nowadays, study of such responses would u
considered as worthy of an academic project!)

Whipsnade Wild Animal Park

In the first edition of this book, the yak herd at Whipsnade was featured
the point previously made, that yak can survive and reproduce well un⸍
are atypical of those in the native habitats of the yak. It is of interes⸍
provide updated information on this small but successful herd, by courte⸍
Whipsnade, Nick Lindsay, and the chief veterinarian, Edmund Flach.

The park lies on the edge of the Dunstable Downs (elevation a⸍
approximately 52°N) in England. The climate is typically temperate.
in 1944, though records of the source are not now available. This v
importations from Alberta (Canada), Berlin (Germany) and from S
Currently, the herd numbers about 30 animals with a second sm
another park with animals originating from the Whipsnade herd.

The information provided is that the yak cows do not calve an⸍⸍⸍
average, approximately two calves in every three years. The animals grow normally and
survive extremely well. Small numbers of yak have been sent to other countries (e.g.
Turkey). There is no obvious seasonality to the breeding and calves (all pure yak) have
been born in March, April, May, July, August, September and November. It appears that
some of the yak at Whipsnade may breed as early as their second year of life. Since the
foundation of the yak herd in 1944, there have been more than 100 yak in the Whipsnade
herd (with the offshoot herd in addition) and the vast majority of them have been born at
the park.

In summer, the animals are said to seek shade under trees and shed much of their fleece but
show no obvious discomfort. The only recurrent health problems were found to be
associated with copper deficiency. Following diagnosis of the condition, it has been fully
controlled by regular supplementation and occasional copper injection for many years
(Edmund Flach, personal communication, 1995). This matter was referred to more fully in
Chapter 9 as there is a possibility that yak may be prone to this deficiency for genetic
reasons because other cattle in the park are not equally affected, although receiving the
same diet. Other data from the herd are presented in Chapter 4.

A note from the curator states that as of 2002, breeding of this long-standing herd was
being suspended temporarily, as there has been insufficient demand for surplus animals.
But the matter is under review.

References

Agir, (1997). Elevages exotiques en Suisse. *Actualités*, 30 Août 1997

Deakin, A., Muir, G.W. and Smith, A.G. (1935). Hybridization of domestic cattle, bison and yak. Publication 479, Technical Bulletin 2, November 1935, Dominion of Canada, Department of Agriculture.

Lensch, J., Sley, P. and Zhang, Rongchang (1996). Der Yak (*Bos grunniens*) in Zentralasien. Duncker & Humblot, Berlin. (IBSN 3-428-08443-8)

White, W.T., Phillips, R.W. and Elting, E.C. (1946). Yak and yak-cattle hybrids in Alaska. J. of Heredity, 37, 355-358.

Wiener, G. (2002). Adaptation of yak to non-typical environments: A preliminary survey of yak in North America. *Proceedings of the third international congress on yak, in Lhasa, China, 4-9 September 2000.* International Livestock Research Institute (ILRI), Nairobi, pp. 373-379.

12 SOCIAL, CULTURAL AND ECONOMIC CONTEXT OF YAK PRODUCTION

by Wu Ning[1]

OVERVIEW

Yak keeping is closely bound up with the social and cultural life of the people, most particularly in the vast rangeland grazing areas of the Qinghai-Tibetan Plateau and other parts around the Himalayan mountain range. The yak is, moreover, a component of the religious practices and manifestations of Tibetan Buddhism.

Yak production underpins the economy of much of this region. To meet the challenges of a harsh and often unfriendly environment on the "roof of the world", herders have developed a complex system of management and land use involving the sharing of grazing lands and their use, for the most part in a nomadic fashion resulting in rotational use of the grazing lands. Much of this developed through agreements between families and within villages. Traditionally, pastoralists relied on their yak primarily for subsistence, but status was also conferred by possessing large numbers of yak. With the more recent moves towards a market-oriented economy, changes have been imposed or at least suggested that affect both the traditional patterns of yak keeping and the purpose of keeping the animals.

In particular, not only have the animals themselves passed into the private ownership of the herders, but, over large parts of the yak-keeping provinces of China, land has been allocated to individual families. This has been in an effort to encourage settlement in place of unrestricted movement – in other words, to change from a mobile to a sedentary method of production. There are both positive and negative aspects to these developments. In respect of range management and making best use of forage resources in times of plenty (the short summer) for the times of feed shortage (the long winter and early spring), the problems created may well be paramount.

Better opportunities for marketing yak and yak products and the attractions of a market economy encourage increased production and technological inputs to assist yak keeping. A move from traditional to modern practices, however, can create tensions and problems if these modern practices are not sensitively integrated with the vast, accumulated knowledge and experience of the herders.

This chapter aims to set out the principal considerations in the relationships of the yak, the land and the people.

---

[1] Wu Ning is a Professor of Restoration Ecology and Assistant to the Director at the Chengdu Institute of Biology of the Chinese Academy of Sciences, Chengdu, Sichuan, China.

Cultural role of yak in Tibetan tradition

The primary importance of the yak is in the economy of the so-called "roof of the world", the Qinghai-Tibetan Plateau. A number of researchers (Alirol, 1976; Goldstein and Beall, 1990; March, 1977) have discussed the importance of yak for pastoralists in the Himalayas. However, domestic yak are also of great cultural importance to the people of the Himalayan region. They are closely linked to the cultural and ritual activities of these herding societies. As illustrated with examples by Cayla (1976), the yak takes its place alongside other animals, both real and mythical, in the history, legends and mythology of the Tibetan region and neighbouring territories. For example, the use of the yak as a provider of components for local medicines is one aspect of the near mystical importance of the yak. In Nepal, especially in the Mustang area in the months of July and August, yak blood is taken from the juvenile vein and fed to weak persons. Meyer (1976) described some of the medicines and remedies associated with the yak. Olsen (1991) considered the yak to have been so important to the Tibetan people that prior to the Second World War their society could legitimately be referred to as a "yak culture" similar in many ways to the "buffalo culture" of the native Indian peoples of America (see Chapter 1).

There is a long history of interaction between the yak and Tibetan pastoral societies. Even the phenomenon of yak totem can be found in some areas on the Tibetan Plateau (Yang, 1987) – and yak are sacrificed at certain festivals. Bovine deities, believed to include yak-headed gods, were important in the religion that preceded the introduction of Buddhism into Tibet from India. In the Tibetan farming areas of Sichuan province of China, there is a special festival to offer sacrifices to "yak gods" or ancestors, called *Gerdorom*, which takes place every November. In Tibetan legend, wild yak are said to be as "stars" living in heaven and the yak is always imagined as a safeguarding god.

Almost all parts of yak body have cultural or religious values. In western Sichuan and Qimdo areas, Tibetan women place on their heads two silver ornaments embedded with coral and yak horn, from which one can imagine they are adherents of ancient yak tribes. Yak horns and skulls are both of religious importance, and they are often carved with mantras and placed in prominent places. On the Tibetan Plateau nomadic people place yak heads or skulls on walls, on the threshold of a gate or *Manidui* (shrine) and may even hang a yak corpse on the doors of monasteries in order to drive out evil spirits. Yak butter sculptures are burnt as offerings to the gods and can be found in most of the monasteries of the Tibetan areas. There is also a popular practice that, in the words of Miller *et al.* (1997), "Sometimes a community will set a domestic yak free. This "god yak", as it is called in Tibetan, is an offering to gods of the locale, a gift back to the environment which sustains pastoralists." Throughout yak-raising regions, yak dances are held by herders, which signify typically the vital role that yak play in the cultural and spiritual values of the pastoral society.

Religion, ceremony, social customs and attitudes to wealth and its symbols are all intertwined with each other in the life of the people and with the integral role of the yak in all aspects. Yak are always used as a dowry when a Tibetan girl marries a young herder. Therefore, yak, apart from being indicators of wealth, play an important role in maintaining social relationships. Complex forms of social organization have developed within yak-raising societies that aid in the allocation of rangeland resources and, through trade networks with other nomadic and agricultural communities, help to secure goods not otherwise available in pastoral areas. However, with socio-economic development, especially the process of modernization, "it is possible," as suggested in the first edition of this book and repeated in Chapter 1, "that the cultural and social importance of the yak may diminish in the life of the herdsmen." And "it is also possible that the spread, however slow, of modern concepts of feeding, management and breeding, and the pressures from those proffering such technological advice on yak husbandry, may further diminish the force of traditional values." It would be a pity if these values were lost without an understanding of their profound importance and further lead to the disappearance of cultural diversity. The conservation of biodiversity and cultural diversity are of the same importance in the development of yak keeping.

Socio-economic significance of yak keeping

Over the centuries, herders have developed complex and, very often, extremely efficient pastoral systems for managing rangelands and livestock in the harsh, high altitude environment where yak are found. Herders possess great knowledge about the rangelands and the animals they herd. As Miller and Steane (1996) concluded, "The fact that numerous unique and, in many cases, prosperous yak herding societies remain to this day bears witness to the extraordinary skills of yak herders." In recent decades, however, the modernization process has brought improved access and services to previously remote pastoral areas and an increased demand for yak products (Miller, 1997; Wu and Richard, 1999). Along with reforms in land and animal tenure, the changed socio-economic issues are transforming traditional yak production systems and grazing use patterns on the rangelands.

From subsistence to marketing purpose

Many researchers have emphasized that the yak has made life possible for man in one of the world's harshest environments. In purely pastoral areas, where cultivated agriculture is not possible, yak allow people to subsist and, in many areas, to live quite well (Miller, 1997). A wide variety of yak products are produced for home consumption and marketing. In the mixed pastoral areas where both animal husbandry and cropping is found, yak and yak-hybrids are also an important component of agricultural production systems. Apart from the home consumption of yak products, yak husbandry is also the mainstay of the regional economies. For example, in western Sichuan, an important yak-raising area in

China, 72 percent of the milk, 45 percent of the beef, 42 percent of bovine skin and 34 percent of animal fibre (including fine wool) come from yak. Because of improved outlets for yak products, the number of yak more than doubled in every yak-raising area of China in the period 1950 - 1990, and in some cases increased by as much as two and a half-fold.

In grazing areas where pastoralists rely for their subsistence mainly upon their yak, the wealth of the nomads is judged, as in other traditional pastoral societies, by the number of animals owned (Wu, 1997a). However, prestige and social status are not the only reasons for keeping as many animals as possible; possession of a large number is also thought by many nomads to provide extra insurance against death of animals in times of severe cold or drought (Scholz, 1981; Huebl, 1986). Wu (1997b) elaborated on this point by suggesting that as an insurance against disasters nomads need to strive to increase stock numbers so that in the event of severe losses of animals an adequate remainder is left to rebuild the herd. Thus, the expansion of herd size in good times is a survival strategy adopted by yak herders, which is analogous to "r-selection" in bionomic strategy. Maintaining a large stock, therefore, becomes an ecological strategy selected by nomads. Among the causes for loss of yak, cold stress is the single most harmful factor on the Tibetan Plateau and some other regions of Central Asia (Wu, 1997a; Humphrey and Sneath, 1999).

In the past two decades, alternative sources of feed and improved veterinary facilities have been reducing the losses of animals during hard winters in some areas. However, the maximizing of livestock numbers by herders has been widely perceived as having caused rangeland degradation in pastoral areas through overgrazing (Linziduojie, 1996; Li and Yong, 1993; see also Chapter 13). It has also been suggested by (Ellis *et al.*, 1991) that, provided an impending climatic disaster could be predicted sufficiently well in advance and provided good market outlets exist, a sensible and potentially profitable move by herders would be to sell out their stock before disaster strikes. However, this seems optimistic, as prediction of climatic disaster is at best uncertain and might not even become known to herders in advance, and the requisite market outlets may not exist. The only thing likely to be known, ahead of time, is the condition of the animals at the start of winter. If the preceding summer has been dry and vegetation growth inadequate, the condition of the animals is likely to be poor, and they will be at greater risk of death if the winter is then especially harsh. Most of the disastrous losses of yak that appear to occur in different areas every few years have resulted from a combination of a poor summer followed by an especially bad winter (Wiener, 1996).

Trade of yak products is also an important way of capital accumulation. Income can be derived from most of the products, from the sale of pack animals and from animals for breeding. Herders also try to exploit year-to-year fluctuations in resources in order to optimize herd productivity.

If reproductive rate is higher than normal in "good" years, or if supplementary feed has been available during winter, herd size increases and greater opportunities are created for marketing.

The present commercialization in China and other countries of Central Asia with histories of centrally planned economies has accelerated the development of marketing of yak products. Many attempts have been made by governments to force pastoralists to reduce their stock numbers and to integrate the subsistence pastoralism with a market economy (Humphrey and Sneath, 1999; Miller, 1998). The market-pricing process has made pastoralists more aware of the possibilities inherent in slaughtering livestock earlier in the season. Moreover, pastoralists now own their livestock, and there clearly is an open market in animal products, especially for those in the proximity of urban areas. This is starting to alter the traditional attitudes of the pastoralists. In the more remote yak-raising areas, the marketing of yak products is still limited due to only a few market outlets and at great distance, weak communications and high transport costs. Without market intelligence for yak products, it is also difficult to evaluate trends in the market or in price changes. Reliance on individual traders with poor management and financial capabilities does not provide a good basis for large-scale marketing. Because the remoteness of most yak-raising areas from good market outlets is still a fact of life, there continues to be substantial reliance on the use of yak products for subsistence and on marketing traditional products through traditional channels. In particular, yak herders have not yet been able to tap into speciality markets for products that could bring higher prices. Moreover, the reluctance of marketers or processors to advertise and develop high-value yak products also limits these developments (Miller, 1997). However, as described in Chapter 10, the development of cheese factories in Nepal provides an example of how substantial marketing outlets for yak milk can be created.

The development of the pastoral economies is the key to poverty alleviation and to improving food security, as well as to the wider goal of creating sustainable livelihoods. Ellis *et al.* (1991) suggested that the most important development intervention for promoting pastoral survival might be to reduce isolation and to consolidate links between the pastoral ecosystem and external resources. This involves encouraging the movement of goods and livestock through trade or marketing systems and linking the pastoral area to external economies both for consumption and distribution of products. As herders' incomes and access to goods increases, their dependence upon the local environment for subsistence decreases. Helping herders explore and adopt new marketing strategies requires support from governments to safeguard the social fabric of the communities by providing credit, insurance, relief funds and market outlets. Improving the infrastructure should reduce reliance on herd number maximization as an insurance against disasters (cf. Williams, 1996; Wu and Richard, 1999).

From mobile to sedentary system

Developments in the science and technology of yak husbandry do not alter the physical conditions of the region. Seasonal mobile keeping of livestock, therefore, still characterizes most of the highland animal husbandry.

On the Tibetan Plateau, the sparseness and limitation of natural pastures and their geographic and/or orographic location encourage nomadic livestock production. Yak herds are regularly moved between different areas at different seasons and, if necessary, between different pastures within a season. Scholz (1986) emphasized that mobile livestock keeping is an "optimum active human adaptation to the physical environment of arid and semi-arid areas and is probably the only possible way of putting the barren pastures of these regions to economic use without an immense expenditure of capital". In ecological terms, the exploitation of heterogeneity in pastoral society involves optimizing forage use through local strategies of habitat division and the dispersal of grazing pressure (Wu, 1997a; see also Chapter 13).

From studies in the eastern Tibetan Plateau, Wu (1997b) suggested that an appropriate management strategy for a mobile system of yak raising used by local herders depends on finding the right starting and termination times of the grazing season. Critical factors involved include the time of greening of the summer pastures, the height of the sward, tillering and the requirements of re-growth of the vegetation. Termination of grazing of the summer pastures in the autumn also impacts on the yield of vegetation in the following year – so this must not be left too late in the season. Detailed consideration of the ecosystem and of range management and grazing practices is found in Chapter 13.

The aim of the nomadic system is to use animals to harvest limited amounts of vegetation scattered over large distances that cannot easily be gathered by any other method. In energy terms, it is inefficient as only a very small proportion of incoming solar energy is converted into usable material; yet without this system, no benefit at all would accrue (Scholz, 1995). With the various nomadic groups following a regular pattern of movement from one grazing ground to another at different times of the year, they can always aim to be where biological productivity is at its maximum.

The rangelands on the Tibetan Plateau are ecologically heterogeneous. Exploiting environmental heterogeneity (or so-called ecosystem diversity) can also be considered an important ecological justification for nomadic movement (Wu, 1997b). Miller (1990), in his account of the rangelands of the Tibetan Plateau, regards the pastoral grouping and mobile keeping of yak as well-adapted responses to different range and environmental conditions and as ecologically sound and sustainable.

However, sedentarization has become a worldwide trend in all pastoral areas of the Old World Dry Belt (Scholz, 1995), marking a gradual move from a nomadic to a more sedentary way of life (Salzmann, 1980). Forced by external circumstances, yak herders have settled down in most yak-raising areas. While this has merit in providing an infrastructure for the community and raising the standards of social services for yak herders, there are a few potential risks. Perhaps the most important is the increased risk of environmental degradation. Lack of mobility is a key factor leading to the degradation of rangelands in many yak-raising areas (Sneath, 1998, Thwaites *et al*, 1998, Williams, 1996, Wu and Richard, 1999). The nomads' ability to track environmental conditions and mobilize herds to seek pockets of good forage is effectively eliminated when grazing areas become partitioned. Enclosure of pastures almost always accompanies settlement. The general trend is that the more productive rangeland areas are fenced first, leaving residual open range prone to faster degradation, especially in areas where some winter areas are fenced and others are not.

Traditional mobile livestock raising is founded upon a traditional social system, which secures the realization of multiple resource goals beyond the purely economic (Behnke, 1984). If the whole system changes from mobile to sedentary in the yak-raising areas, communally based local institutions are likely to be weakened or even eliminated without being replaced by an effective local administration. Excessively centralized settlements, undue expansion of enclosed pastures, irrational encouragement of longer grazing periods in winter pastures along the main roads and abandonment of seasonal migration will inevitably require higher input levels per household and can lead to a breakdown in systems of social cooperation and conflict resolution. With enthusiasm for modernization, people often ignore the fact that a nomadic society responds in its entirety to the change of environment and the availability of resources (Wu and Richard, 1999). Simply to focus on pasture or livestock development fundamentally ignores the tight linkages between culture and the land. This in turn can lead to failure of such projects in the long term – in part through unintended social consequences resulting in a breakdown of traditional institutions. Moreover, because yak are an integral component of the nomadic system on the Qinghai-Tibetan Plateau, changes from a mobile to a sedentary system with consequent changes in management and production could adversely affect the yak species. Reduced need for hardiness and survivability in a harsh environment, which may accompany such changes, could, in time, lead to a loss of these valuable attributes of the yak.

From common to private ownership

In today's market-oriented environment, there is a growing trend to promote increased agriculture and livestock production through intensification of rangeland. Generally, intensification measures are initiated through changes in tenure arrangements from communal to individual, based on the assumption that pastoral strategies involving the use of grazing commons are inefficient.

Privatization of rangeland has been regarded by some as a precondition for the protection of natural resources; and the systems of common and collective pasture ownership are regarded as the primary causes of the degradation of rangelands (Koocheki, 1993; Li and Yong, 1993). Hardin's (1968) concept of "the tragedy of the commons" strongly influenced land tenure policies. Using grazing as an example, Hardin argued for private tenure on the assumption that access to a common resource leads to overexploitation because the livestock owner will view the grazing resource as a free commodity, thus maximizing herd size at the expense of other herders. This view has been refuted extensively in the academic literature, as his argument fails to recognize the common property arrangements generally made among herders and in reality reflects a situation of open (or unregulated) access. That situation is the exception rather than the rule in pastoral regions of the world (Wu and Richard, 1999). Despite the overwhelming evidence against Hardin's argument, his concept still holds sway among policy-makers around the globe, resulting in inappropriate land tenure policies for marginal lands.

In yak-raising areas, large sectors of pastoral societies have been involved in a privatization process coordinated by national governments, especially in Central or Inner Asia. Since the implementation of the "Household Responsibility" system" in China, the pastoral system has moved slowly away from State control and ownership (centrally planned economy) towards a more market-oriented economy, with policies to encourage private-sector initiatives and investment. Communal livestock has been divided among every family, but the tenure of pastures has remained with the State and land has not been individually allocated. Without control of pasture resources, the situation could lead to one of open access, although local agreements generally avoid this (see also Chapter 13). However, to change the perception, the Government started the individualization of rangelands from the middle of the 1980s, first in Inner Mongolia, then in Xinjiang and finally in Qinghai and Sichuan. This programme aims to substantially increase livestock off-take and pastoral incomes through more intensive management to raise the nomads' enthusiasm for rangeland management and to rationalize land use by limiting livestock numbers to carrying capacity.

The individualization programme started with the traditional winter grazing lands; each nomad family was allocated an area of rangeland on a long-term contract (50 years) in what was essentially a privatization of the previously communally managed grassland (cf. Wu and Richard, 1999). Land allocation was based on the supposed carrying capacity of the rangeland and the number of livestock each family had. The construction of houses for nomads, sheds for livestock, fencing and a development of artificial pastures was also heavily subsidized. At the heart of these changes are the policies affecting common property tenure, not least the policies to convert land to individual tenure-ship.

CAMERON, Rev David Alexander 1942. Univ of Reading BA(Hons) 1963. Leeds Dip.TP 1968. MRTPI. Dioc St Andrew TFM 1980. D, 1990. P, 1993. D, St Catharine's, Blairgowrie, St Anne's, Coupar Angus, St Ninian's, Alyth 1990 & Asst P 1993-.
Firgrove, Golf Course Road, Rosemount, Blairgowrie PH10 6LF
01250 873272 / 01786 824225, Business - Tel/Fax - 01250 874583
E-mail - dacameron@talk21.com

CAMERON, Rt Rev Douglas Maclean 1935. Edinburgh Theo Coll 1959-61. Univ of the South, Tennessee 1961-62. D, 1962. P, 1963. C, Christ Ch, Falkirk 1962-65. Mission P, Eiwo, Papua New Guinea (PNG) 1966-67. P-in-C, Movi, PNG 1967-72. R, St Francis Church, Goroka, PNG 1972-74. Archd of New Guinea Mainland 1972-74. P-in-C, St Fillan's, Edinburgh 1974 & R 1978-88, & R, St Hilda's, Edinburgh 1977-88. R, St Mary's, Dalkeith & St Leonard's, Lasswade 1988-92. Canon, St Mary's Cath & Synod Clerk, Edinburgh 1990-92. Dean of Edinburgh 1991-92. Consecrated Bishop of Argyll & the Isles, 6 Jan 1993.
The Pines, Ardconnel Road, Oban PA34 5DR Tel/Fax 01631 566912
E-mail - bishop@argyll.anglican.org

CAMERON, Rev Janice Irene 1943. Reading Univ BA(Hons). St Andrews TFM 1987. Prov TISEC 1993-96. D, 1996. P, 1996. Asst P, St Catharine's, Blairgowrie and St Anne's, Coupar Angus and St Ninian's, Alyth 1996-99. R, St Mary's Dunblane 1999-.
The Rectory, Smithy Loan, Dunblane FK15 0HQ 01786 824225
E-mail - janice.cameron@iescotland.net

CAMERON, Rev Dr Peter Scott 1945. Univ of Edinburgh LLB 1967, BD 1976. Univ of Cambridge PhD 1979. D, 1997. P, 1997. M, St Philip's C of S, Edinburgh 1984-7. Lect in New Test, New College, Univ of Edinburgh 1987-90. Principal, St Andrew's College, Univ of Sydney 1991-6. C, St John, Perth 1997-8. R, St Mary's, Birnam and St Andrew's, Strathtay 1998-.
St Mary's Rectory, St Mary's Road, Birnam, Dunkeld PH8 0BJ Tel/Fax: 01350 727329

CAMPBELL, Rev David 1970. St Andrews MTheol. CECM, Edinburgh MTh. D, 1994. P, 1995. C, St John the Bapt, Perth 1994-96. P-in-C, St Mary's, Newport w St Margaret's, Tayport 1996-99. Diocesan Youth Officer 1996-. R, Holy Trinity Dunfermline 1999-. P-in-C, St Margaret of Scotland, Rosyth 1999-.
The Rectory, 17 Ardeer Place, Dunfermline KY11 4YX 01383 723901
E-mail - FrCampbell@hotmail.com

CARMAN, Rev Roger Eric 1940. Univ Coll Wales BSc(Hons) 1962. TISEC, 1993-96. Chartered Eng MIEE. D, 1997. P, 1998. Microwave Eng, Decca Radar Ltd 1962-69. Tech Consultant, Racal-MESL Ltd, Newbridge 1969-. Asst, St James the Great, Dollar 1998-.
"Sule Skerry", Lovers Loan, Dollar, Clacks FK14 7PG 01259 742485
E-mail - recarman@telco4u.net

CAVANAGH, Rev Capt Kenneth Joseph 1941. Ch Army Coll 1960-63. Dioc Miss 1964-70. Ch Army Off 1963-. SAMS/Ang Church in Paraguay 1970-83. D, 1977. P, 1977. R, United Benefice, Gt & Lt Snoring w Kettlestone & Pensthorpe, Norfolk 1983-88. Leader of Ch Army Faith Sharing Team & R, Glencarse 1988-94. Co-ord for Ch Army in Ireland & Scotland 1990-95. R, St Luke's, Dundee 1995-.
4 St Luke's Road, Downfield, Dundee DD3 0LD 01382 825165
E-mail - CAVANAGH@tinyworld.co.uk

The real effects of pasture allocation are still unclear because of the short time since the implementation of this programme. Attempts to create private, commercial ranges in some developing countries have not been successful (Mueller, 1999; Scholz, 1995; Williams, 1996). Large-scale pasture allocation has raised a new set of issues regarding long-term sustainability in terms of cost and rangeland health and in terms of social consequences for local communities, partly because of perceived inequalities in the allocation process. All options, therefore, need to be evaluated on a site-specific basis, keeping in mind the socio-economic and ecological realities. Pilot schemes should be carefully evaluated before being expanded to a larger scale.

Nowadays, many prosperous nomadic groups still exist on the Qinghai-Tibetan Plateau, testifying to their adaptability to prevailing socio-economic and environmental conditions. The commonalities among these still-intact pastoral areas are effective communal institutions and relatively little interference by government in land tenure and management. Sneath (1998) looked at the geographic region of northern China, Mongolia and southern Siberia and found that areas in the best condition were places that exhibited low land fragmentation, experienced relatively late land tenure changes by centralist governments and consequently still possessed relatively strong local institutions capable of controlling communal pasture access. These characteristics have also been found in pastoral areas of Africa where communal range management has been found to be more productive than private ranching schemes (de Haan, 1998, Scoones, 1996). These characteristics of success can and should be translated into new and innovative policies that support nomadism, rather than undermine it.

From traditional to modern practices

As already discussed, yak herders have intricate ecological knowledge and understanding of the rangeland ecosystem in which they live and upon which their livestock production depends. Recognition of local climatic patterns and key grazing areas allow herders to select favourable winter ranges that provide protection from snowstorms and sufficient forage to bring animals through times of stress. A wide diversity of livestock and grazing management techniques are employed in these traditional systems that enable yak herders to maintain the rangelands (see also Chapter 13).

Yak herders' knowledge of the complexity and ecological and economic efficacy of traditional yak-herding systems should be used in designing new interventions. Unfortunately, this knowledge is not well appreciated or understood by many researchers, planners and others interested in improving yak production. Too often there is a reliance on "new" technologies and scientific methods that, while practical on government farms or research stations, are often not widely applicable in the pastoral context in which the majority of yak are raised. Many of the so-called "new" technologies derive from results obtained in lowland areas and have then been transferred into the harsh environment of the yak. The appropriateness of the new techniques is then in question if they have not been integrated with the indigenous knowledge of yak-management and adequately tested in the remote yak-raising regions.

In the foreseeable future, improvements in the livelihood and well-being of yak herders in the pastoral areas will have to continue to depend on yak production, even though globally yak are not as important as other bovines. The major issues related to yak management include rangeland degradation and a lack of understanding of the socio-economic characteristics of yak production systems (Miller, 1997), even though the precise extent and severity of rangeland degradation may be open to argument. The relatively low productivity of yak husbandry is one of the main reasons why it is often considered inefficient. However, the productivity has to be seen in the context of the hostile and cold environment of the Qinghai-Tibetan Plateau, the serious nutrient deficit in late winter and early spring and the lack of adequate infrastructure for some of the potential improvements and better marketing. The pastoral system does not allow a regular, balanced food intake because of great seasonal variation of the vegetation resources, in terms of availability and nutritive value. While there is a surplus of fodder during the warm season, there is usually a shortage of feed during the cold season that causes malnutrition or worse, resulting in negative consequences for health and reproduction. Moreover, normal herd off-take, which tends to fluctuate from year to year, is frequently made more difficult by inadequate marketing facilities. Thus, further development of pastoralism in these areas depends more on the development of a whole socio-economic system than on the advance of technologies.

The improvement of services in yak-producing areas, as the pastoral areas develop, should increase the ability of yak herders to obtain a better return for their yak products. For herders to realize these opportunities, however, will require improved extension services to address animal health, product quality and yak-product marketing. A general improvement in the educational level of yak herders would also enable them to organize themselves more effectively to increase the value of their products. Although no uniform concepts can be applied to all "nomadic regions" - the regional differences are too great - certain aspects do have supra-regional applicability. These include maintaining maximum mobility for nomads to safeguard the integrity of the grazing resources, promoting self-help and marketing and recognizing the indigenous knowledge when developing improvement strategies.

References

Alirol, P. (1976). Animal husbandry in the Ganesh Himal Region. An essay in ecological synthesis. Contributions to Nepalese studies. *INAS Journal*, 3(1): 47-61.

Behnke, R. (1984). Fenced and open-range ranching – The commercialization of pastoral land and livestock in Africa. In: Simpson, J. R. and P. Evangelou (eds.), Livestock development in Sub-Saharan Africa – Constraints, Prospects, Policy. Colorado. 261-284.

Cayla, L. (1976). Some mythological aspects of yak in Tibet. In: *Le Yak*. Ethnozootechnie No. 15, France, 23-34.

De Haan, C. (1998). Sustaining the rangelands of central Asia – a global perspective. Conference on strategic considerations on the development of Central Asia. 13-18 September 1998, Urumqi, Xinjiang, China.

Ellis, J. E., Coughenour, M. B. & Swift, D. M. (1991). Climate variability, ecosystem stability and the implications for range and livestock development. In: Cincotta, R. P., Gay, C. W. & Perrier, G. W. (eds.). New concepts in international range management: theories and applications. Proceedings of 1991 International Rangeland Development Symposium. 1-12.

Goldstein, M. C. & Beall, C. M. (1990). Nomads of western Tibet: survival of a way of life. University of California Press, Berkeley.

Hardin, G. (1968). The tragedy of the commons. *Science* 162: 1243-1248.

Huebl, K. (1986). The Nomadic Livestock Production System of Somalia. In: Somalia, Agriculture in the Winds of Change. – *Epi-dokumentation* No. 2: 55-72. Eschborn.

Humphrey, C. & Sneath, D. (1999). The End of nomadism? Society, State and the environment in Inner Asia. Durham, Duke University Press.

Koocheki, A. (1993). Improvement strategies in winter cold temperate rangeland ecosystems with particular reference to extensive grazing lands of Iran. In: Baker, M. J. (ed.), Grasslands for our world. New Zealand: SIR Publishing. 598-602.

Li, B. & Yong, S. P. (1993). Winter cold temperate grasslands – identifying problems. *In* Baker, M. J. (ed.), Grasslands for our world. New Zealand: SIR Publishing. 586-589.

Linziduojie, L. (1996). Environment and development of the Qinghai-Tibetan Plateau. Beijing, China Tibetology Publishing House.

March, K. S. (1977). Of people and naks – the management and meaning of high altitude herding among contemporary Solu Sperpas. Contributions to Nepalese Studies. *INAS Journal*. 4(2): 83-97.

Meyer, F. (1976). Notes on products from the yak and its crosses used in Tibetan medicine. In: *Le Yak*. Ethnozootechnie No. 15, France, 35-45.

Miller, D. J. (1990). Grasslands of the Tibetan Plateau. *Rangelands*, 12 (3): 159-163.

Miller, D. J. (1997). Conserving biological diversity in the HKH-Tibetan Plateau rangelands. Rangelands and pastoral development in the Hindu-Kush Himalayas – Proceedings of a regional experts Meeting (eds. D. J. Miller & S. R. Craig). ICIMOD, Kathmandu, Nepal.

Miller, D. J. (1998). Hard time on the plateau. *Chinabrief* I(2): 17-22.

Miller, D. J. & Steane, D. E. (1996) Conclusions. *In* Miller, D.G., Craig S.R., & Rana, G.M. (eds). *Proceedings of a workshop on Conservation and Management of Yak Genetic Diversity* at ICIMOD, Kathmandu, 29-31 October 1996. ICIMOD (International Centre for Integrated Mountain Development), Kathmandu, pp 191-209.

Mueller, F. V. (1999). Die Wiederkehr des mongolischen Nomadismus – Raeumliche Mobilitaet und Existenzsicherung in einem Transformationsland. *In* Janzen, J. (ed.), Raeumliche Mobilitaet und Existenzsicherung. Berlin: Dietrich Reimer Verlag GmbH. 11-46.

Olsen, S. J. (1991). Confused yak taxonomy and evidence of domestication. Illinois State Museum Scientific Papers, 23: 287-393.

Salzmann, P. (1980). When nomads settle – processes of sedentarization as adaptation and response. Berlin, Praeger Scientific A. J. F., Book Publishers.

Scholz, F. (ed.) (1981). Beduinen im Zeichen des Erd's: Studien zur Entwicklung im beduinischen Lebensraum Suedost-Arabiens. Dr. Ludwig Reichert Verlag, Wiesbaden.

Scholz, F. (1986). Ressourcennutzung und Ressourcenerhaltung. *In* Interaktion Tier und Umwelt, Dt. Stiftung fuer internat. Entw. (DSE) (ed.), 113-122.

Scholz, F. (1995). Nomadismus -- Theorie und Wandel einer sozio-oelogischen Kulturweise. Stuttgart, Erdkundliches Wissen, 118.

Scoones, I. (1996). Living with uncertainty – New directions in pastoral development in Africa. London, Intermediate Technology Publications Ltd.

Sneath, D. (1998). State policy and pasture degradation in Inner Asia. *Science.* 281: 114-115.

Thwaites R., De Lacy T., Li Yong Hong & Liu Xian Hua (1998). Property rights, social change and grassland degradation in Xilingol Biosphere Reserve, Inner Mongolia, China. Society and Natural Resources 11: 319-338.

Wiener, G. (1996). Disasters waiting to happen – yak. *Asian Livestock.* XIX (8): 93-95

Williams, D. M. (1996). Grassland enclosures: Catalyst of land degradation in Inner Mongolia. *Human Organisation* 55 (3): 307-313.

Wu, N. (1997a). Ecological Situation of High-frigid Rangeland and Its Sustainability – A Case Study on the Constraints and Approaches in Pastoral Western Sichuan. Dietrich Reimer Verlag, Berlin.

Wu, N. (1997b). Indigenous knowledge and sustainable approaches for the maintenance of biodiversity in nomadic society – experience from Eastern Tibetan Plateau. *Die Erde*, 128: 67-80.

Wu, N. & Richard C. (1999). The privatization process of rangeland and its impacts on the pastoral dynamics in the Hindukush Himalayas: The case of Western Sichuan, China. In: Eldridge, D.& D. Freundenberger (eds.), People and Rangelands – Proceedings of VI International Rangelands Congress, 14-21. Townsville, Australia.

Yang, J. & He, X. S. (1989). Preliminary analysis of the snow disaster in southern Qinghai Plateau and pastoral development. *Economic Geography* 7(2): 116-121. (in Chinese)

13 ALPINE RANGELAND ECOSYSTEMS AND THEIR MANAGEMENT IN THE QINGHAI-TIBETAN PLATEAU

By Long Ruijun[1]

OVERVIEW

There are about 8.5 million sq km areas of alpine land at an elevation higher than 3 000 m above sea level distributed throughout the world, of which the single largest and the highest plateau is the Qinghai-Tibetan Plateau covering an area of nearly 2.5 million sq km. Thus, it is referred to as the "third pole" or "the roof of the world". Given the high altitude and extreme harsh environmental conditions, this high elevation grazing land ecosystem might, up to the present, be among the least affected by modern society. The alpine rangeland ecosystem of the Qinghai-Tibetan Plateau displays inherent characteristics that lead the system to being relatively stable. The alpine pastures have retained a certain level of productivity over thousands of years. It has also resulted in a weaker and slower response to some arguably advantageous management measures, and consequently they are very difficult to rehabilitate once destroyed. Temperature and moisture are thought to be two key factors that drive formation and development of the alpine rangelands. Heat (temperature) seems to play a predominant role in limiting growth and the reproductive pattern of alpine vegetation growth, while the annual rainfall mostly determines the distribution of ecozones of alpine rangelands.

In general, the yield of native alpine pastures is low and seasonal, thus leaving a feed gap between annual pasture provision and the requirements of the grazing animals. Since agricultural cultivation is not possible, continuous year-round extensive grazing - either transhumance grazing on the vast plain of the central Plateau, or seasonal rotation within certain mountain regions – is the land-use pattern throughout the Tibet-Qinghai Plateau. Thus, both livestock (including yak, Tibetan sheep and goats) and wildlife species largely depend on alpine pastures for survival. The alpine native forages have characteristically high protein, fat and sugar contents with relatively low fibre content compared with lowland plants. Another advantageous feature of these plants is that they contain a reasonable quantity of tannins, which potentially enhance the absorption of nitrogen by the host animal. The high quality of fresh alpine forages allow grazing yak and sheep to recover the bodyweight loss sustained over winter through compensatory growth during a short growing season of 90 - 120 days.

---

[1] Long Ruijun is Professor of Pastoral Science and Dean of Faculty of Grassland Science, Gansu Agricultural University, China and Senior Scientist, Northwest Plateau Institute of Biology, the Chinese Academy Science, China. He is also Vice-Chairman of Chinese Grassland Society, China.

Although degradation of alpine rangeland has occurred over decades on the Plateau, it has become worse during the past decade due to a rapid increase in human and animal populations across the Plateau. This has led, in turn, to increasing demands on the alpine rangelands. A conventional seasonal rotation or transhumance system has been considered an effective way of avoiding the rangeland degradation.

However, the distance that herds can move has been restricted since the start of the "Household Responsibility System" in the 1980s, which was intended to encourage a semi-sedentary or completely sedentary lifestyle.

The nutrient resource of the soil pool is the most important basis for the growth and maintenance of the alpine vegetation. Any small change in this soil nutrient pool will have a profound effect on other components in the system.

The varied topography, altitudes and climate give rise to great diversity in alpine rangeland types. The rangelands include the lush, alpine meadows in the Himalayan mountains and eastern Tibetan Plateau, semi-arid scrublands of the dry valleys of central Tibet, the spacious alpine steppes of Tibet's northern plains and the cold, dry deserts of the Kunlun mountains. Therefore, no single management strategy can be applied to all the alpine rangeland types.

The Plateau's rangeland-livestock husbandry has lasted for centuries. Tibetan nomads acquired complex knowledge about the utilization and management of the alpine rangelands in which they lived and upon which the animals' survival depended. Serious degradation of alpine rangeland over the whole Plateau has brought a great threat to the alpine ecosystem and its nearby environment. Coping with these problems more effectively will require a clear understanding of the vast body of indigenous knowledge of the alpine rangeland ecosystem and herders' traditional experience. This is in order to work out sound utilization and management guidelines for the rangeland and ensure that herders get the best out of their pastures. This chapter aims to contribute to that understanding.

Background and present status

The alpine rangelands where yak can be found currently cover more than 2.5 million sq km of the Qinghai-Tibetan Plateau and its surrounding territories. As referred to in Chapter 1, these rangelands are at altitudes from 2 000 m to 5 000 m with a cold, semi-humid climate. They extend from the southern slopes of the Himalayas in the south to the Altai in the north and from the Pamir in the west to the Minshan mountains in the east. The alpine rangeland resource is vital for the livelihood of the people and their livestock raising. Much of this region offers an important habitat for many wildlife species, such as blue sheep (*Pseudois nayaur*), *kiang* or Asiatic wild ass (*Equus kiang*), Tibetan antelope

(*Pantholops hodgoni*), black necked crane (*Grus nigricollis*) and the endangered snow leopard (*Panthera uncia*) (Miller and Craig, 1996; Richard, 2000). Apart from these, many areas are now designated as protected with a high potential for the development of tourism. The available alpine rangelands of the Plateau cover about 128.2 million ha, or approximately 30.7 percent of China's total area of rangelands (Bureau of Animal Husbandry and Veterinary Medicine, Ministry of Agriculture, China, 1994).

These alpine rangelands consist mainly of alpine steppe (including alpine meadow steppe and alpine desert steppe), alpine desert and alpine meadow (Table13.1). Due to the high altitude and harsh environment, agricultural cultivation is not possible on most alpine plateaux. The only way the land can be used is for livestock grazing (Goldstein *et al.*, 1990). Therefore, ruminant (yak and Tibetan sheep) farming plays the most important role in the socio-economic and environmental systems of the Plateau. These rangelands, especially the verdant pastures of the eastern Plateau, offer great reserves of forage for grazing livestock, the products of which account for a significant percentage of the gross national product (GNP) of these areas (Wu, 1997).

Table 13.1 Types of available alpine rangeland on the Qinghai-Tibetan Plateau and their theoretical carrying capacity in 1994 [Source: Bureau of Animal Husbandry and Veterinary Medicine, Ministry of Agriculture, China, 1994]

Type	Areas (ha)	Percentage of total (%)	Theoretical carrying apacity (sheep units $(100\ ha)^{-1}\ yr^{-1}$)
Alpine meadow	63 170 937	49.3	91
Alpine steppe	57 505 299	44.9	23
Alpine desert	7 527 763	5.9	8

Thirteen million yak and 41.5 million sheep (Long, *et al*, 1999a) as well as large numbers of wildlife raised on the Plateau support a human population of 9.8 million. These animals are either largely (livestock) or totally (wild herbivores) dependent on the native alpine rangelands for their survival (Long *et al.*, 1999a,b). Consequently, competition for feed between domestic and wild animals is inevitable in areas where they overlap. Continuous year-round extensive grazing (either transhumance grazing on the vast plain of the central Plateau or seasonal rotation within certain mountain regions) is a unique land-use pattern on the Qinghai-Tibetan Plateau. This form of utilization differs from other alpine rangeland ecosystems in the world where the pastures are only grazed by livestock in the summer season. Until the 1950s, a transhumance pastoral system was the main grazing pattern in most of the plateau areas, the distance travelled by herds being dependent on forage availability and quality.

Thus, the distances covered by herders could vary from tens to hundreds of kilometres, or even more, according to the particular rangeland productivity of that area. Pastoral mobility was probably the simplest and the most effective way of optimizing the use of alpine rangeland resources without harming the ecosystem, but only if the rangeland resources were sufficiently abundant to allow the livestock free access, both in space and across time.

From the 1960s to the 1970s, most of the pastoral communities living in the eastern (Sichuan and Gansu) and northern (Qinghai) parts of the Plateau have changed from a migratory lifestyle to semi-sedentary or completely sedentary grazing practices.

However, these changes are still a relatively new phenomenon within Tibetan territory, associated as they are with the Household Responsibility System policy that was implemented in China from the beginning of the 1980s (see Chapter 12). Under this system, communal livestock were divided among every family, based on family numbers, and consequently, some of the pastures used during cold season (the so-called winter-pastures near by the herders' sedentary houses) were also allocated to herders individually in yak-raising areas. The rest of the rangelands are normally situated in remote or alpine mountainous areas grazed mainly during the warm season (the so-called summer pastures). These still belong to the State or are used as communal lands and so engender less concern for graziers than the winter pastures. Of course, the Household Responsibility System is intended to benefit most herdsmen and help raise their income through culling out more livestock, improving animal husbandry and managing their rangelands in a sustainable way. But such changes from a long-ranging and highly mobile yak-herding system in the past to a short-ranging and sedentary lifestyle also carry some potential risks for the alpine rangeland ecosystem since the rangelands of the Qinghai-Tibetan Plateau are more than just a resource to sustain livestock. They form the headwaters of the six major river systems of Asia – in particular, the Yellow River is regarded as the "Mother river", and the Yangtse being the "life river" of Chinese nationality. Their diverse ecosystems of forest-alpine ecozones, shrub alpine meadows and range alpine meadows lead to extensive quantities of water being held underground and regarded as the "underground reservoirs" of the Plateau and also called the Chinese "water tower".

The Plateau, as a natural protective screen for China in its southwest, plays a tremendous role in driving and regulating climate of western and southwestern China, even the northern hemisphere. In the past two decades, animal numbers have increased rapidly. This has, in turn, aggravated grazing pressures and accelerated the rangeland degradation (Table 13.2). This degradation is now one of the most serious environmental and socio-economic issues in the Qinghai-Tibetan Plateau region accounting for 32.1 million ha and 42.5 million ha in the 1980s and 1990s, respectively. In Qinghai, the headwater areas, where the Yangtse and Yellow rivers have their source, are particularly affected. Some pastures have degraded so badly that "black patch" land has formed (i.e. rangelands with a high density of black soil patches) from which most perennial vegetation has disappeared and been replaced by annual grasses or forbs, which are normally consumed completely by animals at some times of the year. These degraded rangelands with black, denuded soil covered 3.79 million ha and 7.03 million ha of alpine rangeland in the 1980s and 1990s, respectively.

Table 13.2 Areas and distribution of degraded rangelands on the Qinghai-Tibetan Plateau [Source: after Long and Ma, 1997] (unit ha x 10 000)

Region	Available rangeland	Degraded rangeland		Percentage of degraded rangeland		Black patch rangeland		Percentage of black patch rangeland	
		1980s	1990s	1980s	1990s	1980s	1990s	1980s	1990s
Tibet	6636.1	1202.6	1990.8	18.1	30.0	184.6	327.3	2.8	4.9
Qinghai	3161.0	910.3	1005.5	28.8	31.8	120.1	213.0	3.8	6.7
Sichuan	1416.0	386.7	467.3	27.3	33.0	34.8	61.7	2.5	4.4
Gansu	1607.2	712.9	787.5	44.4	49.0	57.0	101.1	3.6	6.3
Total	**12820.4**	**3212.4**	**4251.1**			**396.6**	**703.2**		

Ma Yushou *et al.* (1998) reported that in Dari county of Qinghai province, grassland converted to "black patch" due to overgrazing, extended from 0.17 million ha in 1985 to 0.58 million ha in 1994 – an annual increase of 14.7 percent. In these areas, herbage production is only 13.2 percent of that on the non-degraded grassland, and herbage cover is less than 30 percent. Inedible and poisonous grasses accounted for up to 76 percent of the sward.

Thus, rangeland degradation is often manifested by decreased diversity of plant species, reduced sward height and vegetation cover, increased undesirable and unpalatable grass species and even the occurrence of toxic species harmful to animals. Above all, there is a sharp reduction of acceptable biomass production. If the vegetation density is insufficient to cover the ground surface, wind erosion and desertification take place. In general, the alpine rangelands of the Qinghai-Tibetan Plateau are suffering degradation, soil wind erosion and desertification. These problems make the sustainable management and utilization of the rangeland resources more difficult and, in addition, make the alpine ecosystem even more fragile and unstable than before. Overall, overgrazing is recognized as the most fundamental cause of the degradation.

Climate

Air and solar radiation
The average depth of the atmospheric layer above the alpine rangeland of the Qinghai-Tibetan Plateau is about two thirds of that in the coastal areas. The atmospheric pressure and density are only about 50 - 60 percent and 60 - 70 percent, respectively, of those at sea level. These features, together with a smaller proportion of moisture and dust in the air, lead to much short-wave light of blue and particularly ultraviolet passing through the

atmosphere that can then be absorbed by the green leaf material of the alpine vegetation. Annual sunshine is between 2 000 and 3 600 hours and the value of solar radiation varies from 5 000 to 8 000 MJ sq m per year, compared with only 2 000 to 3 000 MJ sq m per year in the eastern lowland area of China at the same latitudes. Hu *et al.* (1988a) calculated the annual energy conversion efficiencies from total solar radiation and physiological radiation to above-ground biomass energy in sedges (Kobresia capillifolia) meadow as 0.11 percent and 0.22 percent respectively, while it reached 0.40 percent for physiological radiation during the growth period. These figures are relatively low compared with corresponding values of 0.16 percent, 0.32 percent and 0.69 percent found in forbs (Polygonum viviparum) meadows in the same region (Hu *et al.,* 1988b). Physiologically, high solar radiation associated with high density of short-wave light has a profound effect on plant development: It limits cell elongation and thus reduces vegetative growth and forces cell division to accelerate reproductive development. Consequently, compact, stubbed and even cushion plant forms appear above ground while a well-developed root system is formed in the topsoil layer.

Temperature

The average annual air temperature is generally below 0°C, while the average temperature in January drops below -10°C. The average in the hottest month (July) does not exceed 13°C (Table 13.3). In meteorological terms, an absolutely frost-free season does not exist on the Plateau. The growing season of native plants varies from 90 to 120 days, but periods of relatively vigorous plant growth are even shorter than that. Temperature differs between day and night by 12° - 17°C, which is propitious for the accumulation of nutrients assimilated. Zhang and Ma (1982) reported that assimilation lost through respiration at night in alpine plants is only equal to about one third of that produced by photosynthesis during the day. Thus, alpine vegetation characteristically has relatively high levels of nutrients in the form of crude protein, fat and sugar (nitrogen-free extract), and a low fibre content compared with that of lowland and tropical pastures. These compositional characteristics also help native plants resist cold weather and other harsh environmental conditions.

Rainfall and wind

Drought is another feature of the plateau climate. More than 65 percent of the area receives less than 300 mm rainfall per year; the rest has an annual rainfall not exceeding 500 mm.

With the rainfall decreasing from southeast to northwest, the alpine rangelands display a diverse assortment of plant communities, including three dominant rangeland types: alpine meadow, alpine steppe and alpine desert (Table 13.1). Alpine shrub meadow appears if rainfall is sufficient on the north slopes of mountains.

Table 13.3 Climatic characteristics of typical regions on the Qinghai-Tibetan Plateau
[Source: adapted from Hu, 2000]

Location	a.s.l.[1] (m)	a.a.t.[2] (°C)	a.t.[3] in Jan. (°C)	a.t.[4] in July (°C)	d.t.d.n.[5] (°C)	a.c.t.[6] (°C)	a.r.[7] (mm)	a.s.h.[8] (hr)
Gaize	4 415	0.1	-11.6	12.1	17.4	1 012.5	166.1	3 168
Shenzha	4 672	-0.4	-10.7	9.3	13.0	1 151.3	298.6.	2 916
Bange	4 700	-1.2	-11.3	8.3	12.7	967.0	308.3	2 945
Anduo	4 800	-3.2	-15.0	7.7	14.4	846.1	441.6	2 847
Tuotuohe	4 533	-4.4	-16.5	7.5	14.5	743.2	284.4	2 829
Meyun	4 468	-4.3	-16.8	6.3	14.6	672.0	299.3	2 480
Zhahe	4 503	-5.3	-17.8	6.3	15.1	545.5	288.9	2 305
Sewugou	4 416	-2.5	-14.1	8.5	14.0	910.3	393.3	2 125
Maduo	4 221	-4.0	-16.5	7.6	13.5	1 098.0	299.4	1 865
Maqin	4 200	-3.7	-15.7	7.2	12.6	1 268.0	457.2	1 721
Zeku	3 826	-1.5	-14.6	8.6	13.0	1 521.0	647.0	1 879

[1]Above sea level; [2]annual average temperatures; [3]average temperature in January;
[4]average temperature in July; [5]differences in temperature between day and night;
[6]annual cumulative temperature above 0°C; [7]annual rainfall; [8]annual sunshine hours.

Disasters from hailstorms occur frequently in summer and from snowstorms in the spring. Strong winds occur throughout the late winter and spring seasons, with a mean wind velocity of 3 - 4 m s^{-1}, even reaching over 5 m s^{-1} in spring. Such winds can blow away about one third of the yield of standing vegetation from winter-spring pastures.

Effect of climate on alpine rangeland formation and evolution

Climate plays the most active and effective role on rangeland formation and evolution. In terms of alpine rangeland, water and heat (temperature) have more profound effects on its formation and development than any other indigenous factor, such as soil and topography. The summer temperature of the whole troposphere above the Plateau is higher than that of surrounding regions (at the same elevation). Moreover, with stronger solar radiation to the Plateau and the low level of moisture in the air, low heat loss through evaporation is yet another feature of the Plateau's climate. Thus, the distributional upper limits of rangeland types are much higher on the Plateau than on solitary or smaller mountains (Chang, 1981). A moisture gradient from humid and subhumid to semi-arid and arid, from southeast to northwest, results in a corresponding series of diverse rangeland ecozones on the Plateau.

In the western part where rainfall is only about 50 mm annually, the vegetation is of suffrutescent desert and desert-steppe types composed mainly of *Ceratoides latens*. In the northwestern part, the climate is very dry and cold by reason of high altitude and the more northerly latitude, and so a sparse alpine desert of low suffrutescent and cushion-like

Ceratoides compacta has developed there. On the vast flat lands of the central Plateau, the annual precipitation increases to about 200 mm, and alpine steppe vegetation of *Stipa* species prevails. In the eastern part of the Plateau there is a cold, low-pressure zone where annual precipitation normally reaches up to 600 mm. With this cold and wet climate, a special kind of alpine meadow has developed, which represents the main body of alpine rangelands. This meadow consists of sedge species and low scrub, such as *Salix* and *Rhododendron* species. This series of alpine vegetation ecosystems, from southeast to northwest, was formed and developed in the Quaternary period (Chang, 1983). Even now, the three main kinds of pastures are still the most common rangeland types in the Plateau (Table 13.1) on which more than 800 forage species are growing. Among them, the two genera of *Carex* and *Kobresia* (grass-like plants having achenes and solid stems, which belong to the *Cyperaceae* family) are by far the most important indigenous plants. This is not only because of their high biomass production, early "green-up", wide distribution and good resistance to extreme climatic conditions, but also due to an incredibly high grazing tolerance.

Grasses such as *Stipa* and *Poa* species comprise a large proportion of the alpine-steppe sward. Forbs, i.e. broad-leaf herbaceous plants, are companion species in the alpine meadow swards or interspersing plants in the alpine desert.

Vegetation characterization

Patterns of production and growth
In general, temperature is the single most important factor determining the distribution, diversity, growth rate and biomass production of alpine vegetation. Fortunately, during the short growing season, warmth coincides with water supply (rainfall). These, as already mentioned, are the most fundamental factors supporting the primary productivity of the alpine rangeland ecosystems. Productivity ranges from 1 to 4.5 tonnes DM per ha per year. Thus, a high-efficiency and unique vegetation growth pattern is formed within the ecosystem.

Three distinct phases of biomass availability to the animals can be identified: Phase I has a surplus of green forage (June - September); Phase II has a relative surplus of more mature and dry forage (October - January) and Phase III has a shortage of dry forage (February - May). Based on seasonal growth, phenological and climatic aspects, the points concerning the growth pattern of alpine herbage can be summarized as follows:

Growth
Green-up (after winter) starts relatively late but growing activity ends early. Consequently, the growth season of the native vegetation lasts for only 90 - 120 days from May to August or September (Long *et al.,* 1999a) as shown in Figure 13.1. The first (July) and second

366

(September) peaks of biomass production are the result of a faster growth of sedges after green-up till July, and then grasses take over.

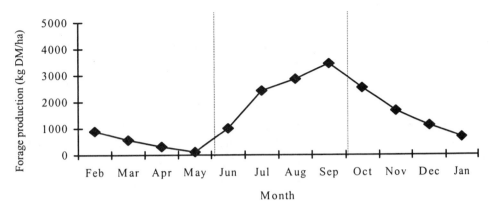

Figure 13.1 Biomass production in alpine meadow in the Qinghai-Tibetan Plateau

In view of this short growing period, the alpine plants, particularly the sedge species, have evolved strong tiller extensibility, since their seeds have poor germination. In order to finish the growth cycle (from germination to seed formation) within a short period, sedge has developed clonal or asexual ways to continue its regeneration.

Accumulation of above-ground biomass
Within the growing season, fresh biomass accumulates quickly but the maximum yield of dry matter does not appear until vegetation growth is finished. Nu Xindai (personal communication, 2002) indicated that *Kobresia littledalei,* a sedge species distributed in Dangxong valley, Tibet, showed a rapid absolute mean growth rate (expressed as DM g m^{-2} per day) of 1.1 from green-up to 15 May, 1.9 from 16 May to 15 June, and thereafter reached 2.8 from 16 June to 15 July from 1983 to 1985. Hu *et al.* (1988b) found that the biggest absolute growth rate (5.8 DM g m^{-2} per day) appeared one month after the green-up in forb (*Polygonum viviparum*) meadow, while its net primary productivity above ground was 481.1 DM g m^{-2} per year. This is higher than the value of 340.1 found in sedge (*Kobresia capillifolia*) meadow in the same part of the eastern Qilian mountain. Due to low temperatures, sedge and grass species are normally not able to generate tillers to contribute to the final biomass production in autumn.

Storage of dry biomass
Wilted herbage remaining on the rangeland from the summer's growth is available to the animals from autumn to winter. Owing to livestock trampling and grazing on the stand, a proportion of stems and leaves fall off the plants to form herbage fractions in the stand. If not consumed timeously, this biomass is liable to be lost by wind or snowstorms during spring. The proportion lost probably reaches up to 30 percent of total biomass yield per year from winter stands.

Defoliation and decomposition

Due to above-ground biomass production being generally low, there is less accumulation of the fallen herbage fractions. While the proportion decomposing varies from 51 to 63 percent annually during the warm season, the decomposition is suppressed to a large extent by relatively low temperatures. Consequently, the senescent herbage is removed by soil fauna mainly between July and September. Other factors, such as grazing activity, may reduce the rate of decomposition; in contrast, improving soil moisture and fertility would lead to enhancing of the degradability of these materials (Li *et al.,* 1982). A lower cellulose decomposition rate occurs where animal access is blocked or the meadows are under-grazed. This results in a considerable amount of the residual herbage mass being left in some areas, particularly under shrubs. In turn, this may reduce the forage growth and yield because the increased amount of dead material relative to vegetative growth creates shading by dead material, and thus reduces photosynthetic capacity.

Absence of legume species

In alpine vegetation communities there is a characteristic lack of forage legume species that, in turn, leads to an insufficiency of forage protein for livestock during the cold season. Moreover, legumes are difficult to establish in the Plateau due to its cold weather. No perennial forage legume has been developed as yet that is well adapted to the Plateau's weather. However, single or mixed grass communities can be easily established by proper selection of adapted grass species for the relatively lower land areas (around 3 000 m a.s.l.).

Accumulation of underground biomass

The underground biomass production is generally higher than that above ground, irrespective of the type of alpine rangeland. The average total underground biomass of different alpine vegetation meadows varies from a lowest of 627 g m^{-2} (*Elymus nutans* meadow) to the highest of 12 827 g m^{-2} (*Carex spp.* meadow). Other types include *Kobresia humilis* meadow (1 265 g m^{-2}), *(Polygonum viviparum)* meadow (5 702 g m^{-2}) and *Dasiphora fruticosa* (shrub) meadow (6 014 g m^{-2}) (Hu *et al.*, 1988b). It is estimated that about 65 percent of total underground biomass is distributed between the surface and 10 cm down in the soil layer. The live root yield accounts for about two thirds of the total underground biomass. Due to the decomposition rate of dead root and fallen herbage lagging behind their accumulation in alpine rangelands, a large quantity of organic matter is preserved in the soil, the proportion varying - depending on soil type - from 0.49 percent in alpine desert soil to 15.7 percent in subalpine meadow soil (Table 13.4) (Xiong and Li, 1987).

Nutritive value of alpine vegetation

The quality of alpine rangelands is influenced by management, environment and plant species. Attaining the optimum stage of growth at grazing is recognized as the most significant management factor, due to the negative relationship between vegetation maturity and forage quality. (The map of the Qinghai-Tibetan Plateau in the Appendix shows most of the locations referred to in subsequent sections of this chapter).

Table 13.4 Variation in organic matter (OM) and total nitrogen (N) contents of alpine soil types to a of 10 cm [Source: adapted from: Xiong and Li, 1987]

Soil type	OM (%)	Total N (%)	Sample No
Alpine meadow soil	10.7	0.47	11
Subalpine meadow soil	15.7	0.69	13
Alpine steppe soil	1.7	0.12	6
Subalpine steppe soil	3.1	0.20	8
Alpine desert soil	0.49	0.04	2
Subalpine desert soil	0.76	0.06	2
Alpine frigid soil	0.79	0.06	7

Chemical composition profile

Sedges, as the fundamental species of many types of alpine sward, are generally components of pasture along with grasses and forbs. Sedge, grass and forb species differ in chemical composition as shown in Table 13.5, and so, their contribution to the pasture composition will also affect forage quality. For example, crude protein (CP) contents of sedge and grass species range from 6 to 16 percent on a dry matter basis - relatively lower than for forbs, which vary from 12 to 22 percent. It seems also that there is no significant variation in contents of crude fat (CF) (about 4 percent) and nitrogen-free extract (NFE) (45 - 50 percent) when samples are harvested during the flowering stage in July. Zhou and Simon (1995) reported similar results for CP content in Sunlian (the southern part of the Plateau) and in Hongyuan (northwestern Sichuan). Long *et al.* (1999a) also indicated that for Tibetan forages, increasing age at harvesting led to a significant decrease in nitrogen (N) content and an increase in neutral detergent fibre (NDF) content of both forbs and shrubs. Nitrogen content in sedges and forbs tended to be greater than that in grasses.

Intake, acceptability and dry matter digestibility

Feeding value of pasture depends on acceptability, dry-matter intake, forage digestibility and the efficiency of utilization of the end products of rumen digestion. On the grazing systems of the Tibetan Plateau, forage intake is largely influenced by pasture availability.

It may reach 4 - 5 kg DM per day for adult yak in summer and autumn, and be reduced to 1 - 1.5 kg DM per day, or even less, during late winter and early spring. Consequently, the animal's live weight varies much among seasons. On the summer pastures, acceptability and digestibility of forages become perhaps the major factors affecting the intake by the animals. Several observations (Ren and Jin, 1956; Zhou, 1984; Zhou and Simon, 1995; Long Ruijun, Hu Z.Z. and Xu Changli, unpublished data 1999) showed that sedges and grasses have a better acceptability than other species. On the basis of these studies it can be estimated that the proportions of the different kinds of forage plants in daily grazing diets in summer were sedges: 30 - 50 percent, grasses: 20 - 50 percent, forbs: 16 - 20 percent and legumes 1 - 3 percent. Cincotta *et al.* (1991) indicated that the proportion of sedge species accounted for 64.1 and 38.4 percent of the diet of yak and sheep, respectively on summer pastures of the Changtan area. Comparison among alpine forages harvested in August, September and October indicated that forbs had the highest 48-hour *in sacco* dry matter degradability, followed by sedge, grass and shrub. Figure 13.2 illustrates profiles of the 48-hour *in sacco* dry matter degradability from monthly samples of three different types of native swards that form the main body of alpine meadow on the Plateau. Although the dominant species varied from type to type and thus affected sward state (sward height, structure and mass), the trends in terms of the *in sacco* dry matter degradability are quite similar (Table 13.6). Obviously, the rates of dry matter degradability for all sward types in general are greater than 50 percent, but a big variation exists between different months throughout a year.

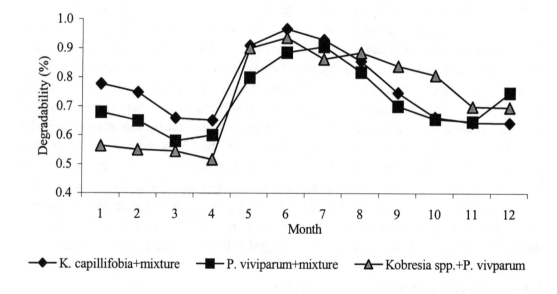

Figure 13.2 The 48-hour *in sacco* DM degradability of natural pasture samples

370

Table 13.5 Chemical composition of alpine plants cut at the end of July (unit: % DM basis) [Source: adapted from Long *et al.* 1999a]

Plant group species	Crude protein	Crude fibre	Ash
Sedge			
Kobresia royleana	14.7	24.1	6.8
K. pygmaea	14.5	26.6	3.5
K. stenocarpa	13.8	26.9	5.7
K. parva	13.6	25.9	5.5
K. capillifolia	13.1	23.3	5.6
Carex scabriolia	10.9	30.2	5.1
K. tibetica	11.3	33.7	4.6
K. bellardii	10.8	33.1	5.5
K. kansuensis	10.4	34.3	6.4
K. humilis	10.2	46.9	9.2
C. trofusca	7.1	33.2	4.0
Grass			
Leymus secalinum	16.6	33.4	8.0
Stipa purpurea	15.6	31.7	5.1
Elymus nutans	12.8	32.4	6.4
Poa annua	10.7	31.7	5.0
Stipa aliena	10.1	32.5	3.8
Roegneria nutans	9.1	37.7	5.9
Helictotrichon tibeticum	8.7	35.7	4.6
Stipa krylovii	6.6	41.6	4.5
Achnatherum splendens	6.3	33.4	3.4
Festuca ovina	6.3	40.2	6.3
Forb			
Triglochin maritimum	22.1	14.8	12.4
Potentilla anserina	20.1	19.5	10.2
Polyonum alatum	15.3	24.9	7.6
Polyonum viviparum	15.2	19.2	7.6
Saussurea superba	12.2	12.8	10.1
Shrub			
Dasiphora fruticosa	19.4	14.3	5.7
Salix oritrapha	16.9	11.4	4.7

Phenolics-related compounds

Ulyatt (1981) suggested that an "ideal" forage would have high protein content, high levels of soluble carbohydrate, some feature such as presence of tannins (that would either slow the release of soluble protein or render it less soluble in the rumen) and concentrations of minerals sufficient to maintain animal health. In most alpine sedge, forb and shrub species, the presence of microbial inhibitory compounds, or phenolics, have been revealed recently (Long *et al.* 1999a). Some of these inhibitory compounds were lately confirmed as being a phenolic-related compound of tannins (Long Ruijun, Hu Z.Z. and Xu Changli, unpublished data, 1999). Figure 13.3 illustrates that an appreciable quantity of tannins in a mixed alpine sward will potentially improve the forage-feeding value. The tannins protect the protein from degradation, thus providing a quantitative saving of nitrogen in the rumen and, further, allowing the bypass protein to be effectively used by the host animal in its small intestine. With a high value in fresh alpine forages, it makes grazing yak and sheep able to recover their previous bodyweight loss through sufficient compensatory growth during the short growing season.

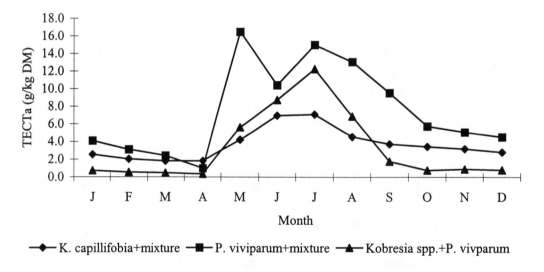

Figure 13.3 Concentration of TECTa from natural pasture samples taken monthly

Table 13.6 *In sacco* dry matter degradability (I.S.D.) of some Tibetan forages at different stages of maturity [Source: adapted from Long *et al.*, 1999a]

Forage group species	Harvesting month		
	Aug.	Sep.	Oct.
	48-hour I.S.D. (%)		
Sedge			
Carex atrofusca	77.8	72.6	59.3
Kobresia capillifolia	80.3	76.0	77.7
K. humilis	75.0	63.5	65.6
K. pygmaea	77.0	70.5	67.5
Grass			
Deschampsia caespitosa	62.1	61.9	70.1
Elymus nutans	69.7	63.1	51.8
Koeleria cristata	63.5	48.4	52.6
K. litwinowii	66.3	47.6	64.5
Leymus secalinum	76.6	77.1	60.6
Roegnevia kamoji	65.0	55.0	81.0
Stipa aliene	75.6	62.2	63.3
Forb			
Ajania frigida	81.7	74.0	65.5
Allium sikkimense	82.6	74.8	66.8
Anaphalis lactea	85.3	89.5	87.1
Carum carvi	78.5	58.3	53.6
Oxytropis ochrocephala	85.4	78.5	71.2
Polyonum alatum	75.0	74.1	53.7
P. viviparum	65.5	60.2	60.9
Potentilla repans	77.4	69.5	78.1
Ranunculus pulchollus	81.1	78.5	74.5
Trigonella ruthehica	90.1	85.0	79.9
Shrub			
Dasiphora fruticosa	51.7	44.6	32.2

Types of alpine rangeland

Alpine meadow

Alpine meadow, also referred to as "Tibetan high-cold meadow", accounts for 49.3 percent of the total available alpine rangeland areas on the Qinghai-Tibetan Plateau. These vast grazing lands, distributed mainly in the eastern and southern parts of the Plateau, extend from 27° to 39° north latitudes and from 82° to 103° east longitudes. Due to the greater rainfall on alpine meadows than on alpine steppes and deserts, its primary productivity, in terms of biomass production and diversity of vegetation, is much higher as well. The vegetation on alpine meadow contains sedge species that include *Kobresia pygmaea, K. microglochin, K. humilis, K. bellardii, K. capillifolia, K. royleana, K. tibetica, K. setchwanensis, K. kansuensis, Carex moorcroftii, C. prewalskii, C. scabrirostris, C. ivanoviae* and *Blymus sinocompresus*; grass species that include *Elymus nutans, Stipa* and *Festuca*; forb species include *Polygonum viviparum, P. sphaerostachyum, Potentilla anserina* and *Artemisia frigida*; and shrub species that include *Hippophae thibetana, Lonicera tibetica, Dasiphora fruticosa and Salix.* Following the uneven annual rainfall and changing elevation, forage yield of alpine meadows with a ground-cover canopy of 80 - 100 percent varies widely, from a low of 1 500 kg DM per ha in eastern Tibet to a high of 4 000 kg DM per ha in southwestern Sichuan. As shown in Table 13.1, the alpine meadows have the highest theoretical carrying capacity of 0.91 sheep unit per ha per year, so that 63.2 million ha of alpine meadows may be expected to support at least 57.5 million sheep units. At present, about 8.5 million yak (60.7 percent of total yak on the Plateau) are raised on alpine meadows, which is equivalent to 34 million sheep units (1 yak = 4 sheep units). Between 15 million and 20 million Tibetan sheep are also grazing these alpine meadows. Although the real carrying capacity of the meadows seems close to theoretical capacity, overgrazing and degradation of meadows are developing extensively on the Plateau.

Alpine steppe

Alpine steppe is widely distributed in the centre of the Qinghai-Tibetan Plateau and on most of the southward-facing slopes of the mountains with a total area of about 55.5 million ha, accounting for 44.9 percent of the Plateau's total available rangelands. Water shortages lead to poor vegetation diversity and an open canopy ranging from 40 to 70 percent ground cover. In consequence, its yield varies from 350 kg to 1 000 kg DM per ha per year. Its community consists of grasses and sedges, such as *Stipa purpurea, S. glareosa, S.capillacea, S. bungeana, S. breviflora, S. krylovii, S. aliena, Festuca ovina, Poa annua, Kobresia parva, K. tibetica, Carex scabriolia* and *C. trofusca.* As suggested in Table 13.1, the theoretical carrying capacities on alpine steppe is 0.23 sheep units per ha per year. The largest proportion of livestock raised is sheep, followed by goats and then yak.

Alpine desert

The alpine desert lies mainly in the western and northwestern flat parts of the Plateau and on some upper areas of the high-altitude mountains. Extremes of dry or of cold can each form the alpine desert. This rangeland accounts for 5.8 percent of the Plateau, with the simple vegetation consisting mostly of *Ceratoides latens, C. compacta, Ajania fruticulosa, Christolea crassifolia, Stipa glareosa, and Carex moorcroftii.* The canopy ground cover reaches down as low as 20 percent and the yield of the sward is very low, varying from 100 kg to 300 kg DM per ha per year. About 12.5 ha are needed to sustain one sheep unit (equivalent to 0.08 sheep units per ha). Compared to alpine meadow and alpine steppe, the desert has less importance and receives less attention in terms of rangeland and livestock management, and goats are the dominant livestock. Some areas, so far with little human activity, are given protection by inclusion in "the national nature-protecting areas" in order to conserve wild animals, such as Tibetan antelope (*Antilope*), wild yak (*Bos mutus* or *Poephagus mutus*) and wild ass (*Equus hemionus*).

Alpine soil type and its characterization

Soil plays the most fundamental role in sustaining the alpine rangeland ecosystem, upon which diverse rangeland communities are established. As a deposited pool, wherein the nutrient transformation and energy flow of the ecosystem take place, it is also a habitat for soil micro-organisms and various animals. Nowadays, most measures to improve alpine rangeland productivity are achieved through amelioration of the condition of the soil pool. A given soil type is always associated with the vegetation community on it and, in the main, there are four different soil types in the Qinghai-Tibetan Plateau, namely that of: alpine meadow (including subalpine meadow, alpine scrubby meadow, subalpine scrubby meadow, peat-bog and peat), alpine steppe (including subalpine steppe), alpine desert (including subalpine desert) and alpine frigid soil. Table 13.4 summarizes the profile of chemical properties of these soil types and shows that the organic matter (OM) and total nitrogen (N) contents of alpine meadow soil types are much greater than those of other soil types. Similarly, the trend is for the amount of forage produced to increase with the OM and N content of the soil.

Soil micro-organisms are the other important component concerned in the status of alpine rangeland. The ecosystem and the activities of the micro-organisms have a profound effect on soil fertility and consequently impact plant growth and pasture production. Zhu *et al.* (1982) indicated that in the alpine meadow ecosystem of eastern Qilian mountain (3 200 m a.s.l.), the population of micro-organisms varies seasonally, being also affected by different soil and vegetation types. The highest numbers of micro-organisms in alpine meadow soil occur in the period from mid-July to mid-September but tend to decline after late October.

The soil mainly covered with forbs tends to have the largest number of bacteria, sedge (*Kobresia humilis*) meadow has the highest actinomycete population and shrub *(Potentilla fruticosa)* meadow has the greatest population of fungi and oligonitrophiles. In the soil of swamp meadow, the cellulose-decomposing micro-organisms are absent.

Zang J.X. *et al.* (1991) investigated the quantity and distribution of trace elements in the alpine meadow ecosystem, eastern Qilian mountain. The results showed that the alpine meadow soil (air-dried sample) is rich in trace elements, with contents as follows:

Fe 36 000 ppm, Mn 652 ppm, F 594 ppm, Zn 127 ppm, Cu 28 ppm and Se 0.23 ppm. There is a view that the Se content is inadequate; however, no plant or animal deficiency symptoms appear to have been reported to date. Significant differences existed among soil types in the concentrations of these elements.

Utilization and management of alpine rangelands

Grazing utilization systems

The zone distribution of alpine rangeland types from southeast to northwest on the Plateau leads generally to a corresponding zoning of livestock production systems. Yak are mainly distributed on alpine meadows and higher proportions of Tibetan sheep are found on alpine steppes, while goats and Tibetan sheep mainly inhabit the alpine deserts. Therefore, there are a variety of different management strategies in use on the Plateau. The pasture itself, whether owned by a family or by a group of herders or a village, can be broadly divided into four seasonal rotation grazing systems according to (i) weather, (ii) landforms, (iii) rangeland availability and productivity and (iv) tradition. The use of different pastures at different seasons and the periodic movement of the animals to new grazing sites is part of the tradition of the herdsmen and finds its counterpart in some of the elements of "modern" rotational grazing systems for which "scientific" justifications have been produced (cf. Chapter 8).

(I) Two-season rotation system
This rotation system involves the summer-autumn pasture used in the warm season and the winter-spring pasture used in the cold season (Table 13.7). The summer-autumn grazing generally occurs some time between June and November and may last 140 - 170 days. The herd then moves to the winter-spring pastures for about 192 - 225 days from November (sometimes sooner) to May - the larger part of the year. In general, the two-season rotation system is used mainly in the wide Plateau areas. During the warm season, a yak herd may be moved every 30 - 40 days, depending on the state of the sward and the size of the herd. The distance between campsites varies from 20 to 40 km.

(II) Three-season system (A)
This rotation system is characterized by summer-pasture, winter-pasture and autumn-spring-pasture (Table 13.8).

Table 13.7 The pattern of utilization on the two-season rotation system (I) of the summer-autumn and winter-spring pastures

Location	Summer-autumn pasture				Winter-spring pasture			
	Grazing period	No. days	Type (%)	Rangeland period	Grazing period	No. days	Type (%)	Rangeland period
Anangren	1/6 - 15/11	168	46	Alpine meadow	16/11 - 31/5	197	54	Riverside shrub, meadow, alpine steppe
Ali, Returebang Zhadarebu	1/6 - 31/10	153	42	Alpine steppe, alpine shrub steppe	1/11 - 31/5	212	58	Riverside meadow, riverside shrub meadow, hill desert steppe
Andu, Bange, Naqu, Senzha, Zhenrong	15/7 - 30/11	138	38	Alpine meadow, alpine steppe	1/12 - 14/7	227	62	Riverside meadow, alpine steppe
Cangdu, Jilong	1/6 - 31/10	153	42	Alpine shrub meadow, alpine meadow	1/11 - 31/5	212	58	Subalpine shrub meadow, riverside shrub meadow
Xietongmen	1/6 - 31/10	153	42	Alpine meadow	1/11 - 31/5	212	58	Riverside shrub meadow

Table 13.8 The pattern of utilization on the three-season rotation system (II) of the summer, autumn-spring and winter pastures

Location	Summer pasture			Autumn-spring pasture				Winter pasture			
	Grazing Period	No. days	Type (%)	Rangeland	Grazing period	No. days	Type (%)	Rangeland	Grazing period	No. days	Type (%)	Rangeland
Hongyuan Luqu, Menyuan, Tianzhu	1/7 - 31/8	62	17	Alpine shrub meadow, alpine meadow	1/9 - 14/12, 16/5 - 30/6	151	41	Alpine steppe, alpine shrub meadow, alpine meadow	15/12 - 15/5	152	42	Alpine meadow, riverside meadow, alpine steppe
Cuomei, Dingre, Dingjie, Langkazi, Lazun	1/6 - 31/8	92	25	Alpine meadow	1/9 - 30/11, 1/3 - 31/5	182	50	Hill steppe, Riverside meadow	1/12 - 28/2	90	25	Riverside steppe, riverside meadow

In a system carried out in the northern piedmonts of the Himalayas, animals remain on both the summer and the winter pastures for about three months each. Livestock graze the autumn-spring pastures twice – once from the beginning of September to the beginning of December and then from March to May. Three-season rotation-grazing systems are commonly found in mountainous regions. In these systems, the herders rarely move during the summer to find different sites and only move when the season ends.

(III) Three-season rotation system (B)
This rotation involves a summer pasture, an autumn pasture and a winter-spring pasture (Table 13.9). The autumn pasture is used in this system for more than two months (61 - 81 days). The activities of the animals on the summer and winter-spring pastures are as for the two systems previously described.

(IV) Three-season rotation system (C)
This rotation involves a summer-autumn pasture, a winter pasture and a spring pasture (Table 13.10). In this system, the spring pasture is separated either from the autumn-spring or from the winter-spring pastures. The livestock remain on it for two to three months. Its rangeland types are mainly alpine riverside meadows or shrub lands. The grazing features of the summer-autumn and the winter pastures are as previously described.

Management of the seasonal pastures

Winter and winter-spring pastures
The winter and winter-spring pastures are normally located on relatively flat meadows, such as riverbank mesas, wide valleys and piedmonts, or south-facing slopes at lower elevations, where pastures have the highest forage output and the best acceptability relative to the other types of pasture. Therefore, these pastures, and particularly the winter pastures, are fenced mainly in order to accumulate the biomass for grazing in winter and spring. Accumulating standing dry forages on the winter and winter-spring pastures is the traditional way of supplying feed for animals during the cold season, as the plants on the Plateau are too short to cut for making hay. This management pattern results in a large proportion of the forage nutrients being wasted and, in consequence, feeding value is much reduced from that of the original green biomass when it was set aside, while a large quantity of above-ground biomass is lost, as discussed earlier. The condition of these pastures has a profound effect on the Plateau's rangeland-livestock production systems, particularly in the provision of feed for the larger herds. Therefore, because calving and lambing takes place on them, herders pay much attention to these pastures and use some improvement practices such as fertilization, flood irrigation, toxic plant removal and rat control. Such measures are usually applied along with enclosures formed with barbed-wire fencing.

Table 13.9 The pattern of utilization on the three-rotation system (III) of the summer, autumn and winter-spring pastures

Location	Summer pasture				Autumn pasture				Winter-spring pasture			
	Grazing Period	No. days	Type (%)	Rangeland	Grazing period	No. days	Type (%)	Rangeland	Grazing period	No. days	Type (%)	Rangeland
Bianba, Biru, Jingqing, Leiwuqi, Suxian	1/6 - 31/8	92	25	Alpine Meadow	1/9 - 31/10	61	17	Alpine & subalpine shrub meadow	1/11 - 31/5	212	58	Subalpine shrub meadow, riverside shrub meadow
Baxu, Caya, Cangdu	15/5 - 31/8	108	30	Alpine meadow	1/9 - 15/11	76	20	Subalpine shrub meadow	16/11 - 14/5	181	50	Riverside shrub, shrub meadow
Jilong, Sage	1/6 - 31/8	92	25	Alpine meadow	1/9 - 15/11	76	20	Hill steppe	16/11 - 30/5	192	55	Riverside steppe, shrub meadow

Table 13.10 The pattern of utilization on the three-season rotation system (IV) of the winter, spring and summer-autumn pastures

Location	Summer pasture				Autumn pasture				Winter-spring pasture			
	Grazing period	No. days	Type (%)	Rangeland	Grazing period	No. days	Type (%)	Rangeland	Grazing period	No. days	Type (%)	Rangeland
Angren, Gangba Kangma, Xietongmen	1/6 - 14/11	168	46	Alpine meadow, shrub meadow	15/11 - 28/2	105	29	Hill steppe, Hill shrub steppe	1/3 - 31/5	92	25	Alpine meadow, riverside meadow
Basu, Mangkan, Zuogong	1/6 - 31/10	153	42	Alpine shrub meadow, alpine meadow	1/11 - 31/3	151	41	Subalpine shrub meadow, riverside shrub	1/4 - 31/5	61	17	Riverside meadow
Geermen, Tuqu, Xiaqulong	15/6 - 31/10	138	38	Alpine steppe, alpine desert	1/11 - 31/1	92	25	Alpine desert, riverside shrub	1/2 - 14/6	135	37	Riverside meadow, riverside shrub
Duilongdeqing Nanmulinmo, Nimu, Zugongqa	1/7 - 31/10	123	34	Alpine meadow	1/11 - 28/2	120	32	Hill shrub steppe, Subalpine shrub meadow	1/3 - 30/6	122	34	Riverside meadow

Summer and summer-autumn pastures

The summer and summer-autumn pastures are generally located either at the higher altitudes, often on the north facing slopes of the terrain or on the relatively flat rangelands furthest from the settled homes of the herdsmen and their families. Most of these pastures are difficult to access or may even be inaccessible except in the warm season as they may become blocked during harsh weather or by poor road conditions. In early summer each year, usually in May but depending on the particular location, the herd may still be grazing the spring, spring-autumn or winter-spring pastures. As soon as the season allows, the herd is taken to the summer pastures. Because these pastures are usually far away from the winter or spring pastures, the herdsmen and their herds may need to travel several days to reach their new campsites. The summer pastures, free from fencing, are usually utilized as communal lands for a group of families or an entire village. Hence, there is free access for the herds, and the herders are accustomed to establishing their campsites at the same places every year. Only when the yield of the summer pasture cannot meet the animals' requirements, because of drought or rangeland degradation, do the herders have to move away. These pastures are effectively managed in the long term through extensive, paper-free agreements among the families of a village. Such agreements are made by three to ten families, or occasionally more, sharing the grazing of the same summer pasture (see Chapter 12). Breeding of the stock occurs on the summer pastures, and so the calving rate is largely dependent on forage quantity and quality of these pastures.

Spring and autumn-spring pasture

The spring and autumn-spring pastures are normally located near the winter pastures and the herders' houses, or they may be situated between the winter and summer pastures. Whether or not these pastures are fenced depends on whether or not they are owned by the herders. Before vegetation turns green in spring, both the quantity and quality of the forage remaining on these pastures are at their lowest for the year. The intake by the animals can be as little as one third of the amount consumed in the autumn. As a result, as much as a third of the live weight the animal achieved in the previous autumn is lost during the late winter to early spring period (before green-up) (cf. Chapter 6). This, in turn, leads to a large number of livestock in the herd becoming sick or weak - the so-called phenomenon of "spring sickness". Some of the sickest or weakest animals may die, especially if heavy snowstorms occur in the absence of sufficient feed supplementation and at the very time when most new calves and lambs are born.

Autumn pasture

The autumn-pasture, which may or may not be fenced, is generally located between the winter and summer pastures and usually closer to the winter pastures. By the end of autumn, the animals have achieved their maximum live weight. Autumn is, therefore, the best season for culling surplus stock.

Critical grazing periods

From the point of view of pasture management on the Plateau, the two critical grazing periods are the approximate two-week periods of early spring immediately after green-up and of the late autumn, before the end of vegetation growth. Grazing activity just after green-up will lead to most growing points of plants being eaten by animals, which is, in turn, harmful to tillering and the ability of plants to re-grow. Areas of the sward that are overgrazed prior to the decline in plant growth in the autumn reduce the storage of nutrients in the root system and will therefore have poorer green-up the following spring. This will lead to less seed being produced for the soil-seed bank. The overall consequences are rangeland degradation.

In practice, it is difficult to avoid the problems associated with the two critical grazing periods unless sufficient supplementary feed can be provided in the early spring or alternative land found for grazing in the late autumn. A traditional approach, developed by herdsmen to avoid or alleviate the above situations, is to have a two- to three-year rotation (crossing-over) system between part of the winter or autumn pastures and the spring pastures. The early spring, as mentioned earlier, is also the critical period for the survival of the animals. Therefore, a sound management of the spring pasture and of the herd grazing will have a large influence on the sustainability of the Plateau's rangeland-livestock production systems. To achieve this, herders, policy-makers and researchers need to reach better mutual understanding and then work together.

The potential for improvement of the alpine rangeland

Irrigation

Flood irrigation is perhaps the most common and economic method used by herders to improve the native rangelands, whenever water is available and easily applied. Due to variation of the landforms, not many pastures can be irrigated by running water. Irrigation is applied mostly on areas of winter or autumn pastures that lie on flat areas of riverside and on open lands down-stream that allow easy flooding. Long Ruijun, Hu Z.Z. and Xu Changli (unpublished data) showed that a sedge-grass meadow developed under an annual mean rainfall of 414 mm and mean temperature of minus 0.1C° responded dramatically to irrigation. Five similar pieces of meadow, each 1.5 - 2 ha in size, were flooded thrice (with an equal amount of water each time) in June. Increasing the quantities of total extra water from zero to 0.45, 1.35, 1.80 to 2.25 tonnes per ha, led to corresponding increases in aerial biomass production with these five treatments. The increases were 1.28 to 3.56, 3.15, 5.38 to 4.79 tonnes per ha, respectively. The response of sedge, grass and forbs to irrigation varied depending on the quantity of applied water. Forbs were more responsive than sedges and grasses when 0.45 tonnes per ha of water was introduced; with 1.80 tonnes per ha water, sedges showed a greater response than forbs and grasses, while grasses were the most responsive when 2.25 tonnes per ha water was supplied. The time of flooding also has a profound effect on yield and structure of swards, the optimum being as soon as possible after green-up of the native vegetation.

Forbs and some toxic plants are considerably restricted by increasing levels of water, thus leaving a larger proportion of acceptable forage in the sward and greatly improving the feeding value of the sward.

Fertilizing

Nitrogen or phosphorus fertilizers are rarely used by herders to improve their grazing pastures due to cost and the difficulty of spreading. Nonetheless, fertilizing can enhance the biomass yield of native pastures, particularly the edible forage. When the sedge-grass meadow referred to above was fertilized once with sulphate of ammonia at the rate of 375 kg per ha (80 kg N per ha) and then flooded with 300 cu m water per ha at the end of June, its edible forage yield reached 5 674 kg DM per ha, an increase of 470 percent compared with the same pasture without any fertilizer. In addition, the green vegetation period of the native sward was extended by an extra two weeks.

Control of toxic plants and rodents

Overgrazing and degradation of alpine rangelands is always associated with an invasion by toxic plants; the greater the overgrazing, the greater is such invasion. The toxic plants commonly found include: *Stellera chamaejasme*, *Achnatherum inebrians*, *Aconitum szechenyianum*, *A. rotundifolium* and some seasonally toxic herbage from plants such as *Ranunculus spp.*, *Pxytropis spp.*, *Gentiana spp.*, *Pediculalis spp.*, and *Senecio spp.* The seasonally toxic plants are avoided by animals during the growing season but are grazed in the standing or dry sward. Winter *et al.* (1992, 1994) reported that species of *Senecio* are the predominant toxic plants found to be causing large numbers of the deaths among yak on overgrazed pastures in Bhutan. This matter is also referred to in Chapters 8 and 9.

Herders rarely use chemical control of poisonous plants. However, removal of the plants by hand is often carried out. Since most of the toxic plants are broad-leaf, the use of a herbicide, such as 2,4-D, with a dose of 0.454 kg per ha, tends to be used on State farms to remove these plants.

Rodent infestation always follows rangeland degradation and in turn, the rodents accelerate the degradation through consuming both aerial biomass and the roots of plants. The rodents also dig up much soil that then covers the surface of nearby swards. Pika (*Ochotona curzoniae*) and Chinese zokor (*Myospalax fontanierii*) are recognized as the most active rodents that invade and destroy degraded meadows, but the alpine steppes and deserts are rarely attacked by these small animals. The pikas move about during the day and *Myospalax baileyi* at night. The density of the pika distribution tends to increase on the alpine meadow in line with increasing degrees of sward degradation. But the largest number of pikas (148 per ha) is found on medium-degraded meadow. Poison bait casting and setting of rat traps are the most common measures used by herders to remove rodents from their pastures, though sometimes they are not very effective in controlling the periodic infestations. Perhaps an alternative, effective and environmentally friendly means of shrinking the rodent population to within harm-free levels, or eliminating the rodents' habitat, would be to increase the numbers of the rodents' natural enemies, such as the eagle and the fox, or to increase sward height and cover by avoiding overgrazing and through irrigation and fertilizing.

Use of forage crops and sown-grass swards

Given a pattern of native forage production in alpine rangelands as shown in Figure 13.2, an obvious imbalance exists throughout the year between feed supply from pasture provision and the requirements of the animals. The traditional way to solve the issue on the Plateau is to practice an effective seasonal rotation or transhumance system. However, an alternative measure used nowadays by many herders who live at a relatively low elevation in Gansu, Sichuan, Qinghai and southern Tibet, is to sow out a supplementary crop or sward near their permanent houses or near rivers in order to fill some of the forage gap during the cold season. Forage crops are normally the first choice for annual production. For example, oats (*Avena sativa*) for making into hay and the root crops of sugar beet (*Beta vulgaris*) and turnip (*Brassica rapa*) are planted in some relatively low-lying areas or where the temperature is sufficient for their growth.

Alternative supplementary forages are from sown perennial-grass swards that are sometimes established on fenced land. There are several cultivated perennial grass species adapted to the Plateau's harsh climate, such as *Clinelumus nutans, Elymus nutans, Bromus inermis, Agropyon cristatum* and *Poa crymophila*. These can be sown in monoculture or in mixture, the latter being the most common. Grass-forage production can be as high as 10 - 14 tonnes DM per ha two years after establishment, i.e. 2- to 5-times higher than the production from enclosed native pasture. In addition, the green-up time of the sown grasses can occur two weeks earlier than that of the native vegetation. However, in the first year of establishment, the sown grasses, because they are insufficiently aggressive, may fail to compete against the native weeds, and so the yield of the sown grass will be lower above ground. However, their root systems can become well established in the year of sowing, and this benefits survival and growth in the second and subsequent years. To achieve both high quantity and quality from the sown sward, an effective control of annual broad-leaf weeds has to be maintained throughout the sward life to ensure persistency.

In terms of haymaking from the cultivated perennial swards, cutting once a year at the early seeding stage and leaving the re-growth for grazing is recommended by Dong (2001). Without a practice of re-seeding, the yield of some monoculture swards begins to decline from the third or fourth year after establishment, while those of mixtures may last for seven to ten years when fertilizer and irrigation are used.

Postscript

The rangelands are not only vast but diverse in climate, topography, soil types and vegetation cover. Sustaining the large populations of yak, sheep, goats and the horses of the herders, as well as wild animals, creates a disequillibrium between the supply of available feed and the requirements of the animals. Typically there is an abundant supply of feed in summer and a significant deficit in winter and spring. Inappropriate but traditional practices have led to substantial degradation of the rangelands, which in turn heightens the difficulties of maintaining an increasing animal population. At the same time, the increasing demands on the rangelands further exacerbate the problems from overgrazing. However, as suggested in this chapter, a study and understanding of the interacting forces and relationships within the ecosystem and the potential for improvements would provide an opportunity for sustainable production from the unique resource represented by the high Plateau and these mountainous regions.

References

Bureau of Animal Husbandry and Veterinary Medicine, Ministry of Agriculture, China (1994). Data on the Grassland Resources of China. Beijing, Agricultural Technological Publishing House, pp. 2-5. (*in Chinese*)

Chang, D. H. S. (1981). The vegetation zonation of the Tibetan Plateau. *Mountain Research and Development*, 1 (1) 29-48.

Chang, D. H. S. (1983). The Tibetan Plateau in relation to the vegetation of China. *Annals of the Missouri Botanical Garden*, 70, 564-570.

Cincotta, R. P. *et al.* (1991). Forage ecology of livestock on the Tibetan Changtan: a comparison of three adjacent grazing areas. *Arctic and Alpine Research*, 23 (2), 149-161.

Goldstein, M.C., Beall, C.M. & Cinotta, R. P. (1990). Traditional nomadic pastoralism and ecological conservation on Tibet's northern Plateau. *National Geographic Research*, 6 (2), 139-156.

Dong, S. K (2001). The stability of mixture grassland of cultivated perennial grass and its regulation in alpine region of Tibet-Qinghai Plateau of China. Ph.D. thesis.

Hu, Z.Z (2000). Prataculture and Environment Development on Qinghai-Tibetan Plateau. Beijing, Tibetanology Publishing House, pp 25-27. (*in Chinese*)

Hu, Z. Z. *et al.* (1988a). Studies on primary production and energy efficiency in Tianzhu alpine Kobresia Capillifolia meadow. *Acta Ecologica Sinica*, 2, 184-192. (*in Chinese*)

Hu, Z. Z. *et al.* (1988b). Studies on primary productivity in Tianzhu alpine *Polygonum viviparum* meadow. *Acta Phytoecologica et Geobotanica Sinica*, 1, 124-133. (*in Chinese*)

Li J., Zhu G., Yang T. & Tang S. (1982). Studies of carbon dioxide evolution and cellulose decomposition in soils at the Haibei Research Station of Alpine Meadow Ecosystem. *In Alpine Meadow Ecosystem-I,* Xia W. (ed). Gansu People Publishing House, pp. 162-172. (*in Chinese*)

Long, Ruijun *et al.* (1999a). Feed value of native forages of the Tibetan Plateau of China. *Animal Feed Science and Technology,* 80, 101-113.

Long, Ruijun *et al.* (1999b). Effect of strategic feed supplementation on productive and reproductive performance in yak cows. *Preventive Veterinary Medicine* 38, 195-206.

Long, Ruijun & Ma, Y.S. (1997). Qinghai's yak production systems. *In Conservation and Management of Yak Genetic Diversity,* Miller, D.J., Craig, S.R. & Rana, G.M. (eds.) Kathmandu, pp.105-114.

Ma Yushou, *et al.* (1998). Improvement of yak production on deteriorated "black soil" grassland. *Grassland of China.* (4): 61-63.

Miller, D. J. & Craig, S. R. (1996). *Rangelands and pastoral development in the Hindu Kush-Himalayas.* Published by International Centre for Integrated Mountain Development, Kathmandu, pp. 75-76.

Ren, J.Z. & Jin, J.H., (1956). Observations on the grazing behaviour yak. *Journal of Animal Husbandry and Veterinary Medicine of China,* (1) p2. (*in Chinese*)

Richard C.E. (2002). The potential for rangeland development in yak rearing areas of the Tibetan Plateau. *Proceedings of the third international congress on yak, in Lhasa, China, 4-9 September 2000.* International Livestock Research Institute (ILRI), Nairobi, pp. 11-18.

Ulyatt, M.J. (1981). The feeding value of herbage: can it be improved? *New Zealand Agricultural Science,* 15, 200-205.

Winter, H. *et al.* (1992). Pyrrolizidine alkaloid poisoning of yaks (*Bos grunniens*) and confirmation by recovery of pyloric metabolites from formalin-fixed liver tissue. *Research in Veterinary Science,* 52, 187-194.

Winter, H. *et al.* (1994). Pyrrolizidine alkaloid poisoning of yaks: identification of the plants involved. *The Veterinary Record,* 134, 135-139.

Wu Ning. (1997). Ecological situation of high-frigid rangeland and its sustainability – a case study on the constraints and approaches in pastoral western Sichuan. Berlin, Dietrich Reimer Verlag. 281 pp.

Xiong, Y. & Li, Q. K. (1987). China soil. (Second Edition), Scientific Publishing House, pp. 284-303.

Zang, J. X., *et al.*(1991). Contents and distribution of trace elements in alpine meadow soil. *In Alpine Meadow Ecosystem-III,* Liu J. & Wang Z. (eds.). Scientific Publishing House, pp 257-266. (*in Chinese*)

Zhang, S. Y. & Ma, Z. Y. (1982). The physiological influence of low temperature at night on some herbage in Tibetan-Qinghai Plateau. *In: Alpine Meadow Ecosystem-I,* Xia W. (ed.). Gansu People Publishing House, pp 52-57. (*in Chinese*)

Zhou, S.R, (1984). Study on the forage and feeding habits of yak. A research on the utilization and exploitation of grassland in the northwestern part of Sichuan province. Sichuan National Publishing House, pp.134-137. (*in Chinese*)

Zhou, S.R & Simon, U. (1995). Evaluation of feeding value on the main rangeland plants on the Tibetan Plateau of China. *Proceedings of the fifth International Rangeland Congress,* pp: 638-639. Salt Lake City, Utah, July 23-28, 1995.

Zhu Guiru *et al.* (1982). Seasonal Changes of the number and constitution of the main groups of soil micro-organism. *In Alpine Meadow Ecosystem-I,* Xia, W. (ed). Gansu People Publishing House, pp 144-161. (*in Chinese*)

14 YAK NUTRITION – A SCIENTIFIC BASIS
by Long Ruijun[1]

OVERVIEW

As discussed in previous chapters, the yak is largely dependent on natural pastures for its survival. Thus, its nutritional state varies seasonally as the supply of supplementary feeds is limited. In most herds, only very weak animals and some pregnant or lactating yak are given access to feeds in addition to grazing. Low calving and growth rates are attributed to the poor nutritional condition of the yak, in the cold season particularly. The traditional way of maintaining the animals is to allow them to put on as much fat as possible during the warm season; fat that is then used over the long cold season as an energy reserve to allow survival beyond the early spring. The tragedy of large numbers of animals dying because of snow disasters is frequent on the Qinghai-Tibetan Plateau. Nowadays, the yak population is increasing rapidly, causing rangeland degradation and, hence, further increasing the gap between feed supply from natural pastures and the animals' feed demand. Thus, the malnutrition that the yak has to suffer is likely to become worse in the foreseeable future. A good understanding of yak nutrition under grazing conditions, which could help to alleviate some of the problems, is still rather inadequate. But this chapter provides some of the evidence that is accumulating and points to several gaps in understanding and the need for validation of some of the preliminary findings.

Feed intake
Generally, yak consume less feed than other cattle, probably because of their smaller rumen capacity. Yak prefer fresh, high-quality forages, and both housing and high temperature can reduce feed intakes. Dry matter intake (DMI, kg per day) of the growing yak under indoor feeding can be estimated as DMI = 0.0165 W + 0.0486 (W is body weight in kilograms), and that of the lactating yak as DMI = $0.008W^{0.52} + 1.369Y$ ($W^{0.52}$ is metabolic body weight, Y is milk yield, kg per day).

Ruminal digestion and metabolism
The rumen of the yak is far smaller than that of other cattle. Outflow rate of rumen fluid ranges from 3.1 to 3.5 litre per hour, hence lower than in cattle. The outflow rate of digesta from the yak rumen stays comparatively constant, ranging from 11.5 percent to 14.9 percent per hour. Total volatile fatty acid (VFA) production in the yak rumen increases with the animal's age. The proportions of propionic acid and butyric acid to total VFA in the yak are higher than those in other ruminants.

---

[1] Long Ruijun is Professor of Pastoral Science and dean of Faculty of Grassland Science, Gansu Agriculture University, China and Senior Scientist, Northwest Plateau Institute of Biology, the Chinese Acadamy Science, China. He is also Vice-Chairman of Chinese Graaland Society, China

The concentration of NH_3-N in the yak rumen varies with the diet composition and feeding behaviour. Mature forages can promote lower NH_3-N concentrations in grazing yak than can young forages. Both feed type and feeding behaviour affect degradability of dietary nutrients in the yak rumen.

Energy nutrition
Lactating yak cows have better utilization of dietary energy than dry yak cows when they are given oat hay at the same level under indoor feeding conditions. An increased feeding level leads to the decreased digestibility of dietary energy in dry cows. The thermoneutral zone of the growing yak is estimated as $8° - 14°C$. The fasting heat production (FHP) of the growing yak can be estimated as FHP = 916 kJ per $kgW^{0.52}$ per day. The metabolizable energy requirement for maintenance (ME_m) in growing yak is around 460 kJ per kg $W^{0.75}$ per day. Metabolizable energy requirement in the growing yak can be estimated as: ME (MJ per day)=$0.45W^{0.75} + (8.73 + 0.091 \text{ W}) \Delta G$ (ΔG is kg per day).

Protein nutrition
There is no difference in the digestibility of dietary nitrogen between lactating and dry cows. A relatively lower excretion of endogenous urinary nitrogen in yak suggests the possibility that the animal has evolved a mechanism to recycle more nitrogen to the rumen than ordinary cattle.

Yak can use non-protein nitrogen as efficiently as other ruminants. The endogenous purine derivative excretion in the yak is only 40 percent of that in cattle but is similar to that in buffaloes. The value of creatinine excretion for the yak when fasting is much lower than for buffaloes and cattle. Rumen degradable crude protein requirement for maintenance ($RDCP_m$, g per day) in growing yak is around $6.09W^{0.52}$ g per day. The crude protein requirements for daily gain (ΔG $RDCP_g$ g per day) in growing yak can be estimated as $RDCP_g = (1.16/\Delta G + 0.05/W^{0.52})^{-1}$. Thus the total crude protein requirement of growing yak could be calculated as RDCP (g per day) = $6.09W^{0.52} + (1.16/\Delta G + 0.05/W^{0.52})^{-1}$.

Mineral nutrition
Mineral nutrition is poorly documented. But the existing information suggests that mineral deficiencies may occur, varying from one yak-raising area to another. Seasonal deficiency of specific elements could be a common issue throughout the Plateau owing to an uneven seasonal supply of feeds. Mineral and trace element deficiencies can cause some problems to yak, but appropriate supplementation will generally improve the conditions.

Feeding
Forages on natural grassland are in surplus in summer but deficient in winter under the traditional grazing system. The nutritional status of yak can be improved by ensuring adequate protein intake in summer – but yak suffer deficiency of crude-protein and of energy from grass in winter. The use of feed supplements seems vital if the productive and

reproductive potentials of grazing yak cows on the Qinghai-Tibetan Plateau are to be developed. Concentrate and urea block supplements are effective in improving the productivity of grazing yak and maintaining the body weight of animals in winter.

Introduction

The yak, like other grazing ruminants, has a highly developed and specialized mode of digestion that has evolved to maximize the utilization of carbohydrates from cellulose (Van Soest, 1987) and thus allow better access to energy in the form of fibrous feeds than that occurring in the non-ruminant herbivores. The yak has adapted, uniquely among cattle, not only to the high cellulose diet of the Qinghai-Tibetan Plateau but also to its extremely harsh climate and, as a result, has developed nutritional and metabolic features that probably differ from those of other cattle species. Yak nutrition is, however, poorly documented compared with some other aspects of yak science, such as biology and ecology characteristics, productive and reproductive performances and aspects of breeding and interspecies hybridization. Knowledge of yak nutrition has been very limited owing to the remoteness and poor infrastructure of yak territories, difficulties of on-farm research and lack of scientific information exchanges.

Until the 1990s, most of the research on digestion and metabolism of protein and energy, as well as supplementation strategies, had been conducted by the Yak Nutrition Research Group of Qinghai Academy of Animal Science and Veterinary Medicine, whose findings were collected in the publication *Recent advances in yak Nutrition* (Hu, 1997). Other researchers (Gansukh, 1997; Long *et al.*, 1997, 1998, 1999; Dong *et al.*, 1997, 2000a,b; Shi *et al.*, 1997) have made contributions to the better understanding of the feeding and nutrition of the yak. Although some nutrition and feeding habits of yak still remain unclear, compared to those of ordinary cattle, the results have been used to improve yak performance on the farm. It is considered that a satisfactory performance of the indigenous animals could be achieved by effective nutritional intervention in the harsh ecological zones.

The aims of this chapter are: (i) to summarize the current advances in yak nutrition research as contained in various scientific reports and (ii) to suggest future research requirements for establishing better guidelines for yak-feeding systems.

Feed Intake

As already noted in Chapter 13, voluntary intake (VI) of the yak varies with the season and sward heights, from 18 to 25 kg of fresh forage in summer to 6 to 8 kg per day, or even much less, of wilted grass in cold-season grazing conditions. Other factors affect the intake levels, including feed types, feeding conditions, environmental climate, as well as age, size and sex of the animal.

Feed types

Han *et al.* (1990a) fed castrated yak (two to three years old) in barns seven diets and found that the dry-matter intake (DMI) of roughage decreased with the increasing content of concentrates in the diets (Table 14.1). Dong *et al.* (2000a) studied the digestion and metabolism of protein and energy in lactating yak given different diets and found that concentrates in the diets decreased the DMI of yak. Preference for fibrous feeds may result in higher intakes of roughages than of concentrates by yak, and a relatively faster passage of high-quality roughage (such as oat hay) leads to reduced mean retention time of digesta (Han, 1996) and thus results in higher intake. In both studies, the authors stated that the intakes of yak were less than those of other cattle, possibly because of the smaller rumen capacity of yak (Liu, 1991).

Feeding conditions

Liu et al. (1997) reported that the DMI of two-year-old yak (as a percentage of body weight) varied from 3.7 percent in the late growing period of forages to 3.4 percent in the mature period under grazing conditions, while that of three-year-olds ranged from 3.7 percent to 3.1 percent. Feed intake per unit of body weight under grazing was greater than in the indoor feeding. Possibly unsuitable housing and restriction to a given diet may be the main factors that reduced the feed intake of the indoor-fed yak.

Climate

Climatic factors, especially temperature, have a profound effect on feed intake and digestibility in the yak. Growing yak increased their intake levels at lower temperatures irrespective of whether they were feeding indoors (Han *et al.*, 1990a) or grazing on natural pasture. The faster rate of passage of feed particles at lower temperatures (Liu *et al.*, 1997) would provide more rumen space to be filled by food.

Greater milk production on cold, cloudy days (cf. Chapter 6) may be partly attributed to the higher forage intakes of lactating yak on such days. The yak can feed normally on grasslands when the temperature is as low as -30° to -40°C, or even lower in a harsh winter. In contrast, the yak moves and grazes less at higher temperatures (cf. Chapter 4), and, consequently, feed intake falls.

Age, size and sex of yak

As shown in Table 14.2, the DMI varies with the age and size (body weight) of the yak. There is a good linear correlation between the DMI of yak and their body weight (W) or metabolic body weight ($W^{0.75}$ or $W^{0.52}$). Han *et al.* (1990a) found it was much better to use body weight than metabolic body weight to estimate the DMI for growing yak. On this basis, Liu *et al.* (1997) deduced the equation: DMI (kg per day) = 0.0165 W + 0.0486 ($r = 0.959$) for growing yak.

Table 14.1 Dry-matter intakes of growing yak from various diets under indoor feeding (± SD) [Source: Han *et al.*, 1990a]

Diets	No. of animals	Body weights (kg)	Daily intakes (kg)	Intake/body weight ratio	Environmental temperature (° C)
87% Concentrate + 13% wheat straw	6	134.1 ± 33.7	3.1 ± 0.87	0.023 ± 0.001	14.2
48% Concentrate + 52% wheat straw	8	159.3 ± 31.3	3.4 ± 0.52	0.022 ± 0.001	14.2
28% Concentrate + 72% wheat straw	8	166.5 ± 31.6	3.0 ± 0.58	0.018 ± 0.001	11.6
40% Fresh grass, 40% fresh bluestem and 20% fresh alfalfa	4	178.3 ± 36.4	3.7 ± 0.37	0.022 ± 0.002	16.7
Oat hay	10	145.2 ± 30.7	3.4 ± 0.88	0.024 ± 0.005	− 6.1
Oat straw	10	145.2 ± 30.7	3.4 ± 0.70	0.024 ± 0.003	− 5.8
Wheat straw	10	145.2 ± 30.7	2.0 ± 0.49	0.014 ± 0.002	− 4.3

For lactating yak, extra feed is needed to meet requirements for milk yield. Therefore, milk production must be taken into account when calculating DMI. The following equation (Dong *et al.*, 2000a) can better describe the relationship: $DMI=0.008W^{0.52}+1.369Y$ (where Y is kg per day of standard milk of 4 percent fat content [$r=0.992$]).

Table 14.2 Feed intake of grazing yak on natural grassland at various growth stages of forages (±SD) [Source: Liu *et al.*, 1997]

Growth stage of forage	Age of animal	No. of animals	Body weight (kg)	Daily DMI		
				kg	g/kg $W^{0.52}$	g/kg $W^{0.75}$
Premature	2 year	7	115.3 ± 2.7	3.9 ± 0.32[a]	311.9	111.4
	3 year	7	154.4 ± 1.4	6.0 ± 0.82[b]	418.5	131.3
Mature	2 year	7	125.9 ± 2.3	3.8 ± 0.53[a]	300.9	98.9
	3 year	7	168.1 ± 1.1	5.8 ± 0.45[b]	393.5	121.0

Note: Means with different superscripts are significantly different (P<0.01).

Feed digestion and metabolism in the rumen

For ruminants, a number of factors, including gastrointestinal size and capacity, rumen fill, rumination, digestive capacity, absorptive gut surface and quality of available forage affect feeding strategy (Van Soest, 1987). Yak, standing apart from other ruminants, have their own rumen characteristics and digestive capacity under different feeding strategies.

Rumen volume

Liu *et al.* (1991) determined the volume of the yak rumen contents (l) by using polyethylene glycol (PEG) as a marker and found that for a yak of 150 kg body weight, the rumen content varied from 32.3 to 35.8 l (Table 14.3). When the rumens of these animals were filled with water after slaughter the mean-water content was 34.8 l (Liu *et al.*, 1991). The maximum size of the yak rumen, reported by Liu Haibo (1989), was approximately 66.8 l. Compared with cattle, yak had a much smaller rumen volume (Liu *et al.*, 1991; Han, 1990a).

Table 14.3 Rumen fluid content of yak and outflow rate of rumen fluid (±SD)
[Source: Liu *et al.*, 1991]

Animal identity	Body weight (kg)	Outflow rate of rumen fluid (l/h)	Rumen content by using PEG (l)		Rumen content by filling with water (l)
			Mean ± SD	C.V.	
A	129	3.1±0.48	33.2 ± 2.4	7.2	
B	117	3.4±0.16	32.3 ± 1.4	4.5	34.8 (mean)
C	196	3.1±0.16	35.8 ± 0.2	0.6	
D	156	3.5±0.48	33.8 ± 1.8	5.3	

Outflow rate of rumen fluid and digesta

Outflow rate of rumen contents is positively correlated with the protein degradability but negatively correlated with the synthesis of microbial protein in the rumen. Many factors, such as feed availability, air temperature, composition of diet, state of feed (solid or liquid) and size of feed particles, can affect the outflow rate (Han *et al.*, 1996).

Table 14.4 shows that dietary intake is positively related to the outflow rate of rumen fluid. A lower outflow rate of rumen fluid with a higher proportion of roughage in the diets indicated that lower quality feeds required more time to be fermented and degraded in the rumen (Han, 1996). The relatively higher intakes under grazing conditions may lead to faster outflow of rumen fluid than under indoor-feeding conditions (Han, 1996). No effects of the level and source of dietary nitrogen on the outflow rate of rumen fluid were observed in yak, although a quicker outflow of rumen fluid with increasing levels of nitrogen in the diet occurred in buffalo (Han, 1990a).

Table 14.4 Outflow rate of rumen fluid and digesta in yak fed with various diets under indoor feeding (±SD) [Source: Han *et al.*, 1996]

Diets	No. of animals	Dry-matter intake (kg/d)	Outflow rate of rumen fluid (%/h)	Outflow rate of digesta (%/h)
CP* level in diet (%)				
8	4	2.8 ± 0.02^{Ab}	10.3 ± 3.3^{A}	13.3 ± 0.9^{a}
12	4	2.7 ± 0.18^{Ab}	9.0 ± 0.9^{A}	13.9 ± 0.6^{a}
Roughage: concentrate ratio				
7:3	3	2.7 ± 0.15^{Ab}	10.4 ± 0.5^{A}	11.8 ± 0.9^{a}
5:5	3	2.8 ± 0.11^{Ab}	12.6 ± 0.8^{A}	14.9 ± 1.8^{a}
3:7	3	1.7 ± 0.36^{Bd}	3.9 ± 0.9^{B}	12.8 ± 0.8^{a}
Source of nitrogen				
Rapeseed cake	3	2.3 ± 0.64^{c}	9.8 ± 3.6^{A}	14.7 ± 1.7^{a}
Pea	3	2.3 ± 0.56^{c}	8.6 ± 3.4^{A}	13.7 ± 1.2^{a}
Bean	3	2.7 ± 0.31^{Ab}	8.5 ± 4.1^{A}	11.5 ± 1.2^{a}

Note: Within columns, the means with different superscript capital letters are significantly different at P <0.01; the means with different lower case superscripts are different at P>0.05.
*CP = crude protein

Outflow rate of rumen fluid in the study of Liu *et al.* (1991) ranged from 3.1 to 3.5 litres per hour, somewhat lower than in cattle.

Irrespective of the composition of the diet, nitrogen level and source, and feed intake, the outflow rate of digesta from the yak rumen remains comparatively constant, ranging from 11.5 to 14.9 percent per hour (Table 14.4).

Volatile fatty acid production

Production of volatile fatty acid (VFA), an original energy substrate, can reflect the fermentative capacity of the rumen. This fermentative capacity is determined to a considerable degree by dietary composition and, therefore, is greatly influenced by feeding behaviour (Van Soest, 1987). The effect of dietary composition and feeding level on fermentation in the yak rumen under indoor-feeding conditions was reported by Xie *et al.*, (1992). According to this report, the production of propionic acid and ratio of acetic acid to propionic acid for a maintenance diet (72 percent of concentrate and 28 percent of roughage, and the intake just meeting maintenance requirements) were significantly lower than those of a roughage diet eaten to appetite (22 percent of concentrate and 78 percent of roughage). The production of total VFA and acetic acid from a concentrate feed eaten to appetite (44 percent of concentrate and 56 percent of roughage) were greater than those from the roughage feed, but the ratios of acetic acid to propionic acid of these two feeds were similar (Table 14.5). A difference in fermentation was observed between indoor feeding and grazing conditions by Liu et al. (1992). Yak grazing fresh forages in the early growing period of grassland produced more total VFA and propionic acid than yak fed indoors with a mixture of concentrate and wheat straw and yak grazing withered and wilted forages. And total VFA production in the rumen was higher for indoor-fed yak than for yak grazing on withered and wilted forages. It was found in both reports that the production of the more efficient energy sources, propionic and butyric acids, were higher in the yak than in other ruminants, such as cattle, deer, goats and buffalo, regardless of whether the animals were fed indoors or grazing. Gansukh (1997) working with yak calves between the ages of 30 and 120 days found that the average amount of total VFA frequently increased with age.

NH_3-N concentration

NH_3-N (ammonia nitrogen), one of the fermentative products of feed in the rumen, is the source of microbial protein. As with VFA production, the concentration of NH_3-N in the yak rumen varied with diet composition and feeding behaviour. Bi et al. (1989) found that more NH_3-N can be provided for grazing yak by alpine steppe (dominated by grass) than by alpine meadow (dominated by sedges). According to Yan (2000), mature forages can provide less NH_3-N to the grazing yak than the young forages. Xie et al. (1989) reported no significant difference in rumen NH_3-N concentration between two- and three-year-old yak under indoor-feeding conditions, although the values were lower than those from yak grazing on the alpine steppe and higher than those from yak grazing on the alpine meadow as already described.

Dry matter and protein degradability

Nutrient degradability in the yak rumen varies with the type of feed and feeding behaviour. Xie et al. (1990) determined in sacco degradability of several protein feeds in the yak rumen under indoor feeding and grazing conditions (Table 14.6). The crude protein degradability of plant materials was significantly higher than that of animal materials, and fishmeal and bone meal had higher crude protein degradability than blood meal among animal materials.

Both dry-matter and crude-protein degradability of bone meal and sesame cake were higher under grazing than under indoor feeding, although no significant differences between feeding situations were observed among other feeds.

Table 14.5 Volatile fatty acid production in the yak rumen at various indoor feeding levels (1×10^{-2} mol/l) ($\pm$SD) [Source: Xie *et al.* 1992]

VFA	Maintenance feed (72 % of concentrate & 28% of roughage)	Roughage feed (22% of concentrate and 78% of roughage, voluntary intake)	Concentrate feed (44% of concentrate and 56% of roughage, voluntary intake)
Total	3.4 ± 0.68^A	3.4 ± 0.30^A	4.1 ± 0.51^A
Acetic acid	1.6 ± 0.35^A	1.5 ± 0.13^A	1.7 ± 0.21^B
Propionic-acid	0.8 ± 0.12^A	1.0 ± 0.10^B	1.2 ± 0.18^B
Butyric-acid	0.8 ± 0.21^A	0.7 ± 0.06^A	1.0 ± 0.11^A
Acetic/ Propionic	2.0^A	1.5^B	1.5^B

Note: Within rows, the means with different superscripts are significantly different ($P<0.01$); means with the same superscripts are not different ($P>0.05$).

Energy nutrition

Dietary energy digestion and metabolism

Differences in the efficiency of the utilization of dietary energy are due to the gastrointestinal capacity for fermentation and the proportion of the diet that is catabolized in that fermentation (Van Soest, 1987). The former depends on animal characteristics that include sex, age and physiological state (growth, lactation, etc.), and the latter is highly related to diet composition and feeding level.

Long *et al.* (1998) observed that lactating yak had better utilization of dietary energy than dry yak cows when they were fed at the same level with oat hay under indoor-feeding conditions. A further study with lactating yak (170 - 200 kg) conducted by the same authors indicated, however, that yak cows had a lower efficiency of metabolizable-energy utilization for milk production (averaging 0.46) than dairy cattle and this in turn suggests that it may be one of the features of energy metabolism developed by the yak under long-term natural selection to concentrate the available energy to withstand the harsh environment and thus ensure survival.

Table 14.6 Dry matter (DM) and crude protein (CP) degradability of various feeds in the yak rumen under indoor feeding and grazing conditions [Source: Xie *et al* 1990]

Feeds		Feeding situation	DM degradability (%)		CP degradability (%)	
			Mean	CV[1]	Mean	CV[1]
Plant materials	Soybean cake	Indoor feeding	94.4	3.4	93.1	3.9
		Grazing	91.2	5.3	90.2	5.5
	Rapeseed cake	Indoor feeding	88.9	0.16	88.2	0.71
		Grazing	88.2	0.68	96.5	0.21
	Sesame cake	Indoor feeding	94.3	0.53	97.9	0.34
		Grazing	87.0	1.4	94.9	1.1
	Average		90.4		93.6	
Animal materials	Bone meal	Indoor feeding	46.4	4.5	83.8	1.5
		Grazing	41.4	1.8	75.3	1.2
	Fish meal	Indoor feeding	60.7	7.8	74.8	8.0
		Grazing	60.6	7.8	69.5	9.5
	Blood meal	Indoor feeding	34.9	15.2	38.2	39.1
		Grazing	34.5	16.4	28.1	24.7
	Average		46.4		61.6	

[1] CV = coefficient of variation

Table 14.7 Features of the energy metabolism of yak fed on various diets [adapted from Han et al. 1990]

Trial	Yak (3 per group)		Intake (DM)		Energy (MJ/d)					Percentages of GE						ΔG/d
	Age	BW	Conc.	straw												
	(yr.)	(kg)	(kg)	(kg)	GE	FE	UE	CH₄E	HP	DE	UE	CH₄E	ME	HP	RE	(kg)
I	2	86-93	0.45	0.40	14.4	5.7	0.24	1.3	11.8	60	1.7	8.8	49	80	-31	-0.26
	3	128-151	0.84	0.40	20.8	7.5	0.46	1.8	15.8	64	2.2	8.8	53	75	-22	-0.47
II	2	86-94	1.00	0.40	23.5	7.4	0.47	1.7	11.8	68	2.0	7.4	59	50	9	0.16
	3	120-143	1.68	0.40	34.7	10.2	0.89	2.6	15.9	71	2.6	7.5	61	46	15	0.20
III	2	87-96	1.40	0.40	30.1	8.7	0.58	2.1	13.9	71	1.9	7.0	62	46	16	0.19
	3	124-156	2.52	0.40	46.5	14.1	1.10	3.4	20.7	71	2.3	7.0	62	43	19	0.57
IV	2	93-103	1.80	0.40	36.7	11.5	0.69	2.5	16.9	69	1.9	6.9	60	46	14	0.39
	3	133-166	3.36	0.40	62.4	15.5	1.11	1.1	25.5	75	1.8	6.6	67	41	26	0.71
V	2	99-109	2.20	0.40	43.0	10.0	0.44	2.8	21.8	77	1.0	6.6	69	51	18	0.35
	3	145-177	4.20	0.40	75.1	17.0	0.83	4.2	35.4	77	1.1	5.6	71	47	24	0.65

BW, Bodyweight; Conc, Concentrate; Straw, Wheat straw; GE, Gross energy content of diet; FE, Faecal energy; UE, Urine energy; CH₄E, Methane energy; HP, Heat production; DE, Digestible energy; RE, Retained energy; ΔG/d, daily weight gain.

Table 14.7 demonstrates that shifting the dietary proportions of concentrate and wheat straw has a profound effect on efficiency of feed energy utilization in growing yak. The ratios of retained energy in body tissues to gross energy content of diet range from minus 31 percent to plus 26 percent when changing animal diet from I (lowest amount of concentrates) to V (highest amount of concentrates). The lower metabolic hormone levels of growing yak reflected a slower growth rate related to an adverse eco-environment (Han, 1994). Another experiment (Dong *et al.,* 2000b) indicated that digestibility of dietary energy decreased by 2.9 - 6.8 percent with increasing forage feeding levels in dry cows.

Fasting heat production

Basal metabolism is generally defined as the heat production of a completely quiescent animal in a post-absorptive state, within a thermoneutral environment. Although this state can be achieved with human beings, it is extremely difficult to achieve with animals like the yak. Consequently, the term "fasting metabolism" has been adopted for them. Table 14.8 shows a profile of fasting heat production (FHP) (kJ per kg $W^{0.75}$ per day) in growing yak that remained fairly constant compared to that in the Qinghai yellow cattle. The comparatively stable FHP in yak may be related to the ability of yak to take in more oxygen, particularly at the higher altitudes (see Chapter 4). At the elevation of 2 261 m, the absolute FHP for the growing yak was higher than that of the growing Qinghai yellow cattle, but the reverse was the case at higher altitudes. Clearly, basal metabolism of animals living at higher elevations, like the yak, is lower than that of animals living at lower elevations. In Table 14.8, there is a significant difference between age groups in both yak and Qinghai yellow cattle (i.e. the FHP value for a one-year-old calf is higher than that for a three-year-old heifer). This difference is also found in other species of animals.

Hu (1994) suggested that the respiratory quotient (RQ) of the growing yak determined by metabolism significantly declined with increasing altitude, from 0.744 (2 261 m) to 0.696 (3 250 m) and 0.545 (4 272 m). But with no significant difference among age groups, the values less than 0.7 indicate disordered metabolism (perhaps ketosis). Lower atmospheric pressure and oxygen contents in the air at higher altitudes may be the main factors that lead to reductions in the respiratory quotient of growing yak. Corresponding information from other species would be interesting but appears not to be available. Hu (1994) also indicated that ambient temperature has a great effect on FHP and other physiological indices in the yak (see Tables 14.9 and 14.10). But the FHP remained fairly constant and, correspondingly, the body temperature, heart rate and respiratory rate of yak were stable in the environmental temperature range of 8° - 14°C. So the thermoneutral zone of the yak was estimated as 8° - 14°C (see Chapter 4).

Further work by Hu (1994 and 1997) on the measurement of the relationship of bodyweight (W) and surface area of the growing yak, by using the method of plaster (pasting paper) on the animalûs body, showed that the highest correlation existed between surface area and $W^{0.52}$. An equation of FHP = 916 kJ per kg $W^{0.52}$ per day (n=25 r=0.8469, P<0.01) was obtained.

In the light of the equation, Hu concluded that yak calfûs FHP value is clearly lower than that of the dairy cattle calf and Holstein heifer and that the heat lost per 1 kg $W^{0.52}$ from yak is lower than for other cattle species. The lower fasting heat production of the yak and its stability at different altitudes are probably an adaptive response to life in an alpine-cold and oxygen-depleted environment and to the nutritional deprivation that yak experience in winter and spring. These features could be the result of long-term natural selection.

Table 14.8 The fasting heat production (FHP, KJ per kg $W^{0.75}$ per day) of growing yak and cattle at different altitudes in summer [Source: adapted from Hu, 1994]

Height above sea level (m)	Age (months)	Yak			Qinghai yellow cattle		
		n	BW*(kg)	FHP	n	BW*(kg)	FHP
2 261	12	3	49.9	351.5	3	98.4	292.4
3 250	12	3	44.6	328.8	4	102.6	414.4
4 271	12	3	57.7	376.2	3	115.7	516.4
2 261	24	7	99.5	305.3	4	138.5	250.5
3 250	24	4	104.7	321.4	4	143.9	353.3
4 271	24	3	101.8	324.8	3	140.4	387.9
2 261	36	6	141.1	302.2	4	229.5	219.1
3 250	36	4	126.2	327.7	4	238.1	357.4
4 271	36	3	150.1	281.1	3	212.7	359.9

*Bodyweight.

Metabolizable energy for maintenance

The energy requirement for maintenance is a useful term for expressing the level of the exogenous nutrient supply. It is defined as the metabolizable energy (ME) input per day at which the animals are in energy balance. Han *et al.* (1990b; 1991) used a respiration mask method to estimate the metabolizable energy requirement for maintenance (ME_m) in growing yak and found its value to be 460.2 kJ per kg $W^{0.75}$ per day. In the same experiment, the authors also estimated the efficiency of utilization of metabolizable energy for maintenance (k_m) in growing yak to be around 0.66.

Table 14.9 Regression equations between fasting heat production (FHP) and ambient temperature (T °C) [Source: Hu, 1994]

Range of temperature (°C)	$Y=a+bx$	n	R	r significance
(-30) - (-20)	FHP = 891 - 18.4T	37	-0.2917	P<0.05
(-20) - 0	FHP = 1 188 - 15.5T	40	0.4744	P<0.01
0 - 10	FHP = 1 155 - 13.8T	46	0.2431	P<0.10
8 - 15	FHP = 1 080 + 0.7T	52	0.0066	P>0.10
15 - 23	FHP = 1 017 + 10.5T	48	0.2735	P<0.05

Table 14.10 Critical upper-limit temperature (°C) leading to a rise in physiological indices [Source: Hu, 1994]

Physiological index	Yak	Holstein-Friesian	Jersey	Swiss brown	Indian zebu
Body temperature	14.0	21.1	23.9	26.7	35.0
Heart rate	15.0	32.2	37.8	35.0	37.8
Respiratory rate	13.0	15.6	15.6	15.6	23.9

Energy requirements for standing and walking

As the yak is a grazing animal, two of its most common activities are standing up and moving on. Han *et al.* (1989) compared the energy requirements for standing and walking in yak with those in Qinghai yellow cattle at an elevation of 3 000 m. Table 14.11 shows that the yak (115.3 kg) generates much more heat (J per kg $W^{0.75}$ m) in the course of walking than do the larger Qinghai yellow cattle (170.5 kg) and other cattle or dairy cows. The energy expenditure of the yak is a little higher in the course of standing (V_0) than that of Qinghai yellow cattle. The author attributes the difference in heat production to the difference in body size and breed, as smaller animals are expected to generate more heat during walking (Blaxter, 1962). Table 14.11 also indicates that the higher the speed of moving the more heat is generated both in yak and Qinghai yellow cattle. Correspondingly, the respiratory quotients of the animals in the course of standing and walking with speeds of 1 metre per second or 1.5 m per second are, respectively, 0.68, 0.65 and 0.59 J per kg $W^{0.75}$ per minute for yak, and 0.79, 0.73 and 0.77 J per kg $W^{0.75}$ per minute, respectively, for cattle.

Energy requirements for growth

Han *et al.* (1990b) estimated metabolizable energy requirements for growth (ME_g) in growing yak (n=7) through an energy balance trial on six two- to three-year-old animals by rationing their intakes of concentrate to a series of levels. The daily metabolizable energy requirement of growing yak was estimated as: ME (MJ/d) = $0.45W^{0.75}$ + (8.73 + 0.091 W) ΔG, where W is the body weight and ΔG is daily gain (kg), and the efficiency of utilization of metabolizable energy for growth (k_g) in yak is 0.49.

Such a high value might be considered to apply only to diets rich in concentrates. However, similar results were obtained from other trials when animals were given coarse fodders (Han *et al.*, 1992 and Dong *et al.*, 2000a).

Table 14.11 Energy expenditure (EE, J per kg $W^{0.75}$ m) of yak and other cattle species moving at various speeds at an elevation of 3000m
[Source: adapted from Han *et al.*, 1989]

Animal	Age (months)	Live weight (kg)	EE in movement by speed (V, m/s) of:			Source
			$V*_0$=0	V_1=1	V_2=1.5	
Yak	24 (n=4)	115.3	0.35	1.93	2.35	Han *et al.* (1989)
Qy cattle[1]	24 (n=4)	170.5	0.31	1.48	1.75	Han *et al.* (1989)
Cattle					2.00	Hall&Brody (1934)*
					2.10	Ribeiro (1976)*
Dairy cow					2.00	Ribeiro (1977)*
					2.09	Webster (1978)*
				1.39	1.19	Jiang (1987)*
					2.00	ARC (1980)*

[1]Qy cattle = Qinghai yellow cattle. *J per kg $W^{0.75}$ per minute).

* Quoted by Han *et al.*, 1989

Energy requirements for lactation

Data on energy requirements for lactation are still scarce, as only preliminary studies on dietary energy digestion and metabolism in lactating yak have been conducted by a few researchers (Long *et al.*, 1998; Dong *et al.*, 2000a).

Protein nutrition

The animal needs protein to support its functions, including tissue maintenance, growth of lean tissue, wool and the products of conception and for milk-protein synthesis.

Dietary protein digestion and metabolism

As with dietary energy, utilization efficiency of dietary protein in the yak differs with diet composition and feeding level and with age, sex, body condition and the productive stage of the animal (growth, lactation etc.). Long *et al.* (1998) reported that when yak cows were fed with oat hay *ad libitum* (CP: 8.5 percent), there was no difference between lactating and dry cows in crude protein digestibility, although lactating yak tended to consume more feed than dry yak. However, lactating yak with a milk yield of 1.2 - 1.8 kg per day showed a negative balance of nitrogen, while dry yak were in positive balance.

With regard to excretion of endogenous urinary nitrogen, Long *et al.* (1999a) found that the daily fasting nitrogen excretion of 316 mg per kg $W^{0.75}$ per day for yak cows was similar to that found for buffalo (275 mg per kg $W^{0.75}$) (Chen *et al.*, 1996). Possession of such a low value suggests that yak could have evolved a mechanism to recycle more nitrogen to the rumen than do cattle.

Non-protein nitrogen metabolism

Non-protein nitrogen (NPN) has been used as an extra source of nitrogen for microbial protein synthesis in dairy and beef production but not so in yak. Xie *et al.* (1989) found a higher concentration of NH_3-N in the rumen of growing yak fed with ammonia-treated straw than in animals fed with untreated straw (Figure 14.1). Also pH, VFA production and the density of ciliated protozoa in the yak rumen increased correspondingly with NPN ingestion. Clearly, as a ruminant, the yak can use NPN as efficiently as other ruminants. Chai *et al.* (1996) indicated that when a basal diet (containing 4.2 percent of CP) was supplemented with urea (to give a diet containing 7.3 percent of CP), there was a great increase in the concentration of NH_3-N in the yak rumen that, in turn, improved the microbial protein production (Table 14.12). This shows that the utilization of dietary nitrogen can be improved by adding a source of NPN (such as urea).

Purine and creatinine metabolism

The excretion of total purine derivatives in urine is used to estimate the supply of microbial protein to the host animal in some ruminants (Chen *et al.,* 1990). Long *et al.* (1999a) investigated the profiles of urinary excretion of purine derivatives and creatinine in the yak and found them to be similar to those of cattle and buffalo, irrespective of feed levels or fasting.

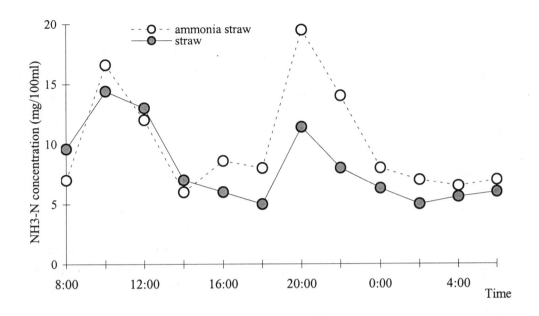

Figure 14.1 Effect of diets on NH₃-N concentration in growing yak rumen
[Source: Xie Aoyun, *et al* 1989]

Table 14.12 Effect of urea additive on degradability of nitrogen and efficiency of
microbial protein synthesis in the rumen of the growing yak (n=3, ±SD)
[Source: Chai *et al.* 1996]

Animal	Source of nitrogen	Nitrogen degradability (%)	Production of microbial protein in rumen (g/d)	Efficiency of microbial protein synthesis (g/kg degradable DM)
Mean	Basal diets*	21.5±1.3	90.6±10.4	64.4±5.2
	Basal diets + urea #	24.4±0.3	125.3±7.7	101.0±6.4

* Basal diet, 70 percent pea straw + 28 percent maize + 1 percent fish meal + 0.5 percent salt + 0.5 percent
additive; # Urea, 1.09 percent

The endogenous purine derivative excretion (0.22 mmol per kg $W^{0.75}$ per day) in the yak is
only 40 percent of that noted in cattle but is similar to that found in buffaloes (Chen *et al.*,
1990, 1996). The relationships between total purine derivative excretion in yak urine
(mmol per kg $W^{0.75)}$ and digestible dry matter intake and digestible organic matter intake
were significant (P<0.001), but this was not so for creatinine excretion (Table 14.13). The
value of creatinine excretion (0.25 mmol/kg $W^{0.75}$ per day) for fasting yak was much lower
than the findings reported for buffalo and cattle (Chen *et al.*, 1992, 1996).

Protein requirements for maintenance

Protein requirements for tissue maintenance, growth, lactation and wool and hair growth have been well discussed for many ruminants other than the yak. There is as yet little information to define the protein requirement for maintenance in yak. Xue *et al.* (1994) used the comparative-slaughter method to measure the rumen degradable crude protein requirement for maintenance ($RDCP_m$) (n = 9, age: one and a half years) and obtained a value of $6.09W^{0.52}$ g per day for growing yak.

Protein requirements for growth

For growing yak, the protein requirements include that for maintenance ($RDCP_m$) and for body weight gain ($RDCP_g$). According to Xue *et al.* (1994), the latter can be calculated as follows, $RDCP_g = (1.1548/\Delta G + 0.509/W^{0.52})^{-1}$. Combining the value of $6.09W^{0.52}$ (for $RDCP_m$), the protein requirement of growing yak can be calculated as RDCP (g per day) = $6.09W^{0.52} + (1.16/\Delta G + 0.05/W^{0.52})^{-1}$, where ΔG is daily gain (g per day). However, these calculations need more experiments to validate them.

Table 14.13 Feed intake, dry-matter digestibility (DMD), daily intake of digestible dry matter (DDMI) and daily urinary excretion of purine derivatives (PD), creatinine and nitrogen in three yak
[Source: Long *et al.*, 1999a]

Intake level	Live weight (kg)	DMD	DDMI (g/kg $W^{0.75}$)	Allantoin (mmol/kg $W^{0.75}$)	Uric acid (mmol/kg $W^{0.75}$)	Total PD (mmol/kg $W^{0.75}$)	Creatinine (mmol/kg $W^{0.75}$)	Nitrogen (mg/kg $W^{0.75}$)
0.3 VI*	175	0.66	17.2	0.32	0.07	0.39	0.67	275
0.6 VI	180	0.63	32.1	0.46	0.08	0.54	0.60	309
0.9 VI	186	0.56	38.1	0.61	0.09	0.70	0.52	283

*Voluntary intake.

Protein requirements for lactation

To date, little information on protein requirements for lactation is available. Only preliminary studies on protein digestion and metabolism in lactating yak have been conducted by some researchers (Long *et al.*, 1998; Dong *et al.*, 2000a).

Mineral nutrition

Compared with energy and protein nutrition, mineral nutrition in the yak is poorly documented. Long *et al.* (1999c) indicated that inorganic phosphate (P) is sufficient for various categories of yak (calf, heifer, dry cow, lactating cow) (n = 30) during the warm season when grazing was on alpine meadows, with good quality pasture as the sole food. But in the spring and early summer, dietary phosphate failed to meet yak requirements. Dong *et al.* (2000a) analysed the calcium (Ca) and phosphorus (P) balance of three lactating yak (170 - 200 kg) fed indoors on various diets (Table 14.14) or on an oat and hay diet at different levels (Table 14.15). Either or both Ca and P showed negative balance. Yan Ping *et al.* (2002) suggested that yak living in the Qinghai Lake area were suffering sodium (Na) and copper (Cu) deficiency but not of other minerals. It seems that there may be a shortage of molybdenum on Tianzhu alpine rangelands (Zhou Zhiyu, personal communication, 2002).

Mineral and trace element deficiency

Effects of mineral or trace element deficiency or imbalance on yak health conditions are not adequately documented throughout the Qinghai-Tibetan Plateau (but see reference to possible Cu and Mb deficiency earlier). However, the symptoms of copper deficiency in yak have been recorded at Whipsnade Wild Animal Park in England, where they noted a difference in the uptake of copper between yak and other *Bovidae* and local domestic cattle (see chapter 9 on disease). Zhang (1998) demonstrated that milk production of Tianzhu White yak was lifted significantly when animals were supplemented with urea molasses multi-nutrient blocks (UMMB) containing 10 percent urea, 0.1 percent mixed minerals and trace elements (Fe, Zn, Mg, Cu, etc.) during lactation (see Chapter 6).

Though yak living in different regions may face different kinds of mineral problems, deficiencies and imbalances could well exist on the Qinghai-Tibetan Plateau as in other parts of the world. However, up to the present, identification of such has not been made and appropriate supplementation has not been much studied in the various yak-raising areas because, understandably, most attention has been given to the animal requirements for the macronutrients.

Feeding

There is as yet insufficient data to describe the nutritional status of the yak accurately under the normal, year-round grazing conditions. However, an approach for developing appropriate feeding strategies for yak on native grasslands can be made with other existing information. Such information relates to forage availability, nutritive values of native forages, known gaps between the supply of feed and the requirements of the animals and the effects of the limited number of supplementary feeding strategies so far investigated (see Chapter 13).

Table 14.14 Balance of calcium (Ca) and phosphorus (P) in lactating yak (n=3) fed with different diets [Source: Dong *et al.*, 2000a]

Content of Ca, P (g/d)	Diets		
	100% oat straw (A)	50% oat straw + 50% maize meal (B)	50% oat straw + 43.5% maize meal +6% rape meal + 0.5% salt (C)
Ca			
Intake	15.3	6.2	7.3
Faeces	24.0	18.0	15.4
Urine	1.1	1.5	2.2
Milk	3.0	2.1	3.7
Retention	−12.8	−15.4	−14.0
P			
Intake	7.0	4.5	6.3
Faeces	7.1	4.3	5.4
Urine	0.49	2.0	5.5
Milk	0.74	0.68	0.65
Retention	−1.4	−2.4	−5.2

Table 14.15 Balance of calcium (Ca) and phosphorus (P) in dry yak (n=3) at different intake levels [Source: Dong *et al.*, 2000b]

Content of Ca, P (g/d)	Intake levels		
	0.3VI	0.6VI	0.9VI
Ca			
Intake	4.9	9.7	13.7
Faeces	8.1	16.0	19.7
Urine	0.8	1.2	1.6
Retention	−3.9	−7.5	−7.6
P			
Intake	2.3	4.5	6.3
Faeces	1.7	4.3	5.4
Urine	1.0	2.4	2.8
Retention	−0.4	−2.2	−1.9

Forage availability to grazing yak

Several researchers have reported the feed availability on the Qinghai-Tibetan Plateau (Xie *et al.*, 1996a; Long *et al.*, 1999b). The uneven feed supply throughout a year suggests that grazing yak require feed supplements in the harsh winter on the Plateau. Harvesting oats and some productive perennials or imported crop residues (agricultural by-products) from nearby farming areas could be alternative feed sources to partly alleviate feed deficiency of yak in winter, provided this can be seen as cost-effective.

Seasonality of forage nutrients

Nutritive value and nutrient production of native forages vary seasonally on the Plateau, together with the variation of forage yield. Xie *et al.* (1996a) found that nitrogen (N) in the dry matter of native forages on the Qinghai-Tibetan Plateau declined from 2.5 percent in June to 1.0 percent in November (Figure 14.2a), while gross energy (GE) dropped from 17.0 MJ per sq m in August to 10 MJ per sq m in November (Figure 14.2b), resulting in N and GE deficiency in the diet of grazing yak. Consequently yak lost much body weight during late winter and spring (cf. Chapter 6) if without appropriate supplementation.

Relation between the nutrient supply
of forages and physiological states of grazing animals

Long *et al.* (1999c) estimated the nutrition situation of yak (n=43) based on the variation of beta-hydroxybutyrate (BHB) values in the serum of yak cows as the grazing season progressed. These results, together with other data shown in Table 14.16, imply generally poor nutrition rather than a specific nutrient deficiency and reflect the quantity of grazing available as winter progressed. This provides some evidence to explain why yak show large weight loss and a loss of condition over winter and early spring (cf. Chapter 6).

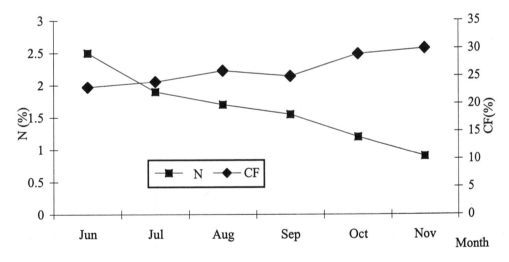

Figure 14.2a. Seasonal variation of nitrogen (N) and crude-fibre (CF) contents in native forages [Source: Xie Aoyun *et al.*, 1996a]

Supplementation feeding

Detailed investigations have shown that supplementation can improve the productivity of grazing yak (Long, 1994; Long *et al.*, 1999c; Zhang, 1998; Xie *et al.*, 1996b, 1997; Wang *et al.*, 1997a & b). Most of these studies were concentrated on energy and protein supplementation.

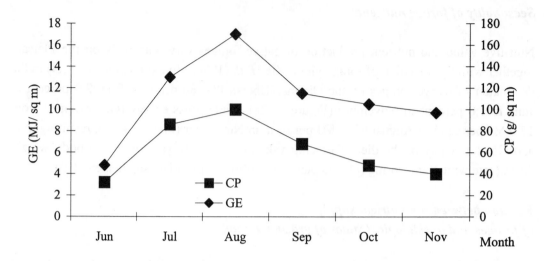

Figure 14.2b. Seasonal yield of crude protein (CP) and gross energy (GE) in the alpine meadow [Source: Xie Aoyun *et al.*, 1996a]

Xiao *et al.* (1996b) and Wang *et al.* (1997a) demonstrated that calving rate and calf growth rate can be greatly improved when grazing animals are supplemented with concentrates at 0.14 - 0.25 kg per day (containing 50 percent maize, 30 percent rape cake, 18 percent wheat bran, 1 percent salt and 1 percent minerals) from July to November.

Table 14.16 The nutrient metabolites of cows before and after calving (n=34) (mean±SD) [Source: Long *et al.*, 1999c]

Season	Stage	No. of animals	Albumin (g/l)	Globulin (g/l)	Urea (mmol/l)	BHB[a] (mmol/l)	Pi[b] (mmol/l)
Spring	Pre-calving	12	31.1 ± 6.5	32.3 ± 8.7	8.2 ± 1.6	0.94 ± 0.2	1.5 ± 0.3
	2 weeks post-calving	13	30.5 ± 6.4	34.1 ± 7.7	6.9 ± 1.1	0.51 ± 0.2	1.5 ± 0.3
Summer	2 months post-calving	26	36.9 ± 2.8	36.6 ± 6.1	5.7 ± 1.3	1.4 ± 0.6	2.6 ± 0.4
Autumn	4 months post-calving	22	44.9 ± 2.6	27.1 ± 7.6	5.5 ± 1.1	1.1 ± 0.3	1.8 ± 0.3

[a] β-hydroxybutyrate [b] Inorganic phosphorus

On the other hand, Long *et al.* (1999c) reported that supplementation with fibrous feeds (oat hay and highland barley straw) had a significant effect on the productivity of yak cows under normal grazing conditions in Tianzhu county, western Gansu province (Table 14.17). Therefore, the practice of supplementation seems important for attaining the productive and reproductive potentials of grazing yak cows and improving their output on the Qinghai-Tibetan Plateau.

Urea blocks can be used as supplementary feed to provide grazing yak with non-protein nitrogen and other necessary nutrients. Xie *et al.* (1997) reported that supplements of urea blocks in winter (from November to the following May) can reduce dramatically the weight loss of yak calves (Table 14.18) and increase their survival rate (Wang *et al.*, 1997b).

Table 14.17 Effect of supplementation with hay or straw on yak productivity (mean ±SD) [Source: Long *et al.*, 1999c]

Item	GNS[a]	GOH[b]	GBS[c]
Number of animals	41	30	33
Body weight:			
Initial (kg)	230±67	216±28	221±34
Final (kg)	187±49	221±23	212±28
Supplementary food:			
Feeding period (months)	-	5	5
Oat hay (kg DM/day)	-	1-15	-
Highland barley straw (kg DM/day)	-	-	1-1.5
Milk yield (kg/day)	$1.0^d\pm0.2$	1.2^d	1.1^d
Milking period (days)	$113^e\pm88$	$142^f\pm55$	$138^f\pm33$
Calving cows (No.)	22	23	24
Calving rate (%)	53.7^e	76.7^f	72.7^g
Live weight change (kg)	$-43.4^e\pm11.6$	$-4.8^f\pm3.1$	$-8.5^g\pm5.9$
Body condition score (1-5)	$2.2^g\pm0.2$	$3.0^h\pm1.0$	$2.6^h\pm0.9$

[a] Grazing nil supplement, [b] Grazing + oat hay, [c] Grazing + highland barley straw; [d,e,f,g,h] values with the same superscript letter (within rows) do not differ significantly. Those with a different superscript letter differ significantly (P<0.05).

Use of the blocks also had a great effect on reproductive performance of adult cows when provided during the summer (June to August) (Zhang, 1998). Urea blocks are an alternative option for maintaining the body weight and productivity of grazing yak in winter when they are facing protein deficiency on the Qinghai-Tibetan Plateau (see Chapter 6 for supplementary feeding in relation to milk production).

Table 14.18 Effect of urea blocks as a supplement on yak body
weight during winter (mean ±SD) [Source: Xie *et al*., 1997]

Age (year)	Group	No.	Initial weight (kg)	Final weight (kg)	Average weight loss (kg/199days)	t-test
2	Control	7	88.4 ± 12.5	65.6 ± 6.1	22.8	P<0.05
	Supplemented	7	85.2 ± 8.8	78.2 ± 11.2	6.9	
3	Control	7	133.2 ± 8.7	107.9 ± 11.8	25.3	P<0.05
	Supplemented	7	136.6 ± 14.7	133.6 ± 10.5	3.0	

References

Bi Xichao *et al.* (1989). Determination on degradability of several kinds of protein feeds in yak rumen. *Journal of Qinghai Animal Husbandry and Veterinary Medicine,* 19(4), 21-22, 6.

Blaxter, K. L. (1962). *The Energy Metabolism of Ruminants.* London, Hutchinson Scientific and Technical.

Chai Shatuo *et al.* (1996). Study on utilization rate of feed nitrogen content in growing yak. *China Herbivores,* (4), 36-39.

Chen, X.B. *et al.* (1990). Excretion of purine derivatives by ruminants: endogenous excretion, difference between cattle and sheep. *British Journal of Nutrition,* 63, 121-129.

Chen, X.B. *et al.* (1992). Effect of feeding frequency on diurnal variation in plasma and urinary purine derivatives in steers. *Animal Production,* 55, 185-191.

Chen, X. B. *et al.* (1996). Urinary excretion of purine derivatives and tissue xanthine oxidase (EC 1. 2. 3. 2) activity in buffaloes (*Bubalis bubalis*) with special reference to differences between buffaloes and *Bos taurus* cattle. *British Journal of Nutrition,* 75, 397-407.

Dong S. K. *et al.* (1997). Effect of feeding level on energy and nitrogen metabolism of dry, non-pregnant yak. *Proceedings of the second international congress on yak, in Xining, China, 1-6 September 1997.* Xining, China, Qinghai People's Publishing House, pp. 117-120.

Dong S. K. *et al.* (2000a). Conversion of energy and metabolism of nitrogen, calcium and phosphorus in lactating yak. Acta Prataculturae Sinica, 9(4), 20-27.

Dong S. K., Long Ruijun & Hu Zizhi. (2000b). A study on conversion of energy and metabolism of protein, calcium and phosphorus in dry yak. Acta Prataculturae Sinica, 9(2), 32-37.

Gansukh S. 1997. Effect of age and grazing on pH value and volatile fatty acid in the rumen of yak calves. *Proceedings of the second international congress on yak, in Xining, China, 1-6 September 1997.* Xining, China, Qinghai People's Publishing House, pp. 100-101.

Han Xingtai, Hu Linghao & Xie Aoyun (1989). Energy expenditure of growing yak and growing cattle in movement. *Journal of Qinghai Animal Husbandry and Veterinary Medicine,* 19(5), 8-10.

Han Xingtai, Xie Aoyun & Hu Linghao (1990a). Feed intake of growing yak. *Journal of Qinghai Animal Husbandry and Veterinary Medicine,* 20(6), 5-6, 39.

Han Xingtai *et al.* (1990b). Energy metabolism of growing yak. *Journal of Qinghai Animal Husbandry and Veterinary Medicine,* 20(4), 31-33.

Han Xingtai & Xie Aoyun (1991). Verificial report on requirement of maintenance energy in growing yak. *Journal of Qinghai Animal Husbandry and Veterinary Medicine*, 21(1), 10.

Han Xingtai *et al.* (1992). Estimate on the energy metabolism of growing yak as they fed coarse fodder. *Journal of Qinghai Animal Husbandry and Veterinary Medicine*, 22(2), 21-22.

Han Xingtai, Xie Aoyun & Hu Linghao (1996). The dilution rate of rumen fluid and digesta in yak receiving various diets. *Journal of Qinghai Animal Husbandry and Veterinary Medicine*, 26(3), 1-4.

Han, Z. K. (1994). Improve performance in yak by study of nutritional ecology and physiology, Proceedings of the first international congress on yak. *Journal of Gansu Agricultural University* (Special issue June 1994) pp. 231-235.

Hu Linghao (1994). Study on energy metabolism and ruminal metabolism in growing yaks. Proceedings of the first international congress on yak. *Journal of Gansu Agricultural University* (Special issue June 1994) pp. 188-195.

Hu Linghao (1997). *Recent Advance in Yak Nutrition*. Xining: Qinghai People's Publishing House.

Liu Haibo (1989). *China Yakology*. Beijing: China Agricultural Publishing House.

Liu Shujie *et al.* (1991). Determination of rumen fluid volume and flow speed of Chinese yak under housing condition. *Journal of Qinghai Animal Husbandry and Veterinary Medicine*, 21(6), 5-6.

Liu Shujie *et al.* (1997). Study on the forage intake at different phonological periods in grazing yak. *Journal of Qinghai Animal Husbandry and Veterinary Medicine*, 27(2), 4-8.

Liu Shujie *et al.* (1992). The rumen fluid VFA of Chinese yak varying with different raising conditions. *Journal of Qinghai Animal Husbandry and Veterinary Medicine*, 22(3), 17-18.

Long R. J. (1994). Milk performance of yak cows under traditional feeding and management on small Tibetan farms. *Acta Prataculturae Sinica* 1, 71-76.

Long R. J. *et al.* (1997). Digestive and metabolic characteristics of lactating yak fed different diets. *Proceedings of the second international congress on yak, in Xining, China, 1-6 September 1997*. Xining, China, Qinghai People's Publishing House, pp 124-126.

Long R. J., Dong Shikui & Hu Zizhi (1998). Nutrient digestion and metabolism in lactating and dry yak cows. *Acta Prataculturae Sinica*, 7(3), 51-55.

Long R. J. *et al.* (1999a). Preliminary studies on urinary excretion of purine derivatives and creatinine in yak. *Journal of Agricultural Science. Cambridge,* 133, 427-431.

Long R. J. *et al.* (1999b). Feed value of native forages of the Tibetan Plateau of China. *Animal Feed Science and Technology*, 80, 101-113.

Long R. J. *et al.* (1999c). Effect of strategic feed supplementation on productive and reproductive performance in yak cows. *Preventive Veterinary Medicine,* 38, 195-206.

Shi J. J. *et al.* (1997). Energy metabolism and nitrogen, phosphorus and calcium balance in suckling yak calves receiving diet consisting of concentrate and straw. *Proceedings of the second international congress on yak, in Xining, China, 1-6 September 1997*. Xining, China, Qinghai People's Publishing House, pp 132-134.

Van Soest P. J. (1987). *Nutritional Ecology of the Ruminant* (second edition). New York: Cornell University Press.

Wang Wanbang *et al.* (1997a). Effect on body weight gain of grazing yak and Tibetan sheep as they fed concentrate supplement. *Gansu Animal Husbandry and Veterinary Medicine*, 27(3), 11-12.

Wang Wanbang *et al.* (1997b). Effect of compound urea block supplement on the anti-disaster of yak and Tibetan sheep. *Feed Technology,* 18(2), 30-31.

Xie Aoyun *et al*. (1989). Study on ruminal digestible metabolism in growing yak under barn feeding conditions. *Journal of Qinghai Animal Husbandry and Veterinary Medicine*, 19 (2), 2-5.

Xie Aoyun *et al*. (1990). Determination on degradability of several kinds of protein feeds in yak rumen. *Journal of Qinghai Animal Husbandry and Veterinary Medicine*, 20(3), 10-11.

Xie Aoyun *et al*. (1992). Effect of different nutritive levels on rumen VFA for Chinese yak. *Journal of Qinghai Animal Husbandry and Veterinary Medicine*, 22(3), 5-7.

Xie Aoyun *et al* (1996a). The herbage yield and the nutrient variation in mountain meadow. *Journal of Qinghai Animal Husbandry and Veterinary Medicine*, 26(2), 8-10.

Xie Aoyun *et al*. (1996b). Effect of concentrate supplementation performance of yak and Tibetan sheep grazed on summer and autumn pasture. *Journal of Qinghai Animal Husbandry and Veterinary Medicine*, 26(1), 17-18.

Xie Aoyun *et al*. (1997). Effect of molasses-urea block supplementation on the performance of yak and Tibetan sheep. *In*: Hu Linghao (Ed). *Recent Advance in Yak Nutrition*. Xining: Qinghai People's Publishing House.

Xue Bai *et al*. (1994). Study on the protein requirement of growing yak. *Journal of Qinghai Animal Husbandry and Veterinary Medicine*, 24(4), 1-4.

Yan Xuebing (2000). Digestibility of natural and cultivated grasslands by yak in alpine pastoral region. MSc. thesis, Lanzhou: Gansu Agricultural University.

Yan Ping *et al*. (2002). Seasonal changes in forage nutrients and mineral contents in water resources, forage and yak blood. *Proceedings of the third international congress on yak, in Lhasa, P.R. China, 4-9 September 2000*. International Livestock Research Institute (ILRI), Nairobi, Kenya. pp. 280-282.

Zhang Degang (1998). Supplementary feeding on urea molasses multinutrient blocks and effect on productive performance of yak cows. *Acta Prataculturae Sinica*, 7(1), 65-69.

15 MOLECULAR AND CYTOGENETICS IN YAK – A SCIENTIFIC BASIS FOR BREEDING AND EVIDENCE FOR PHYLOGENY

by Han Jianlin[1]

OVERVIEW

Genetics provides the basis for developing breeding programs aimed at improving productivity and fitness of yak. However, quantitative genetic characterization is largely absent for the yak because the prerequisite of recording pedigrees and performance has not been widely practised in relation to the yak population. This is due in part to the remoteness and harsh conditions of most of the yak territories, but also because, until now, yak keeping has been more of a way of life than a strictly economic activity.

The techniques of cytogenetics and, more recently, of molecular genetics, which have been used widely to characterize other farm livestock and explore the basis of their heredity, are being applied in the yak, though not, as yet, to the same extent. Much of this work on other species of cattle is, however, proving relevant to yak. Thus, the identification of quantitative trait loci (QTL) and the exploration of marker-assisted selection in cattle may also provide a basis for improving the yak.

These studies in the yak are also providing evidence of the extent of breed differentiation that, in turn, is relevant for conservation policies. Further, the cytogenetics and, more importantly, the molecular information are providing evidence of the relationship of the yak to other cattle species. In this context, the new evidence supports the view that the yak should be assigned to the subgenus *Poephagus* and not to the more widely adopted *Bos*. This chapter reviews the studies in these areas with yak.

Introduction

The aim of yak breeding, as for other livestock, is to improve productivity or to affect other desirable changes. For some traits it is easy to bring about changes because the traits are relatively simply inherited and controlled by a very small number of genes; for example, most coat colours or the presence or absence of horns. Moreover, for such so-called qualitative characteristics, the inherited component is the major and usually the only component responsible for variation in the trait across a population. By contrast, the so-called quantitative traits (variation in quantity rather than quality of the trait), represented by most aspects of performance, such as milk and meat production,

---

[1] Han Jainlin is a molecular geneticist at the International Livestock Research Institute, Kenya. He is also Professor of Animal Genetics and Breeding, Gansu Agriculture University, China and Executive Secretary of the International Yak Information Center and China Breed Association in Lanzhou, China

reproductive rate, health and so on, are also affected to a greater or lesser extent by the environment.

Thus, even if the same complement of genes for growth rate were present in two groups of animals, those that were better fed would grow better. For this reason it is difficult to differentiate between the extent of genetic and non-genetic influences, unless very precise rules are followed in making the comparisons and there are good records of both parentage and performance. The important point is that for the vast majority of traits of the yak, the individual's phenotype is not equivalent to its genotype. However, under uniform conditions for contemporary animals, the better performing will generally be genetically more desirable than less-well performing contemporary individuals. It is by this means that, over generations, livestock breeders have been able to make changes and improvements to their livestock, although as discussed elsewhere in this book, individual yak productivity is, at best, only one of the criteria considered by yak herders in maintaining their herds.

The way to effect genetic change, generally intended to produce some improvement, is to utilize identifiable genetic variation in a herd or larger grouping within a breed by means of selection, or to use differences among breeds (or, for example, between domestic and wild yak) by a process of crossbreeding and, finally, and of particular relevance for the yak, to make use of differences between the yak and other species of cattle by way of hybridization. Each of these routines has its rules and particular consequences, reviewed in relation to yak by Wiener (1994, 1997). Particularly for purposes of selection, the conditions for identifying genetic variation cannot reasonably be met for the great majority of the yak under the normally extensive management, although Goe and Stranzinger (2002) recently proposed a recording scheme they regard as practical under these conditions. Even on the few government or research farms where the potential ought to exist for accurate and sustained recording of parentage and performance, a prerequisite for accurate selection, these opportunities for selection do not appear to have been much exploited (with at least one honourable exception). In consequence, yak have been left out of the revolution in breeding practice of most of the other major livestock species - particularly those kept relatively intensively like poultry, pigs and dairy cattle. Nonetheless, a number of breed development schemes for yak, run by herders, have existed for a long time and some more recent schemes have led to the development of a new breed of yak – based on a cross of domestic and wild yak. These matters are described in Chapter 2 and referred to again in the concluding chapter.

With regard to crossbreeding and to hybridization involving yak, the nature of the genetic reasons for changes in performance, heterosis in particular, have not been quantified because the means for doing so are not usually present (see Chapter 3). Claims for the degrees of heterosis generated by crossbreeding or hybridization with yak will need verification.

New methodologies are emerging, in particular those of molecular genetics and cytogenetics. These aim, in the case of molecular genetics, to identify genetic variation directly from differences within the sequences of the DNA (deoxyribonucleic acid), which is the material of chromosomes on which the genes are located. The cytogenetic approach, which has a longer history, attempts to identify variation in chromosomal structures as seen in preparations under a microscope. The ultimate hope is that such variation, close to the gene or actually involving the gene, can be linked to the differences in fitness and performance in the population or even at an individual animal level. Because such techniques, though complex and demanding, do not depend in the first instance on large-scale herd recording, they provide a challenge for geneticists working with yak as they do for those concerned with other species. A significant start has been made in these areas with yak; the rest of this chapter will provide recent results and, where necessary, some background to the techniques.

Chromosomal work – cytogenetics

As already noted (Chapter 2), yak with 30 chromosome pairs have the same number as other cattle, and domestic and wild yak have similar complements. Li Jiyou *et al.* (1994), Han Jianlin (1996), Zhong Jingcheng (1996) and Nivsarkar *et al.* (1997) reviewed the progress of research on chromosomes of the Chinese and Indian yak in comparison with *Bos taurus* cattle and their hybrids with yak. Zhong Jingcheng found that the structure and size of all 29 pairs of autosomes and the X-chromosome are very similar among five Chinese breeds but that the Y-chromosome shows differences in terms of its relative length and structure (see Table 15.1). However, these differences are small and cannot be taken as markers for distinguishing the species of the yak from either *Bos taurus* or *Bos indicus* cattle (Gupta *et al.*, 1996) or to distinguish the yak breeds from each other (Han Jianlin, 1996).

Halnan (1989) and Zhong Jingcheng (1996) published some detailed G- and C-banded karyotypes of the yak in order to investigate genetic differentiation among the yak breeds. After comparing the C-banded patterns and Ag-NORs between the Maiwa and Jiulong yak, Zhong Jingcheng (1996, 1997) concluded that the visible differences in heterochromatin quantity and distribution between these two breeds were not significant, as similar differences occurred among the individuals within a breed. In spite of proposals for standardization of karyotyping across laboratories, no reliable data are available for use as genetic markers on the chromosome structures of different yak breeds (Han Jianlin, 1996).

Table 15.1 X- and Y-chromosome polymorphisms in yak*
[Source: Zhong Jingcheng, 1996; Nivsarkar *et al.*, 1997]

Population	X-chromosome		Y-chromosome	
	Relative length	Arm ratio	Relative length	Arm ratio
Maiwa	5.11	1.90 (SM)	1.89	2.67 (SM)
Jiulong	4.87	1.77 (SM)	1.71	2.60 (SM)
Tibet	4.59	2.08 (SM)	2.08	(SM)
Huanhu	4.72	1.89 (SM)	2.36	2.46 (SM)
Zhongdian	4.80	1.86 (SM)	2.56	1.87 (SM)
Kyrgyz	5.78	2.32 (SM)		(SM)
Indian	4.95	(SM)	2.44	(M)
Wild yak	4.96	1.96 (SM)	1.57	2.31 (SM)

*Note: Relative length = length of individual chromosome/total length of the haploid with X-chromosome included; arm ratio = length of short arm/length of long arm, with reference to a nomenclature of chromosome, when the arm ratio is between 1 and 1.7, the chromosome is referred to as metacentric (M), between 1.7 and 3 as submetacentric (SM), between 3 and 7 as subtelocentric and beyond 7 it is called telocentric.

A few studies (cf. Chapter 7) have tried to link the differences in the sex chromosomes between the yak and *Bos taurus* or *Bos indicus* cattle to the sterility of the F1 male hybrids (Guo Aipu, 1983). However, this seemed to be an unlikely approach for resolving the problem because crosses of *Bos taurus* and *Bos indicus* produce fertile male offspring in spite of there being differences in the Y-chromosome between these two cattle species (Nivsarkar *et al.*, 1997).

The similarities between the yak and cattle chromosome structures and the relevant linkage maps, may have one beneficial consequence for yak, if indeed it can be shown that cattle provide an adequate model for yak in respect of quantitative trait loci (QTL), which is referred to more fully in ensuing sections (for a general description, see Fries and Popescu, 1999).

Biochemical markers in blood and milk of yak

One of the aims of the molecular technology, which is discussed later, is to provide genetic markers that may be related to performance traits or to health (or disease) and which might also provide information about relationships among the animals examined. The search for such markers in blood and in milk has a much longer history, and before discussing the molecular technology, it is useful to draw attention to the biochemical marker work with yak.

Zhang Yuezhou *et al.* (1994), Zhong Jingcheng (1996, 1997) and Nivsarkar *et al.* (1997) reviewed the advances in yak genetic diversity in terms of blood and milk protein and enzyme polymorphisms used to estimate the genetic differentiation and relationship among the yak breeds. Han Jianlin (1996) and Zhang Caijun (1997) noted that in these investigations there were a total of 54 genetic loci consisting of 14 protein or enzyme loci detected in plasma or serum, 35 proteins or enzymes in erythrocytes and five milk protein loci. As reported by these authors, the methods used in different laboratories for these determinations, as well as the nomenclature employed in description, were not uniform. Moreover, sampling from different breeds of yak was mostly rather limited. For these reasons, comparisons across investigations cannot readily be made and these studies have contributed less to the genetic characterization of yak populations than had been hoped. Most importantly as noted by Han Jianlin (1996) and Zhang Caijun (1997), only a few of these genetic markers showed polymorphisms. For example, nine out of the 41 loci studied, or only 24.5 percent of the proteins or enzymes in the blood of yak, were found to be polymorphic, which is a far lower proportion than that found in the ordinary cattle (Hines, 1999). Consequently, these studies have provided relatively little information by which to differentiate the genetic relationships among yak breeds.

In another comparative study conducted in one laboratory with more loci involved, Tu Zhengchao *et al.* (1997) reported that in the Datong, Tianzhu White, Bazhou, Zhongdian, Maiwa and Jiulong yak (5 - 56 samples), only four out of the 34 blood protein and enzyme loci were polymorphic. The percentage of polymorphic loci was 11.8 percent, and the mean individual heterozygosity across the breeds calculated to be only 0.015. This suggests a very low level of genetic diversity in the Chinese yak breeds. The average genetic distance among the breeds was estimated as 0.0006 and the average coefficient of gene differentiation across the breeds as 0.0313. This implies that at the level of blood protein polymorphisms only 3 percent of the nuclear genetic constitutions detected in these six yak breeds could be attributed to the differences between the breeds. The rest (97 percent) was most likely to be due to variation within breeds. They suggested that such a low genetic diversity in these six Chinese yak breeds may have resulted from one or more severe bottlenecks due to diseases or natural disasters in the yak population.

More recently, Tao Shixin and Han Jianlin (2002) used 269 samples from six pure yak populations in Gansu and Qinghai provinces and confirmed that there are no polymorphisms at the Hb loci. Qi Xuebin and Han Jianlin (2002) reported that in 608 yak-milk samples collected from six geographically different yak production areas in Gansu province, the average genetic differentiation between populations at the beta-lactoglobulin locus was only 8.4 percent. The authors suggested that this might have resulted from introgression of cattle genes into the yak population studied, as hybridization is practised in some of the areas from which the yak were sampled.

Rozhkov and Galimov (1990) found, by affinity electrophoresis in the saliva of yak, a new AMY-1 allelic variant (AMY-1^D). The yak was found to be monomorphic for this allele while other cattle types and hybrids studied by these authors had other alleles. Thus, zebu cattle in the northern Caucasus had AMY-1^B and AMY-1^D alleles, Red Steppen cattle in the Caucasus and Holmogor cattle from the Moscow region had AMY-1^A and AMY-1^B alleles while Kazakh White Head cattle in Altai only showed the AMY-1^B allele. Hybrids produced from yak bulls and *Bos taurus* cows had both the AMY-1^B and AMY-1^D alleles, while hybrids of *Bos indicus* and *Bos taurus* cattle had all three alleles (A, B and D). This suggests that this locus can be useful in investigating introgression between the yak and other cattle species.

Molecular genetics

A general background

DNA-based studies
Recent studies have focused on variation at the level of the DNA sequence. DNA has the advantage of allowing the development of relatively robust tests. It can be sampled from almost any tissue and a very large number of different markers can be developed based on DNA sequence variation. To put yak into perspective in relation to the hugely studied human genome, the latter has a genome size of 3 300 mbp, while that of cattle and yak is estimated to be 3 000 mbp in size.

Not all DNA consists of genes. There are two types of DNA in a cell: the nuclear DNA and the mitochondrial DNA (mt-DNA). Nuclear DNA is responsible for most of the physical characteristics of the yak, and a nuclear DNA profile normally points exclusively to a specific yak. The most common type of nuclear DNA consists of unique, or single-copy sequences, which account for about 57 percent of total DNA in cattle (and yak are assumed to be similar). Other DNA is called satellite DNA, which is sufficiently different in density from the major portion of DNA to enable it to form recognizably separate peaks or "satellites" when the total DNA is subjected to certain density gradient tests. Satellite DNA is not dispersed throughout the genome; instead it is located at specific sites in the genome. Cattle DNA contains eight different satellites, which together constitute about 23 percent of the nuclear DNA of cattle. The remaining 20 percent of DNA is characterized by repeat sequences and is called interspersed-repetitive DNA. Vaiman (1999) pointed out that at least 50 percent of the cattle genome consists of repetitive sequences.

These estimated proportions of the three categories of cattle nuclear DNA derive from work in the late 1980s. It is worth noting that these could be subject of drastic revision if recent human genome data provide a clue. Earlier estimates of the proportion of single-copy DNA for the human were around 60 percent – not dissimilar to the cattle values.

However, recent revision suggests that this proportion in humans is only around 25 percent, or has been reduced from about 100 000 (Hwu *et al.*, 1986) to 30 000 - 40 000 protein-coding genes (International Human Genome Sequencing Consortium, 2001).

Mitochondrial DNA (mt-DNA

Under a microscope, yak cells, like the other eukaryotic cells, appear to contain hundreds of smaller organelles within the cytoplasm of the cell. Many of these smaller structures are the mitochondria, each containing its own DNA. The mitochondrial genome is much smaller than the nuclear genome in terms of the DNA quantity – there are only 16 338 base pairs (bp) in cattle, a tiny fraction of the amount of nuclear DNA (and yak are thought to be similar) (Anderson *et al.*, 1982). Its structure is also relatively simple. Mammalian mt-DNA is very compact and simple compared to the nuclear DNA. Mitochondria have essential functions in the energy metabolism of cells; but for purposes of this chapter it is not their function that is of primary interest but the fact that their DNA profile can be used to differentiate individual animals.

The genetics of mt-DNA differs from that of nuclear DNA in several important ways: The most important feature that distinguishes mt-DNA from nuclear DNA in the present context is its maternal inheritance. The egg harbours several hundred thousands mt-DNA from the mother, while the sperm has only a few hundred mt-DNA. Thus, the few sperm mt-DNA that enter the egg have almost no effect on the mitochondrial genotype. Therefore, a yak mitochondrial DNA profile would be identical to his/her mother's and all of his/her maternal relatives. This means that the mt-DNA profile of a yak is not unique to that individual but rather points to his/her maternal lineage.

Molecular genetic markers

Several molecular approaches have been applied to investigate the yak's genetic markers in both mt-DNA and nuclear DNA. These are RFLPs (restriction fragment length polymorphisms), microsatellites and VNTRs (variable number tandem repeats), SSCPs (single strand conformation polymorphisms) and SNPs (single nucleotide polymorphisms). They are used in terms of understanding relationships between breeds within the yak species and among various cattle species, as a potential aid to breeding.

RFLP is a technique in which organisms may be differentiated by analysis of patterns derived from cleavage of their DNA at a precisely defined length, such as the whole mt-DNA or a specific DNA fragment amplified through a polymerase chain reaction (PCR). If two organisms differ in the distance between sites of cleavage of a particular restriction endonuclease, the length of the fragments produced will differ when the DNA is digested with a restriction enzyme. The similarity of the patterns generated can be used to differentiate species (and even yak breeds) from one another.

Polymorphisms detected by RFLP are inherited differences found among the individuals in a population. Yak mt-DNA RFLPs have been employed as a tool to demonstrate relationships between and within breeds of the yak (Zhao Xinbo *et al.*, 1994; Tu Zhengchao *et al.*, 1998). In particular, Tu Zhengchao *et al.* (1998) using 20 endonucleases and 90 samples collected from Jiulong (20 samples), Maiwa (20), Zhongdian (21), Huanhu (20) and Tianzhu White (9) yak breeds found that six out of the 20 enzymes detected polymorphisms with five haplotypes (I to V) across a total of 56 digestion sites, of which the haplotype II, III and IV were derived from the haplotype I by changing the digestion sites and V subsequently from the II, respectively. The divergence times among these five haplotypes are from 0.045 - 1.295 million years ago, among which the haplotype I is thought to have separated from III 0.635 million years ago, I from II 0.725 million years ago and III from II 1.295 million years ago. The average genetic diversity (H_T) is 0.1065 across the five breeds and the average net genetic distance between either two of the five breeds is 0.000201 (see Table 15.2). The gene differentiation coefficient is only 0.0291, or only 3 percent of the total population differentiation is attributed to the genetic variation among the populations. This indicates a very low genetic differentiation among the yak breeds studied and is similar to the conclusion drawn from protein and enzyme loci (see previous reference). Further clustering of the Jiulong and Huanhu yak into one group and of the Zhongdian and Tianzhu White yak into another group are not in agreement with the knowledge from historical origin and geographic distribution, possibly due to limited and random mt-DNA RFLPs and eventually limited genetic differentiation in yak.

Table 15.2 The nucleotide diversity (upper right) and net nucleotide divergence (left down) between the yak breeds [Source: Tu Zhengchao *et al.*, 1998]

Breeds	No. samples	Zhongdian	Jiulong	Maiwa	Tianzhu White	Huanhu
Zhongdian	21		0.003492	0.003252	0.002460	0.003715
Jiulong	20	0.000352		0.004008	0.003425	0.004293
Maiwa	20	0.000297	0.000151		0.003282	0.004224
Tianzhu	9	0.000112	0.000139	0.000181		0.003650
Huanhu	20	0.000398	0.000038	0.000154	0.000187	

Sulimova *et al.* (1996) using PCR-RFLP investigated the polymorphisms of the 5'-untranslated region and exon 4 of kappa-casein gene in yak and found a new variant in yak compared to other Bovini species.

mt-DNA markers for detecting the introgression of cattle into yak or vice versa. As stated in Chapter 7, the F1 male hybrids and the B1 to B3 male backcrosses from hybridization of yak mated with either *Bos taurus* or *Bos indicus* cattle are sterile. Therefore, the exploitation of heterosis thought to arise in these hybrids usually stops at the F1 generation. However, there is, in the field, a small amount of backcrossing of the fertile F1 females to yak bulls or to bulls of the other cattle species. This opens the possibility for introgression of cattle genes into the yak population (and vice versa).

To assess the level of cattle mt-DNA introgression in yak, Han Jianlin *et al*. (2002), using a cattle diagnostic mitochondrial DNA marker, found that cattle introgression through the female lineages is either absent or low in the five yak populations studied. Out of 239 animals, only one female in the Bhutanese population and two females in the Tianzhu White yak had the cattle mitochondrial DNA. Qi Xuebin *et al*. (2002a) confirmed that in a total of 963 samples from 24 yak populations there were 21 individuals from 13 yak populations carrying a cattle mt-DNA with the frequencies of cattle introgression ranging from 1.5 percent (Tianzhu White yak) to 10.6 percent (Tianzhu Black yak). In general, the introgression of cattle mt-DNA in yak is rare, and it is mostly limited to marginal and agro-pastoral areas where yak and cattle coexists. However, as these results do not take into account possible cattle introgression through the male lineage (in terms of the cattle nuclear DNA from the use of a cattle bull on a yak female at the first step in hybridizing), it is possible that they underestimated the level of cattle introgression in the yak populations.

In a separate study, Bailey *et al*. (2002) found that less than 1 percent cattle mt-DNA in a survey of yak mt-DNA types with samples from Nepal, Bhutan, China and Mongolia. They claimed that this is encouraging for those who are concerned about the effects of introgression of cattle into yak. It is important to note that mt-DNA can remain unperturbed even when high levels of introgression are observed at the nuclear level.

In a study of 11 native cattle breeds in South China using mt-DNA RFLPs based on ten restriction endonucleases' digestion, Yu *et al*. (1999) found that there was an introgression of mt-DNA, at a frequency of two out of seven samples analysed, from yak to a cattle breed (the Diqing cattle kept in northwestern Yunnan province where the Zhongdian yak are also found). They proposed that such an introgression might eventually contribute to the adaptation of the Diqing cattle to the cold weather and high altitude at 2 800 - 3 300 m.

AFLPs or its fluorescent version (fAFLP) are a DNA fingerprinting technique that detects DNA restriction fragments in the animal nuclear genome by means of PCR amplification. It requires no sequence information or probe collections prior to the generation of AFLP fingerprints. This is of particular benefit when studying organisms where very little DNA marker information is available.

Buntjer *et al*. (2002) included three yak in a phylogenetic study of bovine species based on AFLP fingerprinting and all samples produced relatively rich polymorphic markers (see section, Systematics).

Microsatellites (or SSRs, simple sequence repeats) are stable, polymorphic, easily analysed and occur regularly throughout an animal genome, making them especially suitable for genetic analysis. Microsatellites are co-dominant markers, so that all alleles can be scored. The availability of microsatellite markers located throughout the animal genome has also facilitated livestock genome scans for loci affecting quantitative production traits (QTL). Microsatellites are generally recognized as neutral so that selection and environmental pressure do not influence their expression directly.

To identify microsatellite markers from a eukaryotic genome is not as easy as using them. The isolation and characterization of microsatellites, their sequencing and the testing of primers can be time consuming and expensive. However, the conservative flanking sequences at every microsatellite marker allow the primers designed from the sequences to be used across closely related species. Since the late 1990s, Hishida *et al.* (1996), Ritz (1997), Hanotte *et al.* (2000), Wang Minqiang (2000) and Dorji *et al.* (2002) have tried the cross-species amplification of cattle autosomal microsatellite markers in yak and mostly succeeded in getting effective and polymorphic loci. Particularly, Ritz (1997) and Hanotte *et al.* (2000) using the same set of 31 to 39 yak samples collected from Bhutan found that 6 out of 8 and 19 out of 20 cattle microsatellite loci successfully amplified polymorphic yak microsatellite markers, respectively. Wang Minqiang (2000) tried 13 cattle microsatellites for 28 Datong yak and 20 Gannan yak and discovered both breeds showed polymorphic markers at 13 loci (see Table 15.3).

Using a set of eight cattle autosomal microsatellites, including TGLA53, TGLA122, TGLA73, AGLA293, BM2113, BM1824, CSSM066 and ETH3, Dorji *et al.* (2002) found that in a total of 169 yak sampled from three yak populations of western Bhutan (106), central Bhutan (32) and eastern Bhutan (31) all eight loci are polymorphic in the Bhutanese yak. They also found that there is substantial genetic variability within the populations, with average heterozygosity range of 0.644 - 0.680. A neighbour-joining tree constructed from Nei's standard genetic distances grouped western and central Bhutan yak in one clade separate from eastern Bhutan yak. The genetic distances between the yak from eastern Bhutan and from the other two regions suggest that the populations have been separated for at least 4 000 years and that they have exchanged less than two migrants per generation. Based on these results, Dorji *et al.* categorized the Bhutanese yak populations into two types of (1) western and central Bhutan yak and 2) eastern Bhutan yak (cf. Chapter 11, part 2).

Han Jianlin *et al.* (2002) also tried a set of cattle Y-chromosome-derived microsatellite loci and found that INRA124 failed in the amplification of a yak Y-chromosome locus and INRA 126 amplifies microsatellite from both sexes of yak samples.

Table 15.3 Cattle microsatellite loci used in cross-species amplification
in yak and their polymorphisms

Ritz (1997)		Hanotte *et al*. (2000)		Wang minqiang (2000)	
Bhutanese yak		Bhutanese yak		Datong yak and gannan yak	
Loci	Polymorphic	Loci	Polymorphic*	Loci	Polymorphic
BM1824	5	BM1824	4	BM1824	5
ETH003	3	BM2113	4	BM2113	7
ETH010	5	ETH003	2	CSSM66	7
ETH121	7	ETH010	3	ETH152	7
ETH131	5	ETH225	4	ETH185	5.5
ETH225	5	ILST005	Failed	ETH225	5
ILST005	Failed	ILST006	3	HEL1	5.5
CYP21	11	SPS115	Monomorphic	HEL5	4
MHCII	8			HEL9	8
AGLA293	5			HEL13	4
MGTG7	7			INRA005	5
MGTG4B	5			TGLA126	4
TGLA48	5			TGLA127	4
TGLA53	8				
TGLA57	5				
TGLA73	9				
TGLA122	8				
TGLA126	5				
TGLA227	5				
TGLA263	3				

Note: Polymorphic is presented as the allele numbers detected at that loci.

Therefore, neither is suitable for the cross-species amplification yak in this domain. The two microsatellites, BM861 and INRA189, are Y-specific in both cattle and yak with the presence of *Bos taurus*, *B. indicus* and *B. grunniens* diagnostic alleles. This was confirmed by Qi Xuebin *et al*. (2002b) with 252 male yak samples. Both Han Jianlin *et al*. (2002) and Qi Xuebin *et al*. (2002b) found that INRA189 locus is a polymorphic marker in yak with three alleles, the monomorphic locus BM861 reported by Han Jianlin *et al*. (2002) in 83 male yak samples has been shown by Qi Xuebin *et al*. (2002b) to be polymorphic in 252 samples. Meanwhile, Qi Xuebin *et al*. (2002b) also added a third polymorphic Y-chromosome specific locus, BYM-1, in yak being detected with a cattle-derived microsatellite and discovered ten Y-specific microsatellite haplotypes based on the detected combinations among these three polymorphic loci in yak.

From these preliminary reports, it is clearly seen that the cattle microsatellites can be useful in characterizing yak genetic diversity. However, the loci involved in each experiment differ from each other, and the results therefore are not comparable. To efficiently explore the advantage of the these new technologies, the International Livestock Research Institute initiated a project on the genetic characterization of yak with microsatellite genotyping and DNA sequencing in 1999 in collaboration with scientists and institutions in Bhutan, China, India, Kyrgyzstan, Mongolia, Nepal, Pakistan and Russia. A total of about 1 000 samples from up to 30 yak breeds (or populations) have been collected from these countries.

VNTRs (minisatellites) are a short sequence of DNA repeated a number of times on some eukaryotic chromosomes. It is possible to cut out the segment of the chromosome containing the VNTRs, run the total DNA on a gel and identify the VNTRs by hybridization with a probe specific for the DNA sequence of the repeat. The number of repeated segments at a locus varies between individuals. Some VNTR sequence segments are found at only a single locus in the whole genome. Other VNTR sequence segments occur at many loci in the entire genome. These loci are dispersed among the chromosomes and images produced by multi-locus VNTR probes yield more information since one probe is simultaneously probing 10 - 30 loci. In the description above, RFLP is used to detect the variability in the number of repeats. Several PCR-based methods can also be used to detect VNTRs.

Nijman and Lenstra (2001) compared several distinct centromeric satellites, a complex of tandem repeats abundant mostly in eukaryotic genome, among bovine species with yak included. They found that the 1.711b sequence of yak resembles the bison and wisent sequence but in satellite IV yak shares several other heterogeneous nucleotide positions with gaur and banteng.

SSCP is a method for distinguishing between similar-sized DNA fragments according to the mobility of the single-stranded DNA under polyacrylamide gel electrophoresis. In combination with automated detection of fluorescently labelled PCR products, SSCP is a convenient method for screening mutations and typing DNA polymorphisms. SSCPs are codominant markers, like RFLPs.

Prinzenberg *et al.* (2002) found using PCR-SSCP analysis in the Gannan yak that the κ-casein (CSN3) exon IV revealed a two allele polymorphism showing intermediate migration patterns compared to the cattle CSN3*A and B alleles. DNA sequences of these two alleles showed that all yak had nucleotide sequences corresponding to threonine in amino acid position 136 (identical to CSN3*A) and alanine in position 148 (identical to CSN3*B). This is in accordance with a sequence reported from wisent (*Bison bonasus*) (CSN3*G$_{Bison}$) and may represent the common ancestor of CSN3*A and B variants of cattle. Moreover, a 12 bp insertion resulting in a duplicated nucleotide and amino acid motive was found in one yak allele compared to the other. Position of the insertion could not be unequivocally assigned. The duplication is either corresponding to the codons for amino acids 147 - 150 or 148 - 151, which are repeated identically. In 18 yak typed by SSCP analysis, the long variant was found with frequencies about 70 percent and the short variant about 30 percent, implicating the longer variant being the predominant and probably the older allele in yak. The loss of the insertion may have led to the ancestral CSN3 allele from which all variants in *Bos indicus* and *Bos taurus* known today have evolved.

It is worth noting that this pilot study on milk protein polymorphism at the DNA level may shed more light on the understanding of yak genetics as they are coding genes and evolved under both natural and artificial selection over long periods. Consequently, they may also contribute to the detection of genetic markers for use in breeding programmes for genetic improvement, particularly in relation to milk quality and quantity.

SNPs are DNA sequence variations that occur when a single nucleotide in the animal mt-DNA or nuclear genome sequence is altered and detected by traditionally direct DNA sequencing protocol. For example, a SNP might change the DNA sequence AAGGCTAA to ATGGCTAA. SNPs occur at one SNP every 1.9 kilobases in the human genome. SNPs can occur in both coding (gene) and noncoding regions of the genome. Many SNPs have no effect on cell function, but it is believed that others could predispose organism to disease or influence their response to a challenge. SNPs are evolutionarily stable – not changing much from generation to generation – making them easier to follow in population studies. SNPs also have properties that make them particularly attractive for genetic studies. They are more frequent than microsatellite markers, providing markers near to or in the locus of interest, some located within the gene (cSNP), which can directly influence protein structure or expression levels, giving insights into functional mechanisms.

Bailey *et al.* (2002) using sequence data of the D-loop of mt-DNA found two divergent haplogroups, Y1 and Y2, in yak; but there does not appear to be a significant difference between the Chinese, Bhutanese, Nepalese and Mongolian yak. They supposed that a movement of the yak across the mountainous regions in Central Asia eventually reduced the amount of geographical partitioning observed as shown in Figure 15.1 after the domestication estimated to have occurred 5 000 years ago, based on a molecular clock. Nucleotide diversity values have been calculated for both the haplogroups Y1 and Y2 and for all Y (both 1 and 2) and they are very different. Therefore, the authors suggested a dual domestication of the yak. In comparison with European cattle, it is clearly seen that the variability found in yak is of the same order as that found in European cattle.

The total nucleotide variation for both yak haplogroups, is highest because it reflects the whole mt-DNA domestic pool from both centres of domestication. Lower nucleotide diversity for the Y1 and Y2 is thought to be due to both the limited number of samples included and a relatively recent domestication of the yak compared to the other cattle.

However, it would be incautious to adopt this conclusion without further study with a large number of samples collected in a large geographic area covering most of the yak-raising countries.

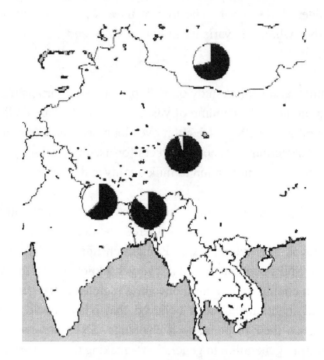

Figure 15.1 A distribution map of the Y1 and Y2 haplogroups in samples from China, Bhutan, Nepal and Mongolia, where the shaded area of the pie is Y1 and the nonshaded area is Y2 [Source: Bailey *et al*., 2002].

Quantitative variations

In contrast to the qualitative traits, most (if not all) characters of morphological, physiological, behavioural and economic importance in yak are quantitative traits that result from the complicated interaction of many genes. Therefore, it is not possible to classify yak into one or another discrete class. For instance, growth rate and the milk yield of yak vary among individuals and are dependent on many different physiological systems with possibly hundreds of genes influencing the phenotype. Such characters are described as quantitative and knowledge of the phenotype of an individual does not allow any specification of its genotype in terms of particular genes.

The genetic basis of quantitative traits is complex

Many pairs of genes influence the expression of any quantitative trait. It is likely that a trait, such as milk yield in yak, must be influenced by many genes relating to hormone production and to the multitude of enzymes involved in metabolism. In reality, however, the contribution of an individual locus to the expression of a trait ranges from small to large. Should one gene play a large role in determining expression of a quantitative trait, it is termed a major gene. For example, major genes are known to affect the expression of double muscling in Belgian Blue cattle and fertility in Booroola sheep and Meishan pig.

Quantitative trait loci – a way forward?

The loci controlling the quantitative traits are called quantitative trait loci, or QTL (It is also found in some publications as ETL to represent the economic trait loci). The identification of the QTLs or closely linked genetic markers would allow genetic selection on the basis of both an individual's breeding value and on genotype using a "marker-assisted" breeding programme. It has been well demonstrated that mapping markers linked to QTLs might identify regions on the chromosomes that may contain genes involved in the expression of the quantitative trait.

Because large-scale conventional selection procedures are rare for the yak – or at best suboptimal - the use of marker-assisted selection might be particularly appropriate for yak once the techniques and the identification of QTLs have been made. Some discussion of the potential merits was provided by Wiener and Bishop (2002) who noted that, in general, marker-assisted selection is considered to be most beneficial for traits that are difficult or expensive to measure, traits that only occur in one sex (e.g. milk or reproduction) or traits that are expressed late in life (e.g. longevity). A further potential use of markers is for selection for disease resistance (Crawford *et al.*, 2000). If a genetic marker is available that indicates resistance to a particular disease, it should be possible to reduce or even eliminate the disease without having to expose the animals to that disease.

So far, the work of most relevance for yak breeding is that which has taken place in other cattle; for example, the intensive investigation on the marker-assisted selection for milk production in dairy cattle (Sonstegard *et al.*, 2001) or for growth and carcass composition in beef cattle (Casas *et al.*, 2000). However, so far no effort has been made to discover specific QTLs or closely linked markers in the yak.

Molecular-genetic techniques have made it possible to identify differences between individuals at the DNA level. In particular, the development of microsatellite markers as an abundant source of polymorphic and convenient markers has boosted the generation of linkage maps in the most important livestock species. These maps provide the basis for detection and exploitation of genes segregating at the QTLs (Montaldo and Meza-Herrera, 1998). After the development of high-density genetic maps of polymorphic markers, it became possible for the first time to dissect genetically quantitative traits in many species. The analysis of QTL segregating in crosses between inbred lines of animals indicated that in some cases only a small number of genetic loci contributed to a large proportion of the variance of each trait, which confirms the presence of major genes (see above) and provides a tempting target for further molecular investigation (Flint and Mott, 2001).

Major genes have been detected for the carcass characteristics in both pigs and cattle and also for parasite resistance in sheep (Montaldo and Meza-Herrera, 1998). Most dairy-related QTLs have also been identified in Holstein grandsire families (Sonstegard *et al.*, 2001).

Systematics and phylogeny of the yak

The Bovini species consists of both domestic and wild cattle and buffalo species, which started to diverge more than four million years ago (Lenstra and Bradley, 1999). Many are among the most important species playing a key role throughout the history of mankind and fulfilling many agricultural, economic, cultural and religious functions. According to some authorities, Bovini can be divided into genera Bovina, Bubalina and Syncerina. Bovina are then separated into subgenera of *Bos* and their wild relatives *Bison* (Felius, 1995). Paleontological evidence indicates that taxa within the Bovina diverged from one another within the past 20 million years (Savage and Russell, 1983). As referred to in Chapter 2, there have been several changes in the name and taxonomic position of the yak in the last two centuries and both the *Bos* and the *Poephagus* genera have been used by various authors but with the same species name of *grunniens*.

Morphological array

Numerous attempts have been made to clarify phylogenetic relationships among the genera of the tribe Bovini, including the yak, but the results have been ambiguous. Bohlken (1958, 1961) first grouped the yak with cattle (*Bos taurus*), followed by gaur (*Bos gaurus*) and banteng (*Bos javanicus*) in one clade, which then clustered with the American bison (*Bison bison*) and European bison (*Bison bonasus*). Groves (1981) concluded that the gaur and banteng represented the most primitive members of the *Bos/Bison* clade and that the two species of *Bison* were most closely related to the yak. Olsen (1990, 1991), who provided a useful review of the taxonomic evidence, also found that the yak has the same arrangement of premaxillaries, maxillaries and nasals as in *Bison* and are different from the structure in *Bos*. But Olsen also noted a difference from bison on the intervening extension of the dorsal margin of the maxilla that prevents the nostrils from reaching the premaxillae in the yak – possibly due to a different arrangement of the facial muscles that control the lips and nostrils in yak. This led Olsen to propose a re-establishment of the yak in the genus *Poephagus*, different from the genus *Bos* and *Bison*. In a study of phylogeny of the tribe Bovini, Geraads (1992), using a matrix of 57 (mainly cranial) characters and 32 taxa of fossil and current Bovini, considered *Bos* + *Bibos* + *Bison* + *Poephagus* + *L. etruscus-callisarni* + *Epileptobos* as a mono- or paraphyletic group and concluded that the yak is close to the bison among the current forms.

Molecular evidence

Since the late 1980s, the sequences of mitochondrial DNA of yak have been included in some of the phylogenetic studies of Bovidae. Miyamoto *et al.* (1989) sequenced the 12S rRNA and three tRNA genes, and a 247 bp partial hypervariant D-loop fragment of four taxa in the tribe Bovini and the results showed a similar topology of phylogeny with Groves (1981), the yak grouped with the *Bison bison* first, with an average divergence of 2.6 percent for the conservative rRNA/tRNA genes and 9.1 percent for the D-loop fragment and then followed by *Bos taurus* (Kraus *et al.*, 1992). Ward *et al.* (1999) using a partial mt-DNA control region of 667 base pairs, found that the percentage nucleotide divergence of *Bos indicus* and *Bos taurus* from the yak was 24.23 percent and 29.53 percent, respectively, but that of American bison and European bison from the yak was only 12.28 percent and 16.59 percent, respectively.

Within the nuclear genome alone [on 15 endonucleases' site mapping of nuclear ribosomal DNA (rDNA)], Wall *et al.* (1992) confirmed the position of yak as more closely related to the bison and wisent than to *Bos taurus* and *Bos indicus* cattle as earlier suggested by Groves (1981). Hassanin and Douzery (1999) sequenced the cytochrome b and 12S rRNA of mt-DNA and aromatase cytochrome P-45 and the promoter segment of the lactoferrin-encoding genes of nuclear genomic DNA in the yak alongside other Bovidae species. With the combined data of these four mitochondrial and nuclear markers, the yak clustered with the American bison first and then grouped with *Bos taurus* in the phylogenetic tree.

Ritz *et al.* (2000) used 20 bovine microsatellite markers to determine the phylogenetic relationships in the tribe Bovini, including the yak and found that the yak emerged as a separate subgenus *Poephagus* within the genus *Bos*. Buntjer *et al.* (2002) claimed that the published phylogenies of this tribe Bovini, based on mitochondrial DNA, contain anomalies, while nuclear sequences show only low variation. They used AFLP fingerprinting to detect variation in loci distributed over the nuclear genomes of Bovini species. Computer-assisted scoring of electrophoretic fingerprinting patterns yielded 361 markers, which provided sufficient redundancy to suppress stochastic effects of intraspecies polymorphisms and length homoplasies (co-migration of non-homologous fragments). Tree reconstructions reveal three clusters: African buffalo with water buffalo, ox with zebu and bison with wisent. Similarity values suggest a clustering of gaur and banteng, but bifurcating clustering algorithms did not assign consistent positions to these species and yak. They proposed that because of shared polymorphisms and reticulations, tree topologies are only partially adequate to represent the phylogeny of the Bovini. Principal-coordinate analysis positioned zebu between a gaur/banteng cluster and taurine cattle. This correlates with the region of origin of these species and suggests that genomic distances between the cattle species have been influenced by genetic exchange between neighbouring ancestral populations. The yak clearly stands alone in a separate group but relatively close to the cluster of bison and wisent. In the multivariate image, regression-specific PCR and AFLP analysis (Buntjer, 1997), there was a clustering of yak with both bison and wisent that are clearly different from other non-buffalo Bovini species, in agreement with the morphological study by Geraads (1992). Buntjer (1997) explained this as due to both yak and bison/wisent being adapted to relatively cold conditions, suggesting a correspondence between genetic distance and geographical origin of the species.

In conclusion, it seems clear that the yak is different from *Bos taurus* and *Bos indicus* cattle and closer to the American bison (*Bos bison*) in terms of its cranial morphology and its genome including both the mt-DNA and nuclear DNA markers surveyed, even with inclusive phenotypic characteristics. Therefore, in agreement with Olsen (1991), it seems that in the choice of nomenclature for both the domestic yak and the wild yak, the subgenus, *Poephagus,* seems more appropriate than *Bos.*

References

Anderson, S. *et al.* (1982). Complete sequence of bovine mitochondrial DNA. Conserved features of the mammalian mitochondrial genome. *Journal of Molecular Biology*, 156: 683-717.

Bailey, J.F. *et al.* (2002). Genetic variation of mitochondrial DNA within domestic yak populations. *Proceedings of the third international congress on yak, in Lhasa, China, 4-9 September 2000.* International Livestock Research Institute (ILRI), Nairobi, pp. 181-189.

Bohlken, H. (1958). Vergleichende Untersuchungen an Wildrindern (Tribus Bovini Simpson, 1954). *Zool. Jahrb.*, 68: 113-202.

Bohlken, H. (1961). Haustiere und Zoologische Systematick. *Z. Tier. Zuchtungsbiol.*, 76: 107-113.

Buntjer, J.B. (1997). *DAN repeats in the vertebrate genome as probes in phylogeny and species identification.* Academic thesis, Utrecht University, Netherlands.

Buntjer, J.B. *et al.* (2002). Phylogeny of bovine species based on AFLP fingerprinting. *Heredity*, 88: 46-51.

Casas, E. *et al.* (2000). Quantitative trait loci affecting growth and carcass composition of cattle segregating alternate forms of myostatin. *J. Anim. Sci.*, 78:560-569.

Crawford, A.M., Dodds, K.G. and McEwan, J.C. (2000). DNA markers, genetic maps, and the identification of QTL: general principles. In: Axford, R.F.E. *et al.* (ed.), *Breeding for disease resistance in farm animals, 2nd edition.* Wallingford, U.K., CABI Publishing, pp. 3-26.

Dorji, T. *et al.* (2002). Genetic diversity in Bhutanese yak (*Bos grunniens*) populations using microsatellite markers. *Proceedings of the third international congress on yak, in Lhasa, China, 4-9 September 2000.* International Livestock Research Institute (ILRI), Nairobi, pp. 197-201.

Felius, M. *Cattle breeds – an encyclopaedia.* Misset uitgeverij bv, postbus 4, 7000 BA Doetinchem, Netherlands, pp. 12-15.

Flint, J. and Mott, R. (2001). Finding the molecular basis of quantitative traits: successes and pitfalls. *Nature Review Genetics*, 2: 437-445.

Fries, R. and Popescu, P. (1999). Cytogenetics and physical chromosome maps. In: Fries, R. and Ruvinsky, A. (ed.), *The Genetics of Cattle.* CABI, Wallingford, UK. pp. 247-327.

Geraads, D. (1992). Phylogenetic analysis of the tribe Bovini (Mammalia: Artiodactyl). *Zoological Journal of the Linnean Society*, 104: 193-207.

Goe, M.R. and Stranzinger, G. (2002). Monitoring of traits for yak and yak hybrids. *Proceedings of the third international congress on yak, in Lhasa, China, 4-9 September 2000*. International Livestock Research Institute (ILRI), Nairobi, pp.291-299.

Groves, C.P. (1981). Systematic relationships in the Bovinii (Artiodactyla, Bovidae). *Zeitschrift fuer Zoologische Systematik und Evolutionsforschung,* 19: 264-278.

Guo Aipu (1983). A comparative study on chromosomes of oxen (*Bos taurus*), yak (*Bos grunniens*) and their hybrids. *Acta Genetica Sinica*, 2: 137-143.

Gupta, N. *et al.* (1996). Chromosomes of yak. *Indian Journal of Animal Sciences*, 66: 453-457.

Halnan, C.R.E. (1989). Karyotype and phenotype in cattle and hybrids of the genus. In: Halnan, C.R.E. (ed.), *Cytogenetics of Farm Animals*. Wallingford, UK, CABI, pp. 235-255.

Han Jianlin (1996). Yak genetic resources in China: evaluation of chromosome, protein and mt-DNA polymorphism. *In* Miller, D.G., Craig, S.R. and Rana, G.M. (ed), *Proceedings of a workshop on conservation and management of yak genetic diversity, at ICIMOD, Kathmandu, 29-31 October 1996*. ICIMOD (International Centre for Integrated Mountain Development), Kathmandu, pp. 175-183.

Han Jianlin *et al.* (2002). Low level of cattle introgression in yak populations from Bhutan and China: Evidences from *Y*-specific microsatellites and mitochondrial DNA markers. *Proceedings of the third international congress on yak, in Lhasa, China, 4-9 September 2000*. International Livestock Research Institute (ILRI), Nairobi, pp. 190-196.

Hanotte, O. *et al.* (2000). Cattle microsatellite markers for amplification of polymorphic loci in Asian Bovidae. In: Shrestha, J.N.B. (ed), *Proceedings of the 4th global conference on conservation of domestic animal genetic resources held in Kathmandu, Nepal, 17-21 August 1998*, pp. 47-49.

Hassanin A. & Douzery, E.J.P. (1999). Evolutionary affinities of the enigmatic saola (Pseudoryx nghetinhensis) in the context of the molecular phylogeny of Bovidae. *Proceedings of Royal Society London*, B 266: 893-900.

Hines, H.C. (1999). Blood groups and biochemical polymorphisms. In: Fries, R. and Ruvinsky, A. (ed.), *The Genetics of Cattle*. Wallingford, U.K., CABI, pp. 77-121.

Hishida, O. *et al.* (1996). Cross-species amplification and polymorphism of microsatellite loci in Asian bovidae. *Proceedings of the eighth AAAP Animal Science Congress, 13-18 October 1996. Vol. 2.* Japanese Society of Zootechnical Science, Tokyo.

Hwu, H.R. *et al.* (1986). Insertion and/or deletion of many repeated DNA sequences in human and higher ape revolution. *Proceedings of the National Academy of Sciences of the U.S.A.*, 83: 3875-3879.

International Human Genome Sequencing Consortium (2001). Initial sequencing and analysis of the human genome. *Nature*, 409: 860-921.

Kraus, F., *et al.* (1992). Mis-pairing and compensational changes during the evolution of mitochondrial ribosomal RNA. *Molecular and Biological Evolution*, 9: 770-774.

Li Jiyou, *et al.* (1994). Advance on the research of chromosomes in yak (Bos grunniens). Proceedings of the first international congress on yak. *Journal of Gansu Agricultural University* (Special issue June 1994), pp. 73-76.

Lenstra, J.A. and Bradley, D.G. (1999). Systematics and phylogeny of cattle. In: Fries, R. and Ruvinsky, A. (ed.), *The Genetics of Cattle*. CABI, Wallingford, U.K., pp. 1-14.

Miyamoto, M.M., Tanhauser, S.M. and Laipis, P.J. (1989). Systematic relationship in the artiodactyls tribe Bovini (family Bovidae), as determined from mitochondrial DNA sequences. *Systematic Zoology*, 38: 342-349.

Montaldo, H.H. and Meza-Herrera, C.A. (1998). Use of molecular markers and major genes in the genetic improvement of livestock. *EJB Electronic Journal of Biotechnology*, 1 (2): 1-7.

Nijman, I.J. and Lenstra, J.A. (2001). Mutation and recombination in cattle satellite DNA: a feedback model for the evolution of satellite DNA repeats. *Journal of Molecular Evolution*, 52: 361-371.

Nivsarkar, A.N., Gupta, S.C. and Gupta, N. (1997). *Yak production*. Indian Council for Agricultural Research, New Delhi, 394 pp.

Olsen, S.J. (1990). Fossil ancestry of the yak, its cultural significance and domestication in Tibet. *Proceedings of the Academy of Natural Sciences of Philadelphia*, 142: 73-100.

Olsen, S.J. (1991). Confused yak taxonomy and evidence of domestication. *Illinois State Museum Scientific Papers*, Vol. 23: 387-393.

Prinzenberg, E.M., Han Jianlin and Erhardt G. (2002). Variants of CSN3 in Chinese yak (Bos grunniens). *Proceedings of the 28th International conference of Animal Genetics held in Göttingen, Germany, 11-15 August 2002*, p. 127 (abstract).

Qi Xuebin and Han Jianlin (2002). Introgression makes yak populations genetically different: Evidence from Beta-lactoglobulin variations. *Proceedings of the third international congress on yak, in Lhasa, China, 4-9 September 2000*. International Livestock Research Institute (ILRI), Nairobi, pp. 202-208.

Qi Xuebin *et al*. (2002a). Cattle mitochondrial DNA introgression in yak (*Poephagus* or *Bos grunniens*). *Proceedings of the 28th International conference of Animal Genetics held in Göttingen, Germany, 11-15 August 2002*, p.102 (abstract).

Qi Xuebin *et al*. (2002b). Y-chromosome specific microsatellite polymorphism in Chinese yak. *Proceedings of the 7th world congress on genetics applied to livestock production held in Montpellier, France, 19-23 August 2002*, 33, 509-512.

Ritz, L.R. (1997). *Genetic diversity in the tribe Bovini*. PhD dissertation of University of Bern, Switzerland, 79 pp.

Ritz, L.R. *et al*. (2000). Phylogenetic analysis of the tribe Bovini using microsatellites. *Animal Genetics*, 31: 178-185.

Rozhkov, YuI and Galimov, I.R. (1990). Salivary gland amylase polymorphism in pigs and cattle detected by affinity electrophoresis. *Animal Genetics*, 21: 277-283.

Savage, D. and Russell, D.E. (1983). *Mammalian paleofaunas of the World*. Reading, MA., U.S.A., Addison-Wesley.

Sonstegard, T.S., Van Tassell, C.P. and Ashwell, M.S. (2001). Dairy cattle genomics: Tools to accelerate genetic improvement. *Journal of Animal Science*, 79 (E. Suppl.): E307-315.

Sulimova, G.E., Badagueva, IuN and Udina, I.G. (1996). Polymorphism of the kappa-casein gene in populations of the subfamily Bovinae. *Genetika*, 32:1576-1582. [in Russian]

Tao Shixin and Han Jianlin (2002). Population genetic variations of haemoglobin in yaks, cattle and their hybrids. *Proceedings of the third international congress on yak, in Lhasa, China, 4-9 September 2000*. International Livestock Research Institute (ILRI), Nairobi, pp. 213-215.

Tu Zhengchao, Zhang Yaping and Qiu Huai (1997). Genetic diversity and divergence in Chinese yak (*Bos grunniens*) populations inferred from blood protein electrophoresis. *Biochemical Genetics*, 35: 13-16.

Tu Zhengchao, Zhang Yaping and Qiu Huai (1998). Mitochondrial DNA polymorphism and genetic diversity in Chinese yak. *Acta Genetica Sinica*, 25: 205-212.

Vaiman, D. (1999). The molecular genetics of cattle. *In* Fries, R. and Ruvinsky, A. (ed.), *The Genetics of Cattle*. Wallingford, U.K., CABI, pp. 123-161.

Wall, D.A., Davis, S.K. and Read, B.M. (1992). Phylogenetic relationships in the subfamily Bovinae (Mammalia: Artiodactyla) based on ribosomal DNA. *Journal of Mammalogy,* 73: 262-275.

Wang Minqiang (2000). *Study on some germplasm characteristics of Datong yak.* Doctoral dissertation of Northwest Science & Technology University of Agriculture and Forestry, Shaanxi, China, 94 pp.

Ward, T.J. *et al.* (1999). Identification of domestic cattle hybrids in wild cattle and bison species: a general approach using mt-DNA markers and the parametric bootstrap. *Animal Conservation*, 2: 51-57.

Wiener, G. (1994). Opportunities and constraints for genetic improvement with reference to the yak. *Proceedings of the first international congress on yak. Journal of Gansu Agricultural University* (Special issue June 1994), pp. 35-44.

Wiener, G. (1997). Yak breeds and the utilization of genetic diversity. *Proceedings of the second international congress on yak, in Xining, China, 1-6 September 1997.* Xining, China, Qinghai People's Publishing House, pp. 50-53.

Wiener, G. and Bishop, S.C. (2002). Opportunities for the improvement of yak production with particular reference to genetic options. *Proceedings of the third international congress on yak, in Lhasa, China, 4-9 September 2000.* International Livestock Research Institute (ILRI), Nairobi, pp. 225-234.

Yu, Y. *et al.* (1999). Mitochondrial DNA variation in cattle of South China: origin and introgression. *Animal Genetics*, 30: 245-250.

Zhang Caijun (1997). Advances of studies on biochemical genetics in yak. *Proceedings of the second international congress on yak, in Xining, China, 1-6 September 1997.* Xining, China, Qinghai People's Publishing House, pp. 55-58.

Zhang Yuezhou *et al.* (1994). Current status and future development of the studies on protein polymorphism on yak. Proceedings of the first international congress on yak. *Journal of Gansu Agricultural University* (Special issue June 1994), pp. 62-66.

Zhao Xinbo, Zhong Guanghui and Cai Li (1994). Studies on mitochondrial DNA RFLP of yaks and cattle. Proceedings of the 1st international congress on yak. *Journal of Gansu Agricultural University* (Special issue June 1994), pp. 96-98.

Zhong Jingcheng (1997). The genetic diversity of Chinese yak and its significance. *Proceedings of the second international congress on yak, in Xining, China, 1-6 September 1997.* Xining, China, Qinghai People's Publishing House, pp. 65-69.

Zhong Jingcheng (1996). *Yak genetics and breeding.* Sichuan Scientific and Technology Press, Chengdu, China, 271 pp.

16 CONCLUDING THOUGHTS – A PERSPECTIVE FROM A DISTANCE

by Gerald Wiener[1]

Background and problems

The final chapter of the first edition of this book reviewed briefly the current situation and aims of yak keeping. It considered the impact of research on yak production and attempted to suggest gaps in knowledge. It ended, perhaps rashly, with thoughts about the future.

A similar approach seems appropriate here but with the need to add some thoughts on how the situation appears to have changed in the eight-year interval since the first edition was published by FAO.

Clearly, what has not changed are the principal territories with their harsh and demanding climate and environment where yak are still of great importance to the livelihood of the people and the economy of the region. What has also not yet changed to a major extent is the generally nomadic system of exploiting the vast rangelands of "the roof of the world" and the mountainous territories of western China and adjacent countries. Changes are, however, in the process of taking place. Over important parts of the yak territories of China, the policy of "Household Responsibility" has now moved on from the individual ownership of the animals to individual responsibility for land through a system of land allocation to families. The move towards settlement in place of a mainly nomadic lifestyle has progressed further. Thus, a traditional system of yak-keeping and rangeland utilization that had not altered fundamentally perhaps in centuries is now in the process of change (see Chapter 13 dealing with the management of the ecosystem and Chapter 12 for the social implications).

These changes are likely to have far-reaching consequences for yak production and for a way of life. Settlement of families, fencing of land, more roads and greater access to markets inevitably steer a subsistence animal husbandry towards a market driven one where the products from yak may need to compete with animal products from elsewhere. The enhanced opportunities of herders to purchase goods they want, require in turn a need to sell the products from yak rather than retain them largely for home consumption. Monetary costs and returns from yak production and concepts of cost-effectiveness of different methods of production - as well as the idea of efficiency of production – could well become more important considerations for yak keeping in the future. Thus, a change in the economics of yak-keeping may bring a consequent change in objectives and in the concepts of what constitutes "improvement" as far as the yak is concerned.

However, there are other factors that may not only put a brake on a headlong dash into a purely market-oriented future for yak production but should also be made part of any

---

[1] Honorary Professor, Gansu Agricultural University, China; Centre for Tropical Veterinary Medicine, University of Edinburgh and Roslin Institute, Edinburgh, UK.Deputy director of former Agricultural and Food Research Council's Animal Breeding Research Organization, UK

process of change. It was pointed out more than once in the first edition of this book that yak-keeping in the past has not been just an economic activity, but that it has been inextricably linked with the culture, religion, social customs and life experience of the people. This is still true now. Hence any technological changes, based on scientific knowledge, should be integrated with, rather than imposed upon, the traditions and experiences of the herdsmen. The fuller attention given to these matters in Chapter 12 makes it unnecessary to elaborate this point further.

It is as well to be aware that tensions can arise between those who advocate husbandry practices based on traditional experience and the scientists, technologists and legislators who may sometimes be impatient to advance new practices based on a better understanding of physiology, nutritional biochemistry and genetic principles.

The authors and editors of this book belong, of course, to the tribe of the scientists. This does not mean that they hold uncritically to the view that science and technology should be the main, less still the only, driving force or consideration for change in yak husbandry practices. That would be foolish and counter-productive. Every change interacts with many other components of the yak production system and the interactions are among the least studied of the factors. Technological changes also impinge on the social fabric of the people who keep yak for their living. But what each of the authors and not least the late Professor Cai Li whose name is perpetuated in this book would claim is that knowledge itself is of fundamental importance. It is the basis for the understanding of the complex system that is yak production and hence for the opportunities to improve the living standards of the people who depend on yak. The contribution to knowledge and understanding of yak and yak keeping remains the sole purpose of this book.

What is needed is mutual understanding and dialogue. But part of that dialogue should also be recognition that it is easy to romanticize a traditional "way of life" and its cohabitation with raw nature – especially when sitting snugly in a town dwelling (or conference chamber!). Ultimately, it is for the herders and their families alone to decide whether to retain their way of life and the traditions and practices that support it. If alternatives were available, would they wish to escape from the undoubted harshness and periodic cruelty of nature, which is part of the life of these regions and abandon their system of yak keeping – and perhaps even life in these regions. Might yak ranching become an alternative to relatively small-scale yak keeping, with a change of emphasis from milk products to meat? Would less dramatic changes, with improvements in output from the present system and amelioration of its harshest features, meet the aspirations of yak herders and their families and of the younger generation in particular? Answers to questions such as these will determine the role and direction that science and technology can or should play in yak husbandry and range management.

In the study of yak and the yak environment there has been one notable change over the past decade or so. It is symbolized by the passing of Professor Cai Li who dedicated his life to the study of yak to the exclusion of almost everything else. He was one of a small group of notable men in China, the former Soviet Union and some of the other "yak" countries who were recognized as the unchallenged "experts" in their field.

The number from that generation has declined with the passage of time and in its place has grown up a new, young generation of scientists who may be better trained in their own, more specialized subjects, but who are, inevitably, less by way of all-rounders, or "yak experts" – though a few would still claim that honour. It remains to be seen whether the new generation of scholars is, by virtue of specialization, less in tune with the needs of the people, the herders and their families, whom their studies, experiments and surveys are ultimately intended to serve. The integration of new knowledge with tradition and practical needs may therefore have become just that bit more difficult.

The present position

Yak numbers are still increasing in China where most of the world's yak are kept; but of great interest in the context of yak numbers is the recent evidence of a reduction in the size of the yak population in Qinghai, until recently the foremost of the yak-keeping provinces. The speculation is (see Chapter 11, part 1) that this reduction is in response to overgrazing and a loss of herds during natural snow disasters. It underlines the fact that the rangelands on which yak, sheep, goats and wild animals depend are a finite resource and, as documented in Chapter 13, rangeland degradation is an increasingly serious problem. More mouths and less feed is a recipe for problems and potential disasters. From a technological point of view, it seems that the most pressing need is to bridge this deficit – whatever the size of herds or the allocation of land resources. There are a number of different ways of achieving this end. Selective reductions in stock numbers may appear obvious, but represents a difficult choice when animal numbers are still widely regarded as signs of status and wealth for the families owning them and as insurance against exceptional losses. Changes in grazing management are made both easier and more difficult, at the same time, by the subdivision and fencing of rangeland intended also to accommodate social and political aims. The use of supplementary feed, especially over late winter and early spring, is equally obvious in theory, but the provision of such feed on the scale required is still an unsolved problem although new plant varieties and opportunities for limited cropping hold out good prospects. Changes in the plant communities of the grazing lands and the introduction of legumes and limited areas of sown swards still seem far off - but the work of the plant breeders is of importance here.

In countries other than China but with the probable exception of Mongolia, yak numbers have continued to decline, and changes in patterns of yak keeping are noted. Different reasons are attributed for these trends, some of which were discussed in the first edition of this book. In some areas, these reasons include the provision of alternative employment, for example from tourism. In other areas, market forces and the attractions of a less demanding lifestyle have driven changes. For example, breeding hybrid stock for sale to other herders, rather than keeping yak directly for the sale of milk, has been a consequence of the development of the cheese factories in Nepal. These factories have greatly increased the demand for milk in their vicinity and have provided those with herds distant from the factories with the opportunity for a new enterprise of breeding stock for sale to the milk producers – an enterprise which is not as demanding of time and attention as direct milk production. In some countries, yak production has always been more peripheral and lacking the mutual support which is provided when entire communities, and the neighbours of those communities, all share a similar lifestyle engaged in the business of yak production - as over the vast areas of the Qinghai-Tibetan Plateau. Following the break-up of the Soviet Union and the establishment of independent republics, the decline in the yak population in these countries has been attributed to social and economic problems during the transitional period into new political and economic frameworks. Whether there will be a recovery in yak numbers as economic and social balance is achieved remains to be seen.

Research and gaps in knowledge

The thoughts here will focus on nutrition, breeding (genetics), reproduction and the interactions in the production system.

Over the past decade there has been a significant increase in research on nutritional biochemistry and physiology in relation to the yak and in the development of potential supplementary feeding regimes to overcome, or at least to lessen, the problems of late winter and early spring starvation in yak. Much of this work is reviewed in Chapter 14. At the same time, a more fundamental understanding has arisen, as a result of investigational work and plant trials, into the management and potential improvement – or at least the conservation – of the grazing lands. This work is discussed in some detail in Chapter 13. Clearly, these various investigations have led to a significant advance in the body of knowledge. Subject to finding economically viable strategies for application of this new knowledge into practice, this work is a cause for optimism.

In terms of breeding and reproduction of the yak, the success of research and development in providing a potentially significant advance over traditional practice is still in question. As pointed out in Chapter 3, the interest in crosses of domestic yak with wild yak has taken a step forward (since this matter was noted in the first edition of this book) with the development, at the Datong Yak Farm, of a "new breed" that is based on this crossbred (see Chapter 2). The extent of the recording of pedigrees and performance undertaken for purposes of selection in the development of this new breed is highly commendable and provides a good example for other breeding schemes to follow. Though the jury is still out on the ultimate performance and uptake of this new breed.

In terms of new genetic studies, as shown in Chapter 15, studies of yak DNA, mostly mitochondrial DNA, are being undertaken by several groups. This work is providing new evidence of relationships – or distances – between different types of yak and other bovines and thus provides some help in setting priorities as to which populations of yak should be conserved among those at risk. This work is, however, still a long way from providing associations with performance traits of yak, through the identification of quantitative trait loci (QTL). In fact, the value of the molecular genetics as an aid to "improving" yak is hampered by the absence of any widespread recording of performance, whether in relation to growth, milk production, reproduction, fibre production or disease. Whether the corresponding work on other cattle in different parts of the world will provide pointers for yak has still to be verified.

The DNA work does, however, provide some potential information, at least in theory, for the avoidance of inbreeding – a subject now more widely accepted to be of practical relevance by yak academics and, by all accounts by herders, than it was formerly. But the brief treatise on inbreeding in Chapter 3 is still appropriate, as the harm done by inbreeding to animal performance is substantial, and avoidance measures are relatively simple to apply (without the need for DNA typing!).

The big unknowns in yak breeding are still, as they were ten years ago, the absence of information on 1) the extent of differences in performance among the various yak breeds and 2) the extent to which heterosis might arise from crossing of breeds (as, for example, in crossing domestic yak with wild yak) and in the production of hybrids.

There are certainly claims that some breeds are better, in some respects, than others, and a few limited comparisons support this view. However, the main problem is still that, in general, different breeds are found in different localities often very far apart. In nearly all cases, the breed type is therefore confounded with the environment in which the breed is kept. It is not enough for this purpose to claim that all yak environments are similar. There is sufficient local variation in climate, management and grazing patterns to make a comparison of the performance of breeds across areas invalid. Even for the same breed, published estimates of performance can vary from each other in different studies, as the estimates may relate to different conditions (not only different times) under which the animals were observed – and the precise conditions are not always specified. In general, therefore, it is safest to regard records of performance as guidelines only or as "orders of magnitude".

In order to estimate hybrid vigour (heterosis), a potential but not universal benefit from crossing breeds, strict genetic principles have to be applied, as discussed in Chapter 7. However, the conditions for applying these principles are difficult to meet in practice, and accordingly, even the claims for hybrid vigour in crosses of domestic and wild yak have to be regarded very cautiously. Similar problems arise, as also discussed in Chapter 7, over claims for hybrid vigour from hybrids of yak with other cattle. The necessary contemporary comparisons of the parental breeds and the hybrids are rare (and would occur at best only when local cattle are involved and never with high-producing exotic cattle breeds). Only a couple of instances have been found in the literature where valid comparisons are claimed for estimating the extent of heterosis. Thus in respect of the results from hybridization, the extent of hybrid vigour also remains in question.

The best that can be said is that crosses (wild yak crossed with domestic) are to some extent better than the contemporary domestic yak with which they are compared - and for practical purposes that may be good enough reason to use the crosses or any new breed developed for them. And in respect of hybrids, questions of heterosis apart, there is clearly a useful place for them in some environments and yak production systems where they are a supplement to, but not a replacement for, pure yak. In relation to fundamental knowledge, there is still a large gap to be filled to discover the genetic components of differences between breeds and of the effects of crossbreeding and hybridization - knowledge that when obtained can lead to improved design of breeding schemes.

Still in relation to genetics, it is of interest to note that there continues to be a virtual absence for yak of estimates of heritability of performance traits, genetic correlations among traits, economic values, construction of selection indices and the rest. These have been the stocks-in-trade in the application of quantitative genetics to animal breeding in most parts of the world for well over half a century. As the chapter on Molecular Genetics (Chapter 15) illustrates, the genetics of yak has taken a straight leap from the nineteenth to the twenty-first century, leaving out all that has transformed the livestock of most other species in most countries into high-producing stock. The absence of this information for yak is almost entirely due to the absence of records of performance and of parentage on any significant scale. Clearly the application of such information, even if it were available, would have obstacles to overcome in the yak territories that are unheard of, for example, in the realm of Holstein dairy cows.

Studies on yak reproduction appear to have advanced relatively little, and there still appears to be a preoccupation with the improvement of A.I. techniques. How widely A.I. might be successfully applied in practice and turn out to be cost-effective are still open questions. The use of A.I. in remote areas and the need to time inseminations fairly precisely face massive obstacles at present. From the point of view of genetic improvement, an assurance that the A.I. bulls are in fact genetically better than the females for which they are the mates is a prerequisite for a worthwhile use of A.I. As already said, because of the absence of widespread performance recording the necessary information for this purpose is not generally available or adequate. To set up a performance-recording scheme in order to sustain genetic selection of potential AI bulls would be expensive and in present circumstances perhaps not cost effective – but market forces may change.

In the production of hybrids, particularly through the use of "improved" breeds of cattle mated to yak, A.I. provides the main method of creating the hybrids. And to this end, the continuing studies of insemination procedures and the attempts to induce and synchronize oestrus are welcome.

For the majority of yak herders, however, hybrid animals can at best provide only an adjunct to their herds and not the mainstay of production. Although some argue differently, the view here is still that hybrid production is only a partial answer to increased output from yak-producing areas. The main thrust to increased production, if it is economically desirable, must come from improving the pure yak itself and the feed supply, in part through improved grazing management.

The importance of the feed supply is given support by the performance of yak in North America. Although the population of domestic yak in North America is small (around 2 000 animals) by Chinese standards, they are distributed in relatively small herds over a fairly wide area. The performance information from them, and the reproductive pattern of these yak in particular, shows that most, perhaps all, of the reputation of the yak as reproductively poor in its native areas is due to environment and is not a genetic feature. Although, as noted in Chapter 11, part 3, a proportion of the North American yak show mitochondrial cattle DNA (which has passed through the maternal line but could have been introduced many generations back) this fact is unlikely to account for the differences in reproductive performance or growth rate. The fact is that yak in North America are fed over winter and spring and suffer none of the weight loss of yak in their traditional environment. The yak females respond by growing well, breeding at a relatively young age and thereafter annually. No need for complex physiological explanations here.

In the first edition of this book, the concluding chapter promoted the idea that one of the gaps in yak research and development was the absence of a systems approach. In the light of what has been written in this book and the new chapters that have been added to it, it should be apparent that in yak production there are a host of interacting factors. This is true at the level of a trait (the example was given previously of meat production, which is the end result and interrelationship of several contributory traits). However, interaction is also a highly relevant concept to the production system as a whole where biology interacts with social, cultural and economic forces. We know of no studies in yak that embrace the systems approach – but the resources needed are perhaps too great to make this a realistic expectation, especially as replication would be demanded for different regions and different breeds and environments.

Prospects

Crystal gazing is neither science nor art. Often-times it is practised to deceive. So, why tempt fate (again) by trying to look into the future?

One reason is the strong feeling that yak are, in many respects, a unique genetic resource with an amazing ability to survive, reproduce and provide marketable products under incredibly harsh conditions and with sparse, poor quality feed for long periods. These are attributes to be cherished. Over-production of human food in some parts of the world (more than matched by the human food deficit in others) and of animal produce in particular, makes it unlikely that those with money to invest will populate remote cold and mountainous areas with yak or yak hybrids – though that was the original concept for the projects in Canada and Alaska in the early part of the twentieth century (see Chapter 11, part 3). Today, parts of Northern Canada and Alaska, parts of the Andes, Greenland and further extensions into Siberia are all areas that must spring to mind as underexploited and where the yak or yak hybrids could play a role. Perhaps in a more rational world the day may yet come when meat production from otherwise barren areas will find favour and make economic sense.

Interestingly, the recent proposal put forward by Jack Rutledge (personal communication, 2002), referred to in Chapter 3, extends this idea to milk production from hybrids of yak and cattle for those harsh environments where there are currently no equally good alternative livestock. The proposal, as outlined in Chapter 3, involves the use of relatively new, technology-based procedures to produce the hybrids from a large potential pool of the cattle eggs. Such ideas could well lead to a future extension of some of the adaptive characteristics of the yak to hostile environments, without the more traditional need for importing the pure-bred animals.

Coming back to the present, it is important to ensure that the yak genotype is conserved (perhaps in several forms if the DNA work so suggests) and that the wild yak in particular is not endangered further. This is not just a matter of sentiment but a sound biological need to conserve genetic resources – and especially where, as in the case of the yak, there is good reason to believe there are special, perhaps unique, genes involved.

Changes in yak production systems are on the speculative list of prospects. If indeed social change were to bring about a degree of rural depopulation, as in many rural parts of the world, then the vast rangelands of the Qinghai-Tibetan Plateau and beyond would still be potentially the home for yak. However, with fewer people to tend them, a change to a more ranching-style production system with meat as the principal product (and perhaps fibre) may be foreseen. Large herds managed by few people would call for something different from the traditional systems – and an edition of this book in the more distant future might then have to mourn the passing of a way of life. It is fortunate that this edition of the book is free of that burden.

Map of Qinghai-Tibetan Plateau

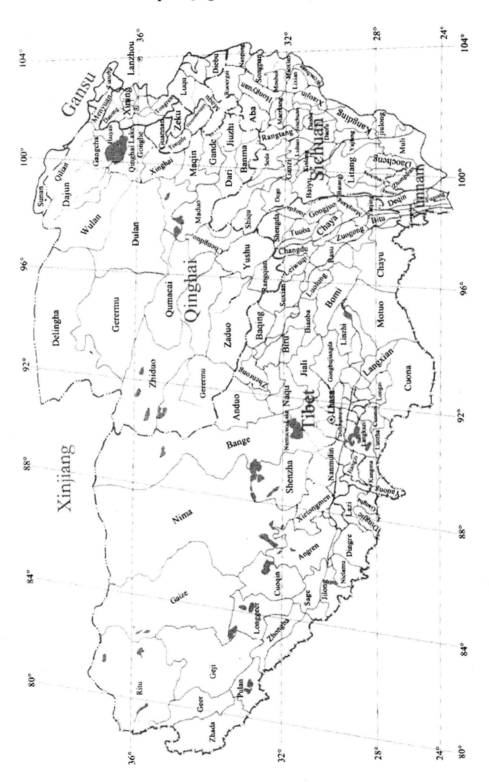

SUBJECT INDEX

(Entries represent substantive information on the topic: "f" after a page number indicates repeat references to the topic on two or more successive, or nearly successive, pages; pages joined by hyphens indicate that the topic is the main subject.)

cashmere 251

castration methods 214

cattle shelters - see enclosures

Caucasus 6, 102, 150, 211, 285f, 296, 420

cellulose 391

Ceratoides sp. 365f

cervix 89, 92

Changtang 11

cheese - see milk products

cheese factories 242, 351, 439

chest circumference - see body dimensions

chest depth - see body dimensions

Chitral 332

Chlamidia infection 224

chromosome number 18, 417

chromosome studies 417-418

churpi - see milk products

CIS - see Commonwealth of Independent States

classification of yak species 17-18, 430-432

climate 2f, 62, 66, 196, 306, 342, 363-366, 392

Clostridium sp. 222

coat - see fleece

coat colour - see colour

Coccidia sp. 230

Coenurosis - see gid

cold insulation - see insulation

cold resistance 65-70

cold stress 350

colostrum, composition 137

colour (see also breed descriptions)
    coat 75, 78, 278, 300, 308, 317, 323, 339
    skin 78

combing down fibre - see fibre harvesting

common grazing 353-355

Commonwealth of Independent States 5, 7, 175, 185, 225, 285-298, 426

composition of products - see products

conception rate (see also pregnancy rate) 97, 100, 177, 310

conformation 65

conservation
    breeds of yak 46-48
    wild yak 48

contagious bovine pleuropneumonia 224

contaminated water - see water

copper deficiency 231-232, 340, 345

coracle 253

corpus uteri 39

courtship 89

Coxiella infection 226

creatinine metabolism 404

crossbreeding (see also hybridizing)
    with wild yak 11, 18, 39, 44-46, 49, 151, 416
        within yak species 41-42, 47, 272, 416

crossbreeding interpretation - see heterosis

cultural factors 348-349

culture 12, 194, 277, 304, 321, 349, 438

Cynobacteria 231

Cyperaceae sp. 198, 303, 366f,

cytogenetics 417-418

D

daily work schedule - see work schedule

dairy herd 199

Danthonia sp 282

defoliation, vegetation 368

dermatitis 231

desertification 363

diarrhoea, viral (see also calf scours) 227

digestion 392, 394-399

diphtheria 227

disasters, natural 222, 266, 269, 327, 341, 350

disease (see also specific diseases) 212, 221-232
    control 195, 221, 267

distribution of yak hybrids 50-51

distribution of yak (see also names of countries)
    historical 3-5
    in relation to environment 62
    outside Asia 6-9, 237-345
    present 5-7

division of yak herd - see management, herd

DNA 341, 420f, 440f

DNA markers 422-428, 440f

domestication 3-4, 259, 427

down fibre - see fibre

449

origins of yak 2-5

ornaments 348

output - see economics

ovaries 101

over-grazing 198, 201-202, 231, 283, 302, 350, 384

over-stocking 266

oviduct 101

ownership, herds - see herd ownership

oxygen

absorption 71, 73

affinity 74

intake 71

retention 73

oxygen, adaptation to - see environmental factors

P

pack carrying 165f, 190, 206, 217f, 304, 339

packed cell volume (PCV) 73, 76

Pakistan 7, 241, 251, 330-333

Pamir 5, 286f, 327-328

para-influenza 227

parasitic disease 198, 227-231

parity effects, 124, 141, 188

parturition 98-104

pasteurellosis 225

pasture (see also herbage, grazing)

types 197-198, 379-382

utilization 197f, 376-383

yield 329

pelt (see also hide products) 253

pens - see enclosures

pH in blood 78

phenolics 372

phosphorus 222, 250, 384, 407f

phylogeny 430-432

physiological state, in nutrition 409

Pian Niu - see hybrids

pituitary gland 179

placenta 101

Plateau yak - see breeds (also type)

ploughing 166f, 190, 217

plucking fibre - see fibre harvesting

pneumonia - see contagious bovine pleuropneumonia

Poa sp. 366f

poison plants - see toxic plants

poisoning 79

polled - see horns

Polygonum sp. 366f

polymorphisms, 419, 423

population size (see also under country names) 7, 198, 258f, 268, 277, 291 301, 306f, 316, 327, 328, 331f, 361

population structure 201

Potentilla sp. 282

pox 227

precipitation (rainfall) 27, 65, 258f, 264, 268, 277, 282, 291f, 307f, 338, 342, 364-366, 373f, 383

predators 82, 205, 213, 229

pregnancy

detection 101f, 212, 310

rate 98-100, 177, 310

pregnancy rate, effect of

age 101, 310

breed (see individual named breeds)

physiological state 101

Primula sp. 282

products from yak - see individual products

progesterone 92, 97, 102

prospects, future 284, 443-444

protein

deficiency 146

digestion 404

feed 249

nutrition 403-406

requirements 406

supplements 146, 325, 404, 407, 409f

pruritis 228

puberty

female 90, 303, 339

male 109

pulmonary pressure 71

pulse rate - see heart rate

pure-breeding 34

purine metabolism 404

pyrrolizideine alkaloid poisoning 79, 202, 231, 303

Q
Qiang people 3
Qianghai province 7, 11, 18f, 34f, 39, 44f, 48, 52, 63f, 74, 91, 96, 99, 105f, 130, 137f, 149, 159, 166, 223f, 264-267, 268f, 354, 419, 439
Qianghai-Tibetan Plateau 2f, 9, 13, 19f, 164, 195f, 258, 264, 348, 353f, 391, 407f, 411, 440. 444, 467
    rangeland ecosystem 359-386
quantitative trait loci (QTL) 429, 441
quantitative variation, genetic 428

R
rabies 227
rainfall - see precipitation
rangeland
degradation 263, 266, 350, 353, 356, 363, 384, 439
    ecosystem 359-386
    formation 365
    management 354, 374-383
    productivity 361, 366f, 373f
rangeland type 307, 373-376
alpine desert 307, 361, 365-366, 369, 373f, 384
alpine steppe 307, 361, 366, 369, 373f, 384
meadow 197, 200, 265, 328f, 361f, 366f, 370, 373f, 379, 383f
Ranunculus sp. 373, 384
rearing - see calf rearing
record keeping 34, 442
rectal palpation - see artificial insemination
red cells - see erythrocytes
religion 12, 194, 277, 348, 438
religious customs 12, 304
replacement rate, reproduction 54,
reproduction
    adaptation of 81
female 89-108, 303, 309-310, 319, 339, 411
    male 109, 112, 303, 310, 339
reproductive
    life 108

organs, female 89
organs, male 109, 178-179
performance (see also breed descriptions) 95, 98, 108, 177, 263, 303
    rate 178, 201, 260, 263, 340
research
activity 264, 267, 270, 271, 296, 304, 310, 440
    gaps in 440-443
genetic (see also molecular genetics) 297, 440f
    grazing ecology 367-375
    nutritional 389-412
respiration rate 64, 166
respiratory quotients 400
restriction length polymorphism (RFLP) 421f
Rhododendron sp. 282
riding, yak 166, 190, 218, 339
rinderpest 22, 227
ringworm 231
rituals 348
river catchment 362
rodent control 384-385
rodents 385
root crops - see forage crops
rope - see fibre products, also hide
rotational grazing 195, 198, 282, 361, 376-379, 383
roundworm 230
rumen volume 80, 394
ruminal digestion 394-397
rumination 80, 209
rump length - see body dimensions
Russian Federation - see Commonwealth of Independent States

S
Salix sp. 366f
salmonellosis 226
salt 145
sausage - see meat products
Sayan 285, 291, 296
scouring - see calf scours
scrotum 65, 109 303
sculptures 241
seasonal activities 196, 311, 317, 323

Switzerland 341
systematics 430-432
systems analysis 443

T
tail, uses 252, 254, 324
Tajikistan 131, 286f, 325-327
tanning 241, 252
tapeworm 229
tea (milk tea) 239, 243, 323
teaser bull 92
teats 78, 149, 210
technological change 195, 349, 438
temperament 18, 82-83, 205, 213, 313
temperature (see also environmental factors)
testes 109
testicular tubules (in hybrid) 179
tetanus 226
tethering 128, 205-206, 210
thorax 70
Tibetan Autonomous Region 3f, 12, 18, 21f, 34, 39, 43, 48f, 63f, 73, 91, 96, 105f, 121, 127, 133, 139, 150, 163, 166, 198f, 222f, 229f, 239, 244f, 248, 251, 258-264, 267, 272, 348f, 362f, 367f, 373f, 385, 418
ticks 228, 303
totem 348
tourism 316, 321, 439
toxic plants 79, 231, 281, 303, 363, 384
trace elements 147, 231, 407
trachea 71
tradition 12, 33, 36f, 97, 190, 193f, 198f, 224, 232, 239, 244, 249f, 253, 283, 313,324, 348f, 376, 383, 437f
traditional medicine 97, 241, 254, 348
training
    bulls 213-214
    yak 82
transhumance - see mobile yak keeping
Trichuris sp. 230
Trollius sp. 200
tsampa - see *zanba*
tuberculosis 226
Tuva 286f

type of yak
    Henduan Alpine 19, 157
    Plateau (see also breed) 19, 157

U
udder 65, 142, 149, 189
United States of America (USA) 337-341
urea - see non-protein nitrogen
USSR (former) - see Commonwealth of Independent States
uterine horns 89, 101
uterus 101-102
utilization of grazing - see grazing utilization

V
vagina 92
vas deferens 214
vasoconstriction 68, 71
vegetation
    characteristics 366-373
    chemical composition 369
    cover 283
    growth 366-367
vertebrae 70
vesicular stomatitis 227
veterinary
    care (see also diseases) 222, 223
    practices, traditional 232
viral diseases 225-227
viscera 248-249
visceral fat 248
volatile fatty acids (VFA) 395-396
vulva 92

W
warble fly - see hypodermiasis
water, contaminated 231, 283
weaning - see calf rearing
West Sayan (see Tuva)
Western High Asia 323-334
whey - see milk products
Whipsnade Wild Animal Park 345
white blood cells 78
wild animal parks - see zoos

wild animals 82, 283, 360
wild yak 9, 43, 51, 272 418
crossbreeding with 11, 18, 39, 44-46, 264
wind - see environmental factors
winter pastures 197, 281, 362, 379
withers height - see body dimensions
wolves - see predators

X
Xinjiang Uigur Autonomous Region (see also Southern Xinjiang) 271-272

Y
yak information centre 271
Yakutia 297-298
Yasin 332
Yunnan province 272

Z
zanba 239, 243, 248
zoos 8, 342-346